S0-AWB-016

Petroleum Geology

Frontispiece. Drilling rig with sandstone cliff in background. Elk Basin, Wyoming. *Photo by Rosskam. Courtesy Standard Oil Company* (*New Jersey*).

Petroleum Geology

KENNETH K. LANDES
Professor of Geology
University of Michigan

New York · JOHN WILEY & SONS, *Inc.*
London · CHAPMAN & HALL, *Ltd.*

PRINTED IN THE UNITED STATES OF AMERICA

Preface

Petroleum geology has grown in 35 years from a stepchild of geology with somewhat questionable parentage to the largest and most vigorous of the geological offspring. In growing it has developed three facets or divisions. These are: (1) the geologic occurrence, by which is meant the origin and accumulation of the natural hydrocarbons; (2) the geographic occurrence or distribution of these substances; and (3) the methods and techniques of searching for oil and gas deposits.

Most authors of textbooks and monographs on petroleum geology published heretofore have tended to restrict themselves to one or at most two of these divisions. The attempt is made in this book to cover all three, and accordingly the book is divided into three parts. The first part, "Techniques of the Petroleum Geologist," should perhaps come after the geologic occurrence, for it is logical that the oil should be formed and trapped before the search for it is begun. The practice is presented before the theory in this book, however, so that the beginner will learn the language of the specialist and observe the sources of evidence and methods of study used in developing the theoretical concepts. However, there is nothing to prevent the reader or teacher from reversing this suggested order if he so desires. The technical aspects of oil-finding are not presented in professional detail in Part I. These are best learned on the job. The objective here is merely to give the embryo petroleum geologist a start.

Part II, "Geologic Occurrence of Petroleum," is the most vital, in my opinion. The more we learn of the origin, migration, and accumulation of oil, the more intelligent will be the prospecting and the more widespread the results. This "academic" side of petroleum geology is actually intensely practical. The emphasis wherever occurrence of oil is discussed in this book is on the manner in which the hydrocarbons have been trapped rather than on details of stratigraphic nomenclature.

The concluding section, Part III, "Present and Future Oil Supplies," is largely devoted to the distribution of oil and gas fields about the globe, and the regional and local controls that have affected accumulation. The final chapter is concerned with the possible hydrocarbon sources of the future. Part III is included mainly for background and reference purposes. It is entirely a compilation and is not intended to be assigned or read *in toto*.

An appendix, "The Literature of Petroleum Geology," is included in order to give the student a concise list of modern references.

This book is written for the student of petroleum geology regardless of whether he is in the classroom or on the job. Petroleum geology evolves with such rapidity that few can keep up with all phases even while practicing the profession. There is no resemblance, except in the name of the course, between the petroleum geology I expounded to students 25 years ago and the current offering which has crystallized into a book. Most of the research papers referred to in this synthesis had not even been written in 1925!

Both the illustrator, John Jesse Hayes, and I have tried to make the reading of this book possible without frequent resort to atlas, gazetteer, or lexicon. Inset maps are included with most oil-field illustrations so that the geographic location and the position relative to other fields can be seen at a glance. For the political subdivisions covered in Chapters 9 and 10 an index map is included on which appear the geographic names referred to in the text. For the benefit of the geologist who does not know the stratigraphy of distant places formation names are followed in parentheses by the name of the geologic period.

It was necessary to close the manuscript to the inclusion of new material on July 1, 1950, when the main part went to the typesetter. The July issue of the *Bulletin of the American Association of Petroleum Geologists* with the annual review of foreign fields arrived after this deadline, as did the July *Journal of Petroleum Technology*, with articles on North Central Texas, South Central Texas, Kentucky, Missouri, and Nebraska.

May you enjoy the rest of this book, whether you be a page skipper, browser, or thorough reader!

KENNETH K. LANDES

January 1, 1951

Acknowledgments

I acknowledge with pleasure and gratitude the help of the following individuals, who read and criticized constructively different sections of the manuscript: Dr. A. L. Morrow, Vincent and Welch, Lake Charles, Louisiana, Chapter 1; Mr. William W. Clawson and Dr. John T. Rouse, Magnolia Petroleum Corporation, Dallas, Texas, Chapter 2; Professor Donald L. Katz, Department of Chemical and Metallurgical Engineering, University of Michigan, Chapters 3 and 4; Mr. G. Moses Knebel, Standard Oil Company (N. J.), New York, Chapter 5; and Mr. W. B. Wilson, Gulf Oil Company, Tulsa, Oklahoma, Chapters 6, 7, and 8. In addition the geologists of the various state geological surveys and bureaus were most helpful by their constructive comments made when sections of the manuscript were sent them for reading. These kind friends include Wilbur T. Harnsberger (Virginia); Stewart J. Lloyd (Alabama); Ralph E. Esarey (Indiana); D. J. Jones (Kentucky); Eugene S. Perry (Montana); Herman Gunter (Florida); H. B. Burwell and H. C. Milhous (Tennessee); G. E. Eddy and Rex Grant (Michigan); John H. Melvin (Ohio); Paul H. Price and R. C. Tucker (West Virginia); C. R. Fettke and Albert I. Ingham (Pennsylvania); Leo W. Hough (Louisiana); John G. Broughton and W. L. Kreidler (New York); Eugene Callaghan (New Mexico); Frank A. Herald (Texas); Harold B. Foxhall and Donald K. Mackay (Arkansas); Gordon B. Oakeshott (California); J. Mark Jewett and R. Kenneth Smith (Kansas); Robert H. Dott and V. E. Monnett (Oklahoma); A. H. Bell (Illinois); H. D. Thomas and J. David Love (Wyoming); W. E. Morse (Mississippi); and Arthur L. Crawford and George H. Hansen (Utah). Hollis Hedberg obligingly read and contributed to the section on Venezuela. Clarence Moody kindly advised me regarding the geology of the Gulf Embayment area. A set of sedimentary basin maps courteously sent me by Lewis G. Weeks has been of great help.

The illustrations are acknowledged individually. Most of them have been adapted from publications of the American Association of Petroleum Geologists, and I am indebted to Mr. J. P. D. Hull, Business

Manager of that organization, for general permission to reproduce these drawings.

Mr. John Jesse Hayes, an associate at the University of Michigan, has been in complete charge of the illustrations. I am grateful for the load thus taken from my shoulders.

Last but not least has been the splendid assistance of my wife, Susan Beach Landes, who has functioned with equal efficiency as editor, critic, and typist.

Contents

INTRODUCTION

Chapter 1

THE PROFESSION OF PETROLEUM GEOLOGY

DEFINITION AND IMPORTANCE. *Petroleum geology is the utilization of geology in the search for, and in the exploitation of, deposits of petroleum and natural gas.* The liquid and gaseous hydrocarbons are so intimately associated in nature that it is customary to shorten the expression "petroleum and natural gas" to "petroleum" or "oil" and assume the inclusion of natural gas. That practice will be followed in this book.

The petroleum industry has profited much by its liaison with geology. During 1949 the sites for approximately four-fifths of the wildcat wells (wells drilled outside the boundaries of known oil fields) drilled were selected for geological reasons; of this number 13 per cent became discovery wells and 87 per cent were failures. However, among the one-fifth of the wildcat wells that were drilled without benefit of geological advice, only 3 per cent became commercial producers and 97 per cent were failures.[1] For this reason every producing company of any magnitude has a geological staff, and more geologists are employed in the oil industry than in any other branch of the profession. It has been estimated that the number of geologists and geophysicists engaged in the petroleum industry on January 1, 1950, was in excess of 7697.[2]

The practical value of geology[3] in oil finding is fairly well known, but the benefits that have accrued to geology through exploration for oil have not been adequately appreciated. The search for new

[1] F. H. Lahee (chairman), "Exploratory Drilling in 1949," *Bull. Am. Assoc. Petrol. Geol.,* Vol. 34 (June, 1950), pp. 995–1013.

[2] A. Rodger Denison (chairman), "Report of Committee on Survey of Geological Employment," *Bull. Am. Assoc. Petrol. Geol.,* Vol. 34 (June, 1950), p. 1359.

[3] Ira H. Cram, "Geology Is Useful," *Bull. Am. Assoc. Peirol. Geol.* (January, 1948), pp. 1–10.

deposits of oil and gas has led to geologic mapping in all parts of the globe, thereby greatly increasing our knowledge of world geology. By drilling thousands of wells, and by sharing with others the geological records of those wells, the petroleum industry has made possible a far more accurate picture of the third dimension in the earth's crust than ever could have been achieved by extrapolation of surface observations. DeGolyer,[4] as long ago as 1921, pointed out some of the geological discoveries that were due to the exploration for oil, and many more could be added to the list today. Examples are the discovery of (1) buried crystalline rock mountains and uplifts, such as the Nemaha granite ridge of Kansas and Oklahoma; (2) the great thickening of the sedimentary rock column in basins of deposition and in embayment areas such as the Gulf Coast; (3) enormous vertical prisms of salt ("salt domes") in the same region; and (4) the existence and location of valuable deposits of helium, carbon dioxide, coal, limestone, natural brines, rock salt, potash, and sulfur as well as oil and gas.[5] From the records of wells drilled for oil, geologists have been able to add many new chapters to the sedimentation and diastrophic histories of the earth's crust.[6] Old shorelines and buried stream beds have been mapped; ancient reefs have been discovered; hidden faults have been recognized; and evidence of volcanism in supposedly "quiet" periods has been found. From a purely scientific standpoint, deep wells drilled for oil have made possible the measurement of earth temperatures in the uppermost four miles of crust.[7]

Illing[8] has aptly stated, ". . . if geology has contributed greatly to the growth of the oil industry the debt is not a one-sided one. Geology owes a great deal to the oil industry in the expansion of its knowledge and the increased efficiency of its methods. . . . It would be well to bury the terms 'Pure' and 'Applied' geology so long as they are used in a separatist sense. There is only one geology. Its purity depends on its truth, not on its application."

[4] E. DeGolyer, "Debt of Geology to the Petroleum Industry," *Bull. Am. Assoc. Petrol. Geol.,* Vol. 5 (May–June, 1921), pp. 394–398.

[5] Hugh D. Miser, "Some Notes on Geology and Geologists, 1907–1947," *Bull. Am. Assoc. Petrol. Geol.,* Vol. 32 (July, 1948), pp. 1340–1348.

[6] F. H. Lahee, "Contributions of Petroleum Geology to Pure Geology in the Southern Mid-Continent Area," *Bull. Am. Assoc. Petrol. Geol.,* Vol. 43 (1932), pp. 953–964.

[7] Hugh D. Miser, "Our Petroleum Supply," *Jour. Washington Acad. Sciences,* Vol. 29 (March, 1939), pp. 93–109.

[8] Vincent C. Illing, "Influence of Oil on Geology," *Oil Weekly,* September, 1946, p. 176.

BRIEF HISTORY OF THE PETROLEUM INDUSTRY.[9] Oil and gas were used by man for many years before their production became an industry. The use of seep oil and asphalt in the Mediterranean area in the calking of water craft (including the Ark of Noah and the amphibious cradle of the infant Moses) extends back into earliest history and no doubt into prehistory. In the New World seep oil in northern Pennsylvania and western New York State was collected by both Indians and pioneer whites for use as lubricant, liniment, and laxative.

In the later pre-industrial history of oil and gas these substances were found by accident while wells were being drilled for water or salt brine. The art of drilling a well is an ancient one; Goodrich [10] reports that a well was drilled in China for salt to a depth of 450 feet *circa* 221 B.C. Brine wells in the Allegheny Mountains were reaching depths of 800 feet by the middle 1800's and an artesian water well at St. Louis was bored to a depth of 2193 feet in 1854.

During the first half of the nineteenth century the most actively drilled area in the United States was a belt extending from New York State across western Pennsylvania and eastern Ohio into West Virginia and Kentucky. Here natural brines, from which salt was obtained

[9] Samuel W. Tait, *The Wildcatters* (Princeton Univ. Press, Princeton, N. J., 1946).

Harry Botsford, *The Valley of Oil* (Hastings House, New York, 1946).

Walter M. Fuchs, *When the Oil Wells Run Dry* (Dover, N. H., 1946).

Paul Giddens, *Beginnings of the Petroleum Industry* (Penn. Historical Commission, 1941).

Paul Giddens, *Birth of the Oil Industry* (Macmillan, New York, 1938).

U. S. Geological Survey, "A Résumé of Geology and Occurrence of Petroleum in the United States," 33rd Congress (Hearings on H. R. 441, 1934).

Gerald Forbes, *Flush Production* (Univ. of Okla. Press, Norman, Okla., 1942).

Harold B. Goodrich, "Early Discoveries of Petroleum in the United States," *Econ. Geol.,* Vol. 27 (March–April, 1932), pp. 160–168.

Harold B. Goodrich, "Early Exploration Methods," *World Petroleum,* Vol. 10 (May, 1939), pp. 32–37.

Eugene A. Stephenson, "The Natural Gas Industry," *Elements of the Petroleum Industry* (*Am. Inst. Min. Met. Engineers*), Chapter 19, pp. 430–452.

Sir Boverton Redwood, *Petroleum* (J. B. Lippincott, Philadelphia, Pa., 1922), 3 vols., 5th edition.

R. F. Bacon and W. A. Hamor, *The American Petroleum Industry* (McGraw-Hill, New York, 1916), 2 vols.

E. DeGolyer and Harold Vance, "Bibliography of the Petroleum Industry," *Bull. A. and M. Coll. Texas,* 1944, Thirty-seven "early historical references" on pp. 695–696.

E. DeGolyer, "Seventy-Five Years of Progress in Petroleum," *Seventy-Five Years of Progress in the Mineral Industry* (Am. Inst. Min. Met. Engineers, New York, 1948), pp. 270–302.

Carl Coke Rister, *Oil! Titan of the Southwest* (Univ. Okla. Press, Norman, Okla., 1949).

[10] Op. cit. (1939).

by evaporation, could be found at relatively shallow depths. In a few places gas was struck. It was used as a fuel in salt processing, and in 1821 it was used to light the community of Fredonia, New York. Other wells struck oil, to the great disappointment of the operators. In a few instances this oil was bottled and sold in the same manner as seep oil, but most was allowed to go to waste.

The curtain could rise on the petroleum industry only after the stage was properly set. By the beginning of the nineteenth century man was rebelling against going to bed at dusk. He was learning to read, and that required a better illuminant than an open fire. The urbanization movement was under way, and street lighting became desirable. A satisfactory lubricant was necessary for the machinery of a growing mechanized civilization. All these demands were to increase manyfold during ensuing decades, and to them new demands were added.

For centuries previously, the relatively modest demand for oil had been met by the whaling industry. But the growing demands of the 1800's soon depleted the whale supply so that by 1850 whale oil was selling for as much as $2.50 a gallon. The rising price had accelerated the search for a substitute, and it was found in kerosene or "coal oil" obtained from coal by distillation. During the decade 1850–1860, 56 plants were built in the United States alone to make kerosene from coal. Although "coal oil" could compete successfully with whale oil, it was still a relatively expensive product. The coal had to be mined, destructively distilled, the resulting oil refined, and the waste ash disposed of. The stage was set for an oil direct from the earth which only needed refining in order to qualify for a rapidly growing market. And the "coal oil" refineries could be, and many of them were, converted readily to the refining of crude oil.

Although petroleum had been marketed in relatively minor amounts throughout historic time, including that from wells dug by hand in Rumania during the later years of the 1850's, a group of individuals operating in the United States, likewise in the late 1850's, is generally credited with initiating the petroleum industry. Among the members of this group were George H. Bissell, youthful New York lawyer; James M. Townsend, New Haven banker; Benjamin Silliman, professor of chemistry, geology, and mineralogy at Yale University; Edwin L. Drake, colonel by courtesy and ex-railroad conductor by vocation; and William A. Smith, brine well driller. In modern terminology these men were respectively promoter, financier, technical adviser, tool pusher (drilling superintendent), and driller. It would be pleasant to record that the location for the well destined to be the discovery well of the world was made by geologist Silliman, but that is not the case. Professor Silliman's contribution was in the form of a chemical analysis and an optimistic report concerning the potential usefulness of the oil which enabled banker Townsend to raise the needed capital, mainly in New Haven. The well was located in June of 1859 near Titusville, Pennsylvania, close by an old oil spring, and on August 27 at a depth of 69½ feet oil began entering the well, and the first oil boom was under way. Literally thousands of wells were drilled in western Pennsylvania within a few months of the completion of the Drake well, as it came to be called, and the search soon extended into neighboring states and far beyond. By the turn of the century oil was being produced commercially in Ohio, West Virginia, Kansas, Oklahoma, Texas, Colorado, Wyoming, California, Canada, and on other continents.

Not even a brief history of the oil industry would be complete without mention of the role played by the automobile and other twentieth-century machines. With the development of the internal-combustion motor and its employment in ever-increasing amount in the automobile and more recently the airplane, the demand for gasoline grew from practically nothing to nearly 100 million gallons daily in 1948. This demand has been met in two ways: (1) by the continued discovery of vast new oil deposits; and (2) by technologic discoveries which permit higher gasoline yield from the hydrocarbons wrested from nature's reservoirs. In the latter category is cracking, a refinery process which increased the yield of gasoline from crude oil from a straight distillation average of 13% in 1912 to 50% by 1938. A more recent development has been hydrogenation, by means of which a barrel of crude oil can be made, theoretically at least, to yield a barrel of gasoline, or any other desired hydrocarbon. The latest innovation in hydrocarbon processing is polymerization, a method of converting natural gas into gasoline.

The mechanical age has also produced an ever-increasing demand for lubricants. The growth of the railroad systems in the latter half of the nineteenth century, and their adoption of petroleum products for lubricants, gave initial impetus to a demand that is now second only to that for gasoline. Other products with a large market today include furnace oil and diesel fuel. The modern merchant marine and the navies of the world are large consumers of fuel and lubricating oil. Kerosene, once the number one product in the United States, still has that rank in countries where electricity is not widely available.

FIG. 1. Then and now (1859–1950). *Courtesy Amer. Petrol. Inst.*

Natural gas, formerly wasted into the air if no market was available in the immediate vicinity, is now piped thousands of miles for use in home and factory. No longer need the geologist worry about lack of sale for his discovery; if oil or gas are present in commercial amounts they eventually will find a way to market regardless of distance or topographic barriers.

EVOLUTION OF OIL FINDING.[11] The methods that are used, and have been used, in the search for new supplies of oil and gas can be classified into non-geologic and geologic. At first the only methods were non-geologic; today, though both non-geologic and geologic methods are used, the latter predominate. Petroleum geology, as employed in oil finding, can be divided into four chronological stages: preprofessional, infancy, adolescence, and maturity.

Non-Geologic Methods Used in Oil Finding. The Drake well and its immediate successors were drilled in creek bottoms. Therefore, the first rule of thumb to be followed in prospecting for new supplies was to stick to creek bottoms. "Creekology" reigned supreme until some rugged individualists drilled successful wells on the uplands. It was next observed that the Appalachian oil pools were much longer than they were wide and that their long axes trended about N 30° E (which is the strike of the rocks in this region). Consequently, following the trend, or "ruler geology," became the vogue, and it is still good practice where the traps tend to be elongate. The discovery of the prolific Spindletop oil field on the Texas Gulf Coast led prospectors to seek topographic mounds similar to the one overlying the Spindletop salt plug. Drilling in the vicinity of gas seepages and associated "paraffin dirt" deposits was also an effective discovery method in the Gulf Coast area, and oil seeps have served successfully as criteria of buried oil pools the world over wherever the rocks have relatively steep dips.

All these methods have had a fair degree of success because they have scientific basis, although the prospector using such a method

[11] J. V. Howell, "Historical Development of Structural Theory of Accumulation of Oil and Gas," *Problems of Petroleum Geology* (Am. Assoc. Petrol. Geol., 1934), pp. 1–23.

Wm. B. Heroy, "Petroleum Geology; Geology, 1888–1938," *Geol. Soc. Am. 50th Anniversary Vol.* (1941), pp. 512–548.

Ralph Arnold, "Two Decades of Petroleum Geology, 1903–1922," *Bull. Am. Assoc. Petrol. Geol.,* Vol. 7 (November–December, 1923), pp. 603–624.

E. DeGolyer, "Development of the Technique of Prospecting," *Science of Petroleum* (Oxford Univ. Press, 1938), Vol. 1, p. 268 et seq.

Paul H. Price, "Evolution of Geologic Thought in Prospecting for Oil and Natural Gas," *Bull. Am. Assoc. Petrol. Geol.,* Vol. 31 (April, 1947), pp. 673–697.

may know little and care less about any possible scientific connection. Even "creekology" can be explained, for in the Appalachian region trellis drainage is common, and many of the streams are subsequent, paralleling the strike of the rock formations. However, there is another group of non-geologic prospecting methods that has no scientific explanation and is no more successful than is possible under the laws of chance. Here we have the dowser, who throughout historic time has sought water, buried treasure, escaped criminals, and, more recently, oil, with a forked stick. The dowser has been largely supplanted in the oil fields by the "doodlebugger" who has a fancy gadget in place of a forked stick, and who glibly uses scientific words, the meaning of which he knows not. In the same category, but perhaps more honest, are those who determine the location of wells by hunches, or because of a commitment made while obtaining a block of leases. It would be quite inaccurate to claim that these unscientific methods never led to the discovery of an oil field; it would be just as untrue to state that no blindfolded child ever succeeded in pinning the tail on the donkey.

The Preprofessional Stage in Petroleum Geology. Howell[12] has published a detailed account of the development of the structural theory of oil and gas accumulation. In 1842 William Logan, pioneer Canadian geologist, noted the presence of oil seeps on anticlinal crests in the Gaspé Peninsula. Nine months after the drilling of the Drake well, in 1860, Professor Henry D. Rogers called attention to the anticlinal location of the new wells in Pennsylvania; the Drake well itself was drilled on an anticline mapped by Rogers years before and published in 1858. The first clear statement of the anticlinal theory was made by another Canadian, T. Sterry Hunt, in 1861. In the immediately succeeding years many others wrote regarding the anticlinal theory. In the meantime, in 1860, Alexander Winchell noted that unfractured sandstones were sufficiently porous to contain oil.

The Infancy of Professional Petroleum Geology. In the early 1880's Professor I. C. White rediscovered the structural theory of oil and gas accumulation and then proceeded to apply his knowledge of geology to the discovery of oil and gas fields. He was singularly successful in this regard. Between 1884 and 1889 he located the discovery wells for the Washington, Pennsylvania, oil and gas field, the Grapefield gas field, the Belle Vernon field, the Mannington field

[12] *Op. cit.*

of West Virginia, and others.[13] Later geologists, working in this same area, have noted the extremely erratic nature of the reservoir sandstones and have questioned the applicability of White's theories to this province, but the fact remains that he did use geology in the

FIG. 2. Professor I. C. White (1848–1927), who first put geology to work in the successful search for oil and gas. *Courtesy Geological Society of America.*

successful search for new oil and gas fields, thereby initiating the profession of petroleum geology.

During the remaining years of the nineteenth century, Dutch geologists were employed professionally in the search for oil in the East Indies, and British geologists were likewise engaged in Mexico. In 1897–1898 geological departments were started in two companies

[13] I. C. White, "The Mannington Oil Field and the History of Its Development," *Bull. Geol. Soc. Am.*, Vol. 3 (April, 1892), p. 195.

in California. During the first fifteen years of the twentieth century, the U. S. Geological Survey published an imposing number of papers and monographs on the geology of various oil fields. The effect was twofold: the oil companies became convinced of the utilitarian value of geology, and those companies extensively raided the U. S. Geological Survey for geologists to establish geological staffs within their organizations. So new is the profession of petroleum geology that most of these "pioneers" are still alive.

Professional Stage—Adolescence. The period 1911 to 1921 was one of great discoveries in the Mid-Continent, Gulf Coast, California, and elsewhere. Most, but not all, of these discoveries were due to the application of geology. By 1915 geological staffs were the rule rather than the exception in company organizations. The American Association of Petroleum Geologists (the Southwestern Geological Society at first) was born in 1917. The geologist was engaged in mapping anticlines or, especially on the Gulf Coast, in searching for surface indications. For this work a general training in geology was adequate.

Professional Stage—Maturity. Beginning in the early 1920's the geologist engaged in the search for new supplies of oil and gas had to become a specialist in petroleum geology. In the first place most of the anticlines discernible at the surface were mapped, and, secondly, it became increasingly obvious that anticlinal folding was but one of a number of factors important to the localization of oil and gas in commercial deposits. New techniques were developed, and knowledge was extended into hitherto unknown or neglected fields. Micropaleontology, geophysics, sedimentation, diagenesis, stratigraphy, and paleogeology have all become essential sciences to the modern petroleum geologist.

The first subsurface laboratory was established in 1919, and micropaleontology [14] was introduced in 1920. The peak years for plane table surveying were 1920 and 1921. Core drilling, which enables the geologist to map the bed rock structures where, for one reason or another, usually inadequate outcrops, such mapping is not possible at the surface, began in 1919 and reached a peak in the 1920's. The torsion balance was introduced in 1920 and the seismograph in 1923. It is interesting to note that the possible applicability of the seismograph to structure mapping was discussed by J. A. Udden, State Geologist of Texas, in a paper read in 1920. The geophysical instruments had their period of maximum return in the later 1920's and

[14] Hubert G. Schenck, "Applied Paleontology," *Bull. Am. Assoc. Petrol. Geol.*, Vol. 24 (October, 1940), pp. 1752–1778.

early 1930's. Since 1917, subsurface geology, which is the study of the lithology, structure, and geologic history of the sedimentary section by means of well records, including both logs and samples, has grown steadily and is now an important part of the organization of every geological department. Today more oil and gas field discoveries are credited to subsurface studies than to any other oil-finding technique.

PRESENT TRENDS IN PETROLEUM GEOLOGY.[15] Petroleum geologists are currently thinking and working in the direction of: (1) rising above the prejudices which have shackled oil-finding from the start; (2) developing new oil territory by extending exploration far beyond previous lateral and vertical boundaries; and (3) continued improvement of the tools and techniques of exploration.

Overcoming the Mental Hazards to Oil Exploration. From the very outset of the oil industry one of the greatest barriers to expanding production has been ultraconservative thinking. "There would be mirth-provoking irony in a map of the United States showing the boundaries, lateral and horizontal, beyond which dogmatists have at one time or another said oil could not be found—which mental barbed-wire fences have snapped under the irrepressible urge of the wild-catter." [16] Throughout the relatively brief history of oil exploration such man-created barriers as "commercial oil deposits cannot occur in limestones," "structural basins cannot contain oil fields," "there is no oil below the Mississippi lime [or the Dundee, or what have you]," "red-bed areas are barren," and "there is no oil west of the Nemaha

[15] E. DeGolyer, "Future Position of Petroleum Geology in the Oil Industry," *Bull. Am. Assoc. Petrol. Geol.*, Vol. 24 (August, 1940), p. 1389; "Notes on Present Status of Problem of Exploration," *Bull. Am. Assoc. Petrol. Geol.*, Vol. 26 (July, 1942), pp. 1214–1220.

A. I. Levorsen, "Trends in Petroleum Geology," *Econ. Geol.*, Vol. 36 (December, 1941), pp. 763–773; "Discovery Thinking," *Bull. Am. Assoc. Petrol. Geol.*, Vol. 27 (July, 1943), pp. 887–928.

R. C. Coffin, "Recent Trends in Geological-Geophysical Exploration and Methods of Improving Use of Geophysical Data," *Bull. Am. Assoc. Petrol. Geol.*, Vol. 30 (December, 1946), pp. 2013–2033.

Research Committee, Am. Assoc. Petrol. Geol., *A Symposium on Petroleum Discovery Methods* (Tulsa, Am. Assoc. Petrol. Geol., 1942).

A. R. Denison, "A Challenge to Geology," *Bull. Am. Assoc. Petrol. Geol.*, Vol. 28 (July, 1944), pp. 897–901.

M. G. Cheney, "The Geological Attack," *Bull. Am. Assoc. Petrol. Geol.*, Vol. 30 (July, 1946), pp. 1077–1087.

Eugene Holman, "Facing Forward," *Bull. Am. Assoc. Petrol. Geol.*, Vol. 30 (July, 1946), pp. 1099–1103.

Earl Noble, "Geological Masks and Prejudices," *Bull. Am. Assoc. Petrol. Geol.*, Vol. 31 (July, 1947), pp. 1109–1117.

[16] Samuel W. Tait, Jr., *The Wildcatters* (Princeton Univ. Press, Princeton, N. J., 1946), p. xiii.

granite ridge" have been demolished by men who had both vision and a capability for courageous thinking. Recent discoveries of oil in the so-called Weber "quartzite" and in sediments of continental origin have blasted two more firmly entrenched prejudices.[17]

Another handicap to discovery has been the tendency to permit a dry hole to condemn an entire township, or county, or even larger area. Actually, of course, a dry hole condemns little more than its own area, and several cases are on record where producing wells have completely surrounded an earlier drilled dry hole.

The fact that the mental hazards listed above, and countless others, have been overcome does not mean that there are no prejudices today. Every district contains geologists who dogmatically confine the occurrence of oil to certain areas and stratigraphic depths. All too often these men are in charge of company exploration programs, and expansion of oil production is impeded by their presumptions. However, the present trend in petroleum geology appears to be in the direction of less prejudiced thinking. The company geologist must also, of course, weigh the costs of a new exploring venture against the probable returns; therefore economic factors as well as prejudices may lead to the rejection of a proposed exploration.

The Development of New Provinces. Oil has become a commodity of such value that no area, no matter how remote, is considered "out of bounds," and geologists are no longer closely restricted in the amount of money they can spend in exploration. As a result, oil is now being sought in such distant places as the polar regions; at greater depths than ever before reached; and beneath "geological masks" heretofore considered too expensive to penetrate. Noble [18] lists, as examples of geological masks: water, thrust sheets, volcanic rocks, high-velocity limestones, and unconformities. Much activity has already been shown in exploring for new oil deposits beneath the waters overlapping the continental shelves. This exploration has met with some degree of success, and submerged areas will no doubt continue to be investigated as potential oil "lands."

Improving the Techniques of Oil-Finding. In the preceding section on the evolution of oil-finding it was noted that during the 1920's and early 1930's the emphasis in exploration method shifted from the surface structure mapping through core drilling and geophysical surveying to subsurface geology. Each one of the first three of these oil-finding techniques reached a peak and then declined fairly rapidly.

[17] Earl Noble, *op. cit.*
[18] Earl Noble, *op. cit.*

This decline has occurred for two reasons: (1) the fact, brought out by DeGolyer,[19] that a technique (a single operation in the search for oil) exhausts its possibilities by being used; and (2) the initial success and resulting popularity of the succeeding new method. However, in regard to the first point, it should be realized that complete exhaustion of possible application is more of a theoretical than an actual end point. Whenever a shift of scale, as from reconnaissance to detailed, is introduced, the entire area can be rerun with the old method, but with the occupation of many more stations. Likewise the opening up of a new territory for exploration, whether it be lateral or vertical, will give further impetus to old methods. Therefore, even though the applicability of an old technique may and does diminish, it may be a long time before it disappears.

The phenomenal successes of geophysical prospecting led to the crowding out of surface geological method in some areas long before it had exhausted its possibilities. Both in the Gulf Coast and Rocky Mountain provinces considerable chagrin has been caused by the realization that oil fields discovered by geophysical means could have been found just as easily by the far cheaper surface method. According to Russell,[20] twenty-four fields in central and northern Louisiana could have been found by surface mapping, but only two actually were so discovered up to 1941. Surface mapping is credited with assisting in the detection of an additional six fields, leaving sixteen in which the possibilities of discovery by surface geology were ignored. The first oil discovery in Mississippi was brought about through surface geology, although the state had previously been covered several times by geophysical surveys. Russell also points out that in 1941 detailed surface structural studies had just made a beginning in the northern Gulf Coast region, including parts of Texas, Louisiana, Arkansas, Mississippi, Alabama, and Florida.

A highly significant trend in petroleum geology has been a growing awareness of the value of combining and coordinating oil-finding techniques. It is now realized that the various exploration methods are not mutually exclusive and should not be considered to be competitive. The exploration department of a modern oil company is so organized that it can support one oil-finding technique by the use of any others that may be applicable. In 1942 approximately 200

[19] E. DeGolyer, "Future Position of Petroleum Geology in the Oil Industry," *Bull. Am. Assoc. Petrol. Geol.*, Vol. 24 (August, 1940), p. 1389.

[20] R. Dana Russell, "Future of Field Geology," *Bull. Am. Assoc. Petrol. Geol.*, Vol. 25 (February, 1941), pp. 324–326.

petroleum geologists contributed opinions to a symposium on petroleum discovery methods.[21] A summary of the replies shows that more geologists favored "improving and coordinating all methods" as a better approach to the problem of oil and gas discovery than any other method.[22]

Of greatest importance to future oil discovery is the growing trend toward more fundamental research. Heretofore, the geologist has been able to find new oil fields by the mere recording of structural data obtained by plane table, well, or seismograph. But most of these relatively easy-to-discover fields have been found, or soon will be, so it becomes necessary for the geologist to learn how to locate the more difficult stratigraphic and combination type oil and gas traps. For this work he must be more than a recorder of formation elevations; he must be an interpreter, a speculative geologist. Interpretation and speculation of practical value can be built only upon accurate knowledge of geologic processes and geologic history; of sedimentation and stratigraphy; of diagenesis and diastrophism. Only by detailed paleogeologic studies can the presence and location of such potential traps as facies changes, porosity wedges, overlaps, and unconformities be determined, or the relative timing of petroleum generation and trap creation be ascertained. Such paleogeologic studies constitute research of the purest type, but unfortunately there are large areas where they cannot be carried out, owing to the paucity of fundamental subsurface information. The more an area of adequate sedimentation has been explored, even unsuccessfully, the greater are the changes of oil discovery.

But no matter how great the improvement in the science of oil-finding it is doubtful that the element of chance can ever be eliminated. "Success in exploration depends upon luck and skill. What the proper proportion of each may be, I do not know. Success can be due, as it has been due many times, to luck alone, but I doubt whether it can ever be due solely to skill. The most perfect of prospects, selected by the most refined and exact of techniques, may be a failure. On the other hand, a prospect drilled at random for mistaken reasons or no reason at all may result in the discovery of a new and important oil field." [23]

[21] Research Committee, Am. Assoc. Petrol. Geol., *A Symposium on Petroleum Discovery Methods* (Am. Assoc. Petrol. Geol., 1942).

[22] C. Don Hughes, "Graphic Arrangement of a Symposium on Petroleum Methods," *Bull. Am. Assoc. Petrol. Geol.,* Vol. 26 (August, 1942), pp. 1410–1412.

[23] E. DeGolyer, "Foreword," in Carl Coke Rister, *Oil! Titan of the Southwest* (Univ. of Okla. Press, Norman, Okla., 1949), pp. viii–ix.

Future of the Oil Industry. There is no reason to believe that the demand for oil and gas will not continue to increase each year as it has done, with few exceptions, from the very beginning. Holman [24] estimated in 1946 that in the United States during the succeeding twenty years we would require 30 billion barrels of new oil, if our 14-year "stockpile" was to remain intact. This 30-billion-barrel figure is equal to the total oil produced in the United States up to 1946.

Future of Geology in the Oil Industry. It is obvious that if the oil industry is to discover and produce as much oil in the two decades 1946–1965 as was produced between the year of the completion of the Drake well, 1859, and 1946, it will need all the help from geology that it can get. The immediate future should see continued expansion of geological staffs in order to meet the enormous demand for oil and gas.

Some have expressed the fear that the discovery of a direct method for locating oil might do away with petroleum geology as a profession. Such a discovery is always a possibility, but it is highly improbable that the device would be so perfect that interpretation on the part of the geologist would not still be necessary. The invention of the X-ray and its application to medicine has not displaced the diagnostician; on the contrary, it has given him an additional and valuable tool.

Pratt [25] has pointed out the permeation of the oil industry by geology, and the trend toward geologic administrators in company organizations.

TRAINING FOR PETROLEUM GEOLOGY.[26] Much time has been spent in recent years in discussing the academic background considered essential to a career in petroleum geology (Am. Assoc. Petrol. Geol. Committee) or to geology in general (Conferences on

[24] Eugene Holman, "Facing Forward," *Bull. Am. Assoc. Petrol. Geol.,* Vol. 30 (June, 1946), pp. 1099–1103.

[25] Wallace Pratt, "Geology in the Petroleum Industry," *Bull. Am. Assoc. Petrol. Geol.,* Vol. 24 (July, 1940), pp. 1209–1213.

[26] Reports of Committee on College Curricula, *Bull. Am. Assoc. Petrol. Geol.,* Vol. 25 (May, 1941), pp. 969–972; Vol. 26 (May, 1942), pp. 942–946; Vol. 27 (May, 1943), pp. 694–697; Vol. 28 (May, 1944), pp. 670–675; Conferences on Training in Geology, *Geol. Soc. Am. Interim Proceedings,* March, 1946; June, 1946; March, 1947 (Fourth and Fifth Conferences); August, 1947 (Final Report and Recommendations); Proceedings of Joint Conference of Committee on Geologic Education and Association of Geology Teachers, *Geol. Soc. Am. Interim Proceedings,* March, 1948, Part 2; Report of the Committee on Geologic Education of the Geological Society of America, *Geol. Soc. Am. Interim Proceedings,* July, 1949, Part 2, pp. 17–21; Bradford Willard, "Post-War Geology," *Science,* Vol. 100 (Oct. 20, 1944), pp. 348–350.

Training in Geology). Before considering any specific recommendations emanating from these groups, it is desirable to emphasize the usually neglected fact that the academic training of any geologist, and especially a petroleum geologist, has maximum value at time of starting professional employment, after which the value of his schooling decreases steadily, approaching the vanishing point twenty years later. Other factors, including native intelligence, industry, personality, and on-the-job learning and experience increase in importance until they become paramount.

However, the fact remains that the nature of the geologist's scholastic training is important in first securing and then in retaining a professional appointment. All agree that the embryo geologist should not neglect to obtain adequate background in the cognate fields of mathematics, physics, and chemistry. Biology is a "must" subject for those intending to specialize in paleontology. English composition and report writing are decidedly helpful, for to reach and remain in a position of responsibility almost always requires the ability to write intelligibly. A majority of the conferees on this subject also recommended acquiring skill in at least one foreign language.

The petroleum geologist must have a thorough training in the fundamental courses in geology. These include physical, historical, structural (both elementary and advanced), and field geology; mineralogy and petrology; stratigraphy, paleontology, and sedimentation; and physiography and geomorphology. A field course of at least one summer's duration is of utmost importance. In addition to, and much more important than, learning techniques of geologic surveying, the student in field geology learns fundamental geology itself. How handicapped is the subsurface geologist attempting to study from samples or electric logs a 50-foot bed of limestone who has never worked over such a section in quarry wall or cliff face! Two other courses especially recommended for geologists pointing toward a career in petroleum are petroleum geology and elementary geophysics. Neither of these courses alone can produce a professional petroleum geologist or geophysicist, but they should give the student a foundation for his subsequent professional training.

A perennial subject for discussion is the extent to which the educational institutions should go in attempting to teach such professional procedures as sample logging and electric log interpretation. Such training in techniques can be acquired only at the expense of other, more fundamental, subject matter. A majority of oil-company chief geologists have expressed a preference for men broadly trained in the fundamentals rather than narrowly trained in highly specialistic subjects.[27]

The feeling is practically universal that four years is an inadequate period for proper coverage of the general educational subjects and the essential fundamental courses in geology and cognate fields. A minimum of five years of academic training is recommended.

[27] Report of the Committee on College Curricula, *Bull. Am. Assoc. Petrol. Geol.* (May, 1942), p. 942.

PART I

TECHNIQUES OF THE PETROLEUM GEOLOGIST

The techniques used by the petroleum geologist, or used by others but with which the geologist should have at least a bowing acquaintance, can be classified under two headings: exploration and exploitation. The geologist is primarily concerned with exploration, but he assists in various phases of exploitation.

Chapter 2

EXPLORATION

Exploration methods are of two types: surface and subsurface. In the younger days of petroleum geology, surface methods were used exclusively, but today the greater part of oil exploration is by means of subsurface methods.

SURFACE METHODS

The surface method of exploration is still valid where it is possible, and it is used extensively in prospecting new territory and in resurveying old areas. Surface methods and observations include direct indications of the presence of underlying hydrocarbons, geological surveying, and the utilization of surface maps.

DIRECT INDICATIONS. According to DeGolyer,[1] Benjamin Silliman defined oil seeps as "natural outcrops of rock oil." Other direct indications of the presence of natural hydrocarbons include gas seeps, oil-impregnated rocks, and solid and semisolid asphalts and waxes.

An active oil seep is in reality an oil spring out of which issues anywhere from a few drops to several barrels of oil daily. Almost invariably such seeps are at topographically low spots where water has also accumulated. The lighter oil rises to the top of the water and covers it with an iridescent ("rainbow") film. In rare cases the seep is large enough to make drawing off and marketing the oil a profitable enterprise.

Gas seeps are difficult to detect unless the gas bubbles through water or issues in such volume that a whistling noise can be detected. If the surface of the gas seep is floored with mud, a *mud volcano* may result. Seep gas may be ignited by natural or artificial means, producing "eternal fire." In the Gulf Coast region of Louisiana and Texas,

[1] E. DeGolyer, "Direct Indications of the Occurrence of Oil and Gas," *Elements of the Petroleum Industry* (Am. Inst. Min. Met. Eng., New York, 1940), pp. 21–25; E. DeGolyer and Harold Vance, "Bibliography of the Petroleum Industry," *Bull. A. and M. Coll. Texas,* 83 (1944), pp. 360–361 (21 references).

escaping gas has apparently been responsible for the formation of *paraffin dirt,* soil which has become impregnated by waxy material containing complex hydrocarbons.

Oil-impregnated rock may be filled with seep oil that has worked its way through a considerable body of pervious rock instead of following a single fissure to the surface, or it may be a true reservoir rock that has been uncovered by erosion. In any event, the oil fills the interstices between the grains of sand or the cavities dispersed through the carbonate rock. The Athabasca tar sands of northeastern Alberta illustrate oil-impregnated rock. This occurrence is described in Chapter 10.

There are no lines of demarcation between very heavy oils, semisolid asphalts, and asphalts. These relatively heavy hydrocarbons may occur as impregnations, as small surface deposits, or in large "lakes." The impregnations are exactly the same as the oil impregnations except that the hydrocarbons have lost their mobility. Small surface deposits of tarry hydrocarbons are common around the world in the areas of outcrop of marine Tertiary sediments. An example is the famous Rancho La Brea deposit in Los Angeles, in which so many animals, some of them now extinct, were trapped and entombed. Brea and tar are two of several synonyms applied to semisolid asphalts. *Pitch lakes* are large deposits of asphalt. Outstanding examples are the famous lake on the island of Trinidad in the West Indies and nearby Bermudez Lake on the mainland in eastern Venezuela.

Natural asphalt is similar to the refinery product which supplies most of the commercial demand. Although very heavy oils may be "young" oils which have not yet evolved into the more common types of petroleum, it is probable that most, at least, of the seep asphalts are residual products from crude oil formed by the escape into the atmosphere of the lighter, more volatile, hydrocarbons. It is also possible that chemical reactions with near-surface ground waters hasten the asphaltization process.

Active or "live" seeps are those which continue to be supplied by oil rising from below. Even the asphalt lake on Trinidad is an active seep, as attested by the fact that more asphalt has been shipped from the lake than could possibly have been there in the first place. However, the asphalt impregnating a rock at the surface is usually the relic of a seep no longer active, but even then the asphalt may be acting as a cork, and seepage would resume were the asphalt to be removed.

The geologist should also be cognizant of *false* indications of the presence of oil or gas. Films of iron oxide on water produce the same iridescence as oil. Such films are easily identified, however, by the fact that they break into flakes when stirred, whereas true oil films cannot be severed, but instead the color bands trail out behind whatever is used as a stirrer. Oil seeps also may be created artificially, by either accident or design. Many short-lived oil "booms" have been started by the escape of gasoline or fuel oil from buried tanks and pipe lines. The oil "seeps" in many farm wells have been due to the generous use of lubricating oil on the pump. A book could be written on maliciously "salted" seeps in which vegetable cooking oil, refinery oil of various grades, and, very rarely, imported crude oil were used.

Marsh gas is difficult, if not impossible, to distinguish from natural gas. Both are dominantly methane, CH_4. Marsh gas is caused by the decay of plant material which has accumulated in marsh, bog, swamp, or lake bottom. All seeping gas which has passed through material of this type should be viewed with suspicion until or unless it can be proved that the gas is coming from underlying bed rock. Mud springs are not mud volcanoes, and the two should not be confused. Mud springs are merely springs in which the water emerges from a mud-covered opening.

Contrary to popular opinion, the presence of oil shale is *not* an indication of the probable presence of oil. An oil shale contains no oil and never did contain any oil. It is so named because oil can be generated from the organic material within the shale by the application of heat; the same thing can be done with coal. As a matter of fact, oil shale is usually a continental rock, and most oil reservoirs are marine formations, so, if anything, the presence of oil shale lessens the chances of finding oil within that rock series.

Use of Seeps in Oil Finding. Seeps have been and can be of utmost importance in leading to the discovery of deposits of oil and gas. Whether they are of value or not depends upon whether the seepage is parallel or transverse to the bedding, and, if parallel, upon whether the rocks are gently or steeply folded. Parallel seepage is movement through the reservoir rock by oil which has escaped from a down-dip trap, perhaps through recent tilting. If the dips are very gentle, as in the Mid-Continent, the "mother lode" may be many miles away. In this case the seep merely affords evidence of the presence of oil in a certain formation; it does not immediately lead to the discovery of an oil pool. However, if the folding has been intense, as in most of the Tertiary oil provinces, the leaking trap may be tapped by a well drilled but a few yards from the seep.

Transverse, or across-the-bedding, seepage is brought about by recent fault or other fissure penetrating to the oil deposit itself. In this case the oil may be exploited by drilling in the immediate vicinity of the seep, the location depending upon the dip of the fissure and the depth of the reservoir. DeGolyer [2] has pointed out that seeps are qualitative but not quantitative guides to oil. They have been the means of discovery of many of the great oil fields of Pennsylvania, the Gulf Coast, Wyoming, California, Mexico, Venezuela, Rumania, Russia, the Middle East, the Netherlands East Indies, and elsewhere. On the other hand, seeps have failed (as yet at least) to guide the way to commercial deposits of oil in Washington, Alaska, Cuba, Madagascar, and New Zealand.

Surface Indications in the Gulf Salt Dome Province. In addition to the usual criteria of the presence of oil, some of the salt domes in the Gulf Coast area are marked at the surface by signs peculiar to this type of structure. The salt domes, which are described subsequently, are immense prisms of salt usually topped by anhydrite-calcite cap rock which in a few localities contains native sulfur. The overlying rock is domed, and the adjacent rock has been upturned and truncated by the upward-moving prism. Oil may occur in the arched overlying strata, in the porous zones in the cap, or in the truncated flanking beds. Direct indications of the presence of salt domes beneath the surface include, besides oil and gas seeps, paraffin dirt, sulfur-bearing clay, salt springs, and outcropping cap rock.

Indirect evidence of the presence of salt domes has also proved of value. The upthrusting of the salt has been so recent in many places that the surface is arched in the form of a low hill rising above the flat coastal plain. Where the hill is too low to be recognizable the radial drainage pattern made by water running off the mound has supplied the clue. In other places leaching of the near-surface salt, followed by collapse into the salt caves, has produced a depression instead of a hill. Where the uplift was not in the immediate past, erosion has truncated the dome producing inliers and a circular pattern to the geologic map, which is the best clue of all to the presence of a structural dome. Even where the different formations have not been recognized and mapped, the preference of vegetation for certain

[2] E. DeGolyer, "Direct Indications of the Occurrence of Oil and Gas," *Elements of the Petroleum Industry* (Am. Inst. Min. Met. Engineers, New York, 1940).

types of rock may lead to the development of circular vegetation patterns. Until the early 1920's, all the salt dome oil fields were discovered by one or another, or a combination, of these direct and indirect surface observations.

Soil Analysis.[3] Soil analysis is an oil-finding technique that is also known as geochemical prospecting. It is an attempt to use what might be called microseeps as a guide to oil deposits in the same way that visible seeps have been used. Soil analysis is based on the theory that no rock is completely impervious, and so the lightest hydrocarbons, especially the gases, will work through the cap rock and overburden to the surface. Geochemical prospecting is a natural evolution from the utilization of gas and oil seeps.[4]

According to the theory underlying the technique of soil analysis, not only will gases escape to the surface but also liquid and solid hydrocarbons will be formed from these gases, and their presence can be determined by means of microchemical techniques. McDermott[5] states that the leaking gases are first adsorbed by earth particles near the surface and then polymerized into liquid and solid hydrocarbons. In addition, the gases moving surfaceward are believed to transport subsurface waters and dissolved minerals, resulting in an increased mineral content near the surface.

Many different techniques have been applied in analyzing the soil for evidence of the existence of microseeps. The usual procedure is to obtain samples from varying depths by soil auger, and then to test the samples for one or more of the following: methane, ethane, surface wax, liquid hydrocarbons, and mineral concentration.[6] One variation from the usual chemical procedure is the so-called "geodynamic"

[3] *Soil Surveys* (Geophysical Service, Inc., Dallas, 1939); Eugene McDermott, "Geochemical Exploration (Soil Analysis)," *Bull. Am. Assoc. Petrol. Geol.*, Vol. 24 (May, 1940), pp. 859–881; Esme Eugene Rosaire, "Geochemical Prospecting for Petroleum" (Symposium on Geochemical Exploration), *Bull. Am. Assoc. Petrol. Geol.*, Vol. 24 (August, 1940), pp. 1400–1433; E. E. Rosaire, Eugene McDermott, R. H. Fash, *et al.*, "Discussion of Geochemical Exploration (Soil Analysis)," *ibid.*, pp. 1434–1463; Leo Horvitz, "Recent Developments in Geochemical Prospecting for Petroleum," *Geophysics*, Vol. 10 (October, 1945), pp. 487–493.

[4] V. G. Gabriel, "Present Status of Geochemical Prospecting," *Oil Weekly*, Vol. 118 (Aug. 6, 1945), pp. 50–53.

[5] Eugene McDermott, "Geochemical Exploration (Soil Analysis)," *Bull. Am. Assoc. Petrol. Geol.*, Vol. 24 (May, 1940), p. 859.

[6] Allen Bronston, "Newer Phases in Geochemical Technique," *Oil Weekly*, Vol. 119 (Oct. 29, 1945), pp. 56–58; Leo Horvitz, "Recent Developments in Geochemical Prospecting for Petroleum," *Geophysics*, Vol. 10 (October, 1945), pp. 487–488.

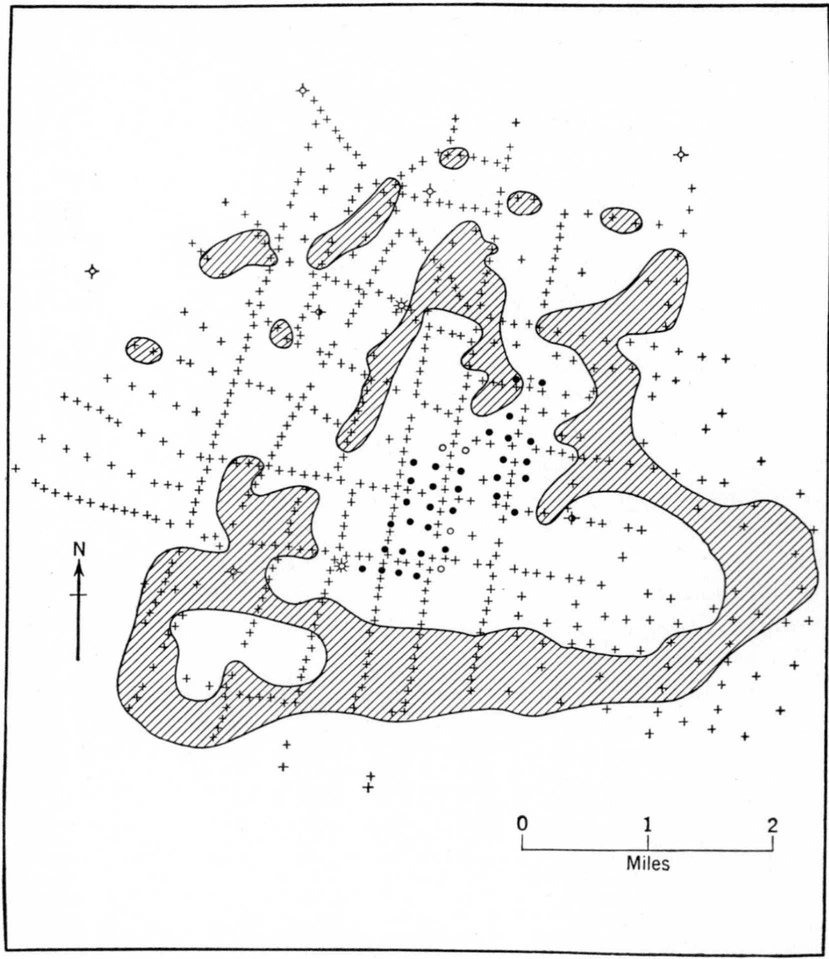

Fig. 3. Soil analysis halos for La Rosa field, Texas. Left: areas of greatest chloride *Geochemical Surveys,*

method, which determines "the time-rate of hydrocarbon leakage through a selected portion of the earth's surface. This phenomenon is essentially dynamic in nature as it measures the volumetric rate of flow of gases escaping from the underground reservoir." [7]

[7] S. J. Pirson, "Recent Development and Success in Geodynamic Prospecting," *Oil Weekly,* Vol. 104 (Jan. 12, 1942), pp. 20 and 24.

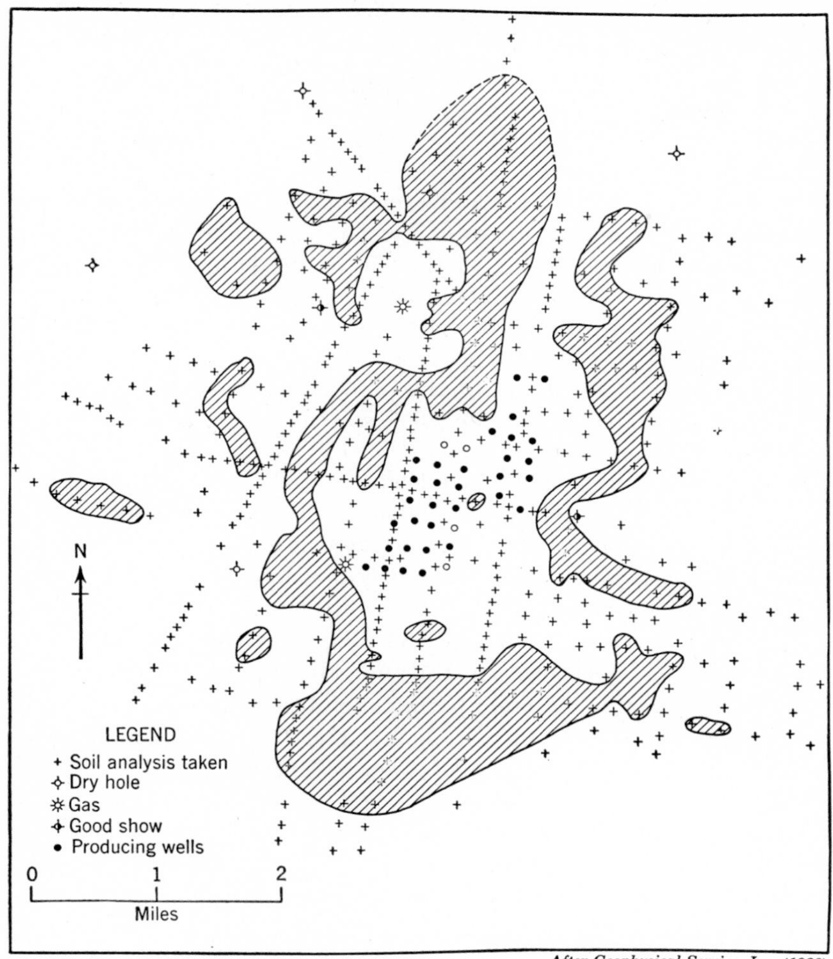

After Geophysical Service, Inc. (1939)

content. Right: areas of greatest concentration of "mineral X." *Courtesy Dallas, Texas.*

Still another variation is the fluorographic method.[8] In this method samples are exposed to ultraviolet light, and the intensity of the fluorescence is measured by a photometer. From the data obtained "isofluors" are constructed which supposedly outline oil fields. Be-

[8] Orton E. Campbell, "The Fluorographic Method of Petroleum Exploration," *World Petroleum,* Vol. 17 (March, 1946), pp. 54–56; E. H. Short, Jr., "Fluorographic Analysis of Soil Samples Used in Search for Oil Deposits," *Oil and Gas Jour.,* Vol. 42 (Dec. 16, 1943), pp. 51 and 53.

cause several million hydrocarbon-oxidizing bacteria per gram have been found in soil soaked in crude oil, it has been suggested that such bacteria might afford a clue to the presence of oil escaping from buried natural deposits.[9] This possible technique has been termed "microbiological prospecting for oil."

The conventional methods of soil analysis appear to show a concentration of minerals in the soil overlying some oil fields, especially those producing from sediments of Tertiary age. The maximum leakage occurs around the edges of the oil accumulation, and so a soil analysis map with its zones of greatest precipitated mineral concentration tends to outline the periphery of an oil pool with a so-called "halo" [10] (Fig. 3). One explanation for the greater activity of gases leaking from the edges of the pool is that oil has clogged the cap rock immediately above the pool, so that escape is possible only about the periphery.

Although some discoveries have been claimed for geochemical prospecting,[11] so far the application of these techniques has resulted in a discouraging number of failures. Greater success has attended the use of soil analysis in the "extension and delineation of established and newly discovered oil pools" [12] than in the discovery of new pools. It has been suggested [13] that geochemical prospecting should be employed over wide areas and that the anomalies found by these surveys be further checked by reflection seismograph before the area of possible accumulation is tested with the drill. The regional reconnaissance can be carried out by soil analysis more cheaply than by seismic surveys, although the seismic survey made to test an area of geochemical anomaly can determine structural detail and the probable depth to the accumulation much better than is possible with soil analysis.

The theory on which geochemical prospecting is based is fundamentally sound. This technique has a major advantage, in theory at least, over all other exploration methods so far developed in that

[9] Claude E. ZoBell, "Influence of Bacterial Activity on Source Sediments," *Oil and Gas Jour.*, Vol. 109 (April 26, 1943), p. 24.

[10] John W. Merritt, "Geochemistry as Aid to Successful Exploration," *Oil Weekly*, Vol. 115 (Oct. 9, 1944), pp. 35–38.

[11] S. J. Pirson, "Recent Development and Success in Geodynamic Prospecting," *Oil Weekly*, Vol. 104 (Jan. 12, 1942), pp. 20 and 24; Leo Horvitz, "Recent Developments in Geophysical Prospecting for Petroleum," *Geophysics*, Vol. 10 (October, 1945), pp. 487–488.

[12] V. G. Gabriel, "Recent Status of Geochemical Prospecting," *Oil Weekly*, Vol. 118 (Aug. 6, 1945), pp. 50–53.

[13] Leo Horvitz, *op. cit.*

it purports to locate the actual presence of a buried oil accumulation, whereas all other oil-finding techniques are for the purpose of locating traps in which oil or gas may be stored. The inadequacies of soil analysis as a prospecting method may be overcome in the future by greater refinement of method. Merritt [14] calls attention to the early difficulties in geophysical prospecting because of lack of cooperation with geologists in matters of interpretation. The development of the same degree of cooperation between geology and geophysics might result in a similar increase in usefulness of soil analysis as a prospecting method. If, and when, soil analysis does evolve into a practical method, it will probably have its greatest success in discovering oil accumulations in the less indurated rocks, especially those of Tertiary age; the tighter, older rocks are much less likely to permit the escape of hydrocarbons to the surface.

GEOLOGICAL SURVEYING.[15] Geological surveying, once the only technique of the petroleum geologist, is now but one of several skills that must be acquired.[16] It is doubtful that field geology will ever disappear as an aid to oil-finding. It is used intensively in exploring new areas, in the re-examination of older regions, and in checking geophysical prospects.

The methods and procedures followed in geologic surveying depend upon whether the survey is reconnaissance or detailed and upon the topography and structure of the country surveyed.

Reconnaissance surveying [17] is for the purpose of determining the oil prospects of a relatively large area in a limited space of time. Fundamental to the survey is a base map on which the observations can be entered. If maps of adequate scale are not available, air photographs must be obtained or the geologist must make his own map by triangulation and plane tabling, by pace and compass, or by other method.

[14] John W. Merritt, "Geochemistry as Aid to Successful Exploration," *Oil Weekly*, Vol. 115 (Oct. 9, 1944), pp. 35–38.

[15] F. H. Lahee, *Field Geology* (McGraw-Hill, New York, 1941), 4th edition; Kenneth K. Landes, *Plane Table Notebook* (Geo. Wahr and Son, Ann Arbor, 1947), 2nd edition.

[16] E. DeGolyer, "Historical Notes on the Development of the Technique of Prospecting for Petroleum," *Science of Petroleum* (Oxford Univ. Press, 1938), Vol. 1, pp. 269–275.

[17] F. G. Clapp, "Fundamental Criteria for Oil Occurrence," *Bull. Am. Assoc. Petrol. Geol.*, Vol. 11 (July, 1927), pp. 683–703; J. J. Zunino, "Evaluation of Oil Exploration Methods," *World Oil*, Vol. 126 (July 7, 1947), pp. 13–20.

The observations made and entered on map or notebook include the following:

I. Environmental and economic.
   a. Accessibility of various parts of an area.
   b. Present and potential transportation media.
   c. Local supply and labor situation.
   d. Local market possibilities.
   e. Location of nearest oil or gas production.
   f. Location and logs of all wells drilled in area and environs.

II. Surface geologic.
   a. Direct or indirect evidences of oil or gas.
   b. Distribution of sedimentary, igneous, and metamorphic rocks. Age of igneous activity and of metamorphism.

III. Stratigraphic.[18]
   a. Thickness of sedimentary rock veneer.
   b. Presence of possible source rocks in section. Age.
   c. Presence of possible reservoir rocks in section. Age.
   d. Presence of possible cap rocks in section.
   e. Position and character of uncomformities.
   f. Lateral changes in facies and especially in permeability.
   g. Convergence.
   h. Presence of soluble rocks in section.
   i. Carbon ratio of any coals present.

IV. Structural.
   a. Size and position of basins and other regional structural features.
   b. Presence of anticlines.
   c. Depths to possible reservoir rocks.
   d. Presence and nature of faults.

The resultant illustrated report contains all the geologic and economic data that were obtained. It also contains a classification of the oil possibilities [19] of different parts of the region and recommendations as to which areas, if any, merit detailed studies or, in some cases, immediate testing without further geological exploration.

The purpose of *detailing* a relatively small area is to determine the areal extent of a surface structural anomaly, its vertical magnitude (closure), and the probable depths to the potential reservoir rocks. The geologist constructs an areal geologic map and a structure map. Positions and elevations are ascertained by plane table, alidade, and stadia rod, or by compass and aneroid, with distance determined by pacing or automobile odometer. However, before the actual mapping

[18] Raymond C. Moore, "Stratigraphical Considerations," *Science of Petroleum* (Oxford Univ. Press, 1938), Vol. 1, pp. 304–305.

[19] Frank Reeves, "Outline for Regional Classification of Oil Possibilities," *Bull. Am. Assoc. Petrol. Geol.,* Vol. 30 (January, 1946), pp. 111–115.

begins, the geological party must prepare and learn a detailed stratigraphic section covering all the rocks involved in the surface work. By means of this section, it is possible to recognize several layers that can be used for elevation determinations and to adjust these elevations to a single datum on which the structure contours are drawn.

A new wrinkle in geological surveying has been the employment of divers to make contact strike and dip readings on the truncated rock layers beneath the sea off the California coast. This information is telephoned to a geologist on the tender, who plots the data on a submarine geological map. Photographs are also taken of the sea-floor outcrops.[20]

The report of the detail party includes the section and other stratigraphic data obtained, as well as the geologic and structural maps. At the same time other branches of the exploration department may have been at work so that concurrent reports are filed covering such possible items as a geophysical survey of the same area and a report from the subsurface department concerning previous tests drilled in the vicinity and their findings. Administrative officers collate these reports and decide (1) whether or not to proceed further; (2) what land to lease; and (3) where to drill the first test. Meanwhile, the geological party has moved to a new assignment.

SURFACE MAPS. The exploration geologist, in addition to using maps and air photographs (exceptionally detailed maps) as an aid in field work, also uses them in the office as a source of much valuable geological information. For example, clues to the presence of structural traps, in which oil may have accumulated, have been found in air photographs and in topographic and geologic maps as well as in structural maps. The leading sources for such maps are the federal, provincial, and state geological surveys.

Air Photos. Although photographs of the ground taken from airplanes were scanned for possible use in petroleum exploration in Oklahoma as early as 1928, it was not until the years immediately preceding World War II that this technique became common in oil-finding. There are two phases in the use of air photos: (1) photogrammetry, which is the transposition into a coherent and accurate whole of the data appearing on many single overlapping photos, and (2) the interpretation of the features appearing in the photographs in terms of geology, engineering, military operations, or other facets of human interest. Among the many geological applications of air photos are

[20] F. P. Shepard and K. O. Emery, "Submarine Photography off the California Coast," *Jour. Geol.*, Vol. 54 (September, 1946), pp. 306–321.

their employment in areal and structural mapping, both reconnaissance and detailed, in the study of shore features and processes, in stratigraphic work, and in mining and glacial geology. The explorer finds air photos invaluable, and the engineer uses them in the construction of topographic maps, for locating pipe lines and highways, and for other purposes. Air photos are used by the agronomist in soil mapping and by the oil company land department for correcting errors in ownership maps and for the inspection of properties.[21]

The petroleum geologist is primarily concerned with the interpretation of land forms in terms of areal and structural geology. This branch of the science has lately been termed "photogeology." It has been the subject of at least two books,[22] one bibliography,[23] and a symposium,[24] as well as many scores of articles.[25]

Although photogeology is possible in regions of widely differing character, including even heavily forested areas,[26] it is most valuable in such provinces as the Rocky Mountains where the terrain is one of "barren topography and naked geology." [27] Under these conditions it is possible actually to see not only the parallel bands of sedimentary rock (Fig. 4) but also the direction and degree of dip of the rock strata. A structure map using strike and dip symbols can be plotted directly on the air photo base; by using photogrammetric techniques it is

[21] Denis S. Sneiger, "Applications for Aerial Photography," *Oil Weekly,* Vol. 80 (Feb. 3, 1936), pp. 19 *et seq.*

[22] Armand J. Eardley, *Aerial Photographs: Their Use and Interpretation* (Harper and Brothers, New York, 1942); H. T. U. Smith, *Aerial Photographs and Their Applications* (D. Appleton-Century, New York, 1943).

[23] G. C. Cobb, "Bibliography on the Interpretation of Aerial Photographs and Recent Bibliographies on Aerial Photography and Related Subjects," *Bull. Geol. Soc. Am.,* Vol. 54 (August, 1943), pp. 1195–1210.

[24] H. T. U. Smith *et al.,* "Symposium of Information Relative to Uses of Aerial Photographs by Geologists," *Photogrammetric Engineering,* Vol. 13 (December, 1947), pp. 531–628.

[25] Especially, A. R. Wasem, "Photogeology Applied to Petroleum Exploration," *World Oil,* Vol. 130 (April, 1950), pp. 64–72; Sherman A. Wengerd, "Newer Techniques in Aerial Surveying," *World Oil,* Part 1 (Sept. 15, 1947), Part 2 (Sept. 22, 1947), Part 3 (Sept. 29, 1947), Part 4 (October, 1947), and Part 5 (December, 1947), which closes with a list of 111 references; W. S. Levings, "Aerogeology in Mineral Exploration," *Quarterly Colo. School of Mines,* Vol. 39 (October, 1944); F. A. Melton, "Aerial Photography Aids Geologist," *Oil Weekly,* Vol. 121 (March 25, 1946), pp. 48, 50, and 65; Bernard M. Bench, "Oil Structure Discovery by Aerial Photography," *Mines Mag.,* Vol. 38 (December, 1948), pp. 101 *et seq.;* Louis A. Woodwood, "Aerial Photogrammetry as Applied to the Petroleum Industry," *Jour. Petrol. Technol.,* Vol. 2 (January, 1950), pp. 9–15; and other articles referred to subsequently.

[26] Laurence Brundall, "La Fotogeologia," *Petroleo Interamericano,* edición de enero, 1948.

[27] Anonymous, "Photogeology Finds Structures," *The Link* (Carter Oil Company, Tulsa, Okla.), Vol. 12 (March, 1947), p. 8.

possible to obtain sufficient thickness and elevation data to draw a structure contour map.[28] Even where the rocks are not so well exposed, structural information may be obtainable from air photos.

Fig. 4. Aerial photograph yielding structural information. Dome, Marfa Basin, Presidio and Brewster Counties, West Texas. *Courtesy Edgar Tobin Aerial Surveys.*

Clues may be had from outcrop, stream, soil color, and vegetation (even submarine) patterns.[29] Some of these patterns, especially soil color and vegetation, may not be visible on the ground, but they are quite

[28] L. E. Nugent, "Aerial Photographs in Structural Mapping of Sedimentary Formations," *Bull. Am. Assoc. Petrol. Geol.,* Vol. 31 (March, 1947), pp. 478–494.

[29] Bernard M. Bench, "Discovery of Oil Structures by Aerial Photography," *Oil and Gas Jour.* (Aug. 26, 1948), pp. 98 *et seq.;* Charles de Blieux, "Photogeology in Gulf Coast Exploration," *Bull. Am. Assoc. Petrol. Geol.,* Vol. 33 (July, 1949), pp. 1251–1259.

prominent in the air photographs. A striking application of air photos to oil discovery took place in eastern Venezuela. The Santa Rosa dome was originally discovered by seismic survey, but the first well, presumably drilled on the top of the dome, was a failure. "Inspection of aerial photographs showed a distinctive, oval patch of light-toned vegetation about 2 miles away from the dry hole. Future investigation proved that the light spot was the top of the Santa Rosa dome." [30] Some of the Gulf Coast salt domes are likewise visible in air photos because of the circular vegetation pattern. Springs in linear arrangement are excellent indicators of fault lines.

In the years immediately following World War II, air photos were employed as a major tool in petroleum exploration in the Rocky Mountain province of the western United States, in the Alberta foothills, in northern Alaska,[31] and in Venezuela.[32]

Prerequisite for acquiring skill in geologic interpretation of air photos are good eyes, training in geomorphology, and field experience. Good eyes are needed to use the various stereoscopic devices by means of which overlapping pairs of air photographs are viewed. A training in geomorphology is essential to the recognition of dip slopes and other geologic features that may have topographic expression. Field experience is vital for the same reason.

Topographic Maps. In addition to their value as base maps for geologic study, topographic maps may also yield structural information of value. The trained eye can recognize dip slopes (Fig. 5), and anticlines can be, and have been, recognized from observations of topographic maps alone. Faults may be traced by their scarps. The recognition of recent domes by circular drainage patterns has already been mentioned. Geological interpretation of topographic maps can be aided by the use of "shaded relief" as shown by the recently published map of the Waldron, Arkansas, Quadrangle. The combination of a little field work and a good topographic map may make possible a geologic map of much greater area than that actually covered in the field.

Geologic Maps. Maps showing the areal geology yield many structural clues. Not only by the presence of inliers but also by the distribution pattern of the outcrops of rocks of varying ages can the struc-

[30] Laurence Brundall, "La Fotogeologia," *Petroleo Interamericano,* edición de enero, 1948.

[31] Norman C. Smith and Sherman A. Wengerd, Photogeology Aids Naval Petroleum Exploration," *Bull. Am. Assoc. Petrol. Geol.,* Vol. 31 (May, 1947), pp. 824–828.

[32] Sherman A. Wengerd, *op. cit.*

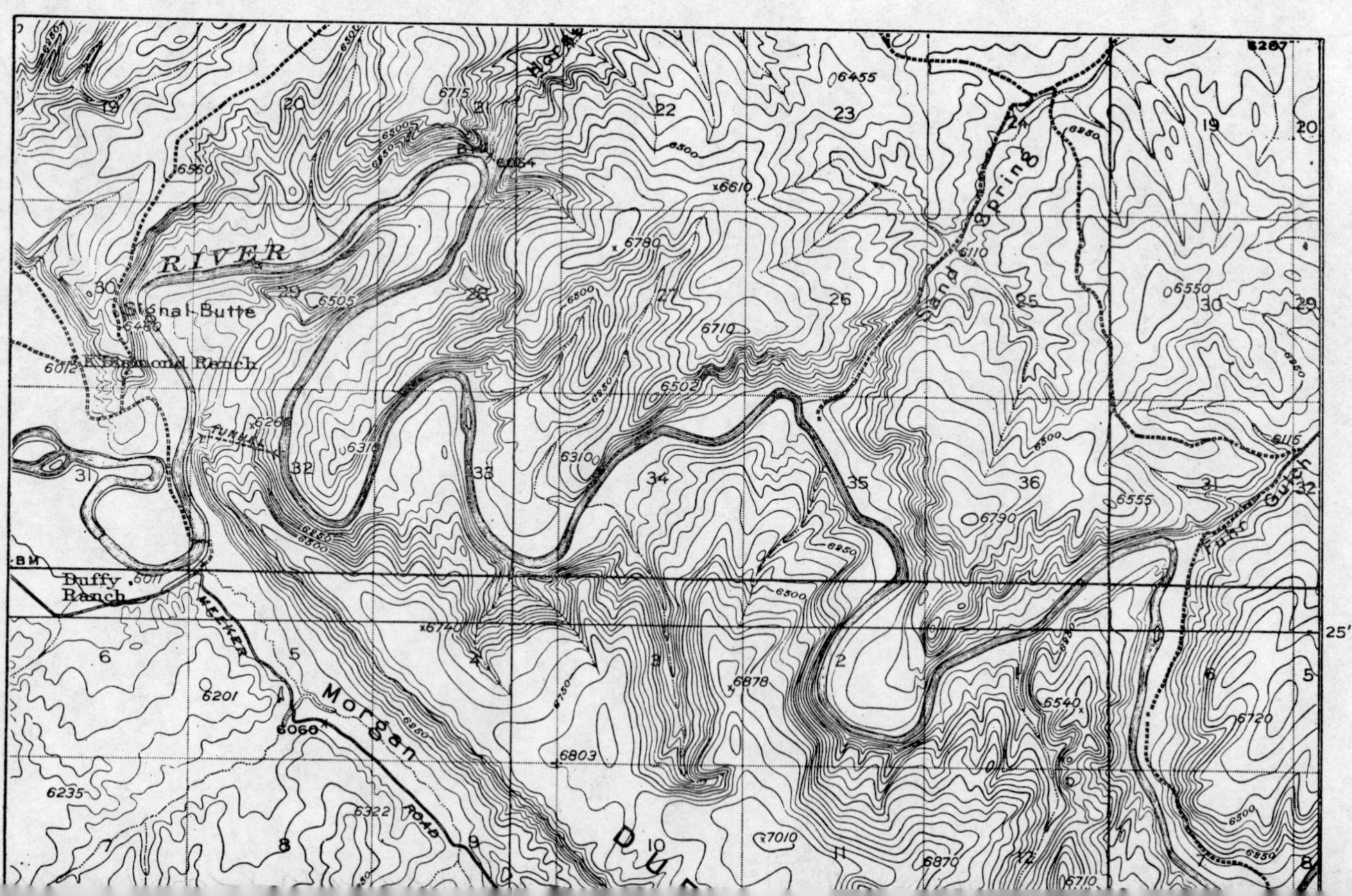
RIVER
Signal Butte
Duffy Ranch
Morgan
MEEKER
ROAD
TUNNEL
Sand Spring
Fuhr Gulch
25'

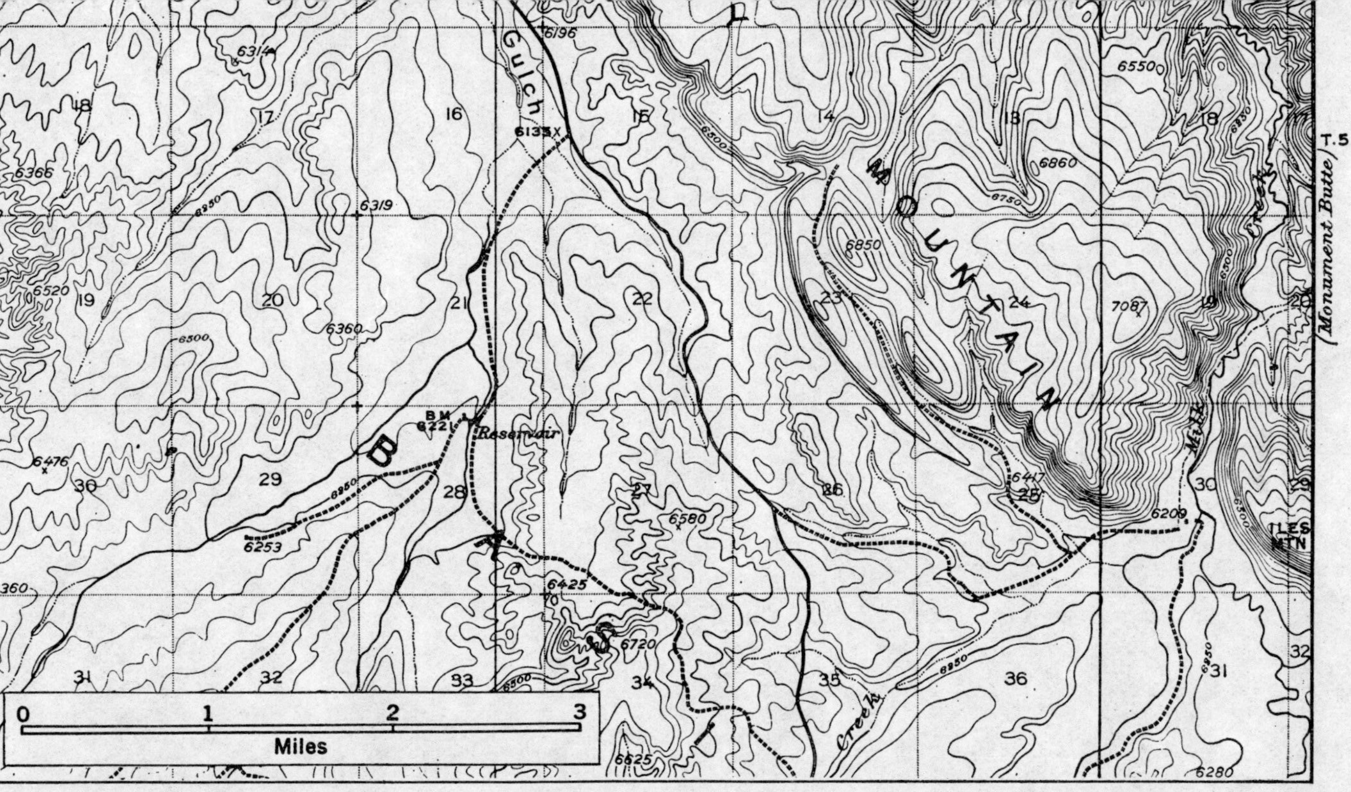

FIG. 5. Topographic map yielding structural information. Duffy Mountain is an obvious hogback, with dip slope to the northeast. Contour interval = 50 feet. *U. S. Geological Survey.*

ture of the bed rock be determined (Fig. 6). In combination with good topographic maps it is possible to determine, by the intersection of contours with formation contacts, the elevation of a stratigraphic

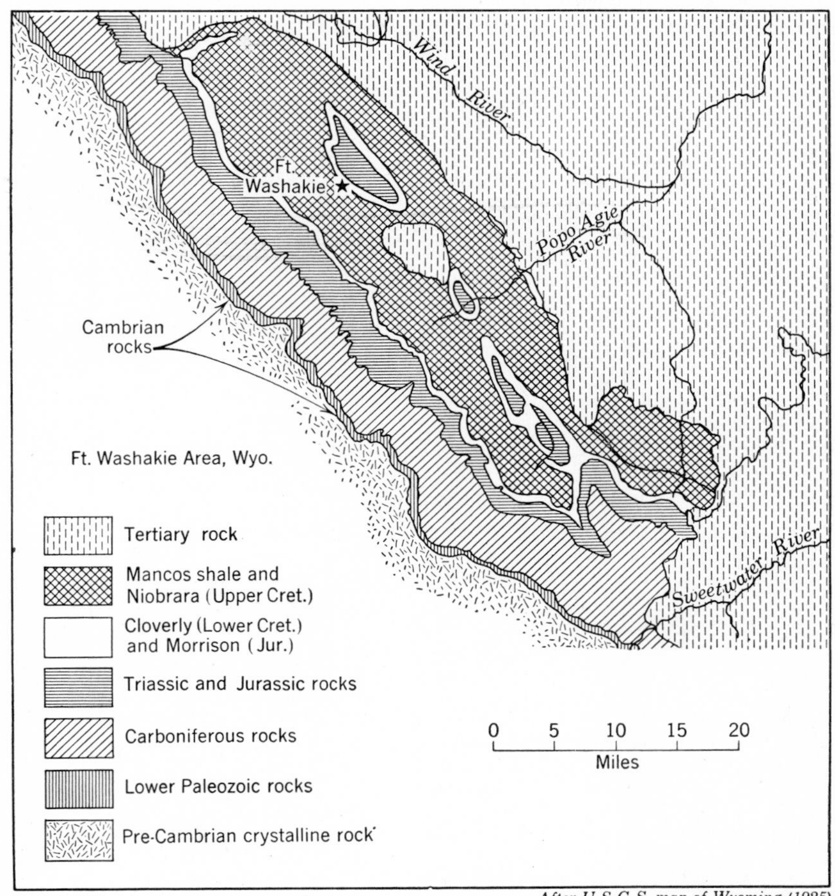

FIG. 6. Geologic map yielding structural information. Syncline, anticline, unconformable Tertiary overlap. *U. S. Geological Survey.*

datum at various points, and from this information a structural contour map can be drawn.

Many oil fields have been discovered through the testing of anticlines and other structural traps mapped and described by a governmental agency such as the Geological Survey, U. S. Department of the Interior.

Structure Maps. Structure maps show, by contours (Fig. 7) or other means, anticlines, synclines, noses, and faults. Many noses that appear on structure maps with large contour interval become closed folds when mapped with smaller interval. Others remain structural noses in the near-surface formations but develop closure in deeper, possibly

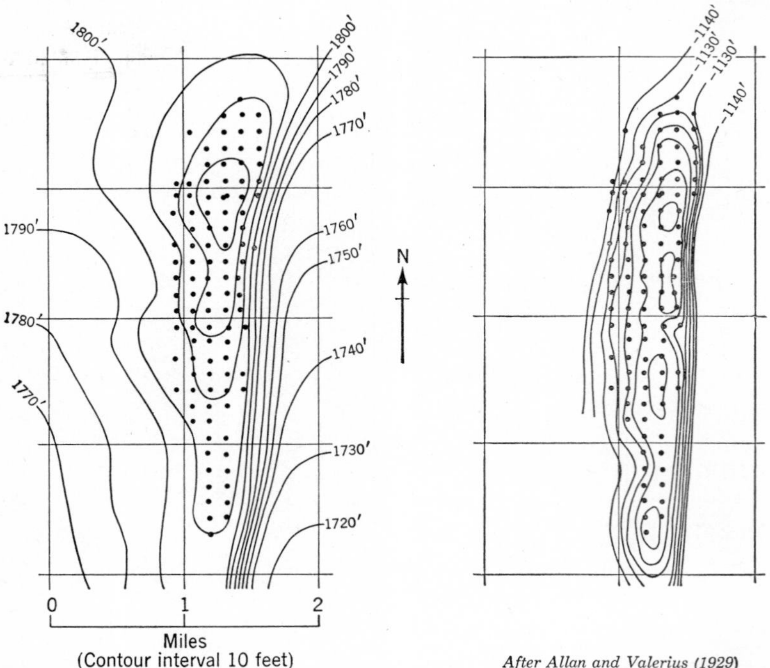

FIG. 7. Structure contour maps. Left: contoured on surface limestone. Right: contoured on subsurface formation. Fairport field, Kansas. *Courtesy American Association of Petroleum Geologists.*

oil-bearing formations. For these reasons structural noses are favorable features for testing.

Even today, after years of exploration in the United States, criteria which lead to testing and discovery are being found by continued study of previously published maps of various types.

SUBSURFACE GEOLOGY [33]

Surface methods of oil exploration can be used only where the bed rock is adequately exposed. If the rock is hidden by a thin capping

[33] L. W. LeRoy and Harry M. Crain, *Subsurface Geologic Methods* (Colo. School of Mines, 1949, Second Edition by L. W. LeRoy, 1950).

of soil, it may be possible by means of dug pits or trenches to expose the underlying bed rock for study. Some oil companies have succeeded in penetrating not only the soil but also recognizable layers of bed rock with hand augers. But where natural outcrops are absent and hand dug or drilled exposures not practicable, or where the sedimentary strata that are exposed cannot be correlated from outcrop to outcrop, structure mapping by surface observations is impossible. By the early 1920's much of the prospective oil territory in the Mid-Continent and the Gulf Coast that could be explored by surface methods had been mapped by some of the older, established oil companies. The oil companies then looked with hungry eyes at the much greater area where the geology was a secret because of a veneer of soil, sand, loess, alluvium, or glacial drift, or because recognition of individual layers in a thick series of red beds or chalky shales was difficult if not impossible. Ever-increasing pressure to find more oil resulted in the development of exploratory tools which in effect give the geologist a "hammer with a longer handle" with which to penetrate the masks that hide the geological picture. The techniques developed to meet this situation include core drilling, geophysical prospecting, and the maximum utilization of the records obtained during the drilling of wells; the practice of these techniques is the relatively young profession of subsurface geology.

CORE DRILLING.[34] One of the earliest uses of the core drill as a device to map possible oil-bearing anticlines was in Kay and Noble counties, Oklahoma, in the early part of 1922.[35] This survey resulted in the discovery of the Tonkawa field, and within a short space of time many core drills were at work in the Mid-Continent and elsewhere. A large number of discoveries, including some major oil fields, can be credited to the geological information obtained by core drilling.

The core drill, as developed for use by the oil industry, is a lightweight rotary drill mounted on a truck. When changing locations, the mast folds forward over the cab of the truck (Fig. 8). Holes can be drilled to depths of over a thousand feet, but most structure drilling is carried on at lesser depths. Soft materials, such as shales, are drilled through with a fish-tail bit; diamond or hard alloy bits are used to cut

[34] E. J. Longyear Company, "Prospecting for Oil" (45 titles), *Bibliography of Diamond Drilling*, 1948 edition, pp. 19–22, and Supplement 1 (March 15, 1949); E. DeGolyer and Harold Vance, "Core Drilling for Structure" (17 titles), "Bibliography on the Petroleum Industry," *Bull. A. and M. Coll. Texas*, 83 (1944), pp. 437–438.

[35] H. G. Officer, Glenn C. Clark, and F. L. Aurin, "Core Drilling for Structure in the North Mid-Continent Area," *Bull. Am. Assoc. Petrol. Geol.*, Vol. 10 (May, 1926), pp 513–530.

(a)

(b)

FIG. 8. Truck-mounted core drills. (a) Shot-hole drilling rig. *Courtesy Seismograph Inc.* (c) Heavy-duty portable rotary rig.

(c)

Service Corporation. (*b*) Rig mast folded over cab. *Courtesy Engineering Laboratories, Courtesy George E. Failing Supply Company.*

a core through rock which may contain the "key beds" which are to be used in determining the elevation of the stratigraphic datum.

The objective of the geologist assigned to a core drill survey is to obtain sufficient stratigraphic elevation data for the recognition and delineation of any structural anomalies that may be present. The usual procedure is to core-drill a series of holes along a straight line in the direction of the regional dip. If any reversal of this dip is noted, additional holes are drilled both along the line of the survey and on both sides in order to map the upfold. It is the duty of the geologist to run elevation lines to the core drill locations and to watch the cores and drill cuttings as they are brought to the surface for the particular stratum, or more often the sequence of strata, which he is using as a datum for a structure contour map. Electric logs are also used to supplement and even replace rock samples in core tests as well as in regular wells. Once the key horizon has been reached, its elevation is determined and entered on the map; at the same time drilling is discontinued and the core drill is moved to the next location.

Core-drilling the geophysical prospects in offshore areas in order to obtain additional geological information has been advocated.[36]

Slim Hole Drilling. The realization, forcibly brought home by the development of the East Texas field in 1931, that oil could accumulate in stratigraphic as well as in structural traps led to a greater interest in subsurface stratigraphy and especially in the tracing of lateral changes in the porosity and thickness of potential reservoir rocks. Inasmuch as most of this information lies beyond the practicable range of the portable core drill, the "slim hole" rig was developed to obtain geological information at greater depths. With this machine, which is merely a light-weight rotary, it is possible to obtain a complete stratigraphic record through thousands of feet of section at lesser cost than with the conventional type of rotary rig. Slim holes have been drilled for geological information in the northern Great Plains and elsewhere, but they have not achieved the widespread use that was anticipated by some geologists at the time of their inception. As at first developed, at least, the slim hole drill could discover but not produce oil, and even in discovery the information was qualitative and not quantitative. Interest in slim hole drilling has recently revived, owing to the success attained by the use of diamond bits in mining operations. It is now anticipated that the oil industry will

[36] J. L. Chase, "Offshore Exploration by Core Drilling," *World Oil,* Vol. 130 (April, 1950), pp. 129 *et seq.*

soon be drilling exploratory wells with diameters ranging from 4 inches down to a mere 1½ inches to depths as great as 10,000 feet.[37]

EXPLORATION GEOPHYSICS.[38] Geophysics is the physics of the earth; exploration geophysics is the application of physics to the search for new mineral deposits. Exploration geophysics has had a long and honorable history in mining geology. Many of the world's great iron-ore deposits were discovered by magnetic surveys, a technique that is now several hundred years old.

It was not until the early 1920's, however, that exploration geophysics became an important tool in oil-finding, but, once it started, the growth and development of this technique were phenomenal. The rapid expansion of the use of geophysical instruments was due to the many successes which followed. Before 1924, thirty-nine salt domes had been discovered in the Gulf Coast of Texas and Louisiana by surface methods. In the succeeding five years sixty-four salt domes were discovered, and many more have been found since. The post-1924 discoveries have been due almost entirely to the use of geophysical instruments. Both gravity instruments and seismic surveys have been successful in this work, and one common procedure has been to use the cheaper gravity survey as a reconnaissance tool, checking the anomalies with the more expensive seismograph survey. The present trend in geophysical prospecting is to combine it with surface observations, using the geophysics to confirm and detail structures whose presence has been suspected by surface observations.

There has been a rather distinct evolution in geophysical instruments since their first application in the search for oil. The dip needle compass of the iron ore surveyor has been superseded by the magnetometer. The pendulum and its first offspring, the torsion balance, have been followed by the readily portable gravity meter or gravimeter, the latest models of which can be carried in automobiles, canoes, and even strapped to a pack board. The refraction method of seismograph surveying has been followed, but not entirely superseded, by the reflection method.

The first important event in the application of exploration geophysics to the petroleum industry was the discovery in March, 1924,

[37] Kenneth B. Barnes, "'Slim' Slim Holes," *Oil and Gas Jour.*, Vol. 48 (Dec. 29, 1949), pp. 34–35.

[38] J. C. Karcher, "Exploration by Geophysical Methods," *Elements of the Petroleum Industry* (Am. Inst. Min. Met. Engineers, 1940), pp. 63–89; Donald C. Barton, "Exploration Geophysics," *Geol. Soc. of Am., 50th Anniversary Vol.* (New York, 1941), pp. 549–569; Harrison E. Stommel, "Subsurface Methods as Applied to Geophysics," *Subsurface Geologic Methods* (Colo. School of Mines, 1949), pp. 695–769.

by means of the torsion balance, of the Nash salt dome in Fort Bend and Brazoria counties, Texas. Within less than a year four additional salt domes were discovered by companies using geophysical methods. Nearly one-half billion dollars' worth of oil and gas have been produced from fields discovered by geophysical methods in the Gulf Coast district alone. The number of parties that are out today at any one time engaged in seismic and other types of geophysical surveys can be counted in the hundreds.

Naturally the great development in exploration geophysics has been accompanied by large-scale publication of articles and treatises. Not only have at least four textbooks [39] been published in English in recent years but also the number of briefer contributions in this field has been enormous. For example, the DeGolyer and Vance bibliography [40] lists 426 titles of articles most of which were published before 1943. The U. S. Bureau of Mines periodically issues *Geophysical Abstracts,* an annotated bibliography of current geophysical papers. The Society of Exploration Geophysicists has commenced the publication of *Geophysical Case Histories.* The first (1948) volume contained sixty papers on case histories of geophysical surveys made principally in the Gulf Coast, Mid-Continent, and California provinces.

Magnetic Methods. All instruments designed to detect magnetic anomalies in the earth's crust, including the currently widely used magnetometer, consist essentially of a magnetized needle mounted so that it will pivot in either the horizontal or vertical plane. The readings taken therefore represent the horizontal or vertical component of the earth's magnetic intensity at that point. Where the fairly common iron-ore mineral magnetite is present in the underlying rocks, the magnetometer or other magnetic instrument records abnormally high readings in that vicinity. Basement rock structures may be reflected in the magnetic map, but usually the prominent anomalies are caused by changes in the character of the igneous rocks within the basement complex. However, the observer may be able to estimate the approximate depth to the crystalline rock floor. The magnetometer also serves to determine the presence of basic igneous rocks, especially dikes and sills, intruded into the sedimentary rock section.

[39] C. A. Heiland, *Geophysical Exploration* (Prentice-Hall, New York, 1940); J. J. Jakosky, *Exploration Geophysics* (Times-Mirror Press, Los Angeles, 1940); L. D. Leet, *Practical Seismology and Seismic Prospecting* (D. Appleton-Century Co., New York, 1938); L. L. Nettleton, *Geophysical Prospecting for Oil* (McGraw-Hill, New York, 1940), 1st edition.

[40] E. DeGolyer and Harold Vance, "Bibliography on the Petroleum Industry" *Bull. A. & M. Coll. Texas* (September, 1944).

The magnetometer has been widely used by the exploration departments of oil companies. It is a highly portable and relatively in-

FIG. 9. Magnetometer in operation. *Courtesy Ruska Instrument Company.*

expensive tool (Fig. 9). Only one man is needed to operate the magnetometer, and he can be trained in its operation in a relatively short period of time. The procedure in making a ground magnetometer survey is to take observations at a series of points according to pre-arranged plans. After being corrected for latitude, the readings are placed on a map, and lines of equal magnetic intensity (isogams) are constructed. Any drawing together or diverging of these lines is indication of a positive or negative anomaly in the intensity of the earth's magnetic field.

The prolific Hobbs, New Mexico, field produces from a structure that was first discovered by the magnetometer and then checked with the torsion balance. The Cedar Creek pool in Bastrop County, Texas, which produces from a serpentine plug, was also discovered by a magnetometer survey.

The latest thing in magnetometer surveys is the air-borne magnetometer. This was developed during World War II as a means for detecting the presence of submarines. The magnetometer is carried in a "trailer" which is towed by an airplane. Immediately upon the close of hostilities this technique was adapted for mineral exploration. It is possible with a single air-borne magnetometer to complete from 500 to 1000 miles of continuously recorded profile per day. In addition the air-borne instrument ignores purely local magnetic disturbances, such as magnetite-bearing erratics, which may make a surface survey completely ineffective. The aerial magnetometer is being employed today as a reconnaissance tool both in oil prospecting[41] and in the search for new deposits of iron ore.

Gravimetric Methods. The motivation for all gravity instruments is the variation in gravitative attraction produced by different masses and different densities. As in the magnetic survey, large anomalies in the gravity picture may be due to differences in the basement rock which have nothing whatsoever to do with the structure in the overlying sedimentary rocks, but the gravimeter is also sensitive to variations in the sedimentary section.

The simplest gravity instrument, the pendulum, does not hang plumb where there is either a mountain or a mass of rock of superior density near by. It is pulled out of the vertical into the direction of the greater mass. Conversely, the presence near by of a depression or of rock of inferior density, such as salt, results in the pendulum's swinging to the opposite side of the vertical because of the superior attraction of the mass in that direction. The pendulum and the torsion balance were the forerunners of the modern gravity meter or gravimeter which is now used almost exclusively in gravity surveys.

The gravity meter is an extremely sensitive instrument which measures variations in gravitative attraction by means of a mass

[41] H. Wayne Hoylman, "Airborne Magnetometer Profiles across Cuyama Valley," *Oil and Gas Jour.,* Vol. 48 (Dec. 29, 1949), pp. 55 *et seq.*

suspended from a balance beam; a suitable spring is attached to the other end of the beam. Readings are in milligals; a milligal is one one-thousandth of a gal, and a gal is an acceleration of 1 centimeter per second per second. The gravity meter, unlike its predecessors,

FIG. 10. Gravity meter. *Courtesy North American Geophysical Company.*

has extreme portability (Figs. 10 and 11), and observations can be taken relatively quickly. When roads are available, the gravity meter is mounted in a truck, at each station a tripod is lowered through the floor, and the gravity meter is moved into position on the tripod from its cradle in the truck bed. Where vehicle progress is impossible, the gravity meter may be carried by hand or in a canoe and periodically set up for readings to be taken. It is also used in offshore surveys.

Underwater gravity work is carried on in at least three ways.[42] The simplest method, possible only in shallow water, is to mount the instrument on a tripod which extends above the water surface. The second method is to lower the gravity meter and the operator to the sea floor in a diving bell (Fig. 12) where the instrument is leveled and the readings taken. In the third method the gravity meter alone is lowered in a pressure-tight case to the sea floor. Leveling and

FIG. 11. Airborne gravity meter. *Courtesy North American Geophysical Company.*

unclamping of the meter are carried out by remote control (Fig. 12), and the readings are taken by a camera enclosed with the gravity meter.

Gravity methods have had their greatest success in the discovery of the piercement-type salt domes because of the marked variations in gravity between the prism of salt and the intruded country rock. In this case, of course, the gravity survey map shows an area of low gravitative attraction above the buried salt mass. Igneous intrusions, on the other hand, appear in the gravity survey map as areas of high gravity attraction. It is likewise possible, as in the Lost Hills anticline of the San Joaquin Valley of California, to identify some anticlines by

[42] R. D. Wyckoff, "Geophysical Exploration," *Oil and Gas Jour.*, Vol. 47 (Nov. 11, 1948), p. 344.

the arched position of a lighter rock such as a diatomaceous shale. It should also be noted, however, that an abnormally heavy rock arched over a domal structure produces quite the opposite results in the gravity map. Inasmuch as upfolds and downfolds may both create the same kind of gravity anomalies, the geologist attempting to interpret gravity records must be acquainted with the local tectonics.

FIG. 12. Gravity meter operated in diving bell. *Courtesy North American Geophysical Company.*

The gravity meter has also had considerable success in the tracing of fault planes.

Seismic Methods. The most elaborate, the most expensive, and the most effective geophysical instrument at the present time is the seismograph. The magnetometer and the gravity meter are generally considered to be reconnaissance instruments, and the seismograph a device for determining the structural geology in detail. Wyckoff [42a] calls attention to the fact that magnetic and gravimetric methods measure forces at a distance and consequently are indirect, whereas seismic methods record sound waves generated at or near the surface, which actually "reach down and touch or traverse the rock strata."

[42a] *Op. cit.*

Seismic surveying is done by either the refraction or the reflection method. Both techniques are based on the fact that shocks created by man-made explosions travel downward into the bed rock and then are refracted and reflected back to the surface by rocks of different density. The length of time involved in that round trip is a reliable indication of the depth of the refracting or reflecting layer. Therefore, these techniques can be used in tracing the structural rise and fall of the rock formations beneath the surface.

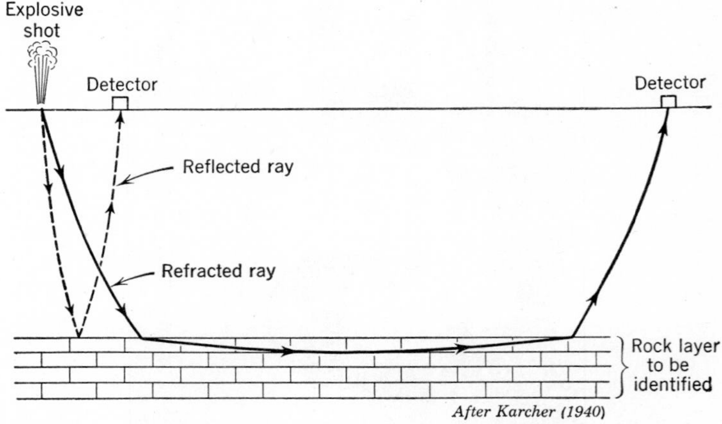

Fig. 13. Reflected and refracted seismic waves. *Courtesy American Institute of Mining and Metallurgical Engineers.*

The difference between the refraction and the reflection methods is shown in Fig. 13. The refraction method was first used in the United States about 1923. It was very successful in the search for new salt domes on the Gulf Coast of Texas and Louisiana. Refraction shooting has recently become important again as a method of detailing rock structure where reflection shooting is not practicable. The reflection method was first used commercially in Texas in 1926. It has been used not only in the salt dome search but also in the search for anticlinal structures. It has largely superseded the refraction method.

In surveying with the reflection seismograph, a shot hole is drilled and an explosive charge is placed in it. For each explosion, or synthetic earthquake, up to 96 detectors ("jugs") are placed on the ground along a line or according to a pattern. The vibration of the detectors converts the earth shock waves into electrical energy which is transmitted by wire to the recording truck. The time taken by the earth waves in traveling from the explosion to the reflecting surface and back to the earth's surface is converted into depths in feet by using different velocities for different types of rock; variations in these depth figures give the interpreter a picture of the geologic structure pattern.

The reflection seismograph is almost a precision instrument. Under favorable conditions, it is possible with this tool to map the three-dimensional aspect of an anticline or a fault with considerable accuracy. Levorsen has pointed out that the degree of accuracy that is available by the seismograph method before the drilling of the discovery well is not entirely an unmixed blessing. "However, the subsurface method, due to the necessity of drilling several wells in order to locate and test the top of the structure, frequently resulted in the discovery of oil in various sand lenses, porosity changes, and other stratigraphic type accumulations. On the other hand, the seismic method by its ability to locate accurately the top of the structure condemns all of the territory intervening between it and the next structure. In other words the seismic method loses oil discovery by its accuracy which in many places the subsurface method gains by its inaccuracy." [43]

Seismic surveying has not as yet been found to be very successful where the bed rock is veneered by a thick cover of glacial drift or where the bed rock itself is composed of high-velocity limestones which lack sharp planes of reflection.

Beginning in 1944 the oil companies began to explore the geology of the floor of the Gulf of Mexico by marine seismic exploration.[44] The procedure is the same as on the land surface except that the explosive is detonated on the sea floor, or below the surface of the water, instead of in a shot hole. The detectors are attached to a cable and let down to the sea floor in a linear arrangement. The recorders are located in a boat instead of a truck. Aside from the weather, which is a most important factor, the only unusual complication in marine work is the problem of exactly locating the detector points. This is done either by triangulation or by electronic surveying, using radar or "shoran," which involves the use of shore range stations.

A recent innovation in seismic prospecting, still in the experimental stage, is the Poulter process of shooting in which the charge, instead

[43] A. I. Levorsen, "Petroleum Geology," *Bull. Am. Assoc. Petrol. Geol.,* Vol. 24 (August, 1940), p. 1355–1360.

[44] R. L. Palmer, "Techniques and Problems in Marine Seismic Exploration," *Oil and Gas Jour.,* Vol. 47, No. 8 (June 24, 1948), pp. 160 *et seq.*

of being placed in a hole in the ground, is placed at the tops of a cluster of poles, 5 to 8 feet above the ground.[45]

Electrical Methods.[46] In the attempt to search for new supplies of petroleum by electrical methods, an electric current is introduced into the ground and the potential effects of the flow of current as it passes through the earth are measured by electrodes at the surface. Unlike the other geophysical methods which purport only to find structures favorable to the accumulation of oil and gas, electrical methods hold out some possibility of locating oil and gas directly. This method has not yet been developed to the point where it has been successful in discovering new deposits of oil and gas, but it has had considerable success in ground-water geology in the location of shallow aquifers.

DRILLED WELLS.[47] The geologist is interested in the techniques of well-drilling for at least two reasons: (1) if he recommended the site for a test ("located the well"), he is much concerned in the adequacy of the well to prove or disprove the presence of oil or gas, and (2), regardless of the success or failure of a well as a producer, it yields geological information, the value of which depends both upon the driller and the drilling method. The geological record obtainable during the drilling of a well consists of logs and rock samples, both cuttings and cores. The character of any oil or gas, and especially of the water, struck during the drilling operations may contribute to the geological record also.

There are two distinct methods of drilling oil wells: the standard and the rotary. The standard method is the older, but rotary drilling has superseded it in most of the newer fields.

Standard Drilling. The standard method is also referred to as cable tool, churn, and percussion drilling. The well is driven downward by the repeated dropping of heavy "tools." The blows struck by the bit at the lower end of the tool string break off pieces of rock,

[45] Charles J. Deegan, "New Seismic Shooting Methods Demonstrated at San Antonio," *Oil and Gas Jour.,* Vol. 47, No. 28 (Nov. 11, 1948), p. 214 *et seq.;* J. E. Kastrop, "The Poulter Method of Geophysical Seismic Exploration," *World Oil,* Vol. 128 (January, 1949), pp. 53–60.

[46] Hubert Guyod, "Can Resistivity Method Discover Oil Directly?" *World Oil,* Vol. 128 (April, 1949), pp. 69–74, and Vol. 129 (May, 1949), pp. 73–77; R. M. Balter, "Electronics Applied to Oil Exploration," *World Oil,* Vol. 131 (July 1, 1950), pp. 72 and 77.

[47] J. E. Brantly, "Oil Well Drilling Machinery and Practices," *Elements of the Petroleum Industry* (Am. Inst. Min. Engineers, New York, 1940), Chapter 10, pp. 116–159.

the "cuttings," which are periodically removed so that deepening of the hole can continue.

The standard drilling rig is illustrated in Fig. 14. It consists of a derrick, usually 84 feet in height, with a sheave arrangement, the *crown block,* at the top. Other essential parts of the rig include the *bit* and other *drilling tools, drilling line, clamps, temper screw, walking beam, pitman, band wheel, bull wheel, sand reel,* and *power plant.* The power plant is some feet away from the base of the derrick. It operates by internal-combustion fuels, steam, or electricity. A belt from the power plant turns the band wheel, and an eccentric on the band wheel operates the pitman, which gives an up-and-down motion to the walking beam. The end of the walking beam opposite the pitman is directly over the hole being drilled. From this end are suspended the temper screw and clamps. The sand reel lies in back of the band wheel and is driven by the band wheel. Across the derrick floor is the bull wheel, which is also turned by the band wheel by means of a large rope belt.

The string of tools consists of the bit, with a V-shaped cutting edge that is sharpened periodically; the stem, into which the bit fits; the jars; and the socket. The jars consist of an inner and an outer section; when the tools are lifted off the bottom, the inner section slides the length of the tool before it takes hold and lifts the underlying tools in the string. This makes a strong upward jerk possible in the event that the bit gets caught in the mud in the bottom of the hole. The socket at the top of the tool string is the means of attachment of the drilling line, which may be either wire cable or manila rope. The drilling line extends from the tool string through the clamps beneath the temper screw at the end of the walking beam and from there over the crown block and down to the bull wheel on which it is spooled.

The up-and-down movement of the walking beam raises and drops the bit at the bottom of the hole. Because of the elasticity of the drilling line, however, the vertical oscillation of the tool string is considerably greater than that of the walking beam. This produces a whiplash effect to the bit, increasing its cutting power on the rock. A few feet of water is kept in the bottom of the hole to soften and emulsify the cuttings. As the hole is deepened the driller adds to the length of the drilling line below the walking beam by turning the temper screw or by slipping the line through the clamps. To "come out of the hole" for any purpose the drilling line is disconnected from the clamps, the rope belt which operates the bull wheel is put

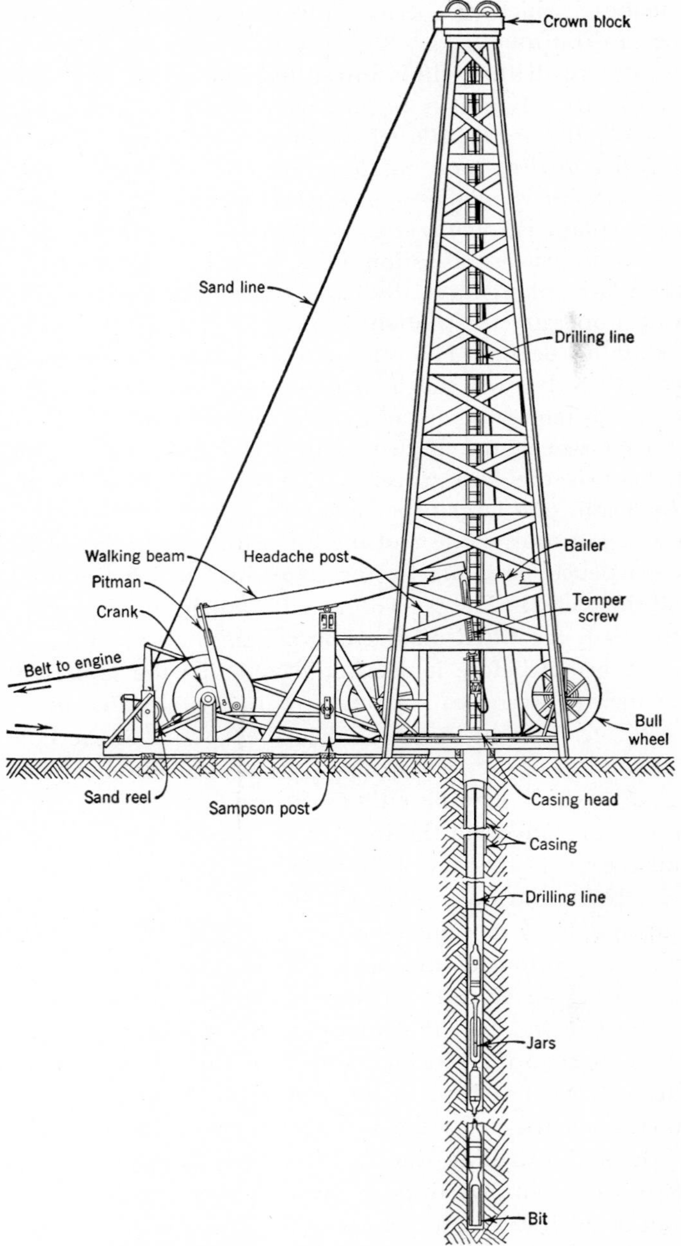

FIG. 14. Cable tool drilling rig. *Courtesy United States Steel News.*

in place, and the line is reeled on the bull wheel until the tools emerge from the hole.

To bail out accumulated rock cuttings and excess water, the bailer, a long steel tube with a valve in the bottom, is dropped down the hole by means of a line spooled on the sand reel. It is brought to the surface and dumped as many times as may be necessary. If a core is desired, the bit may be replaced by a cylindrical core-barrel which has cutting teeth around the lower end. These teeth are driven into the rock, and the core that rises within the barrel is broken off and brought to the surface with the tool string. However, cable tool coring is not as feasible as rotary coring and is resorted to much less often.

The drilling well may encounter a water vein of such magnitude that it is impossible to "dry up" the hole by bailing. Sometimes the water in these aquifers is under so much artesian pressure that it will overflow at the surface. As it is not possible to drill efficiently in a hole full of water, each water vein has to be "cased off." The well must first be drilled below the water sand into a fairly impervious rock such as a shale. Then casing (pipe) is placed in the hole, from the bottom to the top. Cement is forced down the inside of the casing so that it rises for some distance outside the casing, completely filling the annular space between casing and rock wall in order to shut off the water. After the cement hardens, drilling operations are resumed, but a smaller-diameter bit must be used in order to pass through the casing. The cement at the bottom of the well is drilled through, and the hole is deepened to the desired depth. Each succeeding flow of water may have to be cased off in the same manner, and each time this takes place a new and smaller casing must be run inside the preceding casings from the bottom of the well to the top, or "casing head." As a result there may be as many as a half-dozen strings of casing, one within the other, at the surface, and a hole that started with a diameter of 15 inches may end up with a diameter of less than 6 inches.

There is, of course, another reason for the use of casing besides shutting off ground-water flows. Without casing, the wall of a hole may cave. In extreme instances this may block the hole, trapping the tools beneath, and necessitating time-consuming and expensive "fishing" operations. In any event, cavings from above the point where the preceding sample was taken are out of place in the cuttings bailed to the surface, and they tend to confuse the record. For this reason the geologist, in examining cable tool cuttings, must keep in mind the distance below the casing point at which each sample was obtained.

In addition to collecting and labeling the samples, the driller keeps a log in which he enters the depths to the top of each different rock type. He also includes the casing history of the well, the water zones, and any "shows" of oil or gas that may have appeared. Other types of logs also may be made for cable tool wells. These are discussed in a subsequent section.

If the well is successful in finding oil, an innermost line of pipe, the "oil string," is run into the well, higher water is cemented off, and as many of the outer strings of casing are salvaged as possible. The oil flows or is pumped to the surface through the oil string.

Standard or cable tool drilling is ordinarily superior to the rotary method where the rocks are cavernous and where unpredicted oil reservoirs may be present. The cost of the rig is much less than that of a rotary machine, and the drilling costs for shallow wells and for drilling through hard rocks are less. Similarly, the speed is greater in hard rock, and there is much less tendency for crooked holes. Unless one has had long experience with rotary cuttings, the samples obtained by standard drilling are much easier to study.

Rotary Drilling. The turning of the drill pipe in the rotary method of drilling rotates the bit at the bottom of the hole, shaving and grinding off pieces of rock as it turns. The cuttings are removed continuously by a stream of fluid or "mud," which is pumped from the surface down through the drill pipe, out an opening in the bit, and back up to the surface between the drill pipe and the walls of the hole.

The modern derrick for rotary drilling (Fig. 15) is 176 feet or more in height. It can be distinguished from the standard derrick not only by its greater size but also by the presence of a catwalk, or "forble board," around the outside of the derrick, about two-thirds of the distance above the floor. The rotary derrick, like the standard, has a *crown block* at the top and a *power plant* some distance removed from the base of the derrick. The largest machine that has to be powered is the *draw works,* by means of which the drill pipe is hoisted in and out of the hole. Operating by either a "take off" from the draw works or by independent power are the *mud pumps* and the *rotary table.* The latter is circular but has a square slot in the center which turns the kelly (described below). The table rotates in a horizontal plane. Above it, suspended by cables from the crown block, is the *traveling block,* to which the huge *hook* is attached.

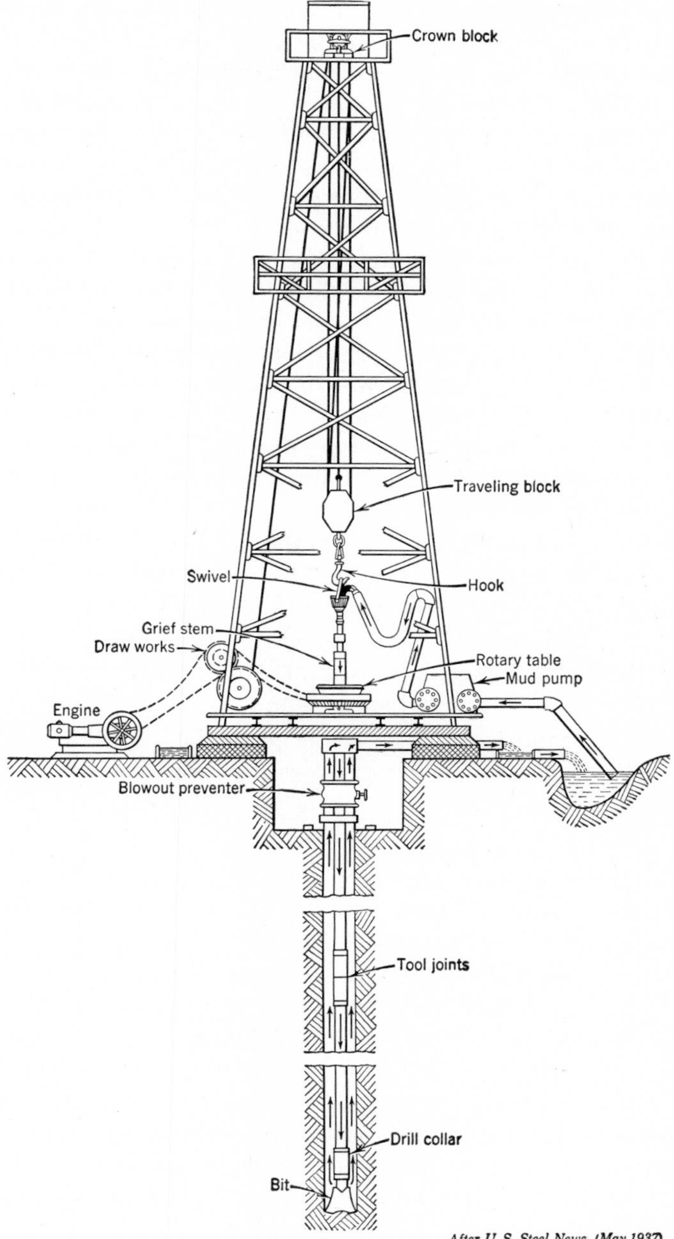

FIG. 15. Rotary drilling rig. *Courtesy United States Steel News.*

The traveling block and hook carry the weight of the tools and drill pipe in the hole. The cable that loops back and forth between the traveling block and the crown block ends up spooled around the reel on the draw works. At the top of the string that extends downward to the bit at the bottom of the hole is the giant *swivel;* the non-rotating section of the swivel is suspended from the hook by steel *elevators.* Next below is the *grief stem,* or *kelly,* which is square in cross section so that it just fits the slot in the rotary table. As the table rotates, at speeds exceeding 300 r.p.m., it turns the kelly which turns the drill pipe which rotates the bit at the bottom of the hole. The *drill pipe,* into the top section of which the kelly is screwed, is circular instead of square in cross section. It serves the dual purpose of turning the bit and acting as a conduit for the drilling mud that is pumped down from the surface. At the bottom of the string of drill pipe, separating the pipe from the bit, are one or more *drill collars.* The bit itself is screwed into the base of the lowest drill collar. Rotary bits [48] are of several types; bits commonly used in cutting rock are shown in Fig. 16. As the bit is rotated on the bottom of the hole, the teeth chip away at the rock. At the same time, a stream of mud issues from the bottom of the bit, keeping the bit and rock formation cool so as to prevent vitrification and simultaneously carrying the cuttings away from the bit and up the hole toward the surface.

The drilling mud is stored in a dug pit or in specially built tanks. The mud is picked up by powerful pumps which drive it through pipe and flexible hose into the top of the swivel, and from there it travels ("circulates") down the drill pipe to the bit at the bottom and then back up the annular space between drill pipe and rock wall to the surface. There the cuttings are removed by screen or settling tank and the mud is returned to storage for re-use. In addition to the lubrication and transporting functions already mentioned, the fluid returning up the hole is under such pressure that it (1) supports the walls and thereby prevents caving; (2) may prevent wasteful and costly "blowouts" when high-pressure gas is encountered unexpectedly; and (3) effectively seals off water veins. The circulating mud may also seal off oil and gas formations; no one can guess the number of reservoir rocks that have been missed in the past in this way. It is now possible to contract the service of a trained crew and a specially

[48] L. L. Payne, "Design and Application of Rock Bits," *Subsurface Geologic Methods* (Colo. School of Mines, 1949), pp. 541–562.

built trailer to aid in detecting pay zones; various devices are used to detect the presence of hydrocarbons, even in exceedingly minute amounts, in the mud returning from the well.

The character of the mud fluid circulated in the well can be, and is, varied to suit different conditions. For drilling through clay, clear

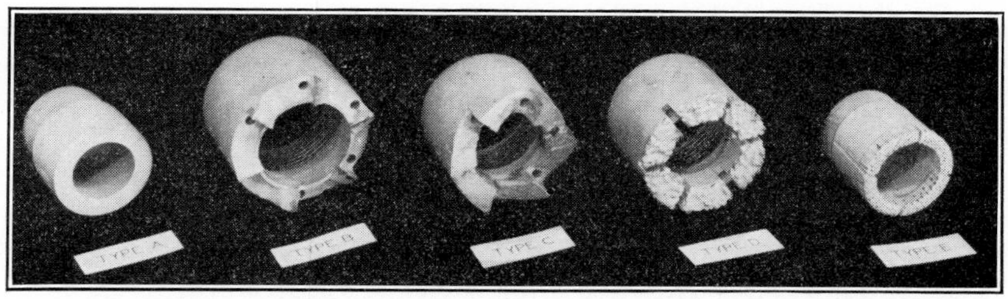

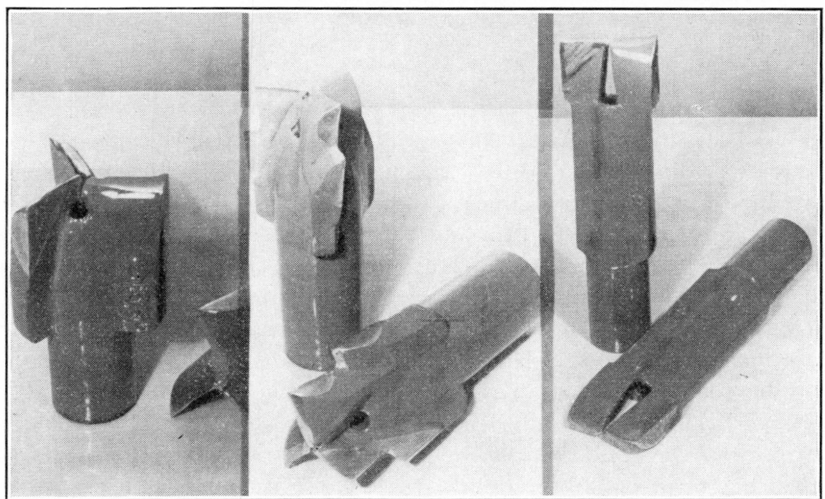

Fig. 16. Types of drilling bits. Top: A, blank bit; B, insert type (soft formations); C, saw-tooth type (soft formations); D, crackerjack type (medium hard formations); E, diamond cast set (hard formations). Bottom: left, three-way bits; center, pilot type; right, fish tail bits. *Courtesy George E. Failing Supply Company.*

water (which weighs 8.35 pounds per gallon) is used. The usual mud is a clay/water mixture that weighs from 9½ to 10 pounds per gallon. For drilling through salt, a saturated brine is prepared so that the liquid will not dissolve the wall rock. A pulverized limestone mud, weighing about 11½ pounds per gallon, is used when drilling cavernous rocks. If strong gas pressures are anticipated, the weight of the mud may be built up to 17 or more pounds per gallon by adding pulverized barite or other heavy minerals. Still other ingredients may be added to change the viscosity or the gel strength of the fluid.

Highly cavernous rocks may cause much trouble because of "lost circulation." Many tons of hay, and even stranger material, may be added to the fluid pumped into the hole in the hope of either filling the caves which are "stealing" the mud or damming the channelways so that circulation can be restored.

Obviously, bringing the bit out for replacement is much more complicated when the bit is at the bottom of a string of rigid steel pipe than when it is suspended by a cable. When the hole is deep, a round trip consumes many hours. In coming out of the hole, the string is first raised above the bottom of the kelly and steel wedges or "slips" placed in position to prevent the string from dropping back down. The kelly with overlying swivel is disconnected from the string and dropped into a slanting hole, the "rat-hole" prepared for this purpose, where they are out of the way. Subsequently, the string is raised, three or four lengths of drill pipe at a time, above the derrick floor, the pipe below is suspended by the slips, and the three- or four-length sections are unscrewed and racked in a corner of the derrick. One member of the crew, mounted on the forble board high up in the rig, assists in the racking. Eventually the bit is brought to the surface and replaced, and the entire procedure is repeated in reverse.

During the drilling of a rotary well, the driller watches a gauge and by means of controls regulates the pressure on the bit at the bottom of the hole in accordance with the character and the structure of the rock. The bit in a rotary-drilled hole can wander off from the vertical for a considerable distance and still be rotated by the drill pipe. Crooked holes in the Seminole District, Oklahoma, reached such magnitude that the depth figures were as much as 800 feet (in 4000 feet) greater than the actual depth. The lateral distance across which the bit wandered was as much as the distance between wells.[49] Obviously, geological records, such as structure contour maps, made from the logs of crooked holes are of questionable value. Since the hectic days at Seminole, however, the technique of drill hole surveying[50] has developed to such an extent that it is now possible to determine the exact position, both horizontally and vertically, of any point in a rotary-driven well. Modern practice is to determine devia-

[49] F. H. Lahee, "Crooked Holes—Next Important Problem," *Oil and Gas Jour.* (March 28, 1929), pp. 38 *et seq.*

[50] J. B. Murdock, Jr., "Oil Well Surveying," *Subsurface Geologic Methods* (Colo. School of Mines, 1949), pp. 470–479.

tion before it becomes serious and resume a vertical course by use of a *whipstock* (Fig. 17), which is placed in the hole and which diverts the bit back into the desired direction.[51]

Not only have the petroleum engineers learned how to prevent "crooked" holes but also they have developed a technique for diverting holes [52] when desired. A very practical application of this technique has been in killing "wild" wells by drilling a new well so as to intercept the blowing or burning well at depth and then pumping water or mud into the wild well until it is finally subdued.[53] Other uses of directional drilling include redrilling the lower part of the stratigraphic section in order to penetrate a laterally inconsistent pay zone missed by the first (straight) hole, and using one expensive drilling site, such as an over-water crib, for the drilling of as many as four diverging holes.

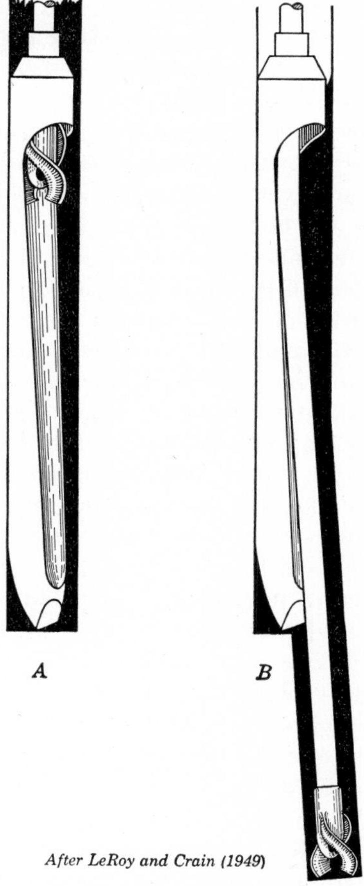

FIG. 17. Whipstock. Left: bit coming into whipstock at top. Right: bit and drill stem, diverted by whipstock, digging new hole. *Courtesy Colorado School of Mines.*

The rock samples obtained in rotary drilling are of two types, cuttings and cores.[54] Rotary drill cores can be obtained in three ways: by conventional core barrel, by wireline core barrel, and by a side-wall corer. The conventional core barrel is placed at the end of the drill pipe string in place of the usual bit. As the barrel rotates, teeth at the bottom cut out a core which rises in-

[51] John R. Suman, "Drilling, Testing and Completion," *Elements of the Petroleum Industry* (Am. Inst. Min. Met. Engineers, New York, 1940), pp. 161–180.

[52] J. B. Murdock, Jr., "Controlled Directional Drilling," *Subsurface Geologic Methods* (Colo. School of Mines, 1949), pp. 433–469.

[53] Gordon B. Nicholson, "Directional Hole Tames Canadian Wild Well," *World Oil,* Vol. 128 (October, 1948), pp. 213 *et seq.*

[54] H. L. Landua, "Coring Techniques and Applications," *Subsurface Geologic Methods* (Colo. School of Mines, 1949), pp. 524–541.

side the barrel as the hole is deepened. When the barrel is filled, the driller must come out of the hole and remove the core. This is a time-consuming process, but it does result in a core of maximum possible thickness.

The wire-line method of coring removes the necessity of making a round trip in order to remove the core. With this method, an outer barrel, or drill collar, with fish-tail type of bit on the end is kept at the bottom of the drill pipe. "Ordinary drilling may be done in the usual manner by dropping a bit plug inside the drill pipe to shut off the main core-barrel passage through the bit and divert circulation through ports to the bit blades. When a core is to be taken, the bit plug is removed by means of an overshot run inside the drill pipe on a wire line. The inner core barrel with a core-catcher assembly in the bottom and a vent valve in the top is then dropped inside the drill pipe and automatically latches into place in the drill collar. After the core has been cut, the inner core barrel is removed by means of the same overshot and wire line used to recover the bit plug." [55]

A fairly recent development in bottom-hole coring has been a return to the use of diamond drill bits. Since the early 1920's, hard-metal rock bits have been used for oil field coring in order to lower costs, but it has been at the expense of complete core recovery. With the growing importance of stratigraphic detail to oil-finding and maximum possible recovery of oil, the geologists and production engineers have found the gaps in the cores, unavoidable with conventional bits, to be decidedly undesirable. The diamond-studded bits enable the driller to obtain from 95 to 100 per cent core recovery. Furthermore, experience has shown diamond drilling to be faster and cheaper in hard formations.[56]

Side-wall coring has proved to be highly practicable, and as a result, several different methods of coring and types of side-wall corers have been developed. These may be classified into three groups: punch, percussion, and rotary.[57] The punch type sends a small core barrel (or several barrels) into the wall of the open hole by the force exerted by the weight of the drill pipe above the corer. The percussion or

[55] John R. Suman, "Drilling, Testing and Completion," *Elements of the Petroleum Industry* (Am. Inst. Min. Met. Engineers, New York, 1940), pp. 181–183.

[56] Karl J. Klapka, "Drilling with Industrial Diamonds," *World Oil,* Vol. 128 (October, 1948), pp. 98 *et seq.;* Joseph J. Sanna and Robert L. Poundstone, "Diamond Drilling in the Oil Industry," *Mines Mag.,* Vol. 39 (December, 1949), pp. 30 *et seq.*

[57] J. E. Kastrop, "Sidewall Sampling Tools and Techniques," *World Oil,* Vol. 128 (Part 1, November, 1948, pp. 100 *et seq.;* Part 2, December, 1948, pp. 76 *et seq.*).

bullet type of side-wall corer shoots a core barrel into the wall, whence it is retrieved by a wire line initially attached to one end of the "bullet." The third type is a laterally directed rotating bit and core barrel operated by electric motor lowered into the hole.

In actual practice, side-wall coring is usually done only after the hole has been drilled and an electric log made. Then side-wall cores are obtained at points which may be indicated by a study of the electric log, or at points where bottom-hole coring was inadequate because of missed sections or incomplete recovery. The advantages of this method are several.[58] Complete bottom-hole coring is expensive and often unnecessary. By first completing the hole and then examining critical parts of the section (as determined from the electric log) by side-wall cores, adequate data regarding porosity, saturation, contacts, facies, and so forth can be obtained at minimum expense. Furthermore, portable core-testing equipment and personnel can be brought to the well for use during this relatively brief period of coring, instead of periodically shipping cores in to the main laboratory.

In addition to noting the data for a time log, the rotary driller also writes up a log based on his identification of the cutting and core samples produced. But much more important in rotary drilling is the opportunity to obtain an electric log, which is not possible in wells drilled with cable tools because of the presence of casing. The running and use of electric and other logs are discussed in a subsequent section.

The usual practice in rotary drilling is to case off the surface water by a relatively short string of casing and then go the rest of the way without casing. However, if the well is to be drilled to depths in the neighborhood of 15,000 feet or more, an intermediate string of casing is set. The mud fluid kept in the hole at all times prevents caving. If oil or gas is struck, casing is run to the producing zone and cemented into place, and the mud is pumped out.

The advantages of the rotary method over standard drilling are such that this method has displaced the standard in most areas, especially where deep drilling is practiced. The necessity of repeatedly inserting a string of casing and then proceeding with a smaller hole places a severe limitation on the depths that can be reached with cable tools. Very few standard wells have been drilled over 5000 feet, and the deepest well on record of this type was bottomed at 10,096 feet.[59]

[58] H. Lee Flood, "Sidewall Coring in the Gulf Coast Area," *Petrol. Engineer*, Vol. 12 (March, 1941), pp. 156–157.

[59] F. M. Van Tuyl and W. S. Levings, "Review of Petroleum Geology in 1945," *Quarterly Colo. School of Mines*, Vol. 41 (July, 1947), p. 10.

On the other hand, there is no known limit to the depth to which rotary wells can be drilled. The deeper wells require larger, heavier, and costlier equipment. The limitation on drilling deeper is purely economic; when drilling costs exceed possible returns there is no point in continuing further.

Other advantages of the rotary method include the shutting off of water sands without resorting to casing, much less caving, lesser blowout hazard, greater completion diameter, less cost per foot for deep wells, greater speed (as much as 1000 feet per day) in soft rocks, and the ready availability of cores and electric logs.

A combination type of rig is very popular with some operators. This rig has both a rotary table and a walking beam. One common procedure is to drill through the upper rocks, especially where shales are abundant, by the rotary method and then to convert ("standardize") to cable tools and drill the well into the potential reservoir rocks by this means. Where the water lies close below the oil, so that the driller wants merely to puncture the top of the reservoir, this procedure is ideal. If he drills in with rotary tools, he might go through the oil and into the water before he knows that he has reached the reservoir rock.

Drilling Depths.[60] The date and depth of the first drilled well are unknown. Goodrich [61] mentions a brine well in China drilled to 450 feet about 221 B.C. By A.D. 1854, wells were being drilled below 2000 feet; an artesian water well in St. Louis reached a depth of 2193 feet that year. After somewhat over 2000 years of well drilling, in 1928, the deepest well was a producer in west Texas which had penetrated 8523 feet into the earth's crust. The deepest well as of October, 1950, was a test in Sublette County, Wyoming, which reached a depth of 20,521 feet before being abandoned as a dry hole. The downward discovery of oil has not, for the time being at least, kept pace with drilling depths; the deepest producer in 1928 was also the deepest well, but the deepest producer in October, 1950, was a California well producing from 15,530 feet, nearly 5000 feet above the bottom of the deepest test.

There is nothing in sight to stop the continuing establishment of new drilling depth records except the complete penetration of the sedimentary rock veneer. Inasmuch as the maximum depth to the

[60] Ernestine Adams, "Deep Drilling Is Finding Oil," *Petrol. Engineer,* Vol. 19 (February, 1948), pp. 43–50.

[61] H. B. Goodrich, "Early Exploration Methods," *World Petrol.,* Vol. 10 (May, 1939), p. 32.

basement rocks in the Gulf Coast and California provinces probably lies somewhere between 30,000 and 50,000 feet or deeper, we can expect the record-breaking testing to continue as long as the price of oil justifies such expensive exploration.

SAMPLES. The materials obtained during the drilling, and after completion, of both exploratory and oil and gas wells are of utmost value to the petroleum geologist and to the petroleum engineer. The petroleum geologist uses the materials obtained from the subsurface to give him a three-dimensional picture of the earth's crust; the engineer decides on the treatment to be given the well itself, and the future development of the area, from these samples. Types of earth materials collected and studied during the life of a well include rock cuttings, cores, water, oil, and gas. The petroleum geologist is most concerned with the rock samples.

Cuttings.[62] Cuttings are the rock fragments broken or torn from the rock being drilled by the bit at the bottom of the hole. Where cable tools are used, the cuttings are broken from the rock by the pounding of the sharpened edge of the bit. They are periodically removed by the bailer, and samples are caught on the derrick floor when the bailer is dumped. The samples are placed in cloth sacks which are labeled as to depth, well name, and location. Rotary cuttings are torn from the rock by the rotating bit and are brought to the surface by the circulation of the drilling mud. There samples are caught by either a "shale shaker" or by a box connected to the mud return line. These samples are likewise sacked and labeled, but determining the depth figure is not the simple procedure it is with cable tool cuttings because of the time lag between the tearing off and the capture of the sample, during which interval the drill has continued to "make hole." However, the circulation time can be calculated by rule of thumb, or by actually timing the circulation of an easily identifiable substance, such as rice or corn. These data, coupled with the time log kept by the driller, will permit a fairly accurate estimate of the true depth. The estimates can be subsequently checked against the electric log for accuracy.

In earlier days of rotary drilling, the samples obtained were of questionable value because of contamination with cavings from higher beds, powdering the sample by the bit, failure of the mud to carry the samples to the surface, and recirculation of the cuttings themselves. Through an intensive study of drilling muds, the engineers

62 John M. Hills, "Sampling and Examination of Well Cuttings," *Bull. Am. Assoc. Petrol. Geol.,* Vol. 33 (January, 1949), pp. 73–91.

have worked out the weights, consistencies, and pressures necessary to "mud off" the higher beds adequately and at the same time pick up the cuttings and bring them to the surface with efficiency and dispatch. Recirculation of rock fragments can be prevented by the use of large settling pits. Although the cuttings differ in appearance, because they are sheared from the rock instead of being hammered off, rotary samples obtained by modern methods are of comparable geologic value to those obtained by cable tool drilling. Some rotary samples are superior to cable tool samples, owing to larger size.

Both types of samples must be "washed" before being used for geologic study. This is in reality a rinsing process which removes the dust or mud film that coats the rock fragments and so makes their recognition difficult, if not impossible.

The size of the sample particles is highly variable because of a number of factors, including drilling method, type of bit, sharpness of bit, hardness of rock, and consistency of rock. Some of these factors are inherent rock characteristics, but others are subject to drilling variations, and so size of particles is not a reliable characteristic for use in correlation. It should be noted that only for a friable clastic rock, such as a sandstone, is the particle size also the grain size.

Well cuttings are examined by the geologist with a binocular microscope. The first step is the identification of the rock or rocks represented in the sample. The purpose of the examination may be either to look for actual or potential oil or gas reservoir rock, or to correlate the rocks with those known elsewhere, or both. In the first case the examiner is especially concerned with possible oil stains and with evidence concerning the character and the degree of porosity and permeability of the rock. He also studies the samples for clues that might lead to nearby reservoir rocks. Coarse sand grains in shale suggest nearby lenses of sandstone, and calcareous zones in shale may be peripheral to limestone reefs.[63] If correlation is the primary objective of the geologist he searches for lithologic and paleontologic characteristics which may be diagnostic. At the same time he looks for evidences of unconformities.[64]

The usual procedure in the examination of well cuttings is to prepare a plotted sample log, which is described in the next section.

[63] Paul Weaver, "The Geological Interpretation of Exploratory Wells," *Oil and Gas Jour.*, Vol. 47 (March 17, 1949), pp. 102–104; *Bull. Am. Assoc. Petrol. Geol.*, Vol. 33 (July, 1949), pp. 1135–1144.

[64] W. C. Krumbein, "Criteria for Subsurface Recognition of Unconformities," *Bull. Am. Assoc. Petrol. Geol.*, Vol. 26 (January, 1942), pp. 36–62.

In special cases, however, the samples may be given unusual treatment. If fossils, especially microfossils, are abundant and are used locally in correlation, they will be sorted out from the inorganic materials and studied by a specialist.[65] Sands and incoherent sandstones can be studied by the usual techniques of the sedimentologist,[66] including the separation and examination of the heavy minerals present.[67] The insoluble residues obtained by the digestion of carbonate rock in acid have been used with success in correlation.[68] Another possible correlation tool is the X-ray; [69] the diffraction pattern obtained from a powdered sample of a rock is due to the mineral composition of that rock and may be diagnostic.

Cores. The cores which may be obtained during the drilling of a well are of utmost value to both production engineer and geologist. The engineer can obtain quantitative data regarding porosity, permeability, and oil saturation; with cuttings, such data are largely qualitative. For core analysis [70] the engineering department has a well-

[65] Martin F. Glaessner, *Principles of Micropalaeontology* (Wiley, New York, 1949); A. Morley Davies, "Paleontology," *The Science of Petroleum* (Oxford Univ. Press, 1938), Vol. 1, pp. 306–308; W. L. F. Nuttall, "Micro-Paleontology," *ibid.*, pp. 309–311; Hubert G. Schenck, "Applied Paleontology," *Bull. Am. Assoc. Petrol. Geol.*, Vol. 24 (October, 1940), pp. 1752–1778; Carey Croneis, "Micropaleontology—Past and Future," *Bull. Am. Assoc. Petrol. Geol.*, Vol. 25 (July, 1941), pp. 1208–1255; L. W. LeRoy, "Micropaleontologic Analysts," *Subsurface Geologic Methods* (Colo. School of Mines, 1949), pp. 58–86.

[66] I. E. Gardescu and M. H. Billings, "Use of Mechanical Sand Analyses for Correlation Purposes," *Bull. Am. Assoc. Petrol. Geol.*, Vol. 21 (October, 1937), pp. 1311–1332; Gordon Rittenhouse, "Detrital Mineralogy," *Subsurface Geologic Methods* (Colo. School of Mines, 1949), pp. 87–111; L. W. LeRoy, four papers on sedimentology, *op. cit.*, pp. 151–168.

[67] R. D. Reed and J. P. Bailey, "Subsurface Correlation by Means of Heavy Minerals," *Bull. Am. Assoc. Petrol. Geol.*, Vol. 11 (April, 1927), pp. 359–368; A. Brammall, "The Correlation of Sediments by Mineral Criteria," *Science of Petroleum* (Oxford Univ. Press, 1938), Vol. 1, pp. 312–314.

[68] Raymond Sidwell, "Aid of Sedimentary Petrology to the Discovery of Oil," *Jour. Sed. Petrol.*, Vol. 13 (December, 1943), pp. 112–116; H. A. Ireland, "Insoluble Residues," *Subsurface Geologic Methods* (Colo. School of Mines, 1949) pp. 111–128.

[69] D. H. Reynolds, Eldon A. Means, Lindsey G. Morgan, "Application of X-Ray Crystal Analysis to a Problem of Petroleum Geology," *Bull. Am. Assoc. Petrol. Geol.*, Vol. 21 (October, 1937), pp. 1333–1339; N. Cyril Schieltz, "X-Ray Analysis," *Subsurface Geologic Methods* (Colo. School of Mines, 1949), pp. 211–238.

[70] E. DeGolyer and Harold Vance, "Bibliography on the Petroleum Industry," *Bull. A. and M. Coll. Texas*, 83 (1944), pp. 355–360 (6 pages of references); John R. Suman, "Drilling, Testing, and Completion," *Elements of the Petroleum Industry* (Am. Inst. Min. Met. Eng., New York, 1940), pp. 187–196; M. D. Taylor, "Determination of the Porosity, Permeability, and Saturation of Core Samples," *Oil and Gas Jour.*, Vol. 40 (Nov. 20, 1941), pp. 40 *et seq.;* G. E. Archie, "Electrical Resistivity an Aid in Core Analysis Interpretation," *Bull. Am. Assoc. Petrol. Geol.*, Vol. 31 (February, 1947), pp. 350–366; John C. Calhoun, Jr., "Methods of Obtaining Poros-

equipped laboratory and in addition may have a truck-mounted portable laboratory for rapid determinations in the field. Porosity, which is expressed in percentage, is the ratio of the volume of pore space to the total bulk volume. Permeability is "the volume of fluid of unit viscosity passing through a unit cross section of the material under a unit pressure gradient in unit time." [71] The unit of permeability is the "darcy," or, more commonly, the "millidarcy," which is 0.001 darcy. Saturation studies are for the purpose of estimating the percentages of pore space occupied by oil and by water.

The geologist can obtain from cores the textural relationship within the rocks, which is not ordinarily possible when dealing with fragments. Even larger features, such as unconformities and rock dips,[72] may be visible in cores, especially in the large-diameter cores now being obtained with diamond bits. The degree of dip can be read directly from the core; the direction of dip can be ascertained only from an oriented core, which can be obtained by one of several methods.[73] Weaver [74] has pointed out the value of petrofabrics [75] in determining the structural position of a single isolated well and in recognizing faults by slip planes and shattering.

Macrofossils may be present in cores to assist in correlation. Clean material is available for chemical analyses for special purposes, such as the determination of the possible source rock by the nitrogen reduc-

ity," *Oil and Gas Jour.*, Vol. 47 (Nov. 18, 1948), p. 121; F. B. Plummer and P. F. Tapp, "Technique of Testing Large Cores of Oil Sands," *Bull. Am. Assoc. Petrol. Geol.*, Vol. 27 (January, 1943), pp. 64–84; James A. Lewis, "Core Analysis, an Aid to Increasing the Recovery of Oil," *Am. Inst. Min. Met. Engineer Tech. Pub.* 1487 (1942), 8 pp.; R. A. Morse, P. L. Terwilliger, and S T. Yuster, "Relative Permeability Measurements on Small Core Samples," *Producers Monthly*, Vol. 11 (August, 1947), pp. 19–25; Anon., "Salt Water Yardstick," *The Link*, Vol. 12 (June, 1947), pp. 8–11; Donuil Hillis, "Colorimetric Method of Determining Percentage of Oil in Cores," *Bull. Am. Assoc. Petrol. Geol.*, Vol. 21 (November, 1937), pp. 1477–1485; John G. Caran, "Core Analysis," *Subsurface Geologic Methods* (Colo. School of Mines, 1949), pp. 238–264.

[71] John R. Suman, *op cit.*, p. 191.

[72] Charles A. Sansom, "The Interpretation of Core Evidence," *Science of Petroleum* (Oxford Univ. Press, 1938), Vol. 1, pp. 502–507; E. F. Stratton and R. G. Hamilton, "Dipmeter Surveys," *Subsurface Geologic Methods* (Colo. School of Mines, 1949), pp. 517–524.

[73] Hugh McClellan, "Core Orientation by Graphical and Mathematical Methods," *Bull. Am. Assoc. Petrol. Geol.*, Vol. 32 (February, 1948), pp. 262–282.

[74] Paul Weaver, "The Geologic Interpretation of Exploratory Wells," *Oil and Gas Jour.*, Vol. 47 (March 17, 1949), pp. 102–104; *Bull. Am. Assoc. Petrol. Geol.*, Vol. 33 (July, 1949), pp. 1135–1144.

[75] Warren W. Wagner, "Petrofabric Analysis," *Subsurface Geologic Methods* (Colo. School of Mines, 1949), pp. 135–150.

tion ratio method,[76] or the search for porous dolomitized limestone by the magnesium/calcium ratio.[77]

The major disadvantage of cores as permanent geologic records is their volume and weight. The mere transportation from field to office may be an item of considerable expense. The construction and maintenance of a "core library" where cores are kept accessible for further study are also fund-consuming, but the costs are much less than those involved in obtaining the core in the first place. The oil industry's revived use of the diamond-studded bit has greatly increased the amount of rock core produced each year.

Water.[78] Many thousands of samples of oil-field waters have been analyzed, probably in part because of the ready availability of water and the relative ease of water analysis. Nevertheless these analyses have assisted in solving a number of engineering and geological problems.

In earlier days of water analysis, a number of misconceptions arose concerning the relationship between the occurrence of oil and the mineral content of the associated water. It is now known that there is no relationship between the two; the associated water in some of the Michigan oil fields is highly concentrated brine, whereas in parts of the Rocky Mountain district it is almost drinkable. About the only generalizations that can be made are (1) the deeper the reservoir the more mineralized the water and (2) the brine concentration increases between outcrop and basin. The waters of different formations may differ sufficiently so that the analyses can be used for correlation locally but not regionally. However, because of these local differences, the engineers have found it possible to identify the source of new water appearing in an oil well so that steps can be taken to prevent further incursion. Similarly, geologists have been able to locate faults by water analyses, and a structural uplift can be suspected by the finding of concentrated mineralized water at a higher level than usual.

[76] Parker D. Trask, "One Way of Finding Oil More Cheaply," *Oil and Gas Jour.*, Vol. 36 (Nov. 12, 1937), pp. 120 *et seq.*

[77] Kenneth K. Landes, "Porosity through Dolomitization," *Bull. Am. Assoc. Petrol. Geol.*, Vol. 30 (March, 1946), pp. 305–318.

[78] L. C. Case *et al.*, "Selected Annotated Bibliography on Oil Field Waters," *Bull. Am. Assoc. Petrol. Geol.*, Vol. 26 (May, 1942), pp. 865–881; C. W. Washburne *et al.*, "Oil Field Waters," *Problems of Petroleum Geology* (Am. Assoc. Petrol. Geol., 1934), Part VI, pp. 833–985; C. E. Reistle, Jr., "Identification of Oil Field Waters by Chemical Analysis," *U. S. Bur. Mines Tech. Paper*, 404, 1927, pp. 1–25; L. C. Case, "Application of Oil Field Water Studies to Geology and Production Studies," *Oil Weekly*, Vol. 119 (Oct. 29, 1945), pp. 48–54; James G. Crawford, "Water Analysis," *Subsurface Geologic Methods* (Colo. School of Mines, 1949), pp. 188–210.

Oil. Ever since Professor Silliman of Yale made an analysis of western Pennsylvania seep oil for the promoters of the Drake well, it has been the practice, where oil is discovered, to obtain samples for examination and analysis. The analyses of crude oils from 283 important domestic oil fields have recently been compiled and published.[79] Although the primary purpose of making these analyses is to determine the value of the oil and to supply essential data to the refiner, geologists have found the character of oil to be of value in solving problems of correlation and migration.

For geological study it is now customary to transform the analytical data into a "correlation index"; [80] this may be applied directly,[81] or it may be used in grouping the crude oils into various types.[82] Where only a small sample of oil is available in core or cuttings, the index of refraction [83] may be used as a substitute for gravity determination and even chemical analysis.

As a general but not invariable rule, crude oils from the same stratigraphic levels in a single oil province are similar, and those from different ages of rock are dissimilar.[84] For this reason, the analyses of petroleums have been used for purposes of stratigraphic correlation; they also can be used to prove the absence of vertical (transformational) migration, as at Oklahoma City where the oils in the Pennsylvanian formations are different from those in the underlying Ordovician rocks. Exceptions to this general rule may signify vertical migration, as on Trinidad [85] and at Garber, Oklahoma, where like oils are found in fourteen superimposed reservoirs.

[79] C. H. McKinney and O. C. Blade, "Analyses of Crude Oils from 283 Important Oil Fields in the United States," *U. S. Bur. Mines Rept. Investigations,* 4289 (May, 1948), 154 pp.

[80] H. M. Smith, "Correlation Index to Aid in Interpreting Crude Oil Analyses," *U. S. Bur. Mines Tech. Paper,* 610 (1940).

[81] L. M. Neuman *et al.*, "Relationship of Crude Oils and Stratigraphy in Parts of Oklahoma and Kansas," *Bull. Am. Assoc. Petrol. Geol.,* Vol. 25 (September, 1941), pp. 1801–1809.

[82] J. G. Crawford and R. M. Larsen, "Occurrences and Types of Crude Oils in Rocky Mountain Region," *Bull. Am. Assoc. Petrol. Geol.,* Vol. 27 (October, 1943), pp. 1305–1334.

[83] Hollis D. Hedberg, "Evaluation of Petroleum in Oil Sands by Its Index of Refraction," *Bull. Am. Assoc. Petrol. Geol.,* Vol. 21 (November, 1937), pp. 1464–1476.

[84] Donald C. Barton, "Correlation of Crude Oils with Special Reference to Crude Oil of Gulf Coast," *Bull. Am. Assoc. Petrol. Geol.,* Vol. 25 (April, 1941), pp. 561–592; L. M. Neumann *et al.*, "Relationship of Crude Oils and Stratigraphy in Parts of Oklahoma and Kansas," *Bull. Am. Assoc. Petrol. Geol.,* Vol. 30 (May, 1946), pp. 747–748; Charles Bohdanowicz, "Stratigraphic Comparison of Polish Crude Oils," *Bull. Am. Assoc. Petrol. Geol.,* Vol. 21 (September, 1937), pp. 1182–1192.

[85] K. W. Barr, F. Morton, and A. R. Richards, "Application of Chemical Analysis of Crude Oils to Problems of Petroleum Geology," *Bull. Am. Assoc. Petrol. Geol.,* Vol. 27 (December, 1943), pp. 1595–1617.

Gas. There is considerable variation in natural gases from different reservoirs, and from different parts of the same reservoir, in terms of percentages of methane, gasoline, other hydrocarbons, and extraneous substances such as hydrogen sulfide, nitrogen, helium, and carbon dioxide. However, geologists have made but little use of analytical data of natural gases. It has been suggested that an effective method of search for new oil deposits might be developed from gas analyses.[86] The lightest gases tend to migrate the farthest from the source oil; therefore, the plotting of "isoethane" lines, drawn through points of equal ethane content in a gas field, might show the direction in which to prospect for the "mother lode," and the spacing of the lines might be indicative of the distance.

LOGS.[87] In oil-field terminology, a "log" is a record made during or after the drilling of a well. It furnishes, directly or indirectly, a report of the geological formations penetrated. Some logs are relatively simple, giving the driller's identification of the rocks drilled or the time consumed in drilling each foot of hole; other logs are more complex, made only after a thorough study of the drill cuttings or from observations taken with the help of elaborate physical or chemical equipment.

It would be difficult to overemphasize the importance of logs in oil-searching. By means of the subsurface geological information available in logs, it is possible to determine the structural pattern of the rocks and to recognize lateral changes in facies. Both of these are important in discovering oil- or gas-bearing traps.

Driller's Logs.[88] The first well logs were lithologic identifications and depth figures stored in the mind of the driller, and some water-well drillers still operate on a memory basis. The next step was to write the data down in a "log book" kept by the driller. For thousands of wells drilled during the earlier decades of the present century,

[86] H. C. Allen, "Chemistry Reveals Important Facts," *Oil and Gas Jour.*, Vol. 28 (Oct. 24, 1929), pp. 42 *et seq.;* Paul H. Price and A. J. W. Headlee, "Geochemistry of Natural Gas in Appalachian Province," *Bull. Am. Assoc. Petrol. Geol.,* Vol. 26 (January, 1942), pp. 19–35.

[87] Harold Vance, *Elements of Petroleum Subsurface Engineering* (St. Louis, 1950), Chap. 3, pp. 10–57; E. DeGolyer and Harold Vance, *Bibliography on the Petroleum Industry, Bull. A. and M. Coll. Texas,* 83 (1944), pp. 369–370 and 405; Hubert Guyod *et al.,* "Well Logging Methods Conference," *Bull. A. and M. Coll. Texas,* 93 (1946), pp. 166–171 (6 pages of references); Hubert Guyod, "Well Logging Methods Studied at Texas A. and M.," *Petrol. Engineer,* Vol. 17 (April, 1946), p. 218; *ibid.* (August, 1946), pp. 62–66; Carl A. Moore (editor), A Symposium on Subsurface Logging Techniques (Univ. Book Exchange, Norman, Okla., 1950).

[88] L. W. LeRoy, "Driller's Logging," *Subsurface Geologic Methods* (Colo. School of Mines, 1949), pp. 422–425.

the driller's log is the only record available. Therefore the geologist operating in such areas must learn to interpret the terminology used. It should be remembered that the cable tool driller makes his rock identifications largely by *feel*—the feel of the drilling line while the formation is being drilled, the feel of the cuttings washed out of the bailer, and the feel of the cutting edge of the bit when withdrawn from the hole.[89] The experienced driller is quite capable of distinguishing in this manner the three most commonplace sedimentary rocks, shale ("soapstone"), sandstone ("sand"), and limestone ("lime").

For purposes of correlation and subsurface geologic study the usual procedure is to plot the driller's log on specially prepared paper log strips at a scale of 100 feet to the inch. Colored pencils are used for the different types of rock, usually yellow for sandstone and blue for limestone, with shale denoted by the omission of any color pattern. These strips can be "slipped" up and down on the drafting table in respect to each other until the most likely "match" is obtained; in this way formations are correlated in the subsurface from well to well and eventually from one side of a sedimentary basin to the other side.

Although they are of less relative importance in correlation today, because of the availability of many other data, driller's logs are still kept, and in some companies a two-column strip log is plotted, one column containing the sample log, the description of which follows, and the other column the driller's log.

An additional and important feature of the driller's log, especially in cable tool wells, is his notation of "shows" of oil and gas, and of the presence of water-yielding formations. Some oil shows consist only of a "rainbow" of colors on the surface of the water bailed out of the well; a gas show may be merely a slight bubbling or effervescence noted when the bailer is dumped. These occurrences can be observed only by the men working on the derrick floor; they leave no record in the samples for subsequent consideration by the geologist. And yet even such minor shows of oil or gas may be very significant. The well may be too low structurally; a second or third well drilled near by, but structurally higher, may strike the "jackpot." A second possibility is that the reservoir rock has thinned down to noncommercial thickness, in which event subsequent wells drilled in the direction of divergence (thickening) may find oil in abundance. Still another possibility is that the pay formation is locally "tight" but elsewhere in the same general area it has adequate porosity and

[89] James F. Swain, "Interpretation of Cable Tool Drilling Logs," *Bull. Am. Assoc. Petrol. Geol.*, Vol. 27 (July, 1943), pp. 997–1000.

permeability for commercial oil production. Many an oil field has been discovered through the encouragement given by shows in otherwise unsuccessful wildcat tests. In the same way, the notation in the log by the driller of "HFW" (hole full of water), or other reference to the presence of water in fair abundance in a subsurface formation, may be of great value to the geologist. Such information indicates a porous and permeable stratum which under a more favorable environment may be just as full of oil as it is here full of water.

Sample Logs.[90] Sample logs are plotted strip logs which show the identifications made by a geologist who examined the well cuttings with a binocular microscope. Although basically similar to the plotted driller's log in showing rock types by color patterns, the sample log includes infinitely more detail. The less common, or less easily distinguished, rock types, such as dolomite and anhydrite, are included. Furthermore, approximate percentages of chert in limestone, or anhydrite in dolomite, or other ingredients in a rock mixture, can be shown by lateral thickness of the color pattern in the vertical log column. Because of variations in the occurrence of minor constituents which are ordinarily missed by the driller, it may be possible to obtain more precise correlations with sample logs, and it is certainly true that facies changes can be studied in much more detail. Because a considerable proportion of each sample obtained during the drilling of a rotary well consists of rock sloughed off from a higher level, the percentage type of sample log will not give a true picture of each individual stratum penetrated. Therefore, in some areas the percentage description of rotary samples has been superseded by *interpretive logs,* in the construction of which the geologist attempts to describe only the new material cut by the bit.

In almost all subsurface geologic work, the study of samples and the plotting of sample logs is routine procedure. In order to obtain consistency in textural descriptions from day to day and from person to person, the use of a "textural standard" [91] has been advocated. A process of duplicating sample logs in full color has been developed; [92] this may in time lessen the enormous amount of duplication of effort which now takes place through the separate preparation of sample logs in separate offices.

[90] Bob Greider, "Lithologic Logging," *Subsurface Geologic Methods* (Colo. School of Mines, 1949), pp. 297–302.

[91] Gordon Rittenhouse, "Textural Standard for Sample Log Work," *Bull. Am. Assoc. Petrol. Geol.,* Vol. 29 (August, 1945), p. 1195.

[92] John H. Speer, "Color Reproduction of Well Logs," *World Oil,* Vol. 128 (March, 1949), pp. 68 *et seq.*

Mounted Logs. A variation in plotting sample logs is to mount the samples themselves on log strips at a scale of 20 feet to the inch. First glue is spread over that part of the strip which represents the interval of the sample, and then the cuttings are sprinkled over the glue until the surface is covered. Breaks in the lithology are just as obvious on the mounted as on the plotted logs, and color variations are much more noticeable. Furthermore, the original material rather than an interpretation of the original material is used in slipping the logs for correlation and in tracing facies. Because of the labor of preparation, and their bulk, mounted logs are not widely used.

Time Logs.[93] Drilling-time logs, or rate-of-penetration logs, consist of a curve plotted on a time-depth basis. The slope of the curve designates the speed of penetration; any abrupt breaks show contacts between rocks of unequal penetrability. The major factor in controlling the speed of drilling is the hardness of the rock being drilled, and the hardness is dependent upon the mineral content, the kind of cement and the degree of cementation, the texture, and the porosity. It is obvious that penetration speed is also a function of various equipment and operational factors, such as design and sharpness of bit, the pressure on the bit, the characteristics and velocity of the drilling mud, the rotation speed of the bit, and the skill of the driller. In spite of these variables the drilling-time log is ordinarily a reliable index to the nature of the formations penetrated.

Time logging is done either on the derrick floor by the driller, who manually records the time when each chalk mark, placed at 1-foot intervals on the kelly, reaches the level of the table bushings, or by semi-automatic or completely automatic devices mounted on the derrick or in the doghouse.

Time logs can be used in correcting the lag in sample return, and in correlating from well to well. They are especially valuable during the drilling of a well because of their immediate availability. The passing of a formation contact may be recognized by the time log before the circulation of the drilling mud brings the samples to the

[93] P. B. Nichols, "Mechanical Well Logging," *Bull. A. and M. Coll. Texas,* 93 (1946), pp. 105–118 (15 references); G. Frederick Shepherd and Gordon I. Atwater, "Geologic Use of Drilling Time Data," *Oil Weekly,* Vol. 114 (July 3, 1944), pp. 17 *et seq.; ibid.* (July 10, 1944), pp. 38 *et seq.;* Lester C. Uren, "Recent Developments in Formation Logging," *Petrol. Engineer,* Vol. 14 (February, 1943), pp. 63 *et seq.* (bibliography with 10 references on p. 70); Robin Willis and R. S. Ballantyne, Jr., "Drilling Time Logs and Their Uses," *Bull. Am. Assoc. Petrol. Geol.,* Vol. 26 (July, 1942), pp. 1279–1283; G. Frederick Shepherd, "Drilling-Time Logging," *Subsurface Geologic Methods* (Colo. School of Mines, 1949), pp. 387–404; P. B. Nichols, "Drilling-Time Logging," *op. cit.,* pp. 404–412.

WELL SURVEYING COMPANY, INC.

Location of Well

N½-SW-NE

Elevation 2451'

COMPANY Nogales Oil Co.
WELL Gringo #5
RUN NO. Two
FIELD Bluehills
SURVEY 15-25N-8W
COUNTY Baringer
STATE Texas

Filing No. A-345

COUNTY: Baringer
FIELD OR SURVEY: Bluehills
WELL: Gringo #5
COMPANY: Nogales Oil Co.

First Reading 3972 ft.
Last Reading 1754 ft.
Footage Measured 2218 ft.
Casing Shoe Depth {W. S. Co. / Driller} ft. 1754 ft.
Bottom Depth 3972 ft.
Maximum depth reached 3972 ft.

DIAMETER OF HOLE	MUD CHARACTERISTICS
from ____ to 6½"	NATURE Aquagel
from ____ to ____	WEIGHT 9.5
	VISCOSITY 33
Bottom Temperature ____ °F	RESISTIVITY 1.3 @ ____ °F

REMARKS

DATE Aug. 15, 1947 OBSERVERS J. F. Turner

SELF-POTENTIAL Millivolts	DEPTHS	RESISTIVITY - ohms m²m — Normal Curve — Third Curve --- Fourth Curve
← 20 mv → +		20 40 60 80 / 200 400 600 800
	1800	Third Curve
	1900	

FIG. 18. Electric log. *Courtesy Sch*

Electric logs are most reliable indices of the lithology of a stratigraphic section that consists of alternating layers of sandstone and shale. In areas where the subsurface geology is of this type, electric logs have largely supplemented sample logs and cores. However, the initial determination of the geologic formations in the subsurface section must have been made from samples; the electric log is merely a reaction pattern and can never supplant rock samples in identifying formations in the exploration of new subsurface territory. Where the geologic section consists of carbonate rocks and perhaps anhydrite, as well as shale and sandstone, the lithologic identifications by means of electric logs are more difficult and a closer control with sample logs is necessary. Sections of this sort are especially subject to lateral variation in facies, which is further reason for frequent check of electric log against sample log. The electric log is still a valuable tool in formation correlation, even under these conditions, but its applicability is more local in extent.

An electric log (Fig. 18) is in reality two logs, one (on the left) depicting the so-called self-potential and the other showing resistivity. To log a well the drill stem and drilling tools are removed from the hole but the drilling mud is left in. The recording is done in a truck backed up close to the drilling platform. First a stationary electrode is placed at the surface, usually in the mud pit. Then a traveling electrode assembly at the end of a wire line spooled on a reel in the logging truck is lowered to the bottom of the hole. As this electrode assembly is raised by a power take-off in the truck, electrical currents are intermittently passed through the electrodes, and the electrical meter readings are automatically plotted against depths on the recording drum. The self-potential readings are made while the current is off; resistivity is entered while the current is on.

The self-potential is a measurement of the natural potential between the surface electrode and one of the electrodes in the well. It is measured in millivolts, 1 millivolt being 0.001 volt. The datum of reference, or zero point on the millivolt scale, is the average potential of shales. Readings to the right of this arbitrary datum are referred to as positive anomalies; those to the left, as negative anomalies.

The resistivity curve or curves, appearing on the right side of the electric log, is the result of measurements made of the differences in potential between two electrodes when an outside electric current is sent into the ground by means of a separate pair of electrodes. The unit of measurement is the ohm. Electrical resistivity is that property surface. Coring points may be selected, and the time log may be used to interpret gaps in the core record due to incomplete recovery. This type of log has been of value in locating porous and permeable intervals during the drilling of thick carbonate rock sections. In rotary-drilled holes, the time or rate-of-penetration log is a valuable predecessor of the electric log, which ordinarily is not obtained until the well is completed.

Electric Logs.[94] Electric logs supply indirect but nevertheless effective indices for subsurface stratigraphic correlation, for the determination of strike and dip, and for the identification of faults. They also furnish data useful in forming a tentative opinion of the permeability and fluid content of the rocks traversed. Since the advent of electric logging in the late 1920's, this method has become virtually indispensable; it is now routine procedure to make electric logs of rotary-drilled wells. Electric logging is not possible in a cased well; this rules out most wells drilled with cable tools. An uncased cable tool well can be logged for self-potential by filling the hole with fresh water, and the resistivity log (described in subsequent paragraphs) can be obtained in a dry uncased cable tool well. Conventional electric logs are valueless even in rotary wells once the bit has cut into rock salt, for from then on the drilling mud is contaminated with salt and so it has very low electrical resistance. For this reason, in the salt-bearing sedimentary basins conventional electric logging is confined to the super-salt strata unless the salt-bearing strata are cased off, in which event reliable electric logs can be obtained in the underlying section.

A great advantage of electric logging lies in the continuity and accuracy of the depth measurements. Other methods give a depth correction figure but no indication as to where it should be applied. Electric logging is a rapid procedure, and its cost is insignificant in terms of the total cost of drilling a well. Furthermore, the electric log, unlike the sample log, is a purely mechanical record, uninfluenced by personal factors.

[94] E. DeGolyer and Harold Vance, "Bibliography on the Petroleum Industry," *Bull. A. and M. Coll. Texas,* 83 (1944), pp. 403–404 (52 references); Houston Geological Society Study Group, "Electrical Well Logging," *Bull. Am. Assoc. Petrol. Geol.,* Vol. 23 (September, 1939), pp. 1287–1313; Hubert Guyod, "Electrical Well Logging, a reprint of a series of 16 articles which appeared in various issues of the *Oil Weekly* between Aug. 7 and Dec. 4, 1944," 103 pp.; Hubert Guyod, "Electric Log Interpretation, a reprint of a series of 4 articles which appeared in the *Oil Weekly* dated Dec. 3, 10, 17, and 24, 1945," 27 pp.; Sylvain J. Pirson, "Electric Logging" (4 articles), *Oil and Gas Jour.,* Oct. 4 to Oct. 25, 1947; E. F. Stratton and R. D. Ford, "Electric Logging," *Subsurface Geologic Methods* (Colo. School of Mines, 1949), pp. 302–339.

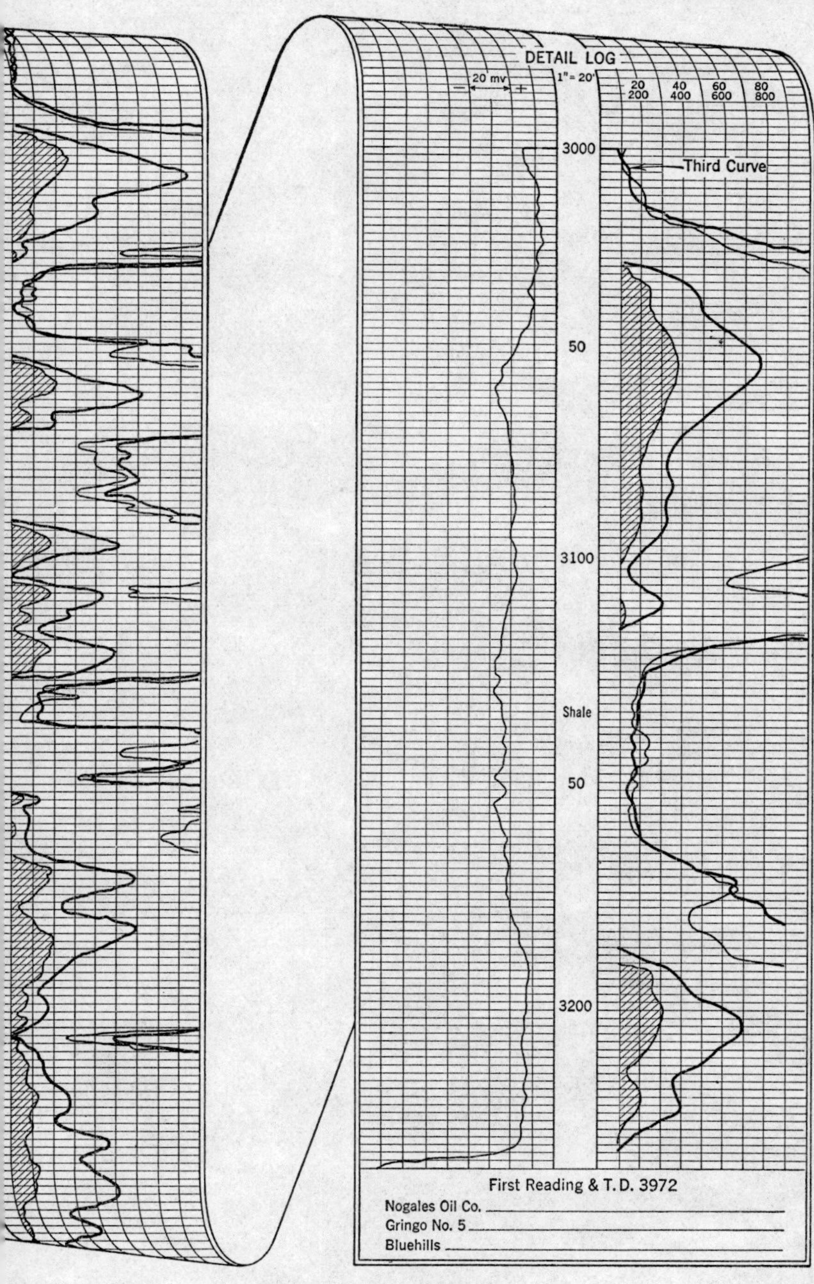

…erger Well Surveying Corporation.

which tends to impede the flow of electricity through a substance. For rocks in a bore hole, the resistivity measurement obtained is the resultant of two resistivities, that of the rock itself and that of the contained fluid. The readings are also modified by the presence of the drilling mud, and in permeable strata the invasion of the wall rock by the mud creates an additional complication. The distance outward from the bore hole which is traversed by the electric currents is directly proportional to the vertical distance between electrodes. The "normal curve" is made by a relatively close spacing so as to record resistivities of thin rock strata, but, in order to measure resistivities out beyond the zone of mud invasion, successively wider electrode spacings may be obtained by different current hook-ups in the electrode assembly. These readings are recorded as additional curves superimposed on the resistivity diagram. Where resistivity lines run off the sheet to the right, because the quantities exceed 100 ohms, the missing data are inserted, at one-tenth the original scale, on the left side of the resistivity diagram with diagonal lines on the inside of the normal curve for purposes of recognition.

In resistivity logging, the mud fluid standing in the hole acts as a conductor between the electrodes and the wall rock. However, oil-base mud is not a conductor, so the conventional procedure cannot be followed where this type of mud is used. "Scratcher" electrodes, which are held by springs against the side of the hole, may be employed under such circumstances, but they are not always satisfactory because of poor contacts with some types of wall rock. To meet this inadequacy in resistivity recording, *induction logging*[95] has been developed. The housing lowered into the bore hole contains a transmitter coil and a receiver coil. Alternating current is made to flow through the transmitter coil; this results in eddy currents which penetrate the formations surrounding the well. The eddy currents in turn create a secondary magnetic field that induces an electromotive force in the receiver coil. The strength of the signal received in the recording instruments at the surface is directly proportional to the conductivity (the inverse of the resistivity) of the bore-hole wall rock. The record is a continuous one from bottom to top of the hole and is very similar to, and applicable in the same manner as, the conventional resistivity log.

[95] H. G. Doll, "Introduction to Induction Logging," *Oil and Gas Jour.*, Vol. 47 (Feb. 24, 1949), pp. 168–174; H. G. Doll, "Induction Logging and Application to Logging of Wells Drilled with Oil-Base Mud," *Subsurface Geologic Methods* (Colo. School of Mines, 1949), pp. 340–345.

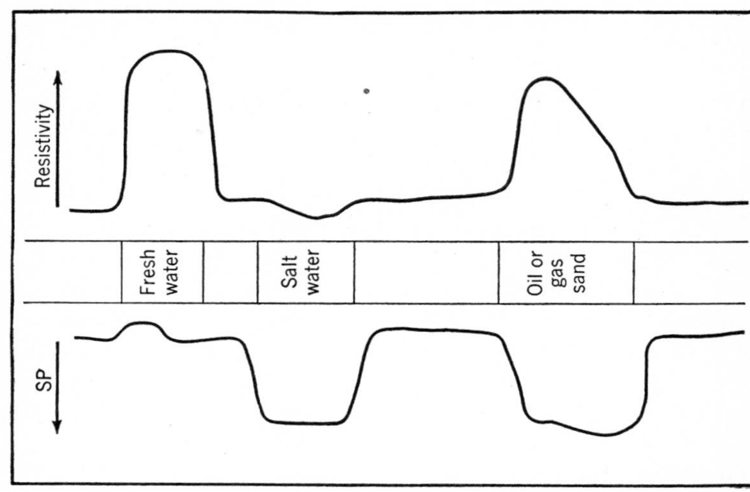

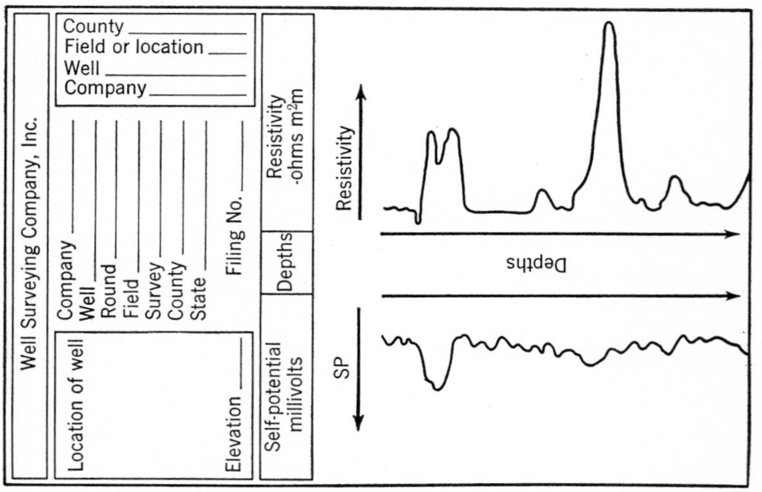

Fig. 19A. Electric log panel showing different reactions. *Courtesy Schlumberger Well Surveying Corporation.*

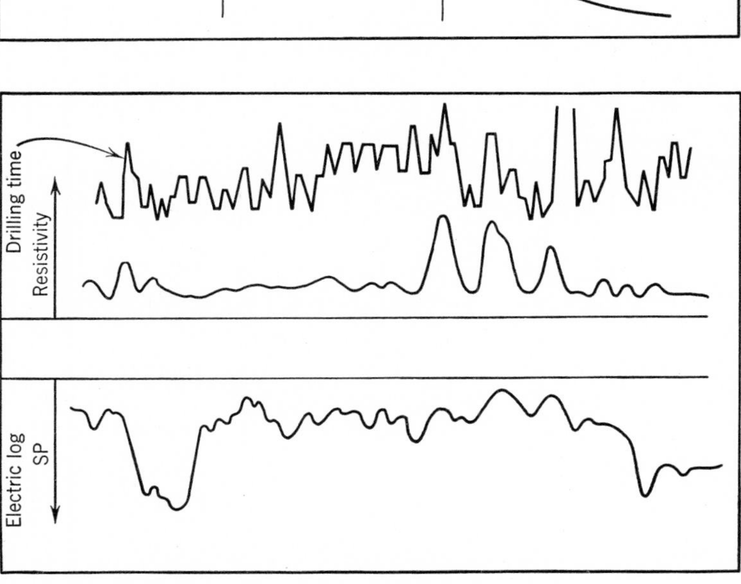

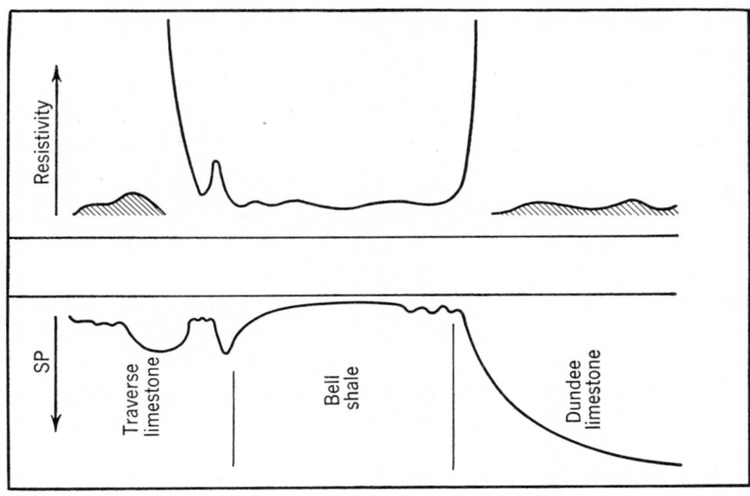

After Schlumberger Well Surveying Corporation

FIG. 19B. Electric-log panel showing different reactions. Drilling-time log has been added to electric log at left. *Courtesy Schlumberger Well Surveying Corporation.*

The center column between the self-potential and resistivity diagrams contains the depth figures. Often two scales are employed; the lower section, where the potential reservoir rocks lie, may be shown at 20 feet to the inch, and the upper section at 50 feet to the inch. Lithologic and even stratigraphic identifications may subsequently be inserted in this column.

It is possible to use electric logs as a subsurface correlation tool with little or no concept of the meaning of the erratic pattern of the curves. Electric logs can be "slipped" alongside of each other in the same way as plotted or mounted logs, and correlations can be made from well to well by the magnitude and spacing of the "kicks" on the curves. If the formations have been identified on one electric log, based on sample studies, it may be possible to carry these formations, with their separate behavior patterns, for considerable distances laterally by electric logs alone. However, many pitfalls can be avoided if the user knows something about the possible reasons for the "kicks" on the curves, and much valuable knowledge of permeabilities and fluid conditions is available to those who can interpret electric logs.

Divergences from the norm in the self-potential curve (Fig. 19) occur only where the well passes through a stratum with a certain degree of porosity and permeability. However, the porosity determinations can be considered only qualitative and not a measurement of absolute porosity. Negative anomalies occur where the sandstones or carbonate reservoirs contain water (with or without oil) that is more saline than the water in the drilling mud. As this is the general rule, negative anomalies are much more common than positive anomalies. The magnitude of the negative self-potential is the resultant of both the porosity and the concentration of the brine; it is for this reason that the millivolt readings cannot be taken as quantitative indications of porosity. In addition to fresh-water aquifers, positive anomalies occur where a pyritiferous layer has been penetrated by the bore hole.

As a general but not invariable rule the harder a rock is to drill, the greater is its electrical resistivity. Therefore, the resistivity curve tends to parallel the plotted drilling-time log (Fig. 19B). As saline waters are good conductors, where they are present within a rock the curve will show low resistivity. On the other hand, fresh water, sulfur water, oil, and gas are poor conductors, and so they produce high resistivities (Fig. 19A). Dry, dense rocks are always highly resistant.

Interpretation of resistivity curves is most profitable when the porosity, or more especially the permeability, as indicated by the self-potential curve, is also taken into account. The table gives some possible interpretations.

	Low Resistivity	*High Resistivity*
Permeable	Salt water in rock	Fresh water (usually at shallow depths only) Sulfur water Oil and gas
Impermeable	Shales and clays containing absorbed saline water	Limestone and dolomite Anhydrite and salt Coal

Figure 19B, right, shows two limestones, both with high resistivity and one with porosity as well. For the second, either sulfur water or oil and gas is indicated.

Extensive and continuous research is being carried on both by service companies and by operators to improve electric logging methods and to make the curves more quantitative. A recent development is "micrologging." [96] By means of electrode spacings of 1 to 2 inches, the individual pay sections can be measured down to fractions of a foot. The electrodes are mounted in an insulating pad which is pressed against the wall of the drill hole. The short-circuiting action of the drilling mud is thereby avoided, so that electrical micrologging can be carried on in brine. This permits electric logging below salt-bearing formations without the necessity of casing.

Radioactivity Logs.[97] Radioactivity logging may actually produce two logs (Fig. 20), one a measure of the natural emanations of gamma

[96] Kenneth B. Barnes, "New Logging Method," *Oil and Gas Jour.*, Vol. 48 (Dec. 29, 1949), p. 35; H. G. Doll, "The Microlog," *Oil and Gas Jour.*, Vol. 48 (March 2, 1950, pp. 62 *et seq.;* "The Microlog, a New Electrical Logging Method for Detailed Determination of Permeable Beds," *Am. Inst. Min. Met. Engineers,* T.P. 2880; *Jour. Petrol. Tech.*, Vol. 2 (June, 1950), pp. 155–164.

[97] Warren J. Jackson and John L. P. Campbell, "Some Practical Aspects of Radioactivity Well Logging," *Am. Inst. Min. Met. Engineers Tech. Pub.* 1923 (September, 1945), 27 pp. (30 references); Robert E. Fearon, "Gamma Ray Measurements," *Oil Weekly,* Vol. 118 (June 4, 1945), pp. 33–41 (66 references); "Neutron Bombardment of Formations," *ibid.* (June 11, 1945), pp. 38 *et seq.;* John L. P. Campbell, "Gamma Ray Logging in East Texas," *Petrol. Engineer,* Vol. 15 (January, 1944), pp. 156–158; Lester C. Uren, "Radioactivity and Geochemical Well Logging," *Petrol. Engineer,* Vol. 14 (January, 1943), pp. 50–58; W. L. Russell and R. B. Downing, "Neutron Logs Find Porous Zones in Western Kansas Limestones," *Oil and Gas Jour.,* Vol. 41 (Aug. 6, 1942), p. 66; Bruno Pontecorvo, "Neutron Well Logging," *Oil and Gas Jour.,* Vol. 40 (Sept. 11, 1941), pp. 32–33; William L. Russell, "Well Logging by Radioactivity," *Bull. Am. Assoc. Petrol. Geol.,* Vol. 25 (September, 1941), pp. 1768–1788; John

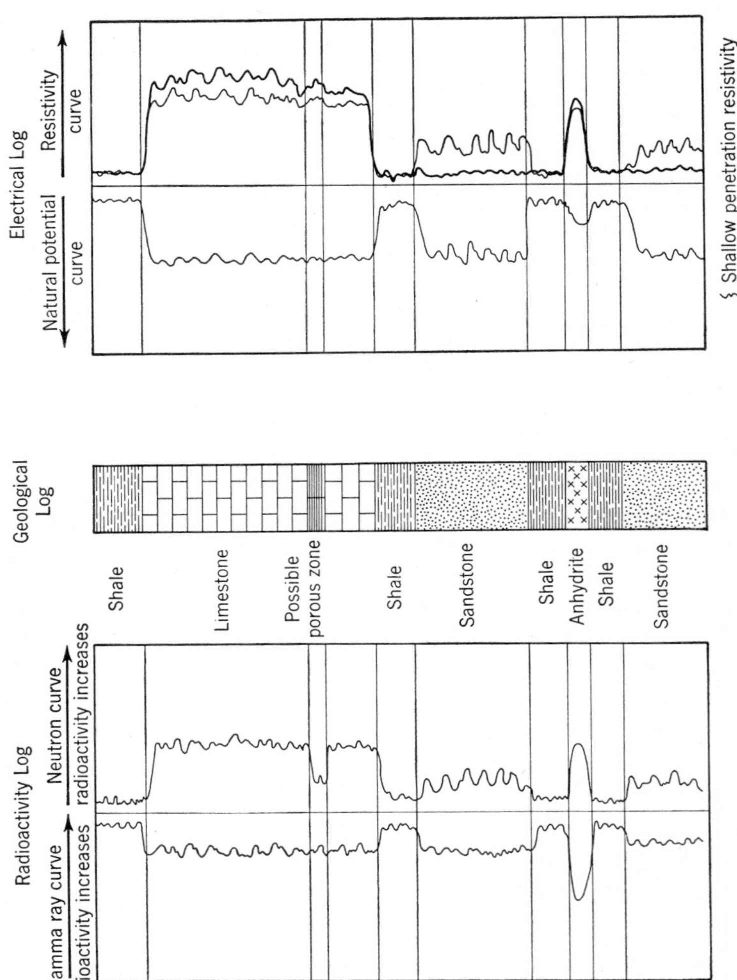

FIG. 20. Radioactivity log, compared with electrical log. Left: gamma ray and neutron logs. Center: lithologic log. Right: electrical log.

rays from the rock formations penetrated by the well and the other a measure of the effect of bombardment of the wall rocks by neutrons from an introduced source. Gamma-ray logging began in 1940 and neutron logging about a year later. A major advantage of radioactivity logs is that they may be obtained through several strings of casing and even through cement. Like electric logs, radioactivity logs are better considered an auxiliary to sample logs than an end in themselves; the curves obtained are subject to various interpretations, and sample logs are necessary to the correct solution.

The theory of the gamma-ray curve is simple. All rocks contain radioactive material, but the amount is highly variable. The radioactive substances are undergoing constant disintegration, in the course of which rays are emitted; the most penetrating of these rays are the gamma rays. As a general rule, shales contain more radioactive material than sandstones and limestones, and so this rock produces a prominent "kick" in the gamma-ray curve. To this extent, gamma-ray logging is also lithologic logging.

The neutron curve, produced by an artificially induced neutron bombardment of the wall rocks, is an inverse measurement of the amount of hydrogen present. Because most hydrogen in rock is in either interstitial water or oil, the neutron curve indicates (by subnormal readings) the presence of fluids and hence is a porosity log. It is not possible to distinguish oil from water in the neutron log. However, this curve does complement the gamma-ray log in that it makes possible the distinction between sandstone and dense limestone. The accuracy of the identifications is increased further by using the radioactive logs in conjunction with electric logs.

Gamma-ray logs are made by dropping down the bore hole a steel cylinder containing an ionization chamber filled with inert gas plus a pair of electrodes. The cylinder is suspended from a wire spooled on a reel in the recording truck. Gamma rays from the wall rock penetrate the ionization chamber and make possible the flow of currents between electrodes. By means of a series of amplifiers, these currents are recorded, with the depth, as a curve on a revolving drum in the service truck. In addition to an ionization chamber, neutron logging uses a properly shielded but strong source of neutrons which bombard the wall rocks, and the effects of the bombardment are measured in the ionization chamber and transmitted to the recording

L. P. Campbell and A. B. Winter, *Bull. A. and M. Coll. Texas,* 93 (1946), pp. 119–120; "Radioactivity Well Logging," 36 pp.; V. J. Mercier, "Radioactivity Well Logging," *Subsurface Geologic Methods* (Colo. School of Mines, 1949), pp. 345–359.

truck. It has not been possible heretofore to log the gamma rays and the neutrons at the same time; two trips were necessary to obtain a complete radioactivity log, but it is claimed that a new instrument will make simultaneous gamma and neutron readings.[98]

Radioactivity logs have demonstrated considerable usefulness. After a well has been drilled, the gamma-ray curve can be used to correct the time lag in the sample return, and the neutron curve has wide and valuable application in cased wells in determining where to perforate in order to test porous zones in the wall rock. Old wells, drilled before the days of accurate logging, are especially fertile fields for radioactivity logging. Porous zones in thick carbonate rock sections may have been missed completely, or the well may be cased too deep in the reservoir rock so that bottom water is produced in profusion with good oil lying outside the casing at a higher elevation; both these possibilities can be explored by radioactivity logging.

In addition to assisting the production engineer, radioactivity logs, especially gamma-ray logs, can be and are used by geologists in subsurface structure mapping. Some formations produce a highly distinctive gamma-ray-curve pattern which remains fairly constant over great distances. A notable example of this is the Chattanooga shale, which is easily recognized by the distinctive gamma-ray "kicks" from the Appalachians to West Texas, and from Canada to Oklahoma.

Caliper Logs.[99] The bore-hole caliper is an ingenious device to determine the variations in well diameter from bottom to top. Because of differences in brittleness, cohesion, and solubility between different rock layers, the bore hole does not have smooth vertical walls. Some formations are especially likely to "cave," or to erode by the jetting action of the mud fluid emerging from the bit, or to wear by the subsequent circulation of the drilling mud. Other rocks, especially salt, are soluble to the water in the circulating fluid, unless previously saturated, so lateral leaching may take place. It is obvious that considerable control on variations in bore-hole diameter can be exercised by drilling procedures, but the control is mainly in the

[98] Charles J. Deegan, "New Logging Method," *Oil and Gas Jour.,* Vol. 48 (March 2, 1950), p. 23.

[99] Hubert Guyod, "Caliper Well Logging," *Oil Weekly,* Vol. 118 (Aug. 27, 1945), pp. 32–35; Vol. 119 (Sept. 3, 1945), pp. 57–61; *ibid.* (Sept. 10, 1945), pp. 65–69; *ibid.* (Sept. 17, 1945), pp. 52–54; C. P. Parsons, "Caliper Logging," *Trans. Am. Inst. Min. Met. Engineers,* Vol. 151 (1943), pp. 35–47; William H. Farrand, "Caliper Well Logging," *Petrol. Engineer,* Vol. 15 (November, 1943), pp. 65–69; Wilfred Tapper, "Caliper and Temperature Logging," *Subsurface Geologic Methods* (Colo. School of Mines, 1949), pp. 359–369.

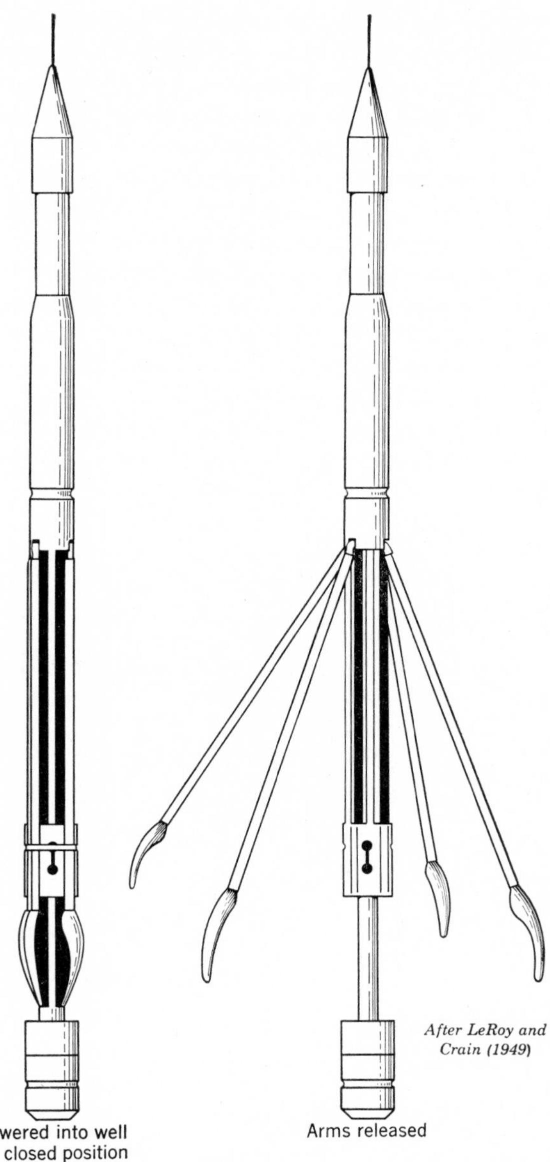

FIG. 21. Bore hole calipers. Left: closed position for lowering into well. Right: open, ready for hoisting to surface. *Courtesy Colorado School of Mines.*

magnitude rather than in the presence of the variations. As a general rule, bore holes, where they pass through massive limestones and indurated sandstones, are but slightly greater in diameter than the diameter of the bit, but in soft, unconsolidated, or poorly cemented rock, such as shale, the diameter may be considerably greater.

The calipers (Fig. 21) consists of four collapsible arms mounted 90° apart on a steel shank. The tool is lowered to the bottom of the hole, where the arms are released. It is then raised to the surface at a rate of about 100 feet per minute. During the trip, individual springs keep each arm pressed against the sides of the hole, and the deviations from the bit diameter are automatically and continuously plotted with the depths by an electrically operated recorder mounted in the service truck.

Caliper logging was first conceived and developed for the purpose of assisting in solving certain engineering problems such as the amount of cement needed to plug a hole, or the amount of material needed to gravel-pack a well. It is also used in surveying the effects of shooting and acidizing. The caliper log is a help in sample examination, giving clues as to both the amount and the source of cavings in the samples. In addition, the peaks and valleys on the caliper profile of a well represent a stratigraphic succession, so the caliper log can be used in well-to-well correlation. It is still essential to have sample logs available for calibrating the caliper logs, however.

Miscellaneous Logs. Various other types of logging procedures have been developed, but none have widespread use, at least as yet. Perhaps the best known of the miscellaneous methods is *mud analysis logging.*[100] Its purpose is to detect the presence of oil and gas in the formations as they are penetrated by the rotary drill. A "gas detector instrument" determines the presence of methane in the drilling mud. Oil is detected by visual examination of samples of the drilling mud placed in an ultraviolet-light viewing box. Accurate estimates of the depth of the point of origin of any hydrocarbons in the drilling mud are made possible by the concurrent use of automatic rate of penetration equipment.

[100] B. Otto Pixler, "Mud Analysis Logging," *Bull. A. and M. Coll. Texas,* 93 (1946), pp. 14–28 (9 references); Robert E. Souther, "Application of Mud Analysis Logging," *Geophysics,* Vol. 10 (January, 1945), pp. 76–90; J. T. Hayward, "Continuous Logging of Rotary Drilled Wells," *Oil and Gas Jour.,* Vol. 39 (Nov. 14, 1940), pp. 100–110; Arthur Langton, "Well Logging by Drilling Mud and Cuttings Analysis," *Subsurface Geologic Methods* (Colo. School of Mines, 1949), pp. 369–378; R. J. Gill, "Composite-Cuttings-Analysis Logging," *op. cit.,* pp. 425–432.

Fluorologs [101] and *geochemical logs* [102] are procedures for identifying chemical substances, particularly hydrocarbons, in the well samples and plotting these determinations in terms of well depth. In this way it may be possible to forecast the penetration of a pay zone by the presence of fugitive hydrocarbons in the overlying rocks. *Spectrochemical logs* [103] have also been suggested. These would show the relative abundance of certain diagnostic elements such as iron, aluminum, and strontium in selected samples taken from the well core and analyzed chemically by the spectrograph. One advantage of this method would be that similar logs could be prepared, for correlation purposes, with outcrop sections.

A newer development has been *permeability logging*.[104] In this procedure, the rate of penetration of a liquid such as water or acid forced into the wall rock of a well by the weight of an overlying column of oil is determined and recorded by electrical means. The oldest physical test to be made in bore holes, namely, temperature determination, is still in use, but so far the principal application of *temperature logging* [105] has been to determine the position in back of casing of recently poured cement. Experimentation has been conducted on *sound wave logging*.[105a]

SUBSURFACE MAPS AND SECTIONS.[106] The logs and rock samples obtained during the drilling of individual wells may be of considerable value when considered alone,[107] but when compiled with

[101] Orton E. Campbell, "Principal Uses of Fluorologs," *Oil Weekly*, Vol. 124 (Dec. 30, 1946), pp. 41–42, 44–45; Tom L. Turner, "Use of Fluorescent Surface Surveys and Subsurface Logs to Find Oil," *Oil Weekly*, Vol. 111 (Nov. 29, 1943), pp. 22–26; Jack DeMent, "Fluoranalysis in Petroleum Exploration," *Subsurface Geologic Methods* (Colo. School of Mines, 1949), pp. 413–422.

[102] Leo Horvitz, "Geochemical Well Logging," *Bull. A. and M. Coll. Texas*, 93 (1946), pp. 29–31; *Geochemical Well Logging* (Geophysical Service, Inc., Dallas, Texas, 1941), 24 pp.

[103] L. L. Sloss and S. R. B. Cooke, "Spectrochemical Sample Logging of Limestones," *Bull. Am. Assoc. Petrol. Geol.*, Vol. 30 (November, 1946), pp. 1888–1898; "Spectrochemical Sample Logging," *Subsurface Geologic Methods* (Colo. School of Mines, 1949), pp. 378–387.

[104] L. B. Swan, "Electric Pilot Applications," *Bull. A. and M. Coll. Texas*, 93 (1946), pp. 146–165.

[105] Hubert Guyod, "Temperature Logging," *idem*, pp. 132–141.

[105a] Charles J. Deegan, "New Well-Logging Device Being Tried by Humble Engineers," *Oil and Gas Jour.*, Vol. 47 (July 15, 1948), p. 62.

[106] F. H. Lahee, "Maps," *Science of Petroleum* (Oxford Univ. Press, 1938), Vol. 1, pp. 276–283; L. W. LeRoy, "Subsurface Graphic Representations," *Subsurface Geologic Methods* (Colo. School of Mines, 1949), pp. 595–626; Julian Low, *Subsurface Maps and Illustrations*, pp. 627–681.

[107] Paul Weaver, "The Geologic Interpretation of Exploratory Wells," *Bull. Am. Assoc. Petrol. Geol.*, Vol. 33 (July, 1949), pp. 1135–1144.

similar information obtained from other wells the resulting maps and cross sections are of inestimable value in oil-finding. It is the task of the subsurface geologist to assemble the individual well records into geologic illustrations which will guide the administrative officers of the company in developing their exploration program. Descriptions of the various types of subsurface compilation follow.

Geologic Maps. In many areas, owing to thick veneers of glacial drift or other types of mantle, the geologic formations of the bed-rock surface can be mapped only by means of well data. This is probably the earliest application of subsurface geology. Water wells, salt wells, and oil wells furnished the information that was needed in compiling the geologic map of the southern peninsula of Michigan, where there are entire blocks of counties without a single outcrop.

The utilization of areal geologic maps in the search for oil was discussed in an earlier section. Such structural features as domes, anticlines, and noses may be discernible on the geologic map by the presence of inliers and other significant outcrop patterns. Faults may be of utmost importance in oil-finding.

Paleogeologic Maps.[108] A paleogeologic map is a map showing the areal geology at a given period in the past. It is, in effect, the result that would be obtained by peeling off the layers of younger rock above an unconformity.[109] Paleogeologic maps are constructed by plotting on a map the formations shown by well data to underlie the plane of the unconformity and then sketching in the formation boundaries after all the well data are plotted.

The paleogeologic map is of immeasurable value to the petroleum geologist. It reveals not only many structural features masked by the unconformity but also much information of the geologic past that is pertinent to the search for sedimentary or stratigraphic traps. "Oil and gas are found as high in their containing reservoir as it is possible for them to move. If true of the present, it must have been true in the past and a study of the changing areal and structural geology during geologic time becomes of prime importance.[110]

One of the earliest uses of the paleogeologic map was in the Mid-Continent, where a map of the pre-Mississippian formations of

[108] A. I. Levorsen, "Application of Paleogeology to Petroleum Geology," *Science of Petroleum* (Oxford Univ. Press, 1938), Vol. 1, pp. 300–303.

[109] W. C. Krumbein, "Criteria for Subsurface Recognition of Unconformities," *Bull. Am. Assoc. Petrol. Geol.*, Vol. 26 (January, 1942), pp. 36–62.

[110] A. I. Levorsen, "Studies in Paleogeology," *Bull. Am. Assoc. Petrol. Geol.*, Vol. 17 (September, 1933), pp. 1107–1132.

Oklahoma and Kansas [111] (Fig. 22) has been widely used in guiding exploration.

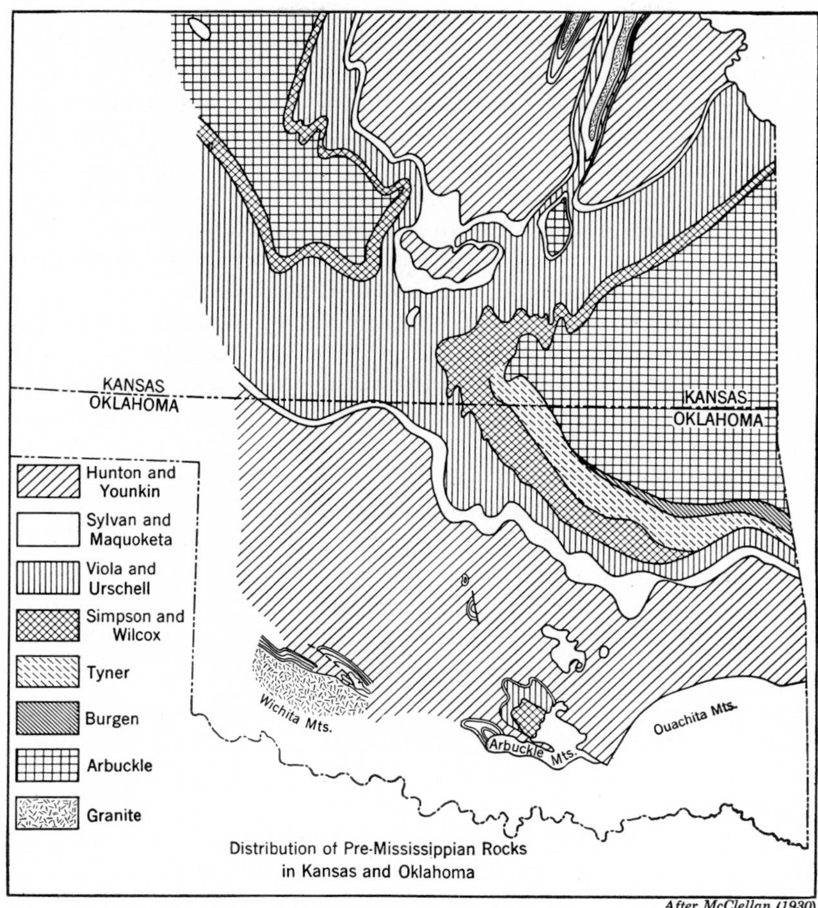

FIG. 22. Pre-Mississippian paleogeologic map, Oklahoma and Kansas. *Courtesy American Association of Petroleum Geologists.*

Paleogeographic Maps.[112] The paleogeographic map purports to show the submergent and emergent areas at a given time in the

[111] Hugh W. McClellan, "Subsurface Distribution of Pre-Mississippian Rocks of Kansas and Oklahoma," *Bull. Am. Assoc. Petrol. Geol.*, Vol. 14 (December, 1930), pp. 1535–1566.

[112] John Emery Adams, "Paleogeography and Petroleum Exploration," *Jour. Sed. Petrol.*, Vol. 13 (December, 1943), pp. 108–111.

geologic past. Most often the shorelines shown are pure guesswork. The data available for the construction of a paleogeographic map for a period of past time are confined to the erosional remnants of the sediments deposited during that time. These residua can be areally mapped in both the surface outcrop and in the subsurface, but almost always the boundaries are the result of erosion, and the original shoreline was an entirely unknown distance out beyond the present boundaries.

True paleogeographic maps can be constructed only where the actual strandlines have been submerged and covered with younger sediments before erosion has destroyed all evidence of the former land-water contact. This ideal situation is rare. However, better paleogeographic maps than those extant today could be made by more thorough studies of the paleoecology of the sediments and contained faunas; this would at least result in a more intelligent guess as to the distance from outermost remaining sedimentary deposit to original land area.

Structure Contour Maps. Obviously a structure contour map based on the reservoir rock (Fig. 7) is much more pertinent in a study of oil accumulation than one based on an outcropping formation. Usually the subsurface structure map shows more relief and greater closure [113] than the surface structure map. The position of the structural summit may shift laterally with depth owing to convergence or unconformity. The oil and water in a reservoir are, of course, in adjustment with the structure of that reservoir and not with the structure of overlying formations.

Subsurface structure contour maps are prepared by first plotting and then contouring the elevations of a buried datum surface (usually a formation top). These elevations may be obtained, with the help of surface elevations, from core-drill information, logs of all types and other well records, sample studies, and geophysical (especially seismic) surveys. Contour maps may be made for any traceable datum; many oil fields have been discovered by subsurface structure maps contoured on a near-surface formation penetrated by water wells, core tests, and shallow exploratory wells.

Isopachous Maps.[114] An isopach is a line drawn through points of equal thickness. The subsurface geologist determines the thickness

[113] The amount of closure is the vertical distance between the lowest possible closed structure contour line and the highest point on the structural feature.

[114] Jay B. Wharton, Jr., "Isopachous Maps of Sand Reservoirs," *Bull. Am. Assoc. Petrol. Geol.,* Vol. 32 (July, 1948), pp. 1331–1339.

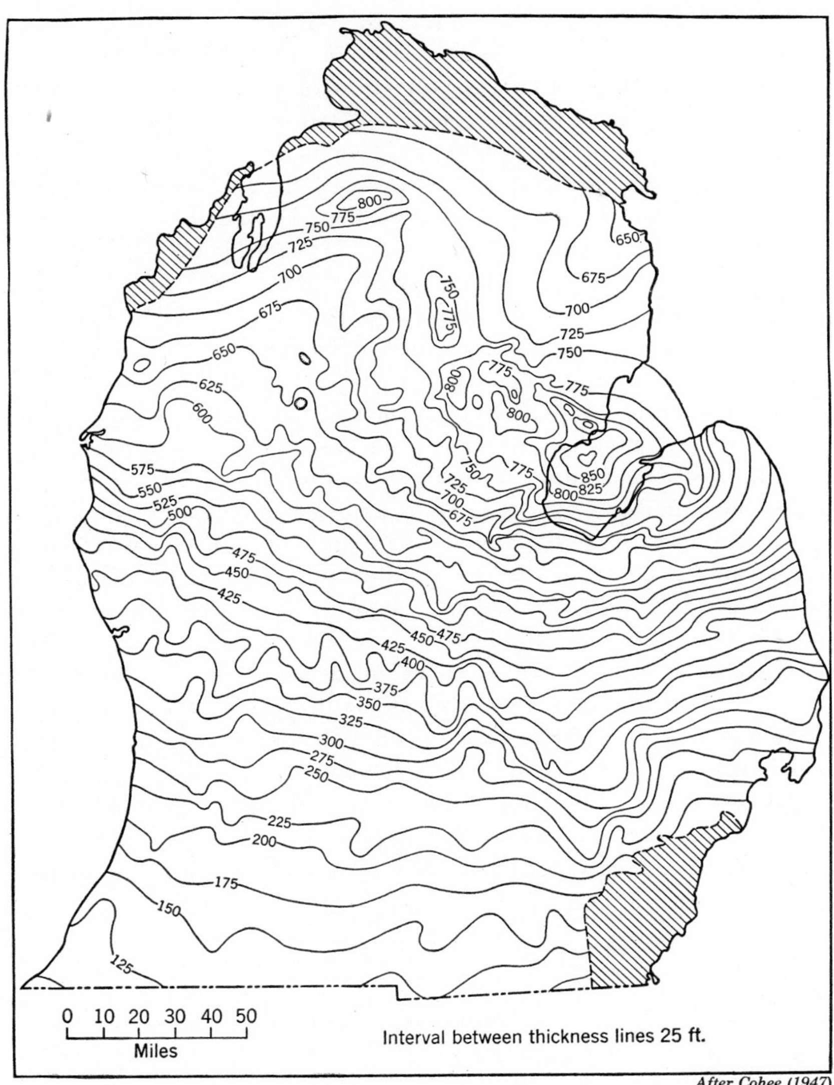

After Cohee (1947)

FIG. 23. Isopachous map, Traverse (Devonian) group, Michigan. Thickness decreases southward toward axes of Kankakee and Findlay arches and northward toward pre-Cambrian shield. Ruled areas show where Traverse rocks have been eroded. *United States Geological Survey.*

of a rock unit and enters these data on a map. Isopach lines can then be drawn in the same manner as contours.

Isopachous maps (Fig. 23) are very commonly employed in the search for oil. They point the direction of possible lateral "pinch-outs," and they may reveal structural features hitherto masked by unconformities. For example, a local reduction in thickness on an isopachous map is quite possibly an anticline or dome which was formed and truncated before the rock that overlies the zone covered by the isopachous map was deposited.[115] Isopachs are also of great value in the discovery and delineation of concealed faults.

By means of a surface structure map and an isopachous map, the structure of the underlying rock can be determined. If the isopachous map shows a thinning or convergence [116] of considerable magnitude, the structure (and especially the position of the anticlinal axes) of the older rocks will be quite different from that shown by the rocks overlying the converging unit. An isopachous map used for the purpose of determining the deeper structure is termed a *convergence map*. The construction of the preconvergence structure contour map is relatively simple and is based on the calculation and plotting of the deeper rock elevations where the higher structure contour lines intersect the isopach or convergence lines.

Isopachous maps are also useful in determining the volume of saturated sand for the purpose of calculating petroleum reserves.

Paleostructure, Paleotectonic,[117] or Palinspastic Maps.[118] Palinspastic maps show the structural or tectonic history of a region (Fig. 24). As will be seen later, under "Accumulation," the dating of the earth movements is of utmost importance. Obviously a trap in which oil has accumulated must have been formed *before* the present oil deposit was caught.

[115] Wallace Lee, "Relation of Thickness of Mississippian Limestones in Central and Eastern Kansas to Oil and Gas Deposits," *Kans. Geol. Survey Bull.* 26 (1939), 42 pp.

[116] Robert R. Wheeler and Robert M. Swesnik, "Stratigraphic Convergence Problems," *World Oil,* Vol. 130 (April, 1950), pp. 57–61; Robert M. Swesnik and Robert R. Wheeler, "Stratigraphic Convergence Problems in Oil Finding," *Bull. Am. Assoc. Petrol. Geol.,* Vol. 31 (November, 1947), pp. 2021–2029; A. I. Levorsen, "Convergence Studies in the Mid-Continent Region," *Bull. Am. Assoc. Petrol. Geol.,* Vol. 11 (July, 1927), pp. 657–682.

[117] A. J. Eardley, "Paleotectonic and Paleogeologic Maps of Central and Western North America," *Bull. Am. Assoc. Petrol. Geol.,* Vol. 33 (May, 1949), pp. 655–682.

[118] George Marshall Kay, "Paleogeographic and Palinspastic Maps," *Bull. Am. Assoc. Petrol. Geol.,* Vol. 29 (April, 1945), pp. 426–450.

The simplest type of paleostructure map is one constructed by eliminating the regional dip.[119] This shows the character of the folding before the regional tilting took place. If that tilting was quite recent, the oil may not yet have become completely adjusted to the new

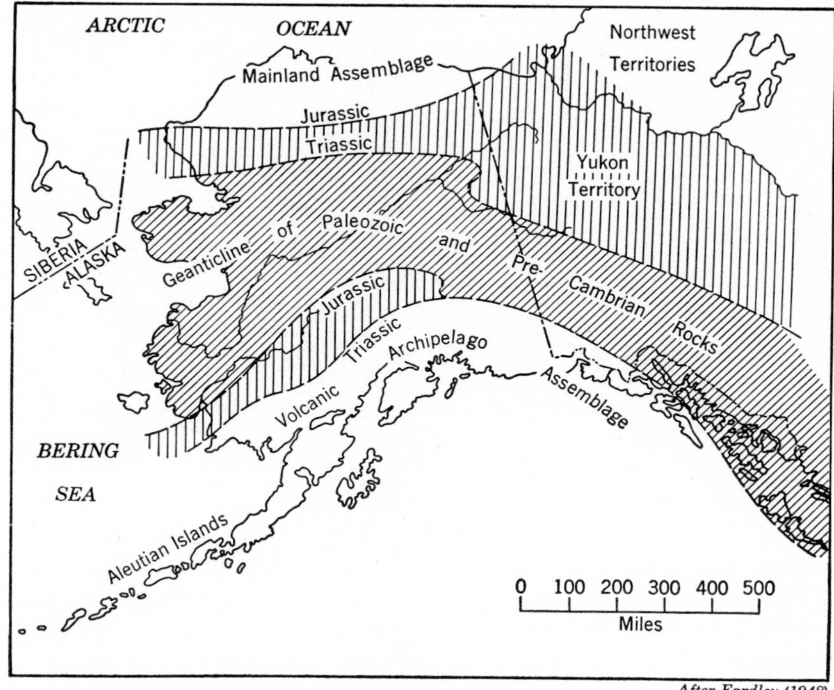

After Eardley (1948)

FIG. 24. Paleotectonic map of Alaska, showing regional structure during the Triassic and Jurassic periods. *Courtesy Journal of Geology.*

structural environment, so a picture of the older structural situation may serve as a guide to oil.

Facies Maps.[120] Differences from place to place in the character of the physical sediment (lithofacies) or in the organic sediment (bio-

[119] John Rich, "Graphical Method of Eliminating Regional Dip" and "Fault-Block Nature of Kansas Structures Suggested by Elimination of Regional Dip," *Bull. Am. Assoc. Petrol. Geol.*, Vol. 19 (October, 1935), pp. 1538–1543; G. D. Hobson, "The Application of Tilt to a Fold," *Proc. Geol. Assoc.*, Vol. 55 (Jan. 26, 1945), pp. 216–221.

[120] W. C. Krumbein, "Sedimentary Maps and Oil Exploration," *N. Y. Acad. Sci. Trans.*, Ser. 2, Vol. 7 (May, 1945), pp. 159–166; W. C. Krumbein, "Lithofacies Maps and Regional Sedimentary-Stratigraphic Analysis," *Bull. Am. Assoc. Petrol. Geol.*, Vol. 32 (October, 1948), pp. 1909–1923; E. C. Dapples, W. C. Krumbein, and

facies) can be shown by means of facies maps (Fig. 25). The usual procedure is to convert the data into numbers, such as percentage figures, and then construct contourlike ("isopleth") maps by drawing lines through points of equal value. The initial data are obtained

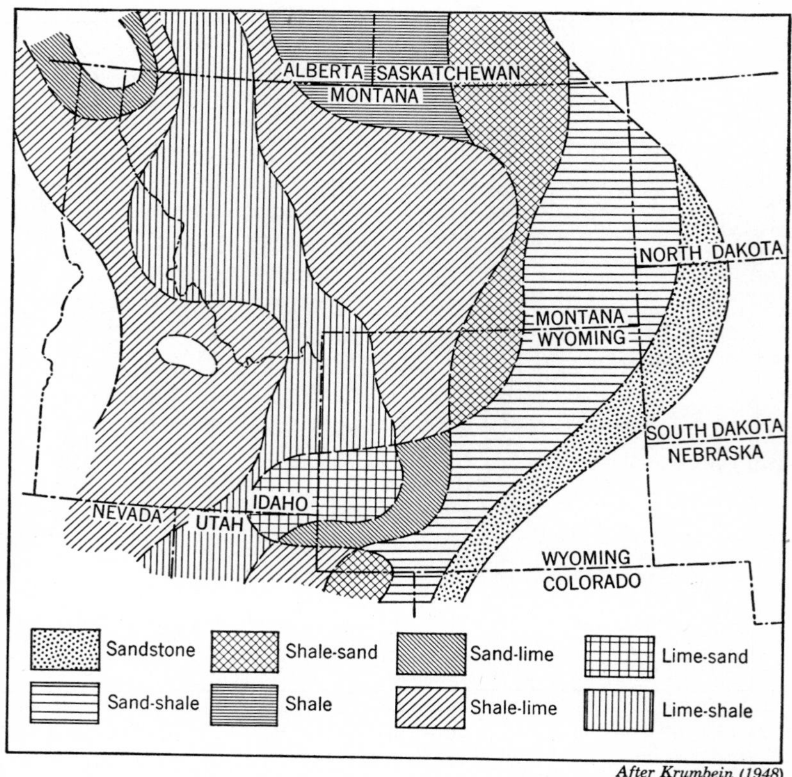

Fig. 25. Lithofacies map showing character of Cambrian deposits in northern Rockies. *Courtesy American Association of Petroleum Geologists.*

from cores or cuttings from wells, or from outcrop samples, or from both.

Krumbein [121] has listed a considerable number of sedimentary rock characteristics that have been or can be used in the construction of facies maps. Examples of lithofacies maps include those showing

L. L. Sloss, "Tectonic Control of Lithologic Associations," *Bull. Am. Assoc. Petrol. Geol.,* Vol. 32 (October, 1948), pp. 1924–1947; W. C. Krumbein, L. L. Sloss, and E. C. Dapples, "Sedimentary Tectonics and Sedimentary Environments," *Bull. Am. Assoc. Petrol. Geol.,* Vol. 33 (November, 1949), pp. 1859–1891.

[121] "Sedimentary Maps and Oil Exploration," *N. Y. Acad. Sci. Trans.,* Ser. 2, Vol. 7 (May, 1945), pp. 159–166.

variations in grain size, porosity, permeability, heavy-mineral content, sphericity of grains, magnesium content, insoluble residues, and degree of cementation. Maps which show lateral changes in sand or shale content are especially valuable. Variations in the character of contained fluids, such as the salt content of the connate water, and in the degree of saturation are readily shown by isopleth maps.

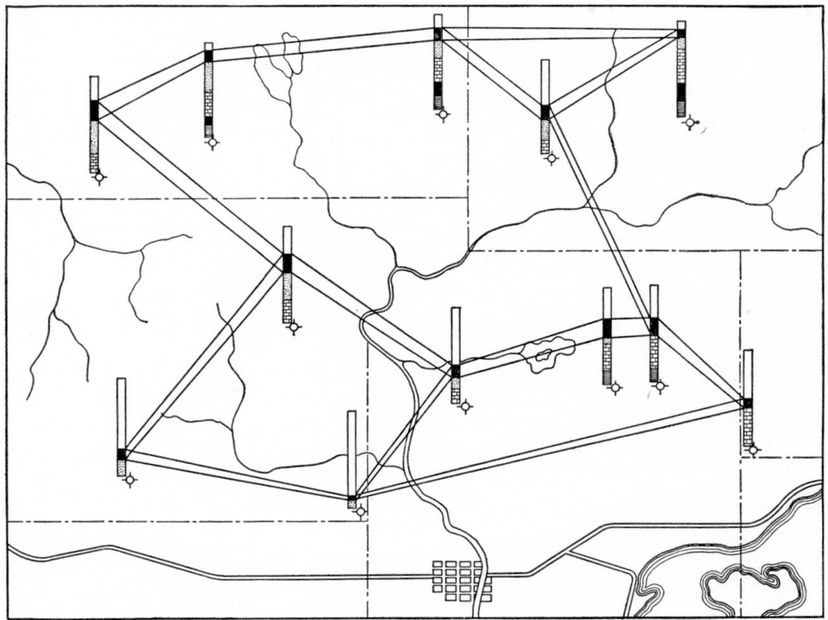

Fig. 26. Log map. The plotted log is drawn beside the location of the well on the map. The relationship between convergence and other lateral changes and geographic position can be seen at a glance. *Drawing by John Jesse Hayes.*

Among types of biofacies maps are those showing variations in percentage of a particular type of organism or in overall organic content.

The importance of facies, and hence of paleogeography, to problems of the origin and accumulation of oil cannot be overemphasized. The environment and character of source material accumulation controlled the creation of oil, and many oil and gas traps have been formed by changes in facies of sediments.

Cross Sections. By means of cross sections, the subsurface geologist can assemble in one drawing information which is spread over several maps. A single cross section can be used to show surface topography, overburden thickness, the stratigraphic column, facies changes, convergence, unconformities, and the structure at various levels. The disadvantage of the cross section lies in its limitation to two dimensions; this handicap can be alleviated by constructing several cross sections which crisscross the area under study.

Cross sections are made by plotting the information obtained from wells and interpolating the formation boundaries and other data

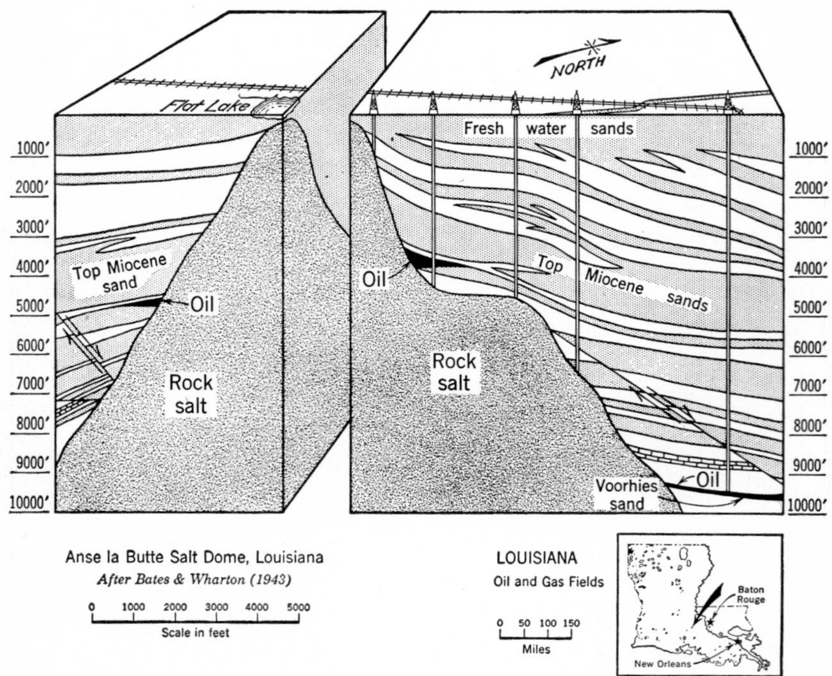

FIG. 27. Block diagram. Anse la Butte Salt Dome, Louisiana. *Courtesy Colorado School of Mines.*

between wells. They can be plotted with sea level as a base, and then the topography can be shown as the structure is as of today, or a formation boundary can be taken as a base in order to emphasize convergence or facies changes.

The usual American custom of exaggerating the vertical scale with respect to the horizontal scale of the cross section has been criticized, and with justification, by Suter.[122] A true dip of 5° becomes 46° if the vertical scale is exaggerated 12 times, which is by no means

[122] H. H. Suter, "Exaggeration of Vertical Scale of Geologic Sections," *Bull. Am. Assoc. Petrol. Geol.,* Vol. 31 (February, 1947), pp. 318–339.

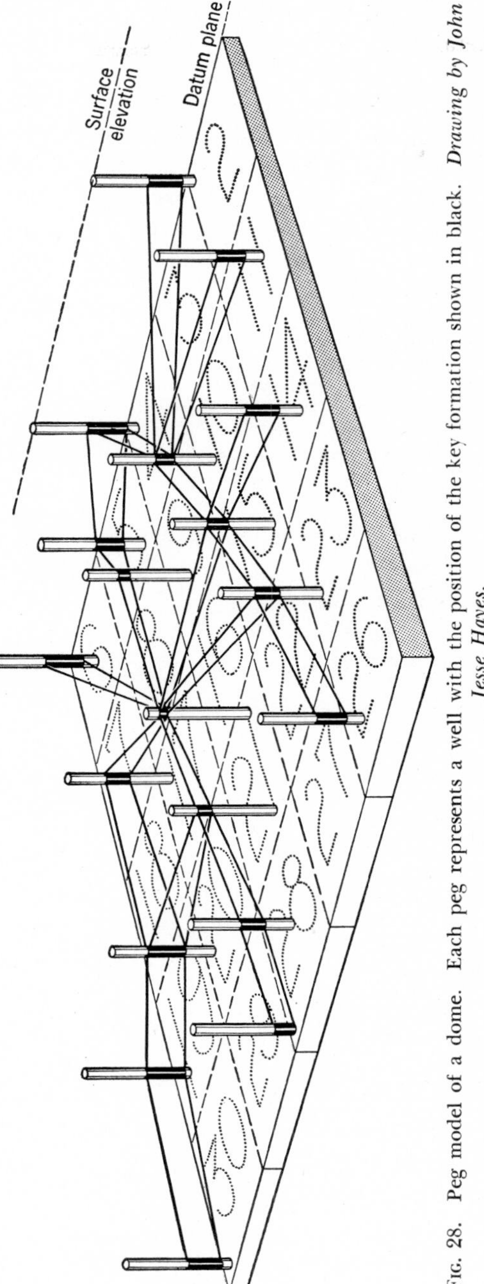

FIG. 28. Peg model of a dome. Each peg represents a well with the position of the key formation shown in black. *Drawing by John Jesse Hayes.*

unusual. The only excuse for the increased vertical scale is to show stratigraphic detail which would be too compressed for visibility if true scale were used.

Miscellaneous methods of geologic illustration include the log map [123] (Fig. 26), the block diagram (Fig. 27), the structure diorama,[124] and the peg model (Fig. 28), which has a wooden rod, on which the formations are marked off in color, for each well. The block diagram was used most effectively by Bass [125] to show reservoir sand thickness; each well is the intersection of two sand "fences" running normal to each other (Fig. 69).

[123] T. H. Bower, "Log Map, New Type of Subsurface Map," *Bull. Am. Assoc. Petrol. Geol.,* Vol. 31 (February, 1947), pp. 340–349.

[124] Frederick Squires, "The Structure Diorama (Lawrence County, Illinois)," *Oil and Gas Jour.,* Vol. 43 (Aug. 19, 1944), pp. 86–93.

[125] N. W. Bass, "Origin of the Shoestring Sands of Greenwood and Butler Counties, Kansas," *State Geol. Survey of Kans. Bull.* 23 (September, 1936), p. 76.

Chapter 3

EXPLOITATION

The duties and interests of the petroleum geologist do not end with the locating of the wildcat test well. Although from there on the work is performed mainly by drilling crews and petroleum engineers, the geologist continues to be concerned with the steps taken to obtain a commercial well and with the subsequent exploitation history of the oil or gas deposit. In some of this development the geologist is an active participant; at other times he may serve in a consulting capacity; and at the very least he is an interested spectator in the operations that follow discovery. For these reasons the geologist should be acquainted with post-exploration procedures.

"DRILLING IN" AND COMPLETING A WELL. Either from the very start or at least after a wildcat well has been drilled to near the top of the possible "pay" zones, a geologist is delegated by the interested company to "sit on the well."[1] It is his job to examine the samples as they are brought to the surface and thereby keep in touch with the stratigraphic progress downward. To implement his cuttings examinations, he may request that a core or cores be taken. He recommends casing points and warns the driller where the pay zones may be expected. His stratigraphic and lithologic identifications are a basis for decisions regarding coring for permeability and saturation data, and testing for potential oil and gas yields.

After a well has been drilled into the potential reservoir rock, as much as two-thirds of the original drilling cost may be spent in testing the formation for production possibilities.[2] Specific items of testing include the porosity, the permeability, the thickness of productive parts of the reservoir, analyses of the hydrocarbons present, and the volume of connate water. These basic reservoir data are obtained largely by the laboratory examination of cores cut from the reservoir rock. It is an increasingly common procedure to core the reservoir

[1] C. A. Caswell, "Sitting on a Well," *World Oil*, Vol. 130 (Feb. 1, 1950), pp. 100 *et seq*.

[2] Anonymous: "Testing Costs Money," *The Link*, Vol. 12 (April, 1947), pp. 12–15.

from top to bottom. The information thus obtained is invaluable in determining the capacity of the well to produce and in estimating the reserve situation.

The actual testing of a well for initial production is a routine operation. If the well flows, its production is gauged over a given period of time and the yield over 24 hours is estimated. A cable tool well which does not flow can be tested by running the bailer and noting the quantity that can be withdrawn per hour without lowering the static fluid level in the hole. If the oil is slow in entering the hole, its flow may be accelerated by *swabbing*. A tool (the "swab") which fits the casing snugly is lowered to the reservoir zone and then hoisted rapidly to the surface. This creates a partial vacuum which pulls the oil from the surrounding rock and may even start a well to flow.

The testing procedure in a rotary well is of necessity quite different. At the time of penetration of the reservoir rock, the well is usually uncased below the surface water zone and the hole is full of mud. In the earlier days of rotary drilling it was necessary to run casing in the well and remove all the mud before the formation could be tested for its capacity to produce. Because of the bother and expense, such testing was often omitted, and without doubt many reservoirs capable of yielding oil or gas in commercial quantities were bypassed in the wildcatting of that period. During the 1920's the method of drill-stem testing which is in use today was developed.

Drill-stem testing [3] uses the drill pipe as a conduit and obviates the necessity of casing the hole and pumping out the mud. An empty string of drill pipe with a valve at the bottom and a packer set so that it will land just above the formation to be tested is run into the hole. The packer seals off the mud from above so that, when the valve at the bottom is opened, the fluids in the reservoir will flow into the empty drill stem. This flow is brought about by the pressure differential between the reservoir rock, which approximates 0.46 pound per foot of depth,[4] and the inside of the drill pipe, where the pressure is atmospheric.

Other things being equal, the amount of fluid entering a well is directly proportional to the area of rock face or "bleeding surface." Therefore, under like conditions more oil will enter a large-diameter well than one with small diameter. Two potent methods of increas-

[3] Roy Edwards, "Mechanics of Drill Stem Testing," *World Oil*, Part 1, Vol. 128 (December, 1948), pp. 83–94; Part 2, Vol. 128 (January, 1949), pp. 82–86.

[4] John R. Suman, "Drilling, Testing, and Completion," *Elements of the Petroleum Industry* (Am. Inst. Min. Met. Engineers, New York, 1940), p. 201.

ing manyfold the area of bleeding surface are shooting[5] and acidizing.[6] Shooting is the detonating of a charge of nitroglycerin which has been lowered into the well. The explosion shatters the rock for a considerable distance, producing many rock faces from which the fluid can drain into the well. Acidizing is the dumping of large quantities of hydrochloric acid into carbonate rock reservoirs. This acid contains an inhibitor which deters corrosion of steel, such as in casing and tools. The carbonate rock, however, is leached outward some distance from the well by the action of the acid. The development of this technique in the early 1930's led to the revival of many declining limestone pools, with a second stage of flush production comparable in magnitude to the initial stage. In addition to increasing the area of the producing rock surface, shooting or acidizing a dry hole may cause a break-through into an oil-filled fracture in pools where the accumulation is largely crevice-controlled.

Another development, also for the purpose of increasing well productivity, is the Hydrafrac[7] process. A viscous gel is forced into the reservoir rock under hydraulic pressure of such magnitude that preexisting fractures are extended and new fractures are formed. Then the gel is removed by injecting a "gel-breaker" solution which decreases the viscosity so that the fluid may be readily displaced from the fractures.

Completing a well includes all the steps taken to transform an exploration test into a producing oil or gas well. Once it has been demonstrated that the well can produce enough hydrocarbon to justify the completion costs, the necessary steps are begun. The simplest procedure can be followed where the well was drilled by cable tools and the reservoir is an indurated sandstone or competent limestone. Under these circumstances casing is run from the surface to the top of the reservoir or consolidated overlying rock, where it is cemented into place. Then smaller-diameter tubing, through which the oil is to travel to the surface, is run inside the casing to near the bottom of the hole, which is open below the casing seat.

Where the reservoir rock is incoherent it is not possible to produce from an open hole. One method, long employed in water wells, is the "gravel pack," in which gravel is poured into the hole below the casing seat in order to discourage collapse of the wall of the bore hole.

[5] E. DeGolyer and Harold Vance, "Bibliography on Petroleum Industry," *Bull. A. and M. Coll. Texas,* 83 (1944), pp. 460–461 (25 references).

[6] *Ibid.,* pp. 528–530 (69 references).

[7] J. B. Clark, "Hydraulic Fracturing of Oil, Gas Formations by Hydrafrac Process," *Oil and Gas Jour.,* Vol. 48 (May 26, 1949), p. 75.

A very common procedure is to attach screens or perforated pipe sections to the casing string at the proper point or points and cement the string into place before running the tubing. Another method with wide application in the newer oil fields is to run a solid string of casing from the surface to the bottom of the hole, cement it into place, and then perforate the casing at the desired levels by means of either a "gun perforator," which shoots bullets through the casing into the wall rock, or a casing perforator, which rips slits in the pipe somewhat in the manner of a can opener.

RESERVOIR PRESSURES.[8] Reservoir pressure is the pressure exerted by the fluids and gases contained in the reservoir rock. This pressure can be measured during flow, or by shutting in the well and lowering a gauge to the reservoir face. Values range from but little above atmospheric pressure (14.4 pounds per square inch) to a maximum recorded reading of 12,635 pounds per square inch.[9] As a general but not invariable rule, the reservoir pressure drops during the lifetime of an oil or gas field from a maximum at time of discovery to a minimum at time of abandonment. The degree of the drop depends upon the proportion of gas present, the hydrostatic pressure of the edgewater, and the percentage of the total volume of the reservoir occupied by the hydrocarbons. Where a large percentage of gas is present, pressure drops of the greatest magnitude occur. If the edgewater pressures are high, the initial reservoir pressure may be maintained throughout the history of the oil field, even after all the oil wells have become water wells. If the reservoir is limited in size and the hydrocarbons occupy the greater part of that reservoir, their removal will obviously be accompanied by a pressure drop because no new supplies of water are available to occupy the relinquished space.

The importance of reservoir pressure to the oil producer cannot be overemphasized. The initial pressures may be of such magnitude as to cause the well to flow, thereby saving pumping expense. Even if the well ceases to flow, or fails to flow initially, the difference in pressures between the reservoir and the well causes the hydrocarbons to

[8] Stanley C. Herold, *Oil Well Drainage* (Stanford Univ. Press, 1941); C. V. Millikan, "Production Practice," *Elements of the Petroleum Industry* (Am. Inst. Min. Met. Engineers, New York, 1940), pp. 255–257; V. C. Illing, "The Origin of Pressure in Oil Pools," *Science of Petroleum* (Oxford Univ. Press, London, 1938), Vol. 1, pp. 224–229; Committees on Reservoir Development and Operation (Standard Oil Co. of New Jersey, affiliated companies, and Humble Oil and Refining Company), *Joint Progress Report on Reservoir Efficiency and Well Spacing* (Standard Oil Development Co., 1943).

[9] Lee S. McCaslin, Jr., "Tide Water's Record Breaker—Bottom Hole Pressure 12,635 Psi," *Oil and Gas Jour.*, Vol. 48 (Sept. 8, 1949), pp. 58 *et seq.*

flow into the well and to rise in the tubing toward the surface so that the pumping depth may be considerably less than the reservoir depth. Furthermore, the maintenance of high reservoir pressure during the lifetime of a pool will result in a far greater yield than is possible if the pressure is allowed to drop appreciably. The principal reason for the higher eventual recovery with maintenance of reservoir pressure lies in the relationship between the gas and oil within the reservoir. The greater the pressure, the more gas the oil can carry in solution; the more gas the oil has in solution, the greater its liquidity. The escape of gas to the surface in disproportionate amounts to the oil produced will result in more and more sluggish oil being left behind in the reservoir. Furthermore, the dropping of the pressure below the point at which the gas begins to come out of solution will cause the formation of minute gas bubbles, which in turn retard the flow of oil. The proportion of gas to oil is known as the gas-oil ratio,[10] and it is modern production practice to attempt to maintain it as near the initial ratio as possible. If the gas in the reservoir initially overlies the oil ("gas cap") or if during exploitation it escapes from the oil upward to the top of the reservoir instead of to the surface, it still maintains a useful function, as will be further explained in a subsequent paragraph. The expansive force of the gas in the gas cap tends to drive the oil downward into wells that have been completed low in the oil zone. If, however, the wells are completed in the gas cap, only gas will be produced and the greater part of the reservoir energy will become dissipated.

Natural gas, because of its high compressibility, is capable of storing up pressures that were the result of some activity in the geologic past which may be no longer existent. It is this "fossil" pressure that supplies the reservoir energy in many oil fields.

Possible Causes of Reservoir Pressure. The pressure in the reservoir that is simplest to explain is that exerted by the water which almost invariably underlies the oil and gas deposit. If the reservoir rock is continuously permeable to the outcrop, the pressure exerted by the edgewater will be approximately equivalent to that of a vertical column of water extending from the oil-water interface upward to the level of the water table below the outcrop of the reservoir rock. This amounts to 44 to 46 (depending upon degree of salinity) pounds per

[10] R. V. Higgins, "Productivity of Oil Wells and Inherent Influence of Gas:Oil Ratios and Water Saturation," *U. S. Bur. Mines, Rept. Investigations* 3657 (September, 1942).

square inch for each 100 feet of water column. In some oil fields lateral permeability of the reservoir rock apparently does extend to the outcrop, for the reservoir pressure is very close to the calculated pressure. At the other extreme, there are cases on record where the deeper reservoirs have much lower pressures than the shallower reservoirs in which event it is obvious that there is little or no connection between the reservoir fluids and the water table. Probably in most fields there is at least an imperfect hydraulic connection with the water table, either by way of the reservoir rock or a trans-stratification fracture system, so that hydrostatic head is one of several forces involved in the reservoir pressure.

Although pure water is only slightly compressible, reservoir brines have considerably higher compressibilities because of the presence of salts and gases in solution. It has been suggested that water expansion, which has accompanied the lowering of reservoir pressure due to the exploitation of the East Texas field, has been the mechanism by which the edgewater has followed behind the oil as the oil has been removed.[11] The artesian movement of water from the outcrop of the Woodbine sand to the zone of oil removal in East Texas is not considered adequate to fill immediately the pore spaces vacated by the oil drawn to the surface. Bugbee[12] emphasizes that only where the volume of edgewater is large (as at East Texas) can water expansion be of great importance. He also points out that in a lenslike reservoir hydrostatic pressures cannot be present, but expansion of compressed water can and no doubt does occur.

Because the hydrocarbons occur in the pore spaces between grains of sand, or in miniature caverns in carbonate rock, they ordinarily do not carry any of the weight of the overlying rock. However, until the associated rock has compacted to its maximum extent, the reservoirs will receive a pressure increment as the result of the squeezing out of the contained liquid in the compacting clay, mud, or calcareous ooze. In a few places, as at Goose Creek, Texas, the production of oil has been accompanied by a settling or a subsidence of the surface, perhaps because of accelerated compaction made possible by the lowering of pressure in the reservoir. In many cases of surface subsidence

[11] R. J. Schilthuis and William Hurst, "Variations in Reservoir Pressure in the East Texas Field," *Trans. Am. Inst. Min. Met. Engineers,* Vol. 114 (Petroleum Development and Technology, 1935), pp. 164–173.

[12] J. M. Bugbee, "Reservoir Analyses and Geologic Structure," *Trans. Am. Inst. Min. Met. Engineers,* Vol. 151 (Petroleum Development and Technology, 1943), pp. 99–111.

of oil fields, however, the removal of large quantities of reservoir sand along with the hydrocarbons has been responsible for the settling.

Some of the pressure in the reservoir may be residual from a past period of diastrophism when lateral compressional forces which accompanied mountain-building activity were added to the static pressures caused by the weight of the overlying sediment.

Another possible cause of reservoir pressure is the generation of oil and gas. If this generation takes place after compaction and lithifaction, the volume increase that accompanies the transformation of organic solid into liquid hydrocarbon would naturally increase the pressures existing in the reservoirs. Furthermore, the various changes which take place in the molecular structure of the hydrocarbons during their post-generation history are also accompanied by an increase or decrease in volume, which will create pressure changes within the reservoir. Pressure control is also brought about by the temperature of the reservoir. The increase in temperature, which normally takes place with increased depth, will also increase the pressure of any confined gas. In addition, the temperature increase will drive some of the gas out of solution in the oil, thereby increasing the quantity of free gas available in the reservoir and at the same time increasing the magnitude of the reservoir energy. Various miscellaneous causes of reservoir pressure have been suggested. According to Waldschmidt,[13] "much of the initial high pressure in some fields may directly result from precipitation of crystalline minerals within the voids of the reservoir rock." He points out that the volume of water with anhydrite in solution is less than the total volume of water with the calcium sulfate precipitated. The natural cementation of clastic reservoir rock would therefore result in an increase in the pressures existing within the reservoir rock, provided that it was a closed system at the time the precipitation of the natural cement took place. The hydration of minerals in the surrounding rocks and the adsorption of water by clay would withdraw water from the reservoir and result in a decrease in pressure. The gradual denudation of an oil field would also result in a decrease in pressure due to the lowering of hydrostatic head, the lowering of temperature, and, in the final phases, to the introduction of surface waters with bacteria and salts in solution. The mineralized ground waters would tend to asphaltize the petroleum, which in turn

[13] W. A. Waldschmidt, "Cementing Materials in Sandstones and Probable Influence of Migration and Accumulation of Oil and Gas," *Bull. Am. Assoc. Petrol. Geol.,* Vol. 25 (October, 1941), pp. 1839–1879.

would produce volume and consequent pressure change. Bacterial activity in the reservoir may result in the release of carbon dioxide, which would affect the pressure.

It can be concluded from this discussion of reservoir pressures that the extent of the connection between the fluids in the reservoir and the water table is of utmost importance. In a completely open system, as where a sandstone is laterally continuous and uniformly permeable from trap to outcrop, the pressure is exclusively due to the hydrostatic head. "Fossil" pressures are impossible, for any increase in the past would have been nullified by outflow at the water table below the outcrop. In a closed system, with no connection between reservoir and ground-water circulation, any or all of the other pressure causes enumerated could be responsible. Probably of greatest importance are the pressures created by the expansive force of water trapped with the hydrocarbons in the closed reservoir and the residual forces that accumulated in the past because of squeezing, increased temperatures, and molecular changes within the hydrocarbons. Timing controls the importance of such possible pressure causes as cementation and petroleum generation. If cementation can take place in volume *after* the hydrocarbons have accumulated in the reservoir, then cementation becomes a potent pressure cause. Similarly, if lithifaction is complete *before* oil is formed, the generation of oil would produce a volume change that would result in an increase in pressure.

In most reservoirs the hydraulic system is probably neither wide open nor tightly closed; an imperfect, tortuous, high-friction connection with the water table may exist so that the reservoir pressure is a combination of hydrostatic and residual forces.

Dissolved Gas Drive. Petroleum is propelled out of the reservoir and into the well by one, or a combination, of three processes: dissolved gas drive, gas cap drive, and water drive. Early recognition of the type of drive involved is essential to the efficient development of an oil field. In dissolved gas drive, the propulsive force is the gas which is in solution in the oil and which tends to come out of solution because of the pressure release at the point of penetration of a well. The movement of oil produced by dissolved gas drive is analogous to the effervescence that results from the uncapping of an agitated bottle of soda water. Dissolved gas drive is most likely to exist in structures of low relief; high structural relief encourages the segregation of gas and oil into separate bodies. Dissolved gas drive is the least efficient type of natural drive. Nothing can be done to control the gas-oil ratio; the bottom-hole pressure drops rapidly, and the total eventual recovery is only from 20 to 40 per cent.

Gas Cap Drive. If gas overlies the oil, beneath the top of the trap, it is compressed and can be utilized to drive the oil into wells which are footed toward the bottom of the oil-bearing zone. The highest-pressure oil fields are of this type, and costly "blowouts" have resulted from the unexpected piercing of the roof of such a gas cap. By producing oil only from below the gas cap it is possible to maintain a high gas-oil ratio in the reservoir until almost the very end of the life of the pool. If, however, the oil deposit is not systematically developed, so that bypassing of the gas occurs, an undue proportion of oil will be left behind. During the life of a properly controlled gas cap field, the decline in reservoir pressure is moderate and the total recovery may be as high as 70 to 80 per cent.

The ultimate in gas caps are the so-called condensate fields in the Gulf Coast area of Texas and Louisiana and in California. These are deep-seated, high-temperature gas accumulations from which liquid hydrocarbons ("condensate") can be recovered at the surface by reduction of pressure and temperature. There remains a large volume of residual gas after the condensate has been removed, and the modern practice is to "cycle" this gas by compressing and reinjecting it into the reservoir. By thus maintaining adequate pressure within the gas cap, condensation in the reservoir is prevented. Such condensation would result in a lesser eventual recovery because of the inevitable loss of the liquid that would remain in the reservoir.

Water Drive. The most efficient propulsive force in driving oil into a well is natural water drive, in which the pressure of the edge-water forces the lighter oil ahead and upward until all the recoverable oil has been flushed out of the reservoir into the producing wells. In anticlinal accumulation, the structurally lowest wells around the flanks of the dome will be the first to come into water, after which the oil-water contact plane will move upward until only the wells at the top of the anticline are still producing oil, and eventually these too will have to be abandoned as the water displaces the oil. In a water-drive field it is essential that the removal rate be so adjusted that the water moves up evenly and as fast as space is made available for it by the removal of the hydrocarbons. If properly practiced, no appreciable decline in the bottom-hole pressure takes place, and the recovery may run as high as 80 per cent. As has already been noted, the force behind the water drive may be either hydrostatic pressure, the expansion of the reservoir water, or a combination of both.

METHODS OF PRODUCING WELLS.[14] Oil may be produced by natural flow, induced flow, or mechanical lift. In most reservoirs the energy is sufficient during the early stages of exploitation to force the petroleum into the wells and up the tubing to the surface, whence it flows to a tank battery. However, some fields initially, and almost all fields eventually, have to be produced by means of help from the surface. The simplest method is the gas lift, in which natural gas is pumped to the bottom of the well through the annular space between the tubing and the casing. The oil that collects in the boring is pushed up the tubing to the surface by the force of the compressed gas. Gas lift merely supplies the natural reservoir with energy that it never had or no longer possesses. The gas used is most often a by-product of the oil from which it has been separated at the surface. During the compression of the gas, any gasoline present ("wet" gas) is removed before the gas is reinjected into the reservoir. If the local gas supply is inadequate, natural gas from other fields may be used. Air can be used in the same manner but has the decided disadvantages of corroding all metal with which it comes in contact and of producing a highly explosive mixture.

By far the most common method of producing oil from non-flowing wells is by means of a pump which provides a mechanical lift to the fluids in the reservoir. A pump barrel is lowered into the well on a string of solid steel rods known as "sucker rods." Up-and-down movement of the sucker rods forces the oil up the tubing to the surface. This vertical movement may be supplied by a walking beam powered by a nearby engine, or it may be brought about through the use of a pump jack, which is connected with a central power source by means of "pull rods."

Substances Which May Be Produced by a Well. A considerable variety of materials may be produced by oil wells in addition to liquid and gaseous hydrocarbons. The natural gas itself may contain as impurities one or more non-hydrocarbon substances.[15] The most abundant of these impurities is hydrogen sulfide, which imparts a noticeable odor to the gas. A small amount of this compound is considered to be advantageous, for it gives warning of leaks when and where they occur. A larger amount, however, makes the gas obnoxious

[14] C. V. Millikan, "Production Practice," *Elements of the Petroleum Industry* (Am. Inst. Min. Met. Engineers, 1940), pp. 260–270; Morris Muskat, *Physical Principles of Oil Production,* McGraw-Hill, New York, 1949).

[15] C. E. Dobbin, "Geology of Natural Gases Rich in Helium, Nitrogen, Carbon Dioxide, and Hydrogen Sulfide," *Geology of Natural Gas* (Am. Assoc. Petrol. Geol., 1935), pp. 1053–1072.

and difficult to market. Such gas is referred to as "sour gas," and much of it is used in the manufacture of carbon black.

A few natural gases contain helium. It is interesting to note that this element occurs in commercial quantities in certain gas fields in Texas, Colorado, and Utah, but it has not yet been found in any volume anywhere else in the world.[16] Nitrogen has also been found in some natural gases. The last few years have seen not only the discovery but also the commercial development of carbon dioxide gas occurring in natural reservoirs in the southwest.[17] Natural carbon dioxide is used in the manufacture of Dry Ice. Because of the great cooling effect of expanding carbon dioxide, the surface pipes and fittings of wells yielding any appreciable volume of this gas become coated with frost, which has led to the appellation "ice cream" wells. Two carbon dioxide fields have been developed in New Mexico and at least one field in each of the states of Colorado, Utah, and California. The origin of the non-hydrocarbon gases is discussed in Chapter 5 under "Origin of Natural Gas."

The liquid hydrocarbons produced by a well may include solid hydrocarbons in solution which separate upon reaching the surface and cause clogging of the pipes and fittings. Both the paraffin hydrocarbons and bitumen [18] are offenders in this regard.

By far the most abundant extraneous material is water. Many wells, especially during their declining years, produce vast quantities of salt water, and its disposal, which is discussed in the following section, is both a serious and an expensive problem. Furthermore, the brine may be corrosive, necessitating frequent replacement of casing, pipe, and valves, or it may be saturated so that the salts tend to precipitate upon reaching the surface. In either case the water produced with the oil is a source of continuing trouble.

Where the reservoir rock is an incoherent sand or poorly cemented sandstone, large quantities of sand will be produced along with the oil and gas. On its way to the surface this sand creates an explosion hazard by the sparks which may be produced, and sand has even been known to scour its way completely through pipes and fittings.

[16] Andrew Stewart, "About Helium," *U. S. Bur. Mines Information Circular* 6745 (September, 1933).

[17] Frank E. E. Germann, "The Occurrence of Carbon Dioxide," *Science,* Vol. 87 (June 10, 1938), pp. 513–521; J. Charles Miller, "Discussion of Origin, Occurrence, and the Use of Natural Carbon Dioxide in the United States," *Oil and Gas Jour.,* Vol. 25 (Nov. 9, 1933), pp. 19–20; Sterling B. Talmage and A. Andreas, "Carbon Dioxide in New Mexico," *N. Mex. Bur. Mines Bull.* 18 (1945?), pp. 301–307.

[18] G. W. Preckshot, N. G. DeLisle, C. E. Cottrell, and D. L. Katz, "Asphaltic Substances in Crude Oils," *Am. Inst. Min. Met. Engineers,* T.P. 1514 (1942).

After it reaches the surface, the sand presents a disposal problem. Some of the European oil wells have great mounds of sand immediately adjacent.

DEVELOPMENT AND CONSERVATION PRACTICES.[19] Conservation of oil and gas is not prevention of their use, but prevention of wastage of not only oil and gas but also of development costs, property, and other natural resources, especially fresh water. An outstanding example of wastage is oil left behind in the reservoir because of bypassing by natural gas or water during exploitation. Another example of wastage is a "wild" well, for not only are the hydrocarbons dissipated into the air or over the surface but also the uncontrolled flow drains off invaluable reservoir energy. Improperly sealed surface equipment will permit leakage of gas and evaporation of the lighter hydrocarbons from crude oil. Further gas wastage takes place at the surface through the indiscriminate use of flares and through valving the gas into the air, if no market is immediately available, in order to produce the associated oil. The amount of energy that has been lost by venting gas into the air has been enormous. The production of carbon black by partial combustion of natural gas is considered an inefficient use of this natural resource and is outlawed by statute in many states except where the gas is "sour."

An outstanding example of the wastage of development costs is the close spacing of wells where the property units are small, as in the case of town lots. It is obviously a wrongful expenditure of stockholders' money to drill from two to ten wells in order to produce the same amount of hydrocarbons that one properly located well would yield. Further economic wastage occurs through property damage caused by fire and explosion.

Perhaps the most insidious wastage is that brought about by the pollution of fresh waters, both surface and underground, by brines produced during the exploitation of an oil deposit.

Certain development practices have evolved for the purpose of minimizing wastage, especially of oil in the underground reservoir. It has been found that, by controlling the rate of production, the spacing of wells, and the development of a reservoir as a unit ("unitiza-

[19] N. Albertson, "Conservation," *Elements of the Petroleum Industry* (Am. Inst. Min. Met. Engineers, New York, 1940), pp. 279–288; Carl Coke Rister, *Oil! Titan of the Southwest* (Univ. of Okla. Press, 1949), pp. 368–377; American Bar Association (Section of Mineral Law), *A Legal History of Conservation of Oil and Gas* (Chicago, 1939); John Forbes, *Flush Production* (Univ. of Okla. Press, 1942).

tion"), the most efficient operation can be obtained. Following these conservation practices increases profits, and so their use is advocated and strongly supported by the petroleum industry. Proper disposal of oil-field brines is a practice which is not, perhaps, so enthusiastically followed but which if ignored leads to expensive lawsuits and loss of good will. Conservation methods are considered in the following paragraphs. Secondary recovery, which attempts to drive the last available drop of oil from the reservoir, is discussed in Chapter 11.

Proration.[20] Proration is the allocation of demand, and hence of production, among competing operators. This allocation may be on a voluntary basis or it may be controlled by a state regulatory body. The history of proration is brief, but its evolution constitutes an interesting chapter in the story of oil in the United States. Proration was first used successfully on a voluntary basis at Seminole, Oklahoma, in 1926. The purpose at that time, and throughout its early years, was to adjust the supply of petroleum so that it did not greatly exceed the demand, thereby depressing the price below all hope of profit. Before proration, oil and gas were produced according to the "law of capture," which meant that the first man into the reservoir helped himself to as much hydrocarbon as he could remove, and of course the faster he got it out the greater would be his immediate return.

The early history of proration was marked by bitter antagonism on the part of many oil producers who insisted that they be allowed to continue to produce according to the traditional law of capture. The discovery of oil in large amounts in the late 1920's, culminated by the East Texas strike in 1929, led to wider and wider application of proration until eventually it became practically industry-wide in the United States. While this development was taking place, the reservoir engineers were learning more and more about the natural conditions controlling oil production, and it became increasingly obvious that reservoir energy was a valuable asset and that its dissipation resulted in low total recovery of oil from the reservoir. Curtailed production helps to maintain the reservoir pressure and the gas-oil ratio, and it lessens the chances of bypassing of oil by tongues of edgewater pushing toward the well with unrestrained output. With this realization, proration evolved from purely a method of production

[20] E. DeGolyer and Harold Vance, "Bibliography on the Petroleum Industry," *Bull. A. and M. Coll. Texas,* 83 (1944), pp. 689–694 (140 titles); Joseph E. Pogue, "Economics of the Petroleum Industry," *Elements of the Petroleum Industry* (Am. Inst. Min. Met. Engineers, 1940), pp. 453–501; Lee S. Miller, "Why Oil Proration?" *Michigan Conservation,* Vol. 12 (November, 1943), pp. 4, 5, and 11.

(and price) control to a most important conservation measure. However, in times of oversupply of oil, it can be and is used for planned production in order to balance supply and demand. In times of scarcity it is practiced solely as a measure of conserving reservoir energy and increasing the eventual yield.

There is no general federal jurisdiction over the output of oil wells. The U. S. Bureau of Mines does attempt to forecast demand and to suggest an allocation to the different oil-producing states. How closely the individual states adjust their production to the Bureau of Mines figure is a matter of local decision. The regulatory body within each state may be the Department of Conservation, the Public Utilities or State Corporation Commission, or even, in Texas, the State Railroad Commission. The states which provide such regulatory machinery are loosely bound together in the Interstate Oil Compact, an organization that meets periodically and discusses quotas and procedures.

In addition to conserving reservoir energy and stabilizing supply and demand, proration has another responsibility: to insure that the equities of the individual property owners and producers are preserved. Most oil deposits are owned by not one but many individuals and companies. However, the deposit itself is a single body of hydrocarbon in a continuous reservoir, and the only way that that reservoir can be efficiently exploited is to operate it as a unit. This may be done by unitization (to be discussed in a subsequent paragraph) or it may be partially carried out by proration. The state regulatory body attempts to assign well production allowables in such a manner as to be equitable to all concerned.

The allowable production for an oil pool is determined by calculating the optimum production rate in terms of conservation of reservoir energy and adjusting that figure to the local market situation. The allocation to individual wells within the pool ("ratable taking") is fixed with due regard to the ownership pattern.

Well Spacing.[21] There is no standard spacing for oil and gas wells. Although some wells have been drilled on tracts as small as town

[21] E. DeGolyer and Harold Vance, "Bibliography on the Petroleum Industry," *Bull. A. and M. Coll. Texas,* 83 (1944), pp. 394–396 (66 titles); Perry Olcott, *et al.* (Houston Geological Society Study Group on Well Spacing), "Problem of Well Spacing," *Bull. Am. Assoc. Petrol. Geol.,* Vol. 26 (January, 1942), pp. 100–122 (121 references); Stuart K. Clark, C. W. Tomlinson, and J. S. Royds, "Well Spacing—Its Effect on Recoveries and Profits," *Bull. Am. Assoc. Petrol. Geol.,* Vol. 28 (February, 1944), pp. 231–256; Committees on Reservoir Development and Operation (Standard Oil Co. of New Jersey, affiliated companies, and Humble Oil and Refining Co.), *Joint Progress Report on Reservoir Efficiency and Well Spacing* (Standard Oil Development Co., 1943); John C. Miller, "Well Spacing and Produc-

lots, the commonest oil spacings are 10 acres, 20 acres, and 40 acres. In large gas fields, a spacing of one well to each 160 acres is common practice, and in the very large fields the spacing is one well to each 640 acres. The primary physical consideration in the discussion of optimum spacing is what spacing between wells will result in the greatest ultimate recovery of oil from the reservoir. There is wide variation of opinion on this subject. At one extreme are those who believe that, given time enough, a single properly placed well would drain a reservoir, regardless of size, as thoroughly as would a multitude of wells. The followers of this school of thought believe that the structural position in terms of type of drive (dissolved gas, gas cap, or natural water drive) is most important and that the spacing between wells should be based solely on economic factors. A much more conservative viewpoint is taken by Miller,[22] who believes that in the sandstone reservoirs of the West Columbia field, Brazoria County, Texas, the drainage range is from 500 to 800 feet out from each well. Miller, therefore, advocates a spacing of 17 to 20 acres for this type of reservoir.

The optimum spacing is the one that produces the most oil at the least cost per barrel. Therefore, the economic factors are of utmost importance. It may not be true that, the more wells drilled, the greater the total ultimate recovery, but it is true that, the more wells drilled, the quicker the reservoir will be emptied.[23] Because of the interest charges on the investment made in exploration and drilling, it is economically advantageous to exhaust the pool as soon as possible without wastage. On the other hand, the more wells drilled, the greater the monetary outlay in obtaining the oil. Every reservoir presents its own problem; the determination of the most efficient spacing pattern is primarily the problem of the reservoir engineer. The present tendency in the deep Gulf Coast and California fields is to increase the spacing because of (1) the high drilling costs and (2) the high recoveries that are possible, regardless of spacing, in the repressured reservoirs.

tion Interference in West Columbia Field, Brazoria County, Texas," *Bull. Am. Assoc. Petrol. Geol.,* Vol. 26 (September, 1942), pp. 1441–1466; Lester C. Uren, "Economic Considerations of the Well Spacing Problem," *Petrol. Engineer,* Vol. 15 (November, 1943), pp. 116–118, 120, and 122.

[22] *Op. cit.*

[23] C. W. Tomlinson, "Closer Well Spacing May Profitably Yield Extra Oil," *World Oil,* Vol. 129 (September, 1949), pp. 47–48; Stuart K. Clark, C. W. Tomlinson, and J. S. Royds, "Well Spacing and Its Effect on Recoveries and Profits," *Bull. Am. Assoc. Petrol. Geol.,* Vol. 28 (February, 1949), pp. 231–256.

It is undoubtedly true that many of the older fields have yielded lower than maximum profits because the spacing was too close. Prior to World War II, 10-acre spacing was the general rule in many fields. The current trend is toward 20-acre and 40-acre spacings. However, there are several types of narrow elongate fields such as fault line pools, dolomite streak pools, shoestring sand pools, and small sharp anticlinal accumulations in which 10-acre spacing is indicated. In fact, some of the pools of this type which are producing today might never have been discovered had a 40-acre plan been followed.

Unitization.[24] A subsurface accumulation of oil or gas has no regard for such arbitrary lines drawn on the earth's surface as state, county, or township boundaries, or property ownership lines. Neither is there any subsurface demarcation between different leases held by oil companies bent upon exploiting the hydrocarbons in the reservoir. In spite of this variegated surface ownership or control pattern, the oil or gas deposit is a single unit and the treatment it receives from the various exploiters is shared by all. Fortunately, proration has tended to cure one of the greatest evils of disconnected independent operation, namely, the rapid dissipation of reservoir energy which was permitted under the law of capture. But in many pools it is not sufficient that deleterious activities only be controlled. In some fields, such as gas condensate fields, it is of paramount importance that the gas, wrung dry of the liquid hydrocarbons, should be repressured ("recycled") and returned to the reservoir. It is obviously impossible for one company to go to the additional expense of a recycling plant if his competitors tapping the same reservoir do not do likewise. The total ultimate recovery of an oil field may be greatly increased by the employment of such secondary recovery methods (see Chapter 11) as artificial flooding. Again it is impractical for a producer to bear this expense alone if others will also profit thereby. In many places where the disposal of oil-field brines is a major problem and expense, it is more feasible for the operation to be carried out as a cooperative enterprise than by individual operators.

[24] E. DeGolyer and Harold Vance, "Bibliography on the Petroleum Industry," *Bull. A. and M. Coll. Texas,* 83 (1944), pp. 396–400 (116 titles); H. S. Gibson, "Scientific Unit Control," *Science of Petroleum* (Oxford Univ. Press, 1938), Vol. 1, pp. 534–540; Anon., "West Edmond Unit Eliminates Waste," *The Link* (Carter Oil Co.), Vol. 12 (November, 1947), p. 19; Leigh S. McCaslin, Jr., "Nation's Largest Voluntary Unit Formed on Texas Gulf Coast," *Oil and Gas Jour.,* Vol. 47 (Sept. 16, 1948), pp. 84 *et seq.*

The systematic development and operation of an oil and gas deposit as a single unit is known as *unitization*. In countries such as Russia, where the state has absolute control over the exploitation of the mineral resources, unitization is automatic. But in a system of free enterprise, it can be carried out only by cooperation. An early and a very successful example of unitization was the Salt Creek field in Wyoming. Only a few companies controlled the leases covering this field, and they placed complete authority in the hands of an operating committee. This committee, initiated long before the advent of state-regulated proration, decided when and where every well was to be drilled and how much it was to be allowed to produce from day to day. Such a procedure tends to produce maximum total recovery and maximum possible profit. The legal machinery has been established in the Gulf Coast area to make easy the formation of unit agreements in the gas condensate fields. Oklahoma passed a new unitization law in 1945, following which the 34 operators in the West Edmond pool voluntarily formed a cooperative unit to be administered by an engineering committee. Secondary recovery and brine disposal activities have led to many cooperative agreements which in effect unitize the solution of one particular problem.

Brine Disposal.[25] Many oil wells yield water as well as oil, and, in the declining months of operation of the well, the amount of water may become enormous. There are many oil wells in some of the older districts that produce over 100 barrels of water for each barrel of oil. This water would not be such a great problem were it not for the fact that it is invariably mineralized. The percentage of sodium chloride and other salts in solution is usually greater than that of the ocean water. Disposing of this concentrated brine without doing irreparable damage to the local economy presents the operator with a serious problem.

Only when the oil field is close to the ocean or other body of salt water is the disposal of oil-field brine a simple matter, for then it can be piped directly into the surface body of salt water. In times past it has been the custom to let the brine escape into the local surface drainage system. The introduction of brine into the rivers killed the fish and polluted the water used for drinking and industrial purposes downstream. When this nuisance had been abated by lawsuit and statute, the next step was to store the brine in artificial ponds near the wells. The water left the ponds either by evaporation or

[25] E. DeGolyer and Harold Vance, "Bibliography on the Petroleum Industry," *Bull. A. and M. Coll. Texas*, 83 (1944), pp. 468–470 (57 titles).

by release into the river during times of high water when the brine would become too diluted to cause appreciable damage. However, both these disposal methods proved to be quite unsatisfactory. Where the climate encouraged evaporation, the concentrated brine that remained in the pond would flocculate the clay floor and escape into shallow ground-water aquifers, spreading into neighboring farm wells and eventually ruining even municipal supplies. The down-river flood-time "booming" was of course dependent upon floods, which usually fail to appear with the necessary regularity.

The next step in the evolution of oil-field-brine disposal was to drill wells into water-deficient sands lying between the surface and the oil reservoir. This proved to be a hazardous procedure because the salt water that was pumped into these sands under pressure often broke through into valuable fresh-water aquifers. The final and logical procedure is to pump the brine back down into the reservoir whence it came. Theoretically this idea is excellent for two reasons: (1) that is one place where there is room for the brine, because it just came from there, and (2) the reservoir energy can be maintained by repressuring the water below the oil. There are, however, some complications to this practice. In the first place, a disposal well must be obtained. This may be a "dry" well which was originally drilled beyond the boundaries of the pool, or it may be a well which initially produced but was later abandoned because the water yield increased beyond the point at which it was possible to operate the well profitably, or, third, the producers may share the expense of drilling a new disposal well beyond the edge of the producing part of the reservoir. The brine must be treated chemically before being returned to the reservoir because in making its trip to the surface the changes in temperature, pressure, and environment may have changed its nature to such an extent that when the brine is returned to the reservoir certain of the compounds in solution will precipitate out, thereby clogging the pores and preventing, or at least retarding, the rate of input. However, these complications have been successfully conquered, and in many areas today it is standard practice to recycle the brine back into the reservoir rock.

VALUATION.[26] The valuation of oil property includes appraising the monetary value of such items as drilling equipment, derricks,

[26] E. DeGolyer and Harold Vance, "Bibliography on the Petroleum Industry," *Bull. A. and M. Coll. Texas,* 83 (1944), pp. 668–674 (151 titles); F. M. Van Tuyl and W. F. Levings, "Review of Petroleum Geology 1945," *Quarterly Colo. School of Mines,* Vol. 41 (July, 1947), pp. 238–239 (6 titles); Paul Paine, *Oil Property Valua-*

buildings, pipe lines, tanks, the oil in storage above ground, the oil in transit, the company's lease holdings, royalty and partnership interests, and the known reserve of oil still in its natural underground storage. The broad problem of valuation is best left to the valuation engineer, but the production engineers and even at times the geologists are called upon to make an estimate of how much oil or gas a field now in production can be counted on to yield before abandonment. The procedures vary somewhat, depending upon whether the field is primarily an oil field or a gas field.

Estimation of Oil Reserves.[27] This discussion is confined to *known* reserves. It is impossible to calculate accurately the reserves of oil not yet produced from a petroleum deposit unless and until enough wells have been drilled so as to outline the area of the accumulation. This is done by drilling enough dry holes about the perimeter to map the production limits. With the data obtained during the drilling, it is possible to make a fairly accurate estimate of the amount of oil that can be produced subsequently. A distinction should be made between such calculations of petroleum reserves in "proved" areas and calculations made on the basis of an insufficient number of wells to obtain all the reservoir data necessary.[28] If a field has been outlined on three sides but not on the fourth side by dry holes, it is possible to obtain from what is known of the structural picture of the accumulation a "probable" area estimate which can be used in making a reserve calculation. If, however, there are only one or two wells so far drilled in a newly discovered field, an ultimate recovery estimate becomes largely guesswork.

Much of the divergence that has been noted between estimates of probable recovery and the actual recovery has been due to acceptance of probable area reserve figures as though they were proved area calculations. Even in proved areas, however, there are factors of uncertainty. An oil field is never abandoned because of complete exhaustion. It is abandoned when it is no longer profitable to pump oil from the reservoir, separate it from the accompanying water, and

tion (Wiley, New York, 1942); David Donoghue, "Note on Appraisal," *Bull. Am. Assoc. Petrol. Geol.,* Vol. 26 (July, 1942), pp. 1283–1289.

[27] F. S. Shaw, "Review of Ultimate Recovery Factors and Methods of Estimation," *Oil Weekly,* Vol. 106 (July 13, 1942), pp. 16–26; V. Bilibin, "Methods of Estimating Oil Reserves," *International Geological Congress, 17th Session, U.S.S.R., 1937* (Preprint, 1936); K. Marshall Fagin, "Notes on Estimating Crude Oil Reserves," *Petrol. Engineer,* Vol. 17 (September, 1946), pp. 92–94.

[28] Frederick H. Lahee, "This Matter of Estimating Oil Reserves," *Bull. Am. Assoc. Petrol. Geol.,* Vol. 25 (January, 1941), pp. 164–166.

market it. Calculations of the recoverable oil are of necessity based on the market situation at the time the calculations are made; fluctuations in the price of oil or in the production cost may cause the abandonment point to be reached earlier or later than originally calculated.

Methods of calculating the amount of oil that can be produced by an oil field fall into three general classes: (1) the production history of older, geologically similar fields; (2) the production history of the pool itself during its early months, and (3) volumetric methods in which the actual bulk of the oil in the underground reservoir is calculated and the recoverable percentage estimated.

The first method cannot be used with any great degree of accuracy. Every natural reservoir has its own specifications and its own behavior pattern, and close parallels are highly improbable. This method is applied by taking the per acre-foot recovery figure for a field which had the same type of reservoir rock and a similar structural setting and multiplying it by the area and thickness of the reservoir of the newer field.

The history written by an oil well or a group of wells during their first few months of production can be used in at least three different ways to estimate future production. One of these is to take the initial daily production, or the cumulative production for the first thirty days, or the first year's production and multiply this figure by a factor in order to obtain the probable eventual yield. Factors that have been used for the initial daily production range from 644 for wells which produce less than 100 barrels a day initially down to 240 for wells producing over 600 barrels a day.[29] According to Moore,[30] a common rule of thumb has been to multiply the wide-open production for the first thirty days by 300 in order to obtain the ultimate yield. Experience has shown that in some of the older California fields the ultimate production was four to six times the first year's production.

Inasmuch as most states now prohibit the unrestricted flow of oil from a well, methods based on wide-open flow over a period of time no longer have much applicability. Before proration the *decline curve* method of estimating underground oil reserves was widely used.[31] In this method the daily production of the well is plotted and a

[29] S. F. Shaw, "Review of Ultimate Recovery Factors and Methods of Estimation," *Oil Weekly,* Vol. 106 (July 13, 1942), p. 24.

[30] Fred H. Moore, informal communication.

[31] Willard W. Cutler, Jr., "Estimation of Underground Reserves by Oil-Well Production Curves," *U. S. Bur. Mines Bull.* 228 (1924).

curve drawn which shows the rapid tapering off from the high flush production to the more slowly diminishing "settled" production. By means of the many such curves that have been made, covering from time of discovery until time of abandonment, it is possible to project into the future the curve from a well but a few months old and to make a fairly reliable estimate of its total yield. The sum of the estimates for the wells in a field gives the total eventual production of that field. A somewhat less exact procedure is to plot the production for an entire field and project it in the same way.

A third method of using history to calculate reserves is to plot the cumulative production against the decline in reservoir pressure and then project this "bottom-hole pressure-production curve" into the future. As discussed in a subsequent paragraph, the pressure decline method is an important means of estimating reserves of natural gas. It is nowhere near as suitable, however, when applied to oil deposits, but it does have the advantage over the two other methods based on yield to date in that it is applicable to wells of restricted production as well as to those with wide-open flow. The lack of accuracy of the pressure decline method applied to oil accumulation is based on the fact that the bottom-hole pressure in an oil reservoir may be only to a minor extent due to the volume and compression of the hydrocarbon in the reservoir. It has already been shown that with a complete natural water drive there is little or no diminution in pressure between the time of first production from the reservoir and its complete exhaustion of oil.

Katz [32] has developed a method of reserve calculation for oil-gas mixtures in a closed system in which data on the oil and gas production to date and the bottom-hole pressure history are combined with information regarding the properties of the oil-gas mixtures.

The volumetric [33] approach to reserve calculations is as old as the exploitation of oil fields. All such methods are fundamentally the same, based on calculating the amount of oil in the underground reservoir from the degree of saturation of the porous volume of a reservoir rock of finite dimensions. The classical formula for determining the oil that a reservoir can be expected to produce is $R = FAtpsr$, in which R is the recoverable oil in barrels, F the factor

[32] D. L. Katz, "A Method of Estimating Oil and Gas Reserves," *Trans. Am. Inst. Min. Met. Engineer,* Vol. 118 (1936), pp. 18–32.

[33] John F. Dodge, Howard C. Pyle, and Everett G. Trostel, "Estimations by Volumetric Method of Recoverable Oil and Gas from Sand," *Bull. Am. Assoc. Petrol. Geol.,* Vol. 25 (July, 1941), pp. 1302–1326; George R. Elliott and William L. Morris, "Oil Recovery Prediction," *Oil and Gas Jour.,* Vol. 48 (June 16, 1949), pp. 84 *et seq.*

7758, *A* the area in acres, and *tpsr,* respectively, average thickness, percentage of porosity, percentage of saturation, and percentage of expected recovery. Multiplying the three factors—area, thickness, and porosity—together gives the number of acre-feet of void space in the reservoir rock in which fluids can be stored. The factor 7758 transforms this volume figure from acre-feet to barrels. The percentage of saturation diminishes the barrel volume of potential oil space to the extent that water is present with the oil in the rock pores. Because it is impossible to recover all the available oil, the last step is to multiply the oil in the reservoir by the percentage of recovery expected.

From drill records and core analyses, it is possible to calculate rather closely the area, reservoir thickness, and porosity percentage. It was originally thought that oil occupied all the interstitial space, which resulted in estimates much too high, both in regard to the oil originally present and in regard to that left in the reservoir after abandonment of the field. It is now known that oil sands have an interstitial water [34] content equal to 10 to 50 per cent or more of the volume of pore space. As a general rule, the lower the permeability of the reservoir, the higher the percentage of interstitial water. The average figure ranges between 30 and 35 per cent, and so on the average only about two-thirds of the available pore space actually contains oil. This interstitial water is commonly referred to as "connate" water, although that terminology is not in exact accord with the original definition. The interstitial waters are present in a thin envelope that surrounds the grains; the oil and gas accumulate in the voids between the watery envelopes and are therefore not in direct contact with the mineral grains of the reservoir rock. If the pores are fine, the water envelopes coalesce and no space whatsoever is left for the accumulation of hydrocarbons.

It has become modern practice to examine and treat the cores obtained from reservoir rocks, so that a fairly close figure can be obtained for the percentage of oil saturation of the void space. There remains only one factor which cannot be closely determined and in which differences of opinion can and do produce divergence in ultimate recovery estimates. This is the percentage of oil that can be extracted profitably from the reservoir. It is not possible, as already pointed out, to forecast the economic situation at 10, 15, or 20 years hence. Neither is it possible to forecast the evolution that may take place in production techniques. On the other hand, it is possible

[34] R. J. Schilthuis, "Connate Water in Oil and Gas Sands," *Trans. Am. Inst. Min. Met. Engineers,* Vol. 127 (1938), pp. 199–214.

to determine the type of reservoir energy that is propelling the oil from the reservoir into the well and to determine through the experience of older fields what percentage of oil can be expected with modern production methods from reservoirs with that particular type of fluid drive. Since it is inevitable, however, that this factor is built in part upon personal opinion, divergences of as much as 20 per cent in final expected recovery figures may occur.

Estimation of Gas Reserves.[35] Because gas is a highly compressible substance, the extraction of a quantity of gas squeezed into a reservoir will result in a measurable drop in the reservoir pressure (except in the presence of an active water drive), and owing to the approximate applicability of Boyle's law, there is a definite ratio between the amount of gas initially in the reservoir, the drop in pressure, and the volume of gas removed. Therefore, unlike oil, it is possible to make an estimate of the gas in the reservoir after the drilling of only one well, providing that that well has produced enough gas to make a measurable decline in the reservoir pressure. The formula used is

$$R = Q \frac{(P_1 d_1 - P_3 d_3)}{(P_1 d_1 - P_2 d_2)}$$

In this formula R is the available gas reserve, Q is the amount of production between discovery and date of appraisal, P_1 is the reservoir pressure at time of discovery, P_2 is the reservoir pressure at time of appraisal, P_3 is the pressure at which abandonment is scheduled, and d_1, d_2, and d_3 are deviation factors at pressures P_1, P_2, and P_3. Since natural gases do not behave exactly according to Boyle's law, it is necessary, for very accurate estimates, to apply deviation factors. These are obtained from published formulas or tables.[36]

Natural gas reserves can also be calculated by decline curve and by volumetric methods. A common volumetric formula obtains the cubic feet of gas per acre-foot at base temperature and pressure by multiplying together six factors: (1) 43,560, the number of cubic feet

[35] P. McDonald Biddison, "Estimation of Natural Gas Reserves," *Geology of Natural Gas,* Am. Assoc. Petrol. Geol., 1935, pp. 1035–1052; E. B. Elfrink, C. R. Sandberg, and T. A Pollard, "Application of Compressibility Factors in the Estimation of Gas Reserves," *Oil and Gas Jour.,* Vol. 47 (March 3, 1949), pp. 89–91; John C. Calhoun, Jr., "Estimating Gas Reserves," *Oil and Gas Jour.,* Vol. 47 (Dec. 9, 1948), p. 115; Henry J. Gruy and Jack A. Crichton, "A Critical Review of Methods Used in Estimation of Gas Reserves," *Petroleum Development and Technology, 1949* (Am. Inst. Min. Met. Engineers), Vol. 179, pp. 249–263.

[36] D. L. Katz, "High Pressure Gas Measurement," Part 2, "A Suggested Standard Method for Calculation of High Pressure Gas Measurement," *Refiner and Natural Gasoline Manufacturer* (June, 1942), pp. 64–69.

per acre foot; (2) porosity percentage; (3) percentage of available void space, obtained by subtracting the interstitial water percentage from 100; (4) reservoir pressure, in pounds per square inch, divided by the base pressure used, which is ordinarily some figure between 14.4 and 16.7 pounds per square inch; (5) 460 plus the base temperature (ordinarily 60° F.) divided by 460 plus the reservoir temperature in degrees F.; (6) $1/Z$, where Z is the compressibility factor at reservoir pressure. This can be determined by laboratory measurements or estimated from published curves. The concluding step is to multiply the figure obtained through the application of this formula by the area of the gas accumulation in acres and by the average thickness of the reservoir in feet. The accuracy of the final result depends largely upon the accuracy of these dimension figures, especially the average thickness estimate.

PART II

GEOLOGIC OCCURRENCE OF PETROLEUM

Chapter 4

PHYSICAL AND CHEMICAL PROPERTIES OF OIL AND GAS

PHYSICAL AND CHEMICAL PROPERTIES OF PETROLEUM AT THE SURFACE.[1] The geologist, in his search for new deposits of petroleum and natural gas, need not be an organic chemist. Nevertheless, some of the physical and chemical properties of the natural hydrocarbons do concern him. An elementary knowledge of the chemistry of petroleum is necessary for proper recognition and evaluation of seeps, for an adequate understanding and interpretation of the natural history of oil, and for an intelligent study of the underground movement of oil once it has been formed. Furthermore, the market value of the oil or gas discovered is dependent upon its chemical constitution, and the economic geologist can never afford to lose sight of the marketability of his wares.

The natural occurring hydrocarbons fall into three main groups: liquids, gases, and solids. The liquid hydrocarbons are the most abundant in the earth's crust, the gaseous hydrocarbons rank second, and the solid hydrocarbons third. The liquid hydrocarbons, however, invariably contain in solution both gaseous and solid hydrocarbons.

Liquid Hydrocarbons. Petroleum, or "rock oil," is the name applied to the liquid hydrocarbons occurring in the earth's crust. Petroleum is a *mixture* of varying proportions of different chemical compounds. For this reason, the properties of each crude oil depend upon the nature and the amount of the different compounds present.

[1] Stewart P. Coleman, "Physical and Chemical Properties of Petroleum and Its Products," *Elements of the Petroleum Industry* (Am. Inst. Min. Met. Engineers, 1940), pp. 4–20; *Science of Petroleum* (Oxford Univ. Press, 1938), Vol. 2; E. DeGolyer and Harold Vance, "Bibliography of the Petroleum Industry," *Bull. A. and M. Coll. Texas,* 83 (1944), pp. 137–144.

Among the *physical properties* of the liquid hydrocarbons, the one most often referred to is the *density* or "gravity." Density may be calculated as specific gravity with unity represented by water. With most liquids, however, it is common to describe the density in terms of degrees Baumé. By this method of calculation, water has a gravity of 10, numbers lower than 10 being used for the gravity of substances heavier than water and numbers above 10 for lighter substances. The common scale in the petroleum industry is the API (American Petroleum Institute) scale, in which the specific gravity is equal to the fraction 141.5 ÷ (degrees Baumé + 131.5).

The gravity of crude oil from different fields ranges from less than 10° to as high as 60° and even higher. An oil below 10 in the Baumé scale is, however, still lighter than the water with which it is associated. Only pure water has a gravity of 10°; the highly mineralized water with which most oils are associated is considerably heavier. As a general rule, the higher-gravity oils contain a higher than average percentage of the profitable gasoline hydrocarbons and a lower percentage of deleterious compounds which increase refining expense. For this reason, much crude oil is priced on a gravity basis. The gravity of the oil may even determine whether a wildcat well of low capacity has discovered a new field or will have to be plugged and abandoned because of the unprofitable character of the oil discovered.

Petroleums vary from colorless to black. The valuable Pennsylvania oil noted for its high yield of premium lubricating fractions is amber in color. Medium-gravity oils such as those of the Mid-Continent are predominantly green, and heavy oils are commonly black. The color of crude oil appears to depend upon the presence of unsaturated hydrocarbons and of hydrocarbons that contain nitrogen, oxygen, or sulfur in addition to the hydrogen and carbon. As a general rule, the lighter the oil in color, the higher its gravity and the greater its value.

The *odor* of crude oil depends upon the character and the volatility of the hydrocarbons within the mixture. Some crude oil has a decidedly aromatic odor, owing to predominance of the aromatic group of hydrocarbons. High-sulfur crudes may have the odor of hydrogen sulfide. On the other hand, light crude oils may have a very noticeable gasoline odor due to the escape from the mixture of this highly volatile material.

Viscosity, or resistance to flow, is measured by the time taken for a given quantity of oil to flow through a small opening. Some oils are so viscous at ordinary temperatures that they must be heated before they can be pumped. On the other hand, some oils that are so light at ordinary temperatures that they are only slightly more viscous than water become highly viscous during the winter because of the congealing of dissolved wax.

The *volatility* of crude oil is dependent upon the boiling points of the various compounds present in the mixture. One common constituent, methane, has a boiling point of $-164°$ C., whereas the boiling points for some of the paraffin compounds are too high to be measured by usual procedures. Inasmuch as petroleum is always at a temperature above the boiling points of some of its hydrocarbons, the more volatile compounds are continuously exerting pressure and tend to escape unless the oil is in a completely sealed unit. Under such circumstances, it is obviously impossible to refer to a single boiling point for any crude oil. Neither is it possible to refer to a freezing point for petroleum. The hydrocarbons present tend to solidify separately at different temperatures. The viscosity increases with lower temperatures until it can no longer be measured and the oil is in a "plastic solid" state, but if the cooling is continued, a truly solid state is finally reached.

The geologist is interested in the *surface tension and capillary force* of petroleum because these physical properties play a role both in the migration of oil through the rocks of the earth's crust and in the permanent retention of some oil in considerable volume in the underground reservoir in spite of most efficient processes of exploitation. The surface tensions of petroleums in buried reservoirs are extremely low. Water has greater capillary force than oil; consequently this fluid may be expected to draw itself into the finest pore spaces of the rock and to force the oil into the larger pores.

The *chemical properties* of crude oils are of greater importance to the refiner than to the geologist, but, because the eventual worth of the oil is dependent upon its chemical characteristics, the geologist also is interested in this subject. The most prominent chemical group in crude oil is, of course, the hydrocarbon group. Within it are a number of subgroups and a large number of individual compounds. Not all these compounds are liquids; both solid and gaseous hydrocarbons occur in solution in the liquid hydrocarbons. The gaseous and the lighter liquid hydrocarbons are the simplest in their chemical composition, containing relatively few carbon atoms. These compounds are easily separated from the crude oil, and their physical and chemical properties can be studied in the laboratory. The heavier hydrocarbons, however, are much less stable and tend to decompose when the oil is heated. Consequently, it is virtually impossible to analyze any crude oil in terms of its original compounds except for the lightest hydrocarbons.

In addition to the pure hydrocarbons, there are also compounds of hydrogen and carbon with sulfur, oxygen, or nitrogen. The sulfur-bearing hydrocarbons are the most prominent, and they present a serious problem to the refiner. These sulfur compounds are heavy, so only the heavier crude oils contain them, and conversely most of the heavy crudes have a relatively high sulfur content. However, hydrogen sulfide can be present without making the petroleum appreciably heavier. The less abundant oxygen-bearing hydrocarbons also increase the density of the crude oil that contains them. Nitrogen-bearing hydrocarbons are relatively insignificant. Analyses of petroleum coke, a solid residue obtained in refining oil, have shown the presence in small but consistent amounts of the elements nickel, vanadium, and phosphorus.

No discussion of crude oil composition, however brief, would be complete without mention of the *base*. It is common to refer to an oil as having a paraffin base, a naphthenic or asphalt base, or a mixed base. A paraffinic oil has a relatively high hydrogen content in relation to the carbon; the reverse is true of a naphthenic oil. Typical of the paraffinic-base oils are those obtained from the state of Pennsylvania; California and the Gulf Coast are sources of naphthenic-base oils. Mixed-base crude oils are found in many places. As a general rule, the gravity of the oil is a good clue to the nature of its base. The paraffin oils are generally of low density and are high in gasoline and kerosene. A paraffin wax, or petrolatum, is obtained in refining this oil. The naphthenic oils are much heavier in weight and contain relatively much less gasoline and kerosene. They do, however, contain a large percentage of viscous, but volatile, lubricating oils. The decomposition of the liquid constituents of the naphthenic-base oils during distillation produces a semi-solid or solid asphaltic residue during the refining process.

In addition to Pennsylvania and other parts of the Appalachian region, paraffin-base crudes are found in Michigan and in parts of northern Louisiana and southern Arkansas. Elsewhere, crude oils of this type have been found in Peru and the Argentine, as well as in the Near East, especially in Iran and Iraq. The Dutch East Indies has also produced some paraffin-base crude, as well as great quantities of naphthenic petroleums. The latter is the principal type of crude oil produced in Venezuela and Colombia. Mixed-base crude oils are called the Mid-Continent type because of their prevalence in Illinois, Kansas, Oklahoma, and in Texas outside of the Gulf Coast. Mexico produces both naphthenic- and mixed-base petroleums, and the same is true in Rumania. Deeper drilling into older formations in all parts of the world has resulted in the discovery of crude oils that are lighter in weight and more paraffinic in base than those found in shallower formations, and so it is becoming much less practicable to classify crude oils geographically.

Gases. The physical properties of a natural gas include color, odor, and inflammability. The principal ingredient of most natural gases is methane, CH_4, which is colorless, odorless, and highly inflammable. The variety of substances present in natural gas is much less than in crude oil. However, in addition to methane, ethane, propane, and other hydrocarbon gases, carbon dioxide, hydrogen sulfide, nitrogen, and inert gases, especially helium, have been found in natural gas in various fields about the globe. Some of these impurities, especially hydrogen sulfide, have a distinct and penetrating odor, and a few parts per million are sufficient to give the natural gas a decided odor. Nitrogen and helium are not inflammable, and where one or both of these elements are present in abundance the natural gas will not burn.

Gasoline in vapor form is present in most natural gas and is extracted and sold as natural gas gasoline (or simply natural gasoline). This product was formerly referred to as casinghead gasoline, and the term is still used to some extent.

Solids. The solid hydrocarbons may be subdivided into four main groups: petroleum bitumens, pyrobitumens, disseminated bitumens, and oxygen-bearing bitumens. The petroleum bitumens can be subdivided into the asphaltic bitumens and the mineral waxes. Examples of asphaltic bitumens include highly viscous liquids, such as the brea deposits in California which ensnared many types of animals (some of them now extinct), and natural asphalt, which occurs on the island of Trinidad and elsewhere in ponds and lakes. The vein asphalts, such as gilsonite, instead of occurring in surface accumulations are found in tabular bodies filling pre-existing cracks in the rocks at or near the surface. The so-called rock asphalts are limestone and sandstones impregnated by asphaltic material which no doubt was originally liquid petroleum. Mineral waxes include ozokerite and other natural paraffins.

The pyrobitumens are similar in physical and chemical properties to the petroleum bitumens, but their probable derivation from petroleum cannot be as readily demonstrated. Some of the pyrobitumens, such as albertite, wurtzilite, and elaterite, occur in veins similar to gilsonite and other asphaltites. Other pyrobitumens are disseminated in rocks like bituminous schists and marbles. Kerogen, or oil shale, is a disseminated bitumen. This rock yields a petroleum-like substance upon distillation. However, the transformation from solid to liquid takes place only under the influence of heat, and repeated tests have failed to show the presence of any oil which can be obtained by solvents or by squeezing the so-called oil shale. Every gradation is possible between a kerogen, or oil shale, and a cannel coal. In both materials, the predominant organic substances present are the spores and pollen of plants. The oxygen-bearing bitumens include resin, peat, and coal.

NATURE OF PETROLEUM IN ITS UNDERGROUND RESERVOIR. Crude oil underground is invariably under a pressure varying from several hundred to several thousand pounds per square inch, depending mainly upon depth. Under such pressures, the oil can and does contain in solution a considerable quantity of gas. As the oil is produced and rises from reservoir to surface, and while it is in storage at the surface, much of this gas escapes from solution with the result that the oil has much less mobility at the surface than it had when it was under high pressure in the reservoir rock. The dissolved gas not only makes the crude oil lighter in density but also considerably increases its liquidity. Crude oil with its dissolved gas is spoken of as "live" oil; after the greater part of the gas escapes it is "dead" oil.

Of equal importance to the mobility of oil underground is the effect of higher earth temperature. Although there is considerable variation from one place to another, the general average increment in temperature is 1° F. for every 60 feet of additional depth. In other words, if the reservoir is at a depth of 6000 feet, the oil will be at a temperature approximately 100° above the average temperature at the surface. It is a commonly observed fact that warm oil has much less viscosity than the same oil at a lower temperature; therefore, oil in the reservoir must have far greater liquidity than oil examined under room temperatures at the surface. Since the liquidity of water also increases with higher temperatures, the "flowability" of both these liquids is higher the deeper the reservoir rock.

Much of the earlier experimentation in migration of oil that was carried on in various laboratories did not take into account the vastly greater mobility due to higher temperature and dissolved gas, and so the results obtained are of little or no value in studying the probable movement of oil underground. Only by simulating as nearly as possible all the environmental conditions (including the wetting effect of interstitial water) can experimental studies of oil migration be of other than questionable value.

Chapter 5

ORIGIN AND EVOLUTION OF OIL AND GAS[1]

Petroleum geologists have written more on the origin of petroleum than on any other subject.[2] Speculation in this field was initiated in the 1860's, and the problem of origin is still with us. "Each year the crop of new papers adds to the fearsome pile threatening to bury the subject by the very dead weight of diversified opinion, and the earnest student, anxiously searching for enlightenment, gets lost in the maze of conflicting opinions." [3] This prodigious amount of research and discussion has not, however, been entirely in vain. Many theories have been tested and found wanting. Although many more theories have appeared to replace those discarded, it is but a matter of time before these too are tested and the inadequate ones rejected until a fairly clear picture is obtained of the origin and evolution of oil and gas.

Investigation of petroleum genesis is not purely academic exercise. When we can determine exactly under what conditions commercial deposits of oil are formed and the date of their formation, we can confine our explorations for oil to (1) places that meet those condi-

[1] William B. Heroy, Jr., "Petroleum Geology," *Geol. Soc. Am. 50th Anniversary Vol.* (1941), pp. 512–548; V. C. Illing, "Origin of Petroleum," *Science of Petroleum* (Oxford Univ. Press, 1938), Vol. 1, pp. 32–38; U. S. Geol. Survey, "Geology and Occurrences of Petroleum in the United States," *Petroleum Investigation,* Hearings, 73d Congress, H.R. 441 (1934), pp. 895–910; E. DeGolyer and Harold Vance, "Petroleum Bibliography, *Bull. A. and M. Coll. Texas,* 83 (1944), pp. 330–338; A. G. Skelton and M. Skelton, "A Selected Bibliography of the Theories of the Origin of Petroleum," *Okla. Geol. Survey, Mineral Rept.* 7 (1942); G. D. Hobson, "Petroleum Geology," *Review of Petroleum Technology* (Inst. Petrol., London, 1947), Vol. 7, pp. 1–16.

[2] G. M. Knebel, "Progress Report of API Research Project 43, The Transformation of Organic Material into Petroleum," *Bull. Am. Assoc. Petrol. Geol.,* Vol. 30 (November, 1946), p. 1945.

[3] V. C. Illing, "Geology of Petroleum," *Jour. Inst. Petrol. Technologists,* Vol. 21 (1935), p. 491.

tions, and (2) to "traps" of oil that have been in existence at the proper time.[4]

PROBLEMS AND STAGES IN THE NATURAL HISTORY OF AN OIL DEPOSIT. The problems in deciphering the evolution of an oil field from source material to commercial accumulation in the earth's crust, and the stages involved in that evolution, are several. The more important ones are:

1. The source of the elements (hydrogen and carbon).
2. The accumulation of the source materials.
3. The burial of the source materials.
4. The transformation from solid to liquid (or gas).
5. Metamorphism of liquid.
6. Migration of liquid.
7. Entrapment of liquid.

These seven topics cannot be given in their exact chronological order, for some overlap may occur between stages, metamorphism of petroleum may take place before, during, or after migration, and no one knows for sure just when the transformation from solid to liquid does take place.

The first five of the items listed above are included in this section on the origin and evolution of oil and gas. The migration and entrapment stages are discussed separately in subsequent chapters.

SOURCE OF HYDROGEN AND CARBON [5]

There can be but little doubt that the carbon and hydrogen in petroleum and natural gas were, in their initial stages, like everything else on this earth, in solution in hot liquid rock or magma. The question here is whether or not these elements, originally inorganic, were removed by plant or animal before conversion into petroleum. In other words, did the carbon and hydrogen pass through an organic phase in the natural history of crude oil? Four lines of evidence should be examined before reaching a conclusion on this subject: (1) experimental data; (2) testimony furnished by the oil (or gas) itself; (3) testimony of associated rocks; and (4) miscellaneous observations.

[4] Harold W. Hoots, "Origin, Migration and Accumulation of Oil in California," *Calif. Div. Mines Bull.*, 118 (August, 1941), p. 259.

[5] F. W. Clarke, "Data of Geochemistry," *U. S. Geol. Survey Bull.* 770 (1924), pp. 744–755.

EXPERIMENTAL DATA. It has been frequently demonstrated in the chemical laboratory that hydrocarbons may be obtained from (1) carbon dioxide, free alkali metal, and water; (2) metallic carbides and water; (3) modern organic materials, both animal and vegetable; and (4) ancient accumulations of organic debris, such as coals and organic shales. The carbon dioxide, alkali, and water method was first demonstrated by Berthelot in 1866. Mendeléef is credited with obtaining hydrocarbons from water and carbides in 1877. Since then both these syntheses have been repeated many times. These are the two principal methods of obtaining hydrocarbons from inorganic materials. It should be noted that both procedures require substances (free alkali metal and metallic carbides) that are unknown or at least as yet undiscovered in nature. On the other hand, hydrocarbon-containing substances have been and are being obtained commercially from both modern and ancient accumulations of organic materials. Examples are whale oil, fish oil, palm oil, shale oil, and coal oil. The last term, coal oil, is used in its original sense to describe an oil obtained from coal by distillation.

TESTIMONY OF OIL AND GAS. Chemical analyses of oil and gas and optical studies of oil have yielded considerable information, some of which appears to have a bearing on the origin of oil. A few natural gases contain helium, a product of radioactive disintegration. It is easier to explain this element as a wanderer from disintegrating radioactive minerals in the underlying crystalline basement rocks, caught in the same trap with natural gas, than to tie its occurrence in with any organic cycle. On the other hand, the presence of nickel and vanadium in some petroleum cokes can probably be best explained by an organic background, for analyses of the ashes left after some types of plants have been burned show the presence of these metals. Such plants appear to remove the metals from the surrounding soil, thereby concentrating them. Other indications of plant origin include the presence of nitrogen compounds in some oils and the optical activity of petroleum hydrocarbons.

Sanders [6] and Waldschmidt [7] have described such microscopic objects as Foraminifera, diatoms, plant remains, insect scales, and spines, as well as fragments of other materials, present in crude oils. These discoveries may or may not be significant in terms of the origin of

[6] J. McConnell Sanders, "The Microscopical Examination of Crude Petroleum," *Jour. Inst. Petrol. Technologists,* Vol. 23 (1937), pp. 525–573.

[7] W. A. Waldschmidt, Progress Report on Microscopic Examination of Permian Crude Oils, *Program 26th Annual Convention, Am. Assoc. Petrol. Geol.* (1941), p. 23.

oil. It may be that the petroleum in the course of its travels through sedimentary rocks rich in organic materials picked up the microscopic objects. Of perhaps greater importance is the presence of porphyrin pigments in crude oils.[8] According to Sheppard,[9] "This is convincing evidence for the animal and vegetable origins of petroleum."

TESTIMONY OF ASSOCIATED ROCKS. The geological associations of oil and gas have led practically all geologists to reject the inorganic theories as entirely inadequate. Over 99 per cent of the world's oil and gas so far produced has come from sedimentary rocks. Furthermore, in every oil-producing region the sedimentary rock section includes beds which either contain or have contained considerable organic material. In fact, Heald[10] expresses the belief that the distribution of oil within the sedimentary series is dependent upon the localization of source material within the rock column. It is his belief that the oil occurring in the beds lying above and below widespread water-bearing rocks must have had its source in that interior zone.

One would expect the crystalline rocks, where porosity exists, to contain more oil than the sedimentary rocks if the source of the oil is inorganic. As a matter of fact, there are instances of oil occurring in commercial quantities in crystalline rocks. "More than 15 million barrels of oil have been produced from igneous and metamorphic rocks; one gas field produces from a basalt flow; and millions of tons of asphalt . . . are known in serpentine in one area. . . ."[11] Many other examples could be cited,[12] but in every instance organic sedimentary rocks which could have been the source of the bituminous material occur near by and, frequently, at a lower elevation.

MISCELLANEOUS OBSERVATIONS. It was stated earlier that hydrogen and carbon are initially magmatic elements; it can be further

[8] A. Treibs, "Chlorophyll- und Haminderivate in organischen Mineralstoffen," *Angew. Chem.*, Vol. 49 (1936), pp. 682–686. Quoted by C. W. Sheppard, "Radioactivity and Petroleum Genesis," *Research on Occurrence and Recovery of Petroleum* (Am. Petrol. Inst., 1943), p. 143.

[9] *Op. cit.*

[10] K. C. Heald, "Essentials for Oil Pools," *Elements of the Petroleum Industry* (Am. Inst. Min. Met. Engineers, 1940), p. 26.

[11] Sidney Powers and F. G. Clapp, "Nature and Origin of Occurrences of Oil, Gas and Bitumen in Igneous and Metamorphic Rocks," *Bull. Am. Assoc. Petrol. Geol.*, Vol. 16 (August, 1932), p. 719.

[12] Sidney Powers *et al.*, "Symposium on the Occurrence of Petroleum in Igneous and Metamorphic Rocks," *Bull. Am. Assoc. Petrol. Geol.*, Vol. 16 (August, 1932); F. M. Van Tuyl and Ben H. Parker, "The Time and Origin of Petroleum," *Quarterly Colo. School of Mines*, Vol. 36, No. 2 (April, 1941), pp. 145–146; John H. Beach and Arthur S. Huey, "Geology of Basement Complex, Edison Field, California," *Program Annual Meeting, Am. Assoc. Petrol. Geol.* (Los Angeles, Calif., 1947), p. 26.

stated that it is probable that the two can and do appear combined in the form of magmatic hydrocarbons, but not in the quantity approaching that needed for commercial exploitation. Black, pitchy hydrocarbons have been found in pegmatites under conditions that are hard to explain in any other way than as truly magmatic. Methane, CH_4, the most stable hydrocarbon, has been found in volcanic gas. Spectrographic studies by astronomers have shown the presence of this hydrocarbon in the atmospheres of the larger planets.[13]

It is also true that the earth does have a heavy center, but studies of the earth's magnetism and of meteorites lead us to believe that this higher specific gravity is due to the concentration of iron and nickel in the core of the earth rather than a free alkali metal or iron carbide. Furthermore, the rock pressures are of such magnitude below the earth's crust that permeability disappears with depth. For this reason, it is impossible to visualize any transfer of materials between the earth's center and the upper parts of the earth's crust.

It should be pointed out that hydrocarbons can be and are produced by normal life processes on the surface of the earth. "The literature contains ample evidence that plants of many kinds produce small, but significant, quantities of hydrocarbons of the paraffin series." [14] Recent studies have shown that modern coral reefs contain a waxy substance which constitutes about 1/7 per cent of the coral and which "consists largely of hydrocarbons and complex alcohols, chemicals similar to those in petroleum." [15]

CONCLUSIONS. To a geologist the conclusion is inescapable that the petroleum hydrocarbons passed through an organic stage. That the literature on the inorganic origin of petroleum has grown to such proportions is apparently due to the failure of geologists to emphasize to the lay public the geological environment of petroleum and to the ignoring by the chemists of this geological environment. "If . . . it had been laid down, as it might have been, that no theory on the origin of petroleum was admissible unless it explained the close association between oil and sediments most of the chemical theories on its origin would not have been put forward." [16]

[13] C. E. Van Orstrand, "Cosmic Origin of Oil and Gas," *World Oil,* Vol. 128 (November, 1948), pp. 150–158.

[14] F. C. Whitmore, Review of API Research Project 43B, *Research on Occurrence and Recovery of Petroleum* (Am. Petrol. Inst., 1943), p. 124.

[15] Werner Bergmann, "Coral Reefs May Add to Petroleum Supply Some Day," *Science News Letter* (Oct. 30, 1948), p. 281.

[16] V. C. Illing, "Geology Applied to Petroleum," *Oil Weekly,* Vol. 122 (July 15, 1946), p. 36.

POSSIBLE SOURCE ORGANISMS

It is not possible to name, with any certainty, the particular organisms that produce the oil in any given oil reservoir. We do know that there are many types of animal and vegetable life capable of yielding oil under the proper conditions. However, between the time of the death of the organism and its transformation to oil many changes take place, during which the organic material tends to lose its identity.

Although many types of animals and plants from highest to lowest are capable of producing oil, we are able by following two lines of reasoning to eliminate some rather broad classes from serious consideration. One of these directions of reasoning involves the timing factor. It is obviously impossible for ancient oils to have been derived from modern organisms. "Inasmuch as petroleum is found in rocks that were formed millions of years before there were such complex forms of life as trees, land animals, or even fishes, it is apparent that very simple forms of life sufficed to provide materials which might be transformed into petroleum. . . ."[17] Another logical factor for consideration is that of opportunities for survival. If an organism lived under such environmental conditions that the chances of its existing long enough after death to become buried in sediment are very slight, then the chances of that organism's being source material for petroleum are also very slight.

These limitations immediately rule out land plants and animals from further consideration. Most of them did not exist at the time the Ordovician oil, for example, was formed. For organisms raised on the land, the chances of escaping destruction by putrefaction or devourment by scavengers are very slight. Possible exceptions are land organisms that can be readily transported by wind, like spores, pollen, and leaves. If these materials settle into bodies of water, they may join the muck on the sea or lake floor and thus become preserved.

Marine life, except the vertebrates, was abundant and fairly well advanced by early Paleozoic time, and it is in these phyla that we suspect the greater part of the source organisms of petroleum belong.

The one-celled plants and animals, such as the Algae, diatoms, and Foraminifera, were abundant in the seas from the earliest Paleozoic to the present and could have contributed to the oil deposits of all ages. The more advanced types of marine life, besides being less abundant

[17] F. C. Whitmore, Review of API Research Project 43B, *Research on Occurrence and Recovery of Petroleum* (Am. Petrol. Inst., 1943).

in the more remote geologic periods, also had lesser opportunity for survival because of the presence and vigor of sea-floor scavengers. It is difficult to visualize the accumulation of the soft body parts of fish (fairly common from the Devonian on), shellfish, or even corals in enough abundance on the sea floor to provide a quantitatively sufficient source of oil. Furthermore, some of the simpler types of marine organisms, such as kelp, produce hydrocarbons during their life processes,[18] so the problem of the generation of petroleum is much simpler for organisms of this kind. In any event, as pointed out by Trask,[19] the original organism may become entombed in the sediments, but the chances are greater that it will be devoured or decomposed by other organisms so that it loses its identity and joins the sea-floor muck as a part of the "waste products of the biota inhabiting the environment in which the source beds accumulate."

It has long been the custom to ascribe differences in petroleums to differences in the relative abundance of the various types of source organisms. For example, Taff, in an article on California, states: "The oil derived from the foraminiferal animal life in prevailing quantity produces a naphthene oil containing little or no tar with more or less wax or paraffin. The oils having their origin in a prevailing abundance of diatomaceous or plant life produce a naphthene oil having a tar base and generally free from wax or paraffin." [20]

Reger, [21] on the other hand, ascribes the high-gravity paraffin-base oils of the Appalachian province to a vegetable origin and storage in sandstone reservoirs. The oil of animal origin, stored in limestone reservoirs, is of lower quality, with tendency toward asphaltic base. These conclusions are exactly opposite to those drawn by Taff. The conditions are hardly comparable, however, because Reger is dealing with Paleozoic plants and animals, and Taff with organisms of Tertiary age.

Although very likely it must be admitted that young oils owe much of their differences in chemical composition and physical properties to differences in the predominant type of source material, it is also probable that differences in nature of mature oils are due more to

[18] F. C. Whitmore, *op. cit.*

[19] Parker D. Trask *et al., Origin and Environment of Source Sediments of Petroleum* (Gulf Publishing Co., Houston, Texas, 1932), p. 234.

[20] Joseph A. Taff, "Physical Properties of Petroleum in California," *Problems of Petroleum Geology* (Am. Assoc. Petrol. Geol., 1934), p. 177.

[21] David B. Reger, "Gravity of Oils in the Appalachian Province," *Problems of Petroleum Geology* (Am. Assoc. Petrol. Geol., 1934), p. 107.

time and environment than to initial differences in source material.[22] In other words, two oils from widely dissimilar source materials, having similar post-generation histories, would tend to become similar in nature.

TIME OF OIL GENERATION

The student of petroleum genesis finds himself dealing with at least five different ages: (1) the age of the source materials; (2) the age of the oil itself; (3) the age of the trap in which the oil accumulates; (4) the age of the actual accumulation; and (5) the age of the reservoir rock. We know least about the first four of these ages, and yet they are of the utmost importance in oil-finding. Ordinarily the age of the producing formation is known, and for the sake of convenience that date is commonly accepted for the oil itself, but actually there is not much justification for this practice.

The following paragraphs contain a discussion of the times at which conversion from solid organic matter to liquid petroleum may take place; the other four ages are considered in subsequent sections.

Geologists differ widely in their opinions regarding time of conversion. At one extreme are those who believe that oil is formed while the organic debris is accumulating on the sea floor. This is the syngenetic ("born with") theory. Next are those who believe that oil is epigenetic, formed later than the enclosing sediments but before lithifaction took place. Last is the post-lithifaction school, some members of which believe that oil is being formed in buried rock strata today.

The possible causes of transformation will be considered later; only the dating of the oil generation will be discussed in this section.

SYNGENETIC OIL. If oil is syngenetic with the sediments, the liquid hydrocarbons must have been formed (or have been already present [23]) while the sediments were accumulating on the sea floor. It can be readily demonstrated by experimental methods that petroleum dispersed through fine sediment will be both carried to the sea floor and retained there by that associated sediment.[24] There are

[22] This conclusion is contrary to that reached by L. C. Snider, "Current Ideas Regarding Source Beds," *Problems of Petroleum Geology* (Am. Assoc. Petrol. Geol., 1934), p. 63.

[23] Werner Bergmann, "Coral Reefs May Add to Petroleum Supply Some Day," *Science News Letter* (Oct. 30, 1948).

[24] F. M. Van Tuyl and Ben H. Parker, "The Time of Origin and Accumulation of Petroleum," *Quarterly, Colo. School of Mines,* Vol. 36, No. 2 (April, 1941), p. 134, includes reference to: (1) Murray Stuart, "Sedimentary Deposition of Oil," *Indian Geol. Survey Records,* Vol. 40 (1910), pp. 320–333; and (2) F. M. Van Tuyl and

also some observational records of the occurrence of petroleum hydrocarbons in sediments accumulating on the sea floor. Van Tuyl and Parker [25] describe numerous instances in which both liquid hydrocarbons and solid bitumens have been observed in recent and modern sediments. Unfortunately, the bituminous material has not been analyzed chemically in most of the cases observed and so we cannot be sure that the oily materials actually were petroleum hydrocarbons in those cases. Four samples of sediment taken from the bottom of Little Long Lake, Wisconsin, were tested with chloroform and ether for substances vulnerable to these solvents. About 0.5 per cent, or 10 pounds per ton, of soluble matter, presumably oil, was obtained.[26] A sample of Cuban mud investigated during the progress of API Research Project 43C at Massachusetts Institute of Technology showed the presence of water-soluble organic material which decomposed at approximately 135° C. into a variety of products, including some light petroleum hydrocarbons. This investigation is continuing.[27] Studies are also being made in an attempt to determine whether the optically active portion of petroleum is derived directly from living organisms.[28]

Howard [29] has described a thin section of oölitic limestone from Alabama which shows that some oölites have a core of calcite, then a ring of bitumen, followed by more calcite. It is difficult to explain the layer of asphaltic material in any other way than that it is syngenetic.

On the other hand, Trask [30] and associates found no liquid hydrocarbons in recent sediments. Up to 1 per cent of the organic content of these sediments consisted of solid paraffin, however. It has been suggested that the scarcity of liquid hydrocarbons in the Trask samples

C. F. Barb, "Notes on the Sedimentary Deposition of Petroleum," *Mines Mag.*, Vol. 24 (October, 1934), pp. 19–20; O. A. Poirier and George A. Thiel, "Deposition of Free Oil by Sediments Settling in Sea Water," *Bull. Am. Assoc. Petrol. Geol.*, Vol. 25 (1941), pp. 2170–2180.

25 *Op. cit.*, pp. 43–53 and 134–136.

26 W. H. Twenhofel and B E. McKelvey, "The Sediments of Little Long (Hiawatha) Lake, Wisconsin," *Jour. Sed. Petrol.*, Vol. 12 (April, 1942), p. 47.

27 W. L. Whitehead, informal communication.

28 T. S. Oakwood, "Review of API Research Project 43B. Transformation of Organic Material into Petroleum—Chemical and Biochemical Phases," *Report of Progress—Fundamental Research on Occurrence and Recovery of Petroleum* (Am. Petrol. Inst., 1949), pp. 189–191.

29 W. V. Howard, "Lithifaction Processes and Early Oil Formation in Sediments," *Oil and Gas Jour.*, Vol. 42 (June 17, 1943), pp. 92–94.

30 Parker D. Trask and C. C. Wu, "Does Petroleum Form in Sediments at Time of Deposition?" *Bull. Am. Assoc. Petrol. Geol.*, Vol. 14 (November, 1930); Parker D. Trask *et al.*, *Origin and Environment of Source Sediments of Petroleum* (Gulf Publishing Co., Houston, Texas, 1932), p. 232.

might possibly be due to the lag between the time of collection and the time of analysis: "The activity of hydrocarbon-oxidizing microorganisms may help to explain why Trask and others have failed to find petroleum hydrocarbons in recent sediments. Even if hydrocarbons were in the sediments *in situ* they might be destroyed rapidly by the increased bacterial activity and other environmental conditions which accompany the collection and storage of sediment samples." [31] It should also be remembered that the environmental conditions under which the recent sediments are being deposited are quite different from those that prevailed during most of the geologic past. During the greater part of the geologic past, the continents were base-leveled, and both the rate and the nature of the sedimentation along the continental margins were different from what they are today.

Many authorities do not believe in syngenetic origin of oil for other reasons. For example, Rich states, "Consideration of various possible sources for this oil indicate that it is not generated until long after the sediments were deposited and that its source cannot logically and consistently be sought in the rocks in the immediate vicinity of the pools." [32] In most oil accumulations, it is obvious that the oil is younger than the enclosing rock. However, this is not in itself evidence that the oil is not syngenetic in some other rock from which it has migrated to its present home.

PRE-LITHIFACTION OIL. The case for the generation of oil after deposition but before lithifaction has been stated well by Hoots: "Burial and its accompanying expulsion of fluids from compressible sediments is an experience necessary to the formation of fine-grained sedimentary rocks. No shales have avoided it. In addition to the effect from burial, lateral compression may cause additional compaction. The resulting movement of large quantities of water offers the most positive opportunity for oil to move along and across the bedding of fine-grained source beds into adjoining permeable beds. Because of this fact most theorists agree that petroleum generation and its migration to the reservoir takes place during compaction." [33] Although he was primarily concerned with the origin of oil in the California oil

[31] Claude E. ZoBell, C. W. Grant, and H. F. Haas, "Marine Microorganisms Which Oxidize Petroleum Hydrocarbons," *Bull. Am. Assoc. Petrol. Geol.*, Vol. 27 (September, 1943), p. 1189.

[32] John L. Rich, "Source and Date of Accumulation of Oil in Granite Ridge Pools of Kansas and Oklahoma," *Bull. Am. Assoc. Petrol. Geol.*, Vol. 15 (December, 1931), p. 1431.

[33] H. W. Hoots, "Origin, Migration, and Accumulation of Oil in California," *Calif. Div. Mines, Bull.* 118 (August, 1941), p. 260.

fields where the source rock is without doubt shale, it is also possible that a calcareous ooze undergoing compaction might likewise be the source of liquid hydrocarbons. Trask [34] found calcareous deposits (as well as siliceous muds) containing relatively high percentages of organic materials. He has observed also that "the period of time shortly after the deposition of sediments is probably of major importance in the generation of petroleum." [35]

In opposition to the theory of prelithifaction oil, there is little evidence that oil in volume is being squeezed out today from compacting sediments. This situation may be due to inadequate exploration, or it may be due to the fact that the conditions of sedimentation in the recent geologic past have not been typical of the more distant past. Walter Link [36] believes that our knowledge is inadequate and advocates for the Gulf of Mexico along the Louisiana or Texas coast a "systematic foot-by-foot analysis of sediments, starting with the youngest and going down to the oldest, in which oil is known to exist. . . ." The American Petroleum Institute is considering a study of the successive changes which source beds deposited under similar conditions through a considerable span of geological time have undergone.[37]

Another argument opposed to prelithifaction oil is the presence in some oil fields of evidence of more than one time of accumulation. Several examples are given by Van Tuyl and Parker.[38] The best-known case is that at Oklahoma City, where drilling has shown the existence of asphaltic residues at the unconformable contact between the Pennsylvanian sediments and the Ordovician reservoir rocks. The natural interpretation of this situation is that oil was migrating up the dipping Ordovician formations and escaping at the truncated surface exposed in pre-Pennsylvanian time. Subsequently, this escapeway was closed by the deposition of the Pennsylvanian sediments and the great oil deposits of the Oklahoma City field accumulated beneath the unconformity. A few other examples of oil residues at uncon-

[34] Parker D. Trask *et al.*, "Origin and Environment of Source Beds of Petroleum" (Gulf Publishing Co., Houston, Texas, 1932).

[35] Parker D. Trask, "Some Studies of Source Beds of Petroleum," *International Geological Congress, Report of the 16th Session, 1933,* Vol. 2 (1936), p. 1011.

[36] Walter K. Link, "Approach to Origin of Oil," *Bull. Am. Assoc. Petrol. Geol.,* Vol. 33 (October, 1949), pp. 1767–1769.

[37] Robert E. Wilson, "API Wildcatting in Some Interesting Areas," Am. Petrol. Inst., 29th Annual Meeting (1949), separate paper, p. 7.

[38] F. M. Van Tuyl and Ben H. Parker, "The Time of Origin and Accumulation of Petroleum," *Quarterly Colo. School of Mines,* Vol. 36, No. 2 (April, 1941), pp. 84–98.

formities are cited by Van Tuyl and Parker, but Rich [39] notes that in proportion to the total number of unconformity accumulations residual asphalt is decidedly rare.

Actually, of course, heavy oil residues at unconformities which are underlain by deposits of "live" oil are not in themselves evidence of multiple or continuous generation of oil. They can be interpreted only as evidence that oil was in motion in the reservoir rock at two widely different periods of time. It is possible that regional tilting during the time that truncated Ordovician formations were exposed at the surface at Oklahoma City permitted some spillage of the oil from a basinward anticline. After the relatively impervious Pennsylvanian sediments had been deposited across the truncated layers, further tilting might have released from below much more oil that accumulated beneath the unconformity, or the new oil might have been driven there by the overlying compacting sediments. Hiestand [40] has observed that oil is adjusted to present structural traps and concludes as a corollary that the oil and associated water "have made migratory adjustments in various directions according as a given trap was destroyed or preserved by structural modifications." Weeks [41] describes "secondary tectonic structures" which cause "secondary redistribution or localization of oil." Similar ideas are expressed by Van Tuyl, Parker, and Skeeters: "It does not necessarily follow that these substances [oil and gas] are generated in the mother rocks continuously or as successive 'crops.' It is possible that they may be stored for considerable periods after generation, either in a disseminated condition or as pools, which may undergo renewed migration as a result of changes in geologic structure. . . . In some instances there may have been renewed migration of oil and gas in pools previously formed as a result of changes in direction or amount of dip, faulting, increase in the vigor of artesian circulation, or other causes." [42]

POST-LITHIFACTION OIL. Several of the theories of oil generation (to be considered subsequently) are based on the assumption that conversion from solid carbonaceous matter to liquid hydrocarbons does not take place until the sediments have been deeply buried and presumably lithified. However, there is little actual evidence that

[39] F. M. Van Tuyl and Ben H. Parker, *op. cit.*, p. 96.

[40] T. C. Hiestand, "Regional Investigations, Oklahoma and Kansas," *Bull. Am. Assoc. Petrol. Geol.*, Vol. 19 (July, 1935), p. 965.

[41] L. C. Weeks *in* F. M. Van Tuyl, Ben H. Parker, and H. W. Skeeters, "The Migration and Accumulation of Petroleum and Natural Gas," *Quarterly Colo. School of Mines*, Vol. 40, No. 1 (January, 1945), p. 53.

[42] *Op. cit.*, p. 56.

oil generation takes place after lithifaction. In many oil reservoirs, especially limestone reservoirs, the age of the local accumulation is obviously post-lithifaction, but that is still not evidence that the oil was generated from source materials in lithified sediments. Stadnichenko [43] determined experimentally that source materials "have different temperature points or zones at which oil and gas are formed, indicating that the petroleum found in our oil fields may contain products generated at several stages in the long course of the devolatization of the organic matter in the sediments." Furthermore, the later the oil generation in a series of generations, the higher the fixed-carbon content of the source rock and the better the quality of the petroleum; when the carbon content rises above 63 per cent, natural gas only is given off.[44] The source materials used in these experiments were oil shales, cannel coals, and other already lithified rocks. But Hoots [45] pointed out that, if the oil is not produced until after lithifaction takes place, one must accept the thesis that large quantities of oil are generated and migrate through rocks that have become compact and relatively impermeable. One naturally wonders why compact shales as a source rock could permit oil to escape outwards but as a cap rock would not allow oil to pass through.

It should also be pointed out that the failure to find any free oil in alleged source rocks in various oil fields of the world shows either that conversion is no longer going on even though the environmental conditions of pressure, temperature, and the presence of possible catalysts or radioactive elements are apparently just as favorable as they have been in the geologic past, or else that this process of autogeneration within the source rock is so slow and the quantities produced are so small that the amount present at any one time would not be measurable.

SEDIMENTATION AND BIOCHEMICAL ACTIVITY

The first phase in the formation of oil is the deposition of the sediment, both physical and organic, which is destined to become the

[43] Taisia Stadnichenko, "Experimental Studies Bearing on the Origin of Petroleum," *International Geological Congress, Report of the 16th Session, 1933,* Vol. 2 (1936), p. 1009.

[44] C. David White, "The Origin of Petroleum," *Petroleum Investigation* (Hearings before a Subcommittee of the Committee on Interstate and Foreign Commerce, House of Representatives, 73d Congress, on H.R. 441, 1934), pp. 908–909.

[45] H. W. Hoots, "Origin, Migration, and Accumulation of Oil in California," *Calif. Div. Mines, Bull.* 118 (August, 1941).

source rock. Concurrent with this sea-floor accumulation are certain chemical changes that take place in the organic sediment as the result of environment and the activity of bacteria.

DEPOSITION OF SEDIMENT. The ecology of source rocks has received considerable attention. The petroleum industry and later the U. S. Geological Survey subsidized a long-continuing program of studies by Parker D. Trask and associates. This research resulted in the publication of numerous papers and two monographs: Parker D. Trask, *Origin and Environment of Source Sediments of Petroleum* (Gulf Publishing Co., Houston, 1932; and Parker D. Trask and H. W. Patnode, *Source Beds of Petroleum,* Am. Assoc. Petrol. Geol., Tulsa, 1942). Another publication in this field is the symposium, *Recent Marine Sediments* (Am. Assoc. Petrol. Geol., Tulsa, 1934).

Environment of Deposition. To those who believe that oil pools occur *only* where restricted deposits of rich source material lie in juxtaposition to reservoir and trap, the environment of deposition is of paramount importance. As stated by Clark: "It is probable that source material is more closely associated with local conditions of sedimentation and environment than has been generally considered. The location of these deposits of rich organic matter is probably controlled by local favorable conditions of sedimentation on the floor of the epicontinental sea, by local favorable climatic conditions, by routes of travel of sea life, by food supply, and by shallow warm water, all these conditions being favorable for the growth, propagation, and accumulation of organic matter." [46]

There is no doubt that the accumulation of source material is subaqueous. Whether the water is invariably saline is open to argument. At one extreme is Van der Gracht,[47] who believes that the richest source materials accumulate where the water is either so saline or so foul with hydrogen sulfide that life can exist only in the uppermost levels and therefore the plankton sinking to the bottom is out of reach of scavengers. "Source rocks of the saline class are found in deposits of concentration basins, before (or after) deposition of actual rock salt, at a time when strong salt solutions prevailed at the bottom, but the less salty upper layers of the water supported life. It is not necessary that the stage of precipitation of actual salt was ever reached; the cycle may have been interrupted. Concentrated brines are not

[46] Frank R. Clark, "Origin and Accumulation of Oil," *Problems of Petroleum Geology* (Am. Assoc. Petrol. Geol., Tulsa, Okla., 1934), p. 309.

[47] W. A. J. M. van Waterschoot van der Gracht, "The Stratigraphical Distribution of Petroleum," *Science of Petroleum* (Oxford Univ. Press, 1938), Vol. 1, p. 58.

only adverse to life, but they also prevent convection currents and access of oxygen to the deeper layers of water. The latter is the real cause of the preservation of organic matter, much more than concentrated salinity."

Nevin[48] believes it probable that the usual association of petroliferous deposits with marine strata "is a direct consequence of salinity. If the water were brackish or fresh, the end product of bacterial breakdown would then be carbonaceous, rather than bituminous, because of the types of microorganisms present and the completeness and intensity of their attack on the organic material." On the other hand, there are now a number of oil fields in which the reservoir rock, at least, is of fresh-water origin. It has been customary to ascribe the oil to some marine organic rock whence it is supposed to have migrated into the continental sediments, but in some of the newer fields this idea is difficult to apply. It is quite possible that deposition in salt water is not necessary for petroleum source material and that the insignificant percentage of known oil pools in continental rocks has been due to less intensive search in such rocks and, more importantly, to the relative scarcity of continental formations in deposits of adequate thickness. The possibility of fresh-water source rocks is considered in more detail in a subsequent section.

The expression used by Van der Gracht for deposits accumulating in waters saturated with hydrogen sulfide is "euxinic facies." Although the water near the surface is near normal and will support life, the deeper layers are practically devoid of oxygen and in addition may contain "poisonous admixtures" which prevent the existence of life at depth. The best example of euxinic facies today is the Black Sea. This environment was more common in the geologic past, according to Van der Gracht, when polar ice caps were not present, and in consequence oxygen-carrying convection currents were much less active in the ocean basins.

It appears much more likely that euxinic conditions rather than supersalinity may have been responsible for unusual accumulations of organic debris. Many black shales, rich in animal and plant matter, are also pyritiferous and were apparently laid down in waters replete with hydrogen sulfide. On the other hand, highly organic shales are uncommon in strata containing evaporite minerals. Trask[49] found

[48] Charles Nevin, "Origin of Petroleum—A Method of Approach," *Bull. Am. Assoc. Petrol. Geol.*, Vol. 29 (March, 1945), p. 288.

[49] Parker D. Trask *et al.*, *Origin and Environment of Source Sediments of Petroleum* (Gulf Publishing Co., Houston, 1932).

that supersalinity was not necessary for the accumulation of abundant organic debris on modern sea floors.

Of great importance in the accumulation of source materials is the configuration of the sea floor and the distance from shore. Trask [50] noted that the organic content of modern sediment is lowest on submarine ridges and highest in sea-floor basins. The reason is that the sediment in the basins is protected from currents; where water is in motion the light organic material cannot come to rest. For the same reason, the usual associate of plant and animal debris deposited on the sea floor is clay or fine silt rather than sand. The distance from shore is a factor because much of the food consumed by the marine organisms is brought to the sea by streams draining the land surfaces. Consequently, life is much more abundant near shore than in the open ocean, and where sanctuary from currents is available, the deposition of organic matter will be much greater near shore.

Composition of Muds. The inorganic or physical sediment accompanying, and far exceeding in volume, the organic sediment is usually mud consisting of clay, silt, or calcareous ooze. More rarely, fine-grained sands may contain sufficient organic matter to be a potential source of oil.[51] The determination of the nature of the organisms that produce petroleum is made difficult by the fact that these types of life leave few, if any, fossil remains. Trask [52] believes that the original source material is plankton, which is taken in by other organisms in succession as food and eventually, but much reduced in volume, comes to rest on the sea floor, where it is incorporated in the physical sediment being deposited. He further believes that the amounts of cellulose, fats, and simple proteins in the marine muds are too small to be the principal source of petroleum. "Petroleum apparently must come mainly from other compounds, such as complex proteins and non-nitrogenous complexes." [53] In the opinion of Brooks: [54] "The principal types of organic substances which are to be considered as the main source material for petroleum include

[50] Parker D. Trask, "Organic Content of Recent Marine Sediments," *Recent Marine Sediments* (Am. Assoc. Petrol. Geol., Tulsa, 1939), p. 428.

[51] Parker D. Trask, "Some Studies of Source Beds of Petroleum," *Proc. XVI International Geological Congress, 1933,* Vol. 2 (1936), p. 1011.

[52] Parker D. Trask, "Inferences about the Origin of Oil as Indicated by the Composition of the Organic Constituents of Sediments," *U. S. Geol. Survey, Dept. Interior Prof. Paper* 186-H (1937), p. 147; "Petroleum Source Beds," *Science of Petroleum* (Oxford Univ. Press, 1938), Vol. I, pp. 42–45.

[53] *Op cit.*

[54] Benjamin T. Brooks, "Origins of Petroleums; Chemical and Geochemical Aspects," *Bull. Am. Assoc. Petrol. Geol.,* Vol. 20 (March, 1936), p. 280.

cellulose, starches, and sugars, proteins, lignins, oleo-resins, waxes, and fatty oils. Fatty oils are to be regarded as the principal source material."

Nitrogenous compounds, of which about half are proteins, are the largest group, totaling about 40 per cent of the organic constituents in modern sediments. Thirty per cent are composed of lignins and humic complexes. The waxes, resins, alkaloids, and alcohols make up about 5 per cent, and the sugars, starches, and organic acids 3 per cent. Carbohydrates comprise 1 per cent. The oils and fats, which chemically are nearest to petroleum, also compose only 1 per cent of the total organic content.[55]

As would be expected, the percentage of organic matter within the sediment varies widely from place to place. The average recent sediment runs about 2.5 per cent by weight organic matter. The figure is lower in deltaic and continental shelf areas where currents are relatively strong; it is higher in closed basins. In bodies of stagnant water, such as the Black Sea, the percentage may be as high as 35; in small lakes the figure may even reach 40 per cent. The average in the open ocean far from land is less than 1 per cent of organic matter.[56]

Although Trask found only solid organic matter in the samples examined, this solid matter yielded liquid hydrocarbons when assayed by dry destructive distillation. Samples were collected from practically every known environment of deposition. These sediments yielded, in the main, from 0 to 3 gallons per ton, although the samples collected from the bottom of an algal lake ran as high as 28 gallons per ton. Some limy oozes had high yields also. As would be expected, the yield increased with finer texture and decreased with distance from shore. The highest yields come from samples collected from sea-floor basins.[57]

Conclusions. There is no doubt that the ecology of sedimentation is an important factor in the accumulation of the organic debris that is to become petroleum. The commonest source rocks are marine, near-shore, shaly or calcareous deposits. Less common, but not ruled out completely, are fresh-water deposits and fine sandstones. The

[55] W. B. Heroy, "Petroleum Geology," *Bull. Geol. Soc. Am. 50th Anniversary Vol.* (June, 1941), p. 170.

[56] Parker D. Trask, "Organic Content of Recent Marine Sediments," *Recent Marine Sediments* (Am. Assoc. Petrol. Geol., Tulsa, 1939), p. 428.

[57] Parker D. Trask, "The Potential Value of Several Recent American Coastal and Inland Deposits as Future Source Beds of Petroleum," *Bull. Am. Assoc. Petrol. Geol.,* Vol. 12 (November, 1928), pp. 1057–1069; also Vol. 14 (March, 1930), pp. 314–316.

richest deposits are those in which the organic debris accumulated either in closed sea-floor basins or in waters so foul with hydrogen sulfide that the organisms were not passed on and on, with consequent diminution of volume.

It is quite possible that local differences in the environment of sedimentation may explain the presence of barren or lean traps within regions of prolific oil accumulations.

PHOTOSYNTHESIS. The possibility of the synthesis of hydrocarbons *before deposition* by the metabolism of plants is being investigated.[58] Sunlight is known to be an important factor in the growth and development of plankton. If hydrocarbons are generated in the organic matter before deposition, the problem of petroleum genesis becomes one of the "selection and concentration" of such hydrocarbon-containing organisms in the sea-floor muds.

BIOCHEMICAL PROCESSES. During the time that the organic matter is accumulating on the sea floor, it is subject to attack and chemical transformation by bacteria. Opinions vary widely as to the relative importance of the biochemical stage in the genesis of petroleum. It is certain that during this period the organic matter becomes *more* petroleumlike chemically; [59] there are those who believe that petroleum itself may be formed.[60]

The role of bacteria on the sea floor has been a subject of active investigation for some years. A paper by Hammer [61] on this subject published in 1934 lists 81 references. ZoBell [62] includes 200 references in a paper published in 1947. In recent years the American Petroleum Institute has sponsored an investigation by ZoBell and associates into the function of bacteria in oil formation which has led to the publication of numerous papers.

58 G. M. Knebel, "Progress Report on API Research Project 43, The Transformation of Organic Material into Petroleum," *Bull. Am. Assoc. Petrol. Geol.*, Vol. 30 (November, 1946), p. 1944.

59 Claude E. ZoBell, "Biennial Report for 1945–1947 on API Research Project 43A—Bacteriological and Sedimentation Phases of the Transformation of Organic Material into Petroleum," *Report of Progress—Fundamental Research on Occurrence and Recovery of Petroleum* (Am. Petrol. Inst., 1949), pp. 100–106; "Bacterial Activities and the Origin of Oil," *World Oil,* Vol. 130 (June, 1950), pp. 128–138.

60 G. D. Hobson, "Biochemical Aspects of the Origin of Oil," *Science of Petroleum* (Oxford Univ. Press, 1938), Vol. 1, pp. 54–56.

61 Harold E. Hammer, "Relation of Micro-Organisms to Generation of Petroleum," *Problems of Petroleum Geology* (Am. Assoc. Petrol. Geol., Tulsa, 1934), pp. 35–49.

62 Claude E. ZoBell, "Microbial Transformation of Molecular Hydrogen in Marine Sediments, with Particular References to Petroleum," *Bull. Am. Assoc. Petrol. Geol.*, Vol. 31 (October, 1947), pp. 1709–1751.

Distribution of Bacteria. Bacteria have been found in recent sediments up to the depth sampled (25 feet). They are most abundant in the top few inches, below which they gradually decrease in numbers.[63] It has been claimed that samples of sedimentary rock collected aseptically from a depth of 1560 feet contained indigenous bacteria,[64] but this conclusion has been questioned. Samples of oil sand from an oil "mine" in Pennsylvania had bacteria where they were exposed to the air but not in the centers of the chunks.[65] It is probable that the bacteria found in samples of ancient sediments, although abundant, are adventitious. It would be extremely difficult, if not impossible, to so control conditions on the drill floor that an uncontaminated sample could be obtained.

Kinds of Bacteria. To the uninitiated it appears that not only are there many varieties of bacteria but also that each type has an opposite number with opposite functions. Thus there are oxidizing (aerobic) bacteria and reducing (anaerobic) bacteria, hydrogen-producing bacteria and hydrogen-removing bacteria, hydrocarbon-producing and hydrocarbon-destroying bacteria, to mention only those of greatest importance to the natural history of oil and gas.

Functions of Bacteria in Oil Formation. The common and abundant anaerobic, or reducing, bacteria liberate oxygen, nitrogen, phosphorus, and sulfur from organic material. As a result, the percentage of hydrogen and carbon is increased, making the material more like petroleum in composition. Where oxidizing conditions exist on the sea floor, only the aerobic bacteria are at work, and this desired result will not follow.

It is common knowledge that bacteria can produce methane from organic debris. This not only is subject to laboratory demonstration but also is illustrated in nature by the production of marsh gas. Whether liquid hydrocarbons are produced by these bacteria is still a matter of conjecture. ZoBell[66] has found that such hydrocarbons can be produced in the laboratory: "It is especially noteworthy that certain anaerobic bacteria, isolated from marine sediments, have been

63 Claude E. ZoBell, "Occurrence and Activity of Bacteria in Marine Sediments," *Recent Marine Sediments* (Am. Assoc. Petrol. Geol., Tulsa, 1939), p. 416.

64 Claude E. ZoBell, "The Role of Bacteria in the Formation and Transformation of Petroleum Hydrocarbons," *Science*, Vol. 102 (Oct. 12, 1945), p. 365.

65 G. M. Knebel, "Progress Report on API Research Project 43, The Transformation of Organic Material into Petroleum," *Bull. Am. Assoc. Petrol. Geol.*, Vol. 30 (November, 1946), p. 1943.

66 Claude E. ZoBell, "Transformation of Organic Material into Petroleum-Bacteriological and Sedimentation Phases," *Fundamental Research on Occurrence and Recovery of Petroleum* (Am. Petrol. Inst., New York, 1943), p. 104.

shown to produce ether-soluble, non-saponifiable, oil-like extracts from naturally occurring lipides or fatty acids." The presence of indigenous liquid hydrocarbons in sea-floor sediment, although reported by several investigators, has not yet been sufficiently verified for general acceptance.

There is ample evidence of the activity of hydrocarbon-oxidizing bacteria. The relatively rapid disappearance of oil spilled upon the ground is caused by such bacteria. It has been noted that the percentage of organic matter in sea-floor sediment may decrease from "10 to 20 per cent in the first two or three inches, and a like amount in the next 2 or 3 feet," [67] because of destruction by bacteria. In fact the hydrocarbon-oxidizing bacteria are so common and so active that it has been suggested that petroleum accumulation can take place only "where conditions are inimical to their activity." [68]

The hydrocarbon-oxidizing bacteria may alter the composition and characteristics of oil by destroying some hydrocarbon compounds ahead of others. Therefore, if the process of destruction is arrested at any time, the residual oil may be quite different from the initial oil.

Hydrogen-producing bacteria might conceivably contribute to the evolution of hydrocarbons by increasing the hydrogen percentage. This "biochemical hydrogenation" can probably take place with methane, CH_4, as well as with straight hydrogen. Hydrogen-oxidizing bacteria are capable of converting organic sulfur into hydrogen sulfide.

Miscellaneous activities of bacteria which may be significant in petroleum accumulation and exploitation include the production of acids that can dissolve carbonate rocks, releasing at the same time carbon dioxide, which adds to the pressure, and the liberation of oil from the surfaces of the grains in the reservoir rock.

The type of decay depends upon the type of bacteria at work. The span of time over which decay occurs depends upon (1) the speed of burial of the organic matter, (2) the degree of stagnation of the overlying water, and (3) the eventual toxicity of the decomposition products to the microbes themselves.

Conclusions. Most, if not all, of the role of bacteria in petroleum generation is confined to the uppermost few feet of the organic sediment accumulating on the sea floor. The principal function of the bacteria is to remove the elements other than hydrogen and carbon,

[67] Claude E. ZoBell, "Changes Produced by Microorganisms in Sediments after Deposition," *Jour. Sed. Petrol.*, Vol. 12, No. 3 (1942), p. 132.

[68] Claude E. ZoBell, "The Role of Bacteria in the Formation and Transformation of Petroleum Hydrocarbons," *Science*, Vol. 102 (Oct. 12, 1945), p. 368.

thereby bringing the organic matter closer to petroleum in composition. Methane can be produced in this way; whether the liquid hydrocarbons can be so generated is an open question.

Differences in the degree and character of the biochemical attack upon the organic debris accumulating upon the sea floor may be another explanation for differences in the composition and properties of petroleums.

BURIAL AND DYNAMOCHEMICAL ACTIVITY

It is the prevalent belief that the close of the depositional phase finds the source organic matter still in solid form. If this view is correct, the transformation from solid to liquid must take place after burial. Much has been written regarding the conditions and processes which might bring about the conversion within the earth's crust of organic debris into petroleum, but in spite of this mental productivity we still do not know how, when, or where oil is formed.

There are two stages in the burial of the organic sediment. The first is the concurrent deposition of the much more abundant physical sediment. In the preceding section it was noted that this material is usually a clay or fine silt because the light organic matter could come to rest only where the water was so quiet that the non-organic sediment would settle out of suspension. The rate of entombment of the organic matter is probably of considerable importance in respect to the percentage to be transformed eventually into petroleum. If the rate of burial is too rapid, the biochemical activity would be obstructed; if too slow, the processes of putrefaction might go so far as to destroy the organic matter.

The second phase in the burial of the organic sediment is the deposition of a non-organic overlying rock, followed by layer upon layer of other rocks of various types. The eventual thickness of this cover varies between wide extremes.[69] It is not possible to state with any certainty the minimum cover which existed at the time transformation took place. The oil fields of eastern Kansas are often cited as examples of oil occurring in rocks which were never very deeply buried. It is true that oil occurs here in upper Pennsylvanian rocks at a present depth of only a few hundred feet, and the addition of the higher Pennsylvanian and Permian formations which crop out

[69] F. M. Van Tuyl and Ben H. Parker, "The Time of Origin and Accumulation of Petroleum," *Quarterly Colo. School of Mines,* Vol. 36 (April, 1941), pp. 79–82.

to the westward would make the total cover less than 2000 feet, but still younger rocks, especially the Cretaceous, may have also covered this area. At the other extreme, we know that oil occurs today beneath a cover of over 15,000 feet, and it probably occurs at considerably greater depths.

At least three changes in physical environment take place with burial. One is an increase in hydrostatic pressure with each foot of cover added. It has been determined that the pressure at a depth of 13,000 feet is over 6000 pounds per square inch.[70] Another change is caused by the rise of the isogeotherms, or levels of equal earth temperature. Sediments buried to a depth of 15,000 feet may be subjected to temperatures as high as 300° F. This combination of strong pressure and high temperature is certainly capable of accelerating, if not initiating, geochemical processes. A third change in environment is the increase in salinity of the formation waters as the sediment is buried to greater and greater depths.

POST-BURIAL CHEMICAL CHANGES.[71] Although not as obvious as the physical changes which take place under load, the chemical composition of an organic sediment does change with burial, and most of the change takes place before the physical metamorphism becomes noticeable. Campbell coined the term "incipient metamorphism" [72] for the chemical changes that take place in organic rocks because of the increase in temperature and pressure which accompanies burial and subsequent loading. The volatiles, especially oxygen, decrease in relative percentage, and the fixed carbon increases. In coals this chemical alteration is responsible for the various grades ranging from lignite to anthracite, with graphite as the rarely reached end point.

The separation of oxygen from the source organic matter is a requisite to the formation of petroleum. However, both Brooks [73] and Hobson [74] have pointed out that petroleum contains hydrocarbons

[70] William B. Heroy, "Petroleum Geology," *Bull. Geol. Soc. Am. 50th Anniversary Vol.* (1941), pp. 512–548.

[71] C. David White, "Progressive Metamorphism ('Carbonization') of the Buried Mother Substances," *Petroleum Investigation* (Hearings before a Subcommittee of the Committee on Interstate and Foreign Commerce, House of Representatives, 73d Congress, on H.R. 441), Part 2, pp. 903–906.

[72] M. R. Campbell, "Coal as a Recorder of Incipient Rock Metamorphism," *Econ. Geol.*, Vol. 25 (November, 1930), pp. 675–696.

[73] Benjamin T. Brooks, "Origins of Petroleum; Chemical and Geochemical Aspects," *Bull. Am. Assoc. Petrol. Geol.*, Vol. 20 (March, 1936), p. 280.

[74] G. D. Hobson, "Biochemical Aspects of the Origin of Oil," *Science of Petroleum* (Oxford Univ. Press, 1938), Vol. 1, p. 54.

that are unstable at high temperatures, so this de-oxygenation must have taken place at relatively moderate temperatures.

POST-BURIAL PHYSICAL CHANGES. The first physical effect on the organic muds to result from burial and loading is compaction. Because of the nature of the material, the sediment may in time become compressed to 50 per cent or more of its original thickness, and the specific gravity of the sediment may increase from an initial 1.3 to more than 2.[75] This compaction is accompanied by the expulsion of a like volume of water or other fluid; the importance of this process in the migration of oil from source rock to carrier or reservoir bed will be considered later (see Migration).

Compaction is accompanied or followed by lithifaction and induration, which transform the incoherent sediment into sedimentary rock. Further dehydration and minor earth movements will create jointing and cleavage in the rock, and if diastrophism or static metamorphism becomes intense, recrystallization and even the development of schistosity will take place. However, the oil generation takes place long before the physical metamorphism stage is reached; in fact it will be shown subsequently that hydrocarbons are destroyed, rather than formed, by metamorphic processes.

AGENTS AND PROCESSES. Among the many agents and processes that have been credited with transforming solid organic matter into liquid petroleum are pressure, bacteria, catalysts, heat with "cracking," intramolecular combustion,[76] natural distillation, and radioactive minerals. Geologic time has also been considered an important contributing factor.

Pressure, to be effective, would have to be of shearing magnitude in order to transform organic solid into oil. Experiments carried on at room temperatures on the application of high shearing pressures to oil shales and cannel coals resulted in some insignificant devolatilization but no oil.[77] Actually, of course, few if any source rocks of petroleum experience pressures of this magnitude. "Skin frictional

[75] G. M. Knebel, Progress report on API Research Project 43, "The Transformation of Organic Material into Petroleum," *Bull. Am. Assoc. Petrol. Geol.,* Vol. 30 (November, 1946), pp. 1948–1949; H. D. Hedberg, "Gravitational Compaction of Clays and Shales," *Am. Jour. Science,* 5th Series, Vol. 31 (April, 1936), pp. 241–287.

[76] E. Berl, "The Origin of Petroleum," *Petroleum Development and Technology* (Am. Inst. Min. and Met. Engineers, Petrol. Div., 1938), Vol. 127, p. 106.

[77] J. E. Hawley, "Generation of Oil in Rocks by Shearing Pressures," I, *Bull. Am. Assoc. Petrol. Geol.,* Vol. 13 (April, 1929), pp. 303–328; II, pp. 329–365; III, Vol. 14 (April, 1930), pp. 451–481.

heat" [78] has been advocated as a factor in the generation of petroleum. This heat is supposed to be generated during the compaction of the source rock, but the speed of movement, which is quite important in frictional heat, is so slight in compaction that it is difficult to visualize a significant temperature increase from this cause.

Just when in the burial process bacteria cease to be active is not known. There are those who believe that bacteria may be responsible for the generation of liquid petroleum. "Conclusive proof is still lacking that bacteria are physiologically active in subterranean deposits of brine or oil, but bacteria are unquestionably functional in recent marine sediments to the greatest depths sampled, around 25 feet." [79] But Illing [80] questions that bacteria, even if present, would produce petroleum: ". . . all studies of such decay have tended to confirm the impression that the ultimate end product of all such decomposition tends to be methane, and until it has been proved conclusively that bacterial decay can produce the higher-molecular-weight hydrocarbons, the bacterial theory can only be regarded as a tentative solution."

Many writers consider a catalyst to be essential to the transformation of buried organic debris into oil.[81] Substances which have been mentioned as possible catalysts include especially fuller's earth and other varieties of clay,[82] limestone, gypsum, potash minerals, salt, and bacteria and their enzymes.[83] The possible role of catalysts in the evolution of oil is discussed in a subsequent section.

Heat and Natural Distillation. Some investigators, including White [84] and van der Gracht,[85] have suggested that the pyrobitumens

[78] Ralph H. Fash, "Theory of Origin and Accumulation of Petroleum," *Bull. Am. Assoc. Petrol. Geol.,* Vol. 28 (October, 1944), pp. 1510–1518.

[79] Claude E. ZoBell, "The Role of Bacteria in the Formation and Transformation of Petroleum Hydrocarbons," *Science,* Vol. 102 (Oct. 12, 1945), p. 365.

[80] V. C. Illing, "The Origin of Petroleum," *Science of Petroleum* (Oxford Univ. Press, 1938), p. 37.

[81] Paul D. Torry, "Origin, Migration, and Accumulation of Petroleum and Natural Gas in Pennsylvania," *Problems of Petroleum Geology* (Am. Assoc. Petrol. Geol., Tulsa, 1934), p. 447; Benjamin T. Brooks, "Catalysis and Carbonium Ions in Petroleum Formation," *Science,* Vol. 111 (June 16, 1950), pp. 648–650.

[82] Ralph E. Grim, "Relation of Clay Mineralogy to Origin and Recovery of Petroleum," *Bull. Am. Assoc. Petrol. Geol.,* Vol. 31 (August, 1946), pp. 1495–1496.

[83] Ben B. Cox, "Transformation of Organic Material into Petroleum under Geological Conditions," *Bull. Am. Assoc. Petrol. Geol.,* Vol. 30 (May, 1946), p. 653.

[84] C. David White, "Effects of Geophysical Factors on the Evolution of Oil and Coal," *Institute of Petroleum Technologists,* Vol. 21 (April, 1935), pp. 308–309.

[85] W. A. J. M. van Waterschoot van der Gracht, "The Stratigraphical Distribution of Petroleum," *Science of Petroleum* (Oxford Univ. Press, 1938), Vol. 1, pp. 59–60.

in organic shales may be decomposed or "cracked" by heat into liquid hydrocarbons. Pratt [86] believes that the initial stage in the formation of oil is a "cracking" of the organic muds during and following compaction to produce methane and a heavy unsaturated oil.

In the Anacacho formation in Texas large quantities of rock asphalt and tar which occur in close juxtaposition to igneous intrusions have been ascribed to the effect of the heat of intrusion on deeper seated bituminous shales.[87]

However, Brooks denies vigorously that petroleum could have resulted from cracking temperatures: ". . . The discovery of chlorophyll porphyrins in asphalt and asphaltic petroleums by Treibs . . . is probably the most significant discovery ever made with respect to the origin of petroleum. Its significance is in showing a complete history of temperatures so low as definitely to preclude the formation of petroleum by thermal decomposition of fatty oils or any other known likely raw material." [88]

Natural distillation involves the expulsion through heat of hydrocarbons in gaseous form from the organic matter in the source rock and the condensation of the vapors in nearby or distant rocks. The requisites are organic sediment raised to the critical temperature, and other rocks, against which the vapors come into contact, below the critical temperature. It has been pointed out that the various constituents of an organic rock would break down into hydrocarbons at different temperatures, and so each source rock might have as many as five or six increasingly higher critical temperatures at which vaporization would take place.[89]

The locale for the condensation would depend upon the regional extent of the elevated temperatures. In areas such as the Michigan and the West Texas basins, which are far removed from zones of intense deformation, nearby rocks could be below the critical temperature and cause condensation. Under these circumstances, the distillation process would be practically *in situ*. At the other extreme is the concept of regional distillation which goes back at least as far as

[86] Wallace E. Pratt, "Hydrogenation and the Origin of Oil," *Problems of Petroleum Geology* (Am. Assoc. Petrol. Geol., Tulsa, 1934), p. 235.

[87] Charles Laurence Baker, "Possible Distillation of Oil from Organic Sediments by Heat and Other Processes of Igneous Intrusion; Asphalt in the Anacacho Formation of Texas, *Bull. Am. Assoc. Petrol. Geol.*, Vol. 12 (October, 1928), p. 995.

[88] Benjamin T. Brooks, "The Chemical and Geochemical Aspects of the Origin of Petroleum," *Science of Petroleum* (Oxford Univ. Press, 1938), Vol. 1, p. 47.

[89] K. C. Heald, "Essentials for Oil Pools," *Elements of the Petroleum Industry* (Am. Inst. Min. Met. Engineers, New York, 1940), Chapter IV, p. 41.

1882 [90] but which has received its strongest support from Rich [91] in more recent years. According to the Rich hypothesis, oil is vaporized in areas of intense mountain folding from carbonaceous shales lying beneath overthrust sheets. It is condensed in cooler zones beyond the area of extreme metamorphism; however, oil vaporized in zones of less intense diastrophism would condense practically *in situ*. After the distillation process is complete, the liquid hydrocarbons would undergo extensive secondary migration under the influence of gas pressure and artesian circulation. Examples of domestic oil fields that border zones of intense thermometamorphism cited by Rich include "the belt bordering the Appalachian folds from New York to Oklahoma; the Rocky Mountain district, and California."

Illing raises an objection to the geologic distillation concept: ". . . all destructive distillation at whatever temperature must leave behind a residue or spent. Such a material is readily identifiable and it is unlikely that material of this type would have escaped recognition in all the oil fields which have been investigated." [92] Russell [93] cites physical, chemical, and geologic evidence to support his contention that geologic distillation of petroleum is not possible.

Radioactivity. The possibility that radioactive emanations may have converted organic matter, buried in the rocks of the earth's crust, into petroleum has been investigated by several scientists in recent years, and the American Petroleum Institute has sponsored a research project in this field.[94] The radioactive elements that may be present

[90] Bailey Willis, "Geologic Distillation of Petroleum," *Mining and Metallurgy*, Vol. 10, No. 157 (January, 1920), pp. 1–7.

[91] John L. Rich, "Generation of Oil by Geologic Distillation During Mountain Building," *Bull. Am. Assoc. Petrol. Geol.*, Vol. 11 (November, 1927), pp. 1139–1151.

[92] V. C. Illing, "The Origin of Petroleum," *Science of Petroleum* (Oxford Univ. Press, 1938), Vol. 1, p. 36.

[93] W. L. Russell, "Is Geologic Distillation of Petroleum Possible?" *Bull. Am. Assoc. Petrol. Geol.*, Vol. 13 (January, 1929), pp. 75–84.

[94] Clark Goodman, K. G. Bell, W. L. Whitehead, "The Radioactivity of Sedimentary Rocks and Associated Petroleum," *Econ. Geol.*, Vol. 34 (December, 1939), p. 941; K. G. Bell, Clark Goodman, *et al.*, "Radioactivity of Sedimentary Rocks and Associated Petroleum," *Bull. Am. Assoc. Petrol. Geol.*, Vol. 24 (September, 1940), pp. 1529–1547; W. J. Mead (Director), "Review of Am. Petrol. Institute, Research Project 43C (Studies of the Effect of Radioactivity on the Transformation of Marine Organic Materials into Petroleum Hydrocarbons)," Am. Petrol. Inst., *Fundamental Research on Occurrence and Recovery of Petroleum, 1943* (1944); C. W. Sheppard, "Radioactivity and Petroleum Genesis," *Bull. Am. Assoc. Petrol. Geol.*, Vol. 28 (July, 1944), pp. 924–952; Roland F. Beers, "Radioactivity and Organic Content of Some Paleozoic Shales," *Bull. Am. Assoc. Petrol. Geol.*, Vol. 29 (January, 1945), pp. 1–22; C. W. Sheppard and W. L. Whitehead, "Formation of Hydrocarbons from Fatty Acids by Alpha-Particle Bombardment," *Bull. Am. Assoc. Petrol. Geol.*, Vol. 30 (January, 1946), pp. 32–51.

in sediments in adequate amounts are uranium, thorium, and potassium. Some organic shales have been found to be highly radioactive. The radium content of limestone decreases with increasing purity whereas that of sandstones is highly variable. Some crude oils are radioactive. But it remains to be seen whether these occurrences are genetically related or merely fortuitous.

It has been demonstrated by the physicists that bombardment of organic material, especially fatty acid, by alpha rays will produce hydrocarbons, free hydrogen, and carbon dioxide. From this fact the conclusion has been reached that alpha-ray bombardment of carbonaceous shales is adequate to explain the origin of petroleum. A possible example that has been cited is the radioactive and carbonaceous Antrim shale of Michigan. According to calculations, based upon a number of assumptions and therefore "to be accepted with some caution," this shale could contribute 208 barrels of crude oil per acre-foot in 10 million years.[95]

So far, at least, the arguments opposed to petroleum genesis on a large scale by radioactivity far outweigh the arguments in favor of it. One wonders, for example, why the Devonian Antrim shale has not yielded 200-plus barrels per acre-foot in the last 10 million years. This shale is over 200 feet in thickness and underlies thousands of square miles; not only should the overlying sandstones be full of oil but also Michigan should be exuding oil from every pore. A similar example is the kolm of Sweden, a Cambrian deposit containing 20 per cent volatile organic matter and nearly 0.5 per cent uranium.[96] An extreme case is the occurrence of thucolite, a solid hydrocarbon, in strongly radioactive pegmatite at Parry Sound, Ontario. In neither the Antrim shale, the Swedish kolm, nor the Ontario thucolite is any liquid petroleum present, although at each locality solid organic matter, or hydrocarbon, has been exposed to strong radioactive bombardment for hundreds of millions of years. As a matter of fact, there is no correlation between the degree of radioactivity and the amount of oil. In addition to organic sediments exposed to radioactivity but without oil[97] are oil deposits where there is, and always has been, little or no radioactivity.

[95] C. W. Sheppard and W. L. Whitehead, *op. cit.*

[96] William L. Russell, "Relation of Radioactivity, Organic Content, and Sedimentation," *Bull. Am. Assoc. Petrol. Geol.*, Vol. 29 (October, 1945), p. 1491.

[97] V. C. Illing, "The Origin of Petroleum," *Science of Petroleum* (Oxford Univ. Press, 1938), Vol. 1, pp. 32–38.

Several writers [98] have pointed out the usual absence of free hydrogen and carbon dioxide in petroleum and natural gas and associated sediments, yet radioactive bombardment should produce copious quantities of these substances, as well as hydrocarbons. Knebel wonders "why after the fatty acids are decarboxylated by radioactivity, the same radiations do not further break up the resulting hydrocarbon molecules, with production of hydrogen and unsaturated hydrocarbons." [99]

Geologic Time as a Factor in the Generation of Oil. It has been demonstrated by several investigators that the formation of bitumen from carbonaceous matter is a function of both temperature and time. Laboratory work by Maier and Zimmerly [100] on samples of Green River oil shale in which a bitumen, not analyzed [101] but soluble in carbon tetrachloride, was produced led to the conclusion ". . . that the amount of bitumen that can ultimately be formed does not depend upon the temperature but that the same amount can be obtained provided that the time of heating is sufficiently long." According to calculations, to convert 1 per cent of organic material into bitumen at 100° C. would take 84,000 years; the same conversion at 80° would take 7,000,000 years, and at 60° the time would be 67,000,000 years. Analogous results were obtained by Trask [102] from recent sediments from the Lake Maracaibo floor.

The theory that a moderate increase in temperature will produce the same results in geologic time that a relatively high temperature will accomplish in a few minutes has been likened to the fact, known to all cooks, that a low oven temperature, given time enough, will do just as thorough a job of cooking as a hot oven.[103] But Illing [104] ques-

[98] Benjamin T. Brooks, "The Chemical and Geochemical Aspects of the Origin of Petroleum," *Science of Petroleum* (Oxford Univ. Press, 1938), Vol. 1, p. 47; Ben B. Cox, "Transformation of Organic Material into Petroleum under Geologic Conditions," *Bull. Am. Assoc. Petrol. Geol.*, Vol. 30 (May, 1946), p. 650; William L. Russell, *op. cit.*

[99] G. M. Knebel, "Progress Report on API Research Project 43, The Transformation of Organic Material into Petroleum," *Bull. Am. Assoc. Petrol. Geol.*, Vol. 30 (November, 1946), p. 1946.

[100] C. G. Maier and S. R. Zimmerly, "The Chemical Dynamics of the Transformation of the Organic Matter to Bitumen in Oil Shale," *Bull. Univ. Utah*, Vol. 14 (1924), pp. 62–81.

[101] C. David White, "Exchange of Time for Temperature in Petroleum Generation," *Bull. Am. Assoc. Petrol. Geol.*, Vol. 14 (September, 1930), pp. 1227–1228.

[102] Parker D. Trask, "Time Versus Temperature in Petroleum Generation," *Bull. Am. Assoc. Petrol. Geol.*, Vol. 15 (January, 1931), pp. 83–84.

[103] W. G. Woolnough, "Geological Extrapolation and Pseud-abyssal Sediments," *Bull. Am. Assoc. Petrol. Geol.*, Vol. 26 (May, 1942), p. 769.

[104] V. C. Illing, "The Origin of Petroleum," *Science of Petroleum* (Oxford Univ. Press, 1938), Vol. 1, p. 36.

tions the general conclusion that bitumen formation will take place at low temperatures regardless of the period of time involved. He found that the reaction velocities of a typical cannel coal that he investigated diminished much more rapidly than the calculated rate below 250° C. and approached "virtual stagnation" at about 220° C. Both Illing and Brooks [105] point out that the survival of organic material in oil shales as old as pre-Cambrian is inconsistent with the theory that such matter would be converted into bitumen at moderate temperatures if given sufficient time. Similarly, there is no significant difference between oil shales of Tertiary age and those deposited during the Paleozoic era.[106] It is probable that each type of carbonaceous matter has its critical temperature below which conversion to bitumen is either impossible or too slow for even geologic time.

EVOLUTION AND METAMORPHISM OF PETROLEUM

The transformation of solid organic matter into liquid hydrocarbon, although essential, is but a single chapter in the natural history of a petroleum deposit. The oil that is generated is, as was the mother material, subject to the geological agents and processes at work within the earth's crust. As a result, the oil changes in nature; the degree of its evolution and metamorphism depends upon the intensity and duration of such geological forces as heat and pressure.

There is no doubt that oil in nature's reservoirs does undergo progressive change. Barton [107] and others have pointed out that in the Gulf Coast, for example, the petroleums occurring in sandstone reservoirs of the same age increase in lighter constituents and Baumé gravity, and decrease in heavier constituents, with depth. The lighter constituents are also more abundant in the oils that occur in the older reservoirs where the depths are the same. From these studies it can be concluded that the heavier oils are the more primitive and that "the varying character of the present normal crude oils represents merely different stages in the alteration of the crude oil." [108]

AGENTS OF EVOLUTION AND METAMORPHISM. The principal agents operating on petroleum are heat and pressure. These

105 Benjamin T. Brooks, "Origin of Petroleums, Chemical and Geochemical Aspects," *Bull. Am. Assoc. Petrol. Geol.,* Vol. 20 (March, 1936), p. 280.

106 Alex. W. McCoy and W. Ross Keyte, "Present Interpretations of the Structural Theory for Oil and Gas Migration and Accumulation," *Problems of Petroleum Geology* (Am. Assoc. Petrol. Geol., 1934), p. 269.

107 Donald C. Barton, "Natural History of the Gulf Coast Crude Oil," *Problems of Petroleum Geology* (Am. Assoc. Petrol. Geol., 1934), pp. 109–156.

108 *Op. cit.,* p. 109.

same forces, with the aid of interstitial water, are the agents of rock metamorphism. However, there is a wide difference between the tolerance limits of oil and rock. Pressure and heat of such magnitude as to cause visible rock metamorphism are too intense to permit the continued existence of petroleum within the rock. Only enough temperature and pressure increase to produce incipient [109] metamorphism of rock, measured by the increased fixed-carbon content of associated coals, apparently is necessary to bring about considerable change in the quality and nature of crude oil.

Petroleum in place underground is ordinarily not affected by the pressures to which the enclosing rock is subjected. It occupies the interstices between the grains of the rocks, and the static weight of the overlying rock, or the lateral forces created by diastrophism, are borne by the rock itself and not by the contained fluids. However, the petroleum is subjected to hydrostatic pressures created by the weight of an overlying column of water extending to the water table. In deeply buried rock these are considerable.

Both the oil and the enclosing rock experience the same earth temperatures. The usual cause of heat is the rise of the isogeotherms, levels of equal earth temperature, which takes place as sediments are buried. The average temperature increment with depth is 1° F. for each 60 feet. Obviously, deeply buried oils are heated to temperatures in excess of the sea-level boiling point of water. Other possible causes of heat include diastrophism and magmatic activity. But diastrophism, in order to produce heat, must be of shearing intensity, and magmatic heat is so local in nature that neither of these causes can be considered to be of widespread application in the evolution of oil. There are still other possible sources of heat, such as radioactivity, about which we know very little.

Another possible agent in changing the character of petroleum underground is ground water. Water, especially if sulfurous, may interact chemically with oil. Whether bacteria are active in the deeply buried oil deposits is debatable, but there is no doubt that bacteria work on oil deposits which have been exposed, or nearly so, by erosion.

DISTRIBUTION OF OIL FIELDS AND METAMORPHIC ROCKS. Oil has not been found in commercial amounts in belts of metamorphic rock. It has not even been found where the coal has

[109] M. R. Campbell, "Coal as a Recorder of Incipient Rock Metamorphism," *Econ. Geol.*, Vol. 25 (November, 1930), pp. 675–696.

been altered to anthracite. Thom[110] estimates the chances of finding oil in areas of semi-anthracite and semi-bituminous coals to be of the order of 1 in 1000; the chances for gas, however, are ten times greater.

An exception to the generalization that oil does not occur in metamorphic rocks may be found where porous and permeable metamorphic rocks are in contact with younger source rocks.

Carbon Ratio. Where the metamorphism is invisible but incipient, it can be determined by the carbon ratio of coals. The carbon ratio is the ratio between the fixed carbon and the volatiles. It can be obtained from the proximate analysis; the percentage of fixed carbon, after recalculating on an ash- and moisture-free basis, is the carbon ratio. The carbon ratio of lignite is below 60, bituminous coal ranges from 60 to 85, anthracite from 86 to 98, and graphite, the end point in the metamorphism of coal, has a carbon ratio of 100.

The carbon-ratio concept can be applied in regions, such as the Appalachians and eastern Oklahoma, where both oil and coal occur. The usual procedure is to enter on a map the localities and carbon ratios of coals for which analyses are available. Then isovols[111] or isocarbs, lines through points of equal carbon ratio, are drawn, usually with an interval of 5 per cent. Actually, of course, the lines mark the outcrop of planes of equal carbon ratio; these planes dip toward the area of more intense deformation so that at a given point the fixed-carbon percentage increases with depth.

The isocarbs in the Appalachian province parallel the strike of the rocks and increase in value to the east in the direction of most intense diastrophism. Both here and elsewhere it has been found that there is very little oil above the 65 isocarb and not much gas above the 70 isocarb. Exceptions do occur, but they are infrequent; an outstanding exception was the discovery of a gas field in Rockingham County, Virginia, close to the 85 isocarb.

The nature of the rocks is a factor in the degree of metamorphism. If the sediments are largely unconsolidated, they can be intensely folded without much metamorphism. For example, the Tertiary sediments of California are more highly folded and less metamorphosed than the indurated Paleozoic rocks of western Pennsylvania. Also rocks which yield readily by folding or faulting will be less metamorphosed than more rigid associated rocks. This is an explanation

[110] William Taylor Thom, Jr., "Present Status of Carbon Ratio Theory," *Problems of Petroleum Geology* (Am. Assoc. Petrol. Geol., Tulsa, 1934), pp. 69–95.

[111] C. David White, "Some Relations in Origin Between Coal and Petroleum," *Jour. Wash. Acad. Sci.*, Vol. 5 (1915), pp. 189–212.

for the occurrence of commercial deposits of oil in some localities of apparent high carbon ratio in the Appalachian province; the metamorphism has been less because of the ability of the rocks to yield.[112]

There are conflicting views as to just why there is little or no oil above the 65 per cent fixed-carbon line. One thought is that the metamorphism, even though it may be only incipient in terms of rocks, has destroyed the oil that existed there at one time. This idea is supported ". . . by evidence that oil pools once existed in the region between the present fields and the metamorphosed belt. Oil-impregnated sands crop out at the surface and have been found by drilling, but the oil is only a residue, wrapped around individual sand grains. . . ." [113] The other view is that metamorphism first creates the oil and then, as intensity increases, drives it out of the rocks.[114]

In conclusion, it is obvious that even the early phases of metamorphism are inimical to the survival of hydrocarbons, especially oil. Where coals are available for analysis, the carbon-ratio concept has decided value, although negative in nature, in the search for new oil and gas fields. Deposits may be found in regions lying above the fixed-carbon limits stated, but the chances of such discovery are very much less than they are in areas of lower carbon ratio.

PROCESSES. The processes by which petroleum evolves are as yet largely conjectural. Trask [115] believes that only a small amount of "ancestral petroleum" need be formed as a starter and that the volume would increase greatly by the solution of organic solids such as pigments, waxes, and fatty acids, which the liquid met in its travels. With the solution of this organic matter, the ancestral petroleum would evolve into true petroleum. According to Lind: ". . . we now know processes either thermal or ionic by which progression both up and down the hydrocarbon series is effected, starting from any member in the series." [116] Processes which might produce hydrocarbon evolution or devolution include cracking, distillation, hydrogenation, poly-

[112] K. C. Heald, "Essentials for Oil Pools," *Elements of the Petroleum Industry* (Am. Inst. Min. Met. Engineers, 1940), Chapter 4, p. 43.

[113] K. C. Heald, "Essentials for Oil Pools," *Elements of the Petroleum Industry* (Am. Inst. Min. Met. Engineers, New York, 1940), Chapter 4, p. 42.

[114] John L. Rich, "Problems of the Origin, Migration, and Accumulation of Oil," *Problems of Petroleum Geology* (Am. Assoc. Petrol. Geol., Tulsa, 1934), p. 339 (footnote).

[115] Parker D. Trask, "Inferences about the Origin of Oil as Indicated by the Composition of the Organic Constituents of Sediments," *U.S.G.S., Prof. Paper* 186-H (1937), p. 156.

[116] S. C. Lind, "Some Chemical Aspects of the Origin of Petroleum," *Science,* N.S., Vol. 73 (Jan. 9, 1931), pp. 19–22.

merization, and contamination. Some of these have already been considered as possible processes in the transformation of solid organic matter into liquid petroleum.

Cracking. According to White,[117] the higher pressures and temperatures accompanying each advance of orogenic stress would cause cracking of the oil held in natural storage. Each such cracking would yield hydrocarbons lighter than before; the end product would be gas and possibly solid or semisolid residual carbon. The cracking concept does explain the presence of light oils and gas only in some regions of high carbon ratio. However, in parts of the Rocky Mountain province the quality of the oil does not appear to be related to the degree of tectonic compression.[118] Cracking of petroleum by alpha radiation has also been suggested.[119]

Distillation. If geologic distillation of petroleum from solid organic matter is possible, it is also conceivable that petroleum could be further distilled by increased earth temperatures. Rich [120] explains the disappearance of oil from the high-carbon-ratio rocks as being due to volatilization, with condensation taking place in the cooler zones.

Hydrogenation. Hydrogenation is a refinery process in which hydrogen is added, with the aid of a catalyst, to low-hydrogen hydrocarbons so as to yield higher-hydrogen hydrocarbons. Pratt [121] has been a foremost advocate of petroleum evolution by natural hydrogenation. He believes that a heavy oil and methane are first produced by cracking of the organic muds, followed by "the slow long-continued hydrogenation or methylation of the unsaturated heavy oil in these reservoirs simultaneously with further slow cracking to lighter and lighter oils."

The availability of sufficient hydrogen for large-scale hydrogenation has been questioned. Pratt utilizes associated methane for the source of hydrogen. Others have postulated hydrogen released from the same source rocks, or from deeper rocks, perhaps owing to radioactive

[117] C. David White, "Effects of Geophysical Factors on the Evolution of Oil and Coal," *Jour. Inst. Petrol. Technologists,* Vol. 21 (April, 1935), pp. 308–309.

[118] C. E. Dobbin, "Exceptional Oil Fields in Rocky Mountain Region of the United States," *Bull. Am. Assoc. Petrol. Geol.,* Vol. 31 (May, 1947), p. 797.

[119] K. G. Bell, Clark Goodman, *et al.,* "Radioactivity of Sedimentary Rocks and Associated Petroleum," *Bull. Am. Assoc. Petrol. Geol.,* Vol. 24 (September, 1940), pp. 1529–1547.

[120] John L. Rich, "Problems of the Origin, Migration, and Accumulation of Oil," *Problems of Petroleum Geology* (Am. Assoc. Petrol. Geol., 1934), p. 339.

[121] Wallace E. Pratt, "Hydrogenation and the Origin of Oil," *Problems of Petroleum Geology* (Am. Assoc. Petrol. Geol., Tulsa, 1934), pp. 235–246.

bombardment.[122] It has also been suggested that a series of reactions starting with calcium sulfate and organic matter would yield hydrogen:

(1) $CaSO_4 + \text{Organic matter} = CaCO_3 + H_2S + H_2O + \text{Organic matter}$

(2) $FeCO_3 + H_2S = FeS + H_2CO_3$ [123]

Polymerization. Polymerization is another refinery process, but it has the opposite result from hydrogenation. By polymerization, light hydrocarbons, especially methane, are converted into heavier hydrocarbons (such as gasoline). The process is favored by high pressure. Whether polymerization takes place in nature is questionable.

Contamination. Most of the chemical compounds that make up crude oil are susceptible of reaction with foreign substances. The contaminating material may be (1) minerals in the rocks with which the oil comes in contact during its travels; (2) compounds in solution in circulating waters; and (3) oxygen and other gases in the atmosphere. Exposure, or for that matter a lessening of the reservoir pressure as the surface is approached, would permit escape of dissolved volatile constituents that would leave a heavier residue. Weathering processes and escape of volatiles may have taken place in the geological past below what are now unconformities. Contamination of crude oil by sulfur or oxygen would reverse natural evolution and produce heavy, unsaturated oils.[124] It has been suggested that the low specific gravities of many limestone oils have been due to "the selective absorption of the lighter constituents by the limestone in the reservoir." [125] On the other hand, Brooks [126] believes that clay and other minerals have a catalytic action that is an important factor in the evolution of petroleums; the absence of such catalysts in carbonate reservoirs is the reason given for the presence of heavier (more primitive) oils in such environments.

[122] W. J. Mead (Director), "Review of API Research Project 43C. Studies of the Effect of Radioactivity on the Transformation of Marine Organic Materials into Petroleum Hydrocarbons," *Report of Progress—Fundamental Research on Occurrence and Recovery of Petroleum* (Am. Petrol. Inst., 1949), p. 194.

[123] E. T. Heck, "Hydrogenation of Oil: Suggested Natural Source of Hydrogen," *Bull. Am. Assoc. Petrol. Geol.,* Vol. 24 (August, 1940), p. 1475.

[124] Wallace E. Pratt, *Oil in the Earth* (Univ. of Kansas Press, Lawrence, Kans., 1942), p. 16.

[125] John Emery Adams, "Origin, Migration, and Accumulation of Petroleum in Limestone Reservoirs in the Western United States and Canada," *Problems of Petroleum Geology* (Am. Assoc. Petrol. Geol., 1934), p. 361.

[126] Benjamin T. Brooks, "Active-Surface Catalysts in Formation of Petroleum," *Bull. Am. Assoc. Petrol. Geol.,* Vol. 32 (December, 1948), pp. 2269–2286.

Conclusions. There is no doubt that oil does undergo change while in natural storage. The initial petroleum is probably a semi-liquid asphaltic material[127] which evolves into lighter oil and eventually, if the process is not interrupted, into gas. The Athabaska tar sands may represent an early stage in this evolution. The heavy oil occurs as a film surrounding sand grains. It is too viscous to migrate. The suggestion has been made that a moderate increase in heat would make the oil more liquid, and abrasion during diastrophism would release the oil from the sand grains so that it could migrate into a trap.[128] Contamination and devolatilization will cause a reversal[129] of the usual evolution and may even result in the re-formation of asphalt.

The processes responsible for the devolution of oil are fairly well understood, but we are still uncertain as to the processes that cause hydrocarbon evolution. It is probable that a moderate increase in temperature acting over a long period of time will cause internal molecular rearrangements that will result in an increase in the lighter hydrocarbons. Whether the actual process is cracking, hydrogenation (or methylation), or something else remains to be seen.

The evolution of petroleum that takes place in nature's laboratory has given rise to certain generalizations, which, like all generalizations, are subject to exception. The two most common ones are "the deeper the oil, the lighter the oil" and "the older the oil, the lighter the oil." A third generalization, with considerably less applicability, is "the sharper the fold, the lighter the oil."

ORIGIN OF NATURAL GAS

Much less, proportionately, has been written about the origin of natural gas than about the origin of petroleum. Apparently it has been assumed that petroleum and natural gas have a like origin, but this is not necessarily so.

The term "natural gas" usually implies hydrocarbons in gaseous form. The commonest and most stable of these gaseous hydrocarbons is methane, CH_4. Also present may be other gaseous hydrocarbons including ethane, propane, and butane, and perhaps pentane, hexane,

[127] E. Berl, "The Origin of Petroleum," *Petroleum Development and Technology* (Am. Inst. Min. Met. Engineers, Petroleum Div., Trans., Vol. 127, New York, 1938), p. 106.

[128] Max. W. Ball, "Steps in the Formation of an Oil Field," *Am. Assoc. Petrol. Geol., Program 25th Annual Meeting* (1940), p. 28.

[129] G. M. Knebel, "Progress Report on A.P.I. Research Project 43," *Bull. Am. Assoc. Petrol. Geol.,* Vol. 30 (November, 1946), p. 1947.

and heptane as vapors. In addition, certain non-hydrocarbon gases either may be present with the hydrocarbon gases or may occur in separate accumulations. Among these erratic constituents are hydrogen sulfide, carbon dioxide, nitrogen, and helium. Their origin will be discussed subsequently.

Natural gas may occur in five different environments: (1) dissolved in petroleum; (2) with the oil but overlying it ("gas cap"); (3) in the same trapping structure as oil but occupying different (usually higher) reservoir beds; (4) in oil-producing districts but occupying separate traps; and (5) in accumulations remote from known oil deposits. History has shown that many gas fields which originally fell in the fifth category have been found, upon further exploration, to belong in either the third or fourth. A number of large gas fields, especially in northern Louisiana, southwestern Kansas, southwestern Wyoming, and eastern Montana, are some distance removed from the nearest known oil. Many geologists believe that it is just a matter of time before large oil deposits are found either beneath or in the vicinity of these gas accumulations.

There are two general theories concerning the origin of natural gas: (1) the gas has separate genesis from oil and may never have been associated with liquid petroleum; (2) gas is a by-product, or an end product, of the origin and evolution of petroleum and was at one time in liquid phase.

NATURAL GAS WITH SEPARATE GENESIS FROM PETROLEUM. There is no doubt that some gas has formed directly from putrefying organic matter without passing through a liquid hydrocarbon phase. The so-called "marsh gas," which is generated during the decay of vegetal matter in bogs and swamps, is a well-known example of this. Bacteria aid in the generation of marsh gas, which is nearly pure methane. A similar gas may be produced by decaying animal matter. Methane from clay or mud that contains an abundance of clams has been reported from at least two places; in one of them, the gas is present in sufficient volume to permit its local use in gas ranges.[130]

Another well-known occurrence of methane gas not connected in any way with the formation of petroleum is the coal gas which is generated from the fresh-water plant remains composing the coals and which accumulates both in the coal seam and in any overlying porous rocks that may be present. It has been suggested (1) that oil

[130] F. M. Van Tuyl and Ben H. Parker, "The Time of Origin and Accumulation of Petroleum," *Quarterly Colo. School of Mines*, Vol. 36 (April, 1941), p. 49.

is derived from organic matter accumulating under marine conditions but that gas comes from land plants, and (2) that oil is generated from source beds which carry a "rich microflora" and that gas is derived in large part from coarse vegetal matter.[131] Price and Headlee [132] in a study of the natural gas in the Appalachian province, found that near-surface and coal gases are high in methane, whereas the deeper gases occurring in the Appalachian oil measures have less methane and more of the other hydrocarbon gases. They conclude that the gas in both places was generated from decaying vegetal matter, but that the deeper gases have interacted with the residual solid organic matter to produce not only the other hydrocarbon gases present but also the liquid hydrocarbons occurring in the associated oil fields.

Methane can also occur through inorganic processes. It has been detected in the gases given off by volcanoes. Baker [133] suggests that methane and other hydrocarbon gases may be produced by contact metamorphism through the combination of carbon from carbonaceous rocks with dissociated water vapor caused by the intrusion of molten rocks.

NATURAL GAS DERIVED FROM PETROLEUM. According to the commonly held concept of the evolution of petroleum, methane is the end product in that chain, and the other hydrocarbon gases lie close to the end. As oil increases in age or in depth of burial or in degree of diastrophism of the enclosing rocks, it changes, with some exceptions, from asphalt to lighter and lighter hydrocarbons, including gaseous hydrocarbons. Perhaps the best example of the application of this theory is the presence of natural gas in considerable abundance in the Appalachian province beyond (to the east of) the "extinction zone," where the carbon ratios run above 65 and the oil fields tend to disappear.[134]

The best testimony, however, for the generation of gas during the natural evolution of petroleum is the almost invariable association of

[131] Paul D. Torrey, "Origin, Migration, and Accumulation of Petroleum and Natural Gas in Pennsylvania," *Problems of Petroleum Geology* (Am. Assoc. Petrol. Geol., 1934), pp. 447–484.

[132] Paul H. Price and A. J. W. Headlee, "Geochemistry of Natural Gas in Appalachian Province," *Bull. Am. Assoc. Petrol. Geol.,* Vol. 26 (January, 1942), pp. 19–35.

[133] Charles Laurence Baker, "Possible Distillation of Oil from Organic Sediments by Heat and Other Processes of Igneous Intrusions; Asphalt in the Anacacho Formation of Texas," *Bull. Am. Assoc. Petrol. Geol.,* Vol. 12 (October, 1928), pp. 995–1003.

[134] C. David White, "Effects of Geophysical Factors on the Evolution of Oil and Coal," *Jour. Inst. Petrol. Technologists,* Vol. 21 (April, 1935), pp. 301–310.

the two together in nature, as outlined in the introduction to this section. Most natural gas occurs either within oil, in the gas cap of an oil deposit, or in a nearby reservoir. Natural gas has considerably greater mobility than oil, and once it has separated from the oil, it may travel through paths which the oil cannot follow and thus accumulate in separated reservoirs. In all probability, the "mother lode" of each currently isolated gas field will some day be discovered. Because of the general wider spread of gas deposits, the discovery of gas has preceded that of oil in most areas in the past.

The direct generation of gas from decaying organic material is not and cannot be denied; it is doubtful, however, that the major accumulations of natural gas have had this origin.

Origin of the Non-Hydrocarbon Natural Gases.[135] Hydrogen sulfide is the only one of the four "erratic" gases considered here that commonly occurs with and has distribution approaching that of petroleum and hydrocarbon gas. At the same time, it is the only non-hydrocarbon gas which may come from the same original source materials as methane gas. Hydrogen sulfide and other sulfur compounds are produced by the decay of organisms under reducing (euxinic) conditions. This sulfur may become "fixed" as FeS_2 (marcasite or pyrite); it may escape in gaseous form or dissolved in water; or it may become trapped with the hydrocarbon-yielding material, to reappear later in natural gas or in high-sulfur crude oil.

Carbon dioxide occurs in a few instances with petroleum and hydrocarbon gas, but this association is probably fortuitous. Most of the known carbon dioxide accumulations, including all the large ones, are in localities which are not (as yet at least) productive of hydrocarbons. Carbon dioxide has been found in volcanic gases and in fumaroles; the calcination of limestone by intrusive magmas should also yield this compound. Generation by bacterial action and release from limestones undergoing ground-water solution are among other possible origins that have been suggested for this gas. There is no general agreement as to which, if any, of these sources has been responsible for the large deposits found in some of the western states.

Helium and nitrogen are usually, but not necessarily, together. Helium is much less abundant than nitrogen, but because of its value, it has received far more attention in the technical publications. Its presence is also easier to explain. Helium is a product of radio-

[135] C. E. Dobbin, "Geology of Natural Gases Rich in Helium, Nitrogen, Carbon Dioxide, and Hydrogen Sulphide," *Geology of Natural Gas* (Am. Assoc. Petrol. Geol., 1935), pp. 1053–1072.

active disintegration; during geologic time, a considerable volume of this gas, which could become trapped in the overlying sediments, might be released from radioactive minerals in the pre-Cambrian crystalline rocks. In this regard it is interesting to note that a pegmatite deposit famous for its radioactive minerals lies at the surface of the stripped pre-Cambrian in the Central Mineral Region of Texas, a few hundred miles southeast of the Cliffside structure in the Panhandle, where Permian reservoirs overlying the buried pre-Cambrian Amarillo Mountains contain the largest known helium deposit. Again it is probably coincidental that some helium occurs with hydrocarbon natural gas; both types of gas merely happened to get caught in the same trap.

The source of the nitrogen is the greatest mystery of all. It is probable that, like the helium, it came from the crystalline basement rocks, but the only explanation that comes to mind for its occurrence there is that it is residual magmatic gas. Nitrogen has been detected escaping from a number of metal mines, in some places in lethal (because of its non-respiratory characteristics) quantities.[136] Ruedemann and Oles [137] have suggested that the nitrogen may be residual from air trapped in the strata at the time of deposition. However, there is a question whether air could be trapped in adequate volume in sediment accumulating beneath water.

PROBABLE SOURCE BEDS IN OIL FIELDS

Many students of individual oil fields have attempted to designate the source rock or rocks that provided the oil. In almost no instances, however, has it been possible to prove definitely that the oil actually came from a certain rock unit. Perhaps the best case for positive identification of the source rock is in the "shoestring" sand pools of southeastern Kansas and northeastern Oklahoma, where the oil-filled sand lenses are completely surrounded by the highly carbonaceous Cherokee shale,[138] but even the designation of this shale as the source rock for the oil in the sandstones has been questioned.[139]

[136] C. E. Dobbin, *op. cit.,* p. 1061.

[137] Paul Ruedemann and L. M. Oles, "Helium—Its Probable Origin and Concentration in the Amarillo Field, Texas," *Bull. Am. Assoc. Petrol. Geol.,* Vol. 13 (July, 1929), pp. 799–810.

[138] L. N. Neumann, N. W. Bass, R. L. Ginter, S. F. Mauney, Charles Ryniker, and H. M. Smith, "Relationship of Crude Oils and Stratigraphy in Parts of Oklahoma and Kansas," *Bull. Am. Assoc. Petrol. Geol.,* Vol. 25 (September, 1944), pp. 1801–1809.

[139] J. L. Rich, "Function of Carrier Beds in Long-Distance Migration of Oil," *Bull. Am. Assoc. Petrol. Geol.,* Vol. 15 (August, 1931), pp. 911–924.

It is not sufficient to find an organic rock in the same section with oil reservoir rocks. Some organic rocks may not have yielded a drop of oil, whereas others may have yielded much oil. The actual source rocks may, as a matter of fact, have less organic content at the present time than other carbonaceous rocks in the section. Since it is unlikely, however, that all the possible oil was generated during the oil-forming period, the source rock should have some carbonaceous matter left.

Attempts to identify the source rock are more than mere academic exercises. When and if it becomes possible to determine, with some certainty, the source rock in an oil field, the lateral changes in the characteristics of that source rock become of utmost importance in oil-finding.

IDENTIFICATION OF SOURCE ROCKS. Many geologists have stated their belief that a certain rock unit was the source of oil in a given oil field, usually basing this conclusion only upon propinquity of an organic rock to the reservoir rock and upon the difficulties of migration from a more distant source.[140] Unfortunately, source rocks contain no obvious clues by which they can be recognized. Although they may have yielded thousands of barrels of oil to the reservoir rocks, they contain today not one recognizable drop. From this, Hoots [141] logically concludes "that the process of oil generation and migration from the shale is now essentially complete."

A few have tried to establish criteria for the identification of source rocks. Heald, for example, believes that the source rock must be between the reservoir rock and the nearest overlying and underlying aquifers: "If, in an area of hundreds to thousands of square miles, some particular permeable formation contains oil where 'traps' or 'structures' exist, and other permeable formations above and below the oil-yielding one commonly contain water and no oil, it follows that the oil must originate in the rocks between the water-bearing formations and the oil-bearing formation. It seems probable that the oil originates either in the formation immediately below the permeable oil-yielding stratum or in the lower part of the formation immediately overlying the oil-yielding stratum." [142] Hedberg, Sass, and Funkhouser [143] believe that the shales immediately above and below each

140 F. M. Van Tuyl and Ben H. Parker, "The Time of Origin and Accumulation of Petroleum," *Quarterly Colo. School of Mines,* Vol. 36 (April, 1941), pp. 13–29.

141 Harold W. Hoots, "Origin, Migration, and Accumulation of Oil in California," *Calif. Div. Mines, Bull.* 118 (August, 1941), p. 260.

142 K. C. Heald, "Essentials for Oil Pools," *Elements of the Petroleum Industry* (Am. Inst. Min. Met. Engineers, New York, 1940), Chapter IV, p. 26.

143 H. D. Hedberg, L. C. Sass, and H. J. Funkhouser, "Oil Fields of Greater Oficina Area, Central Anzoategui, Venezuela," *Bull. Am. Assoc. Petrol. Geol.,* Vol. 31 (December, 1947), p. 2137.

of the productive sands in the Greater Oficina area of Venezuela were the source rocks. They point out that these shales are gray, owing to the presence of finely divided carbonaceous matter, whereas the overlying Freites shales, which are associated with barren sands, are green and lack carbonaceous matter.

The organic composition, especially the amount of microscopic algae present, was considered by Charles David White [144] in identifying probable source rocks. Algae-rich rocks were considered to be source beds, whereas rocks of equal or even greater vegetal content, if the plant material belonged to the higher orders (mainly terrestrial types), were rejected as possible source rocks. In his first investigation, Trask analyzed some suspected source rocks along with the recent marine sediments. He found that two suspected source rocks, the Monterey of California and the Eagle Ford of Texas, are richer than the best marine deposits. On the other hand, some suspected source beds yielded no oil by distillation.[145] In a later investigation Trask and Patnode [146] worked specifically on characteristics of the sediments that might be used as criteria for recognizing source rocks. Four of the eight characteristics—the volatility, the relative volatility, the carbon-nitrogen ratio, and the nitrogen-reduction ratio—gave some promise, especially the nitrogen-reduction ratio. This is simply the ratio of the nitrogen content to the reducing power. Source beds are probably those of relatively low oxygen content, which would be reflected by a low nitrogen-reduction ratio. Trask and Patnode found that the sediments immediately adjacent to reservoir rocks had a lower nitrogen-reduction ratio, as a general rule, than those farther removed. The conclusion to be drawn from this work is that the source rocks tend to occur close by the reservoir rocks (or vice versa).

Snider [147] made an extensive survey of the literature published on oil fields and submitted a list of conclusions. He believes that source beds are usually close to the oil reservoir rocks. The quantity of the organic material in source beds is highly variable. A prolific pool may be due to the presence of rich source material in a restricted area

[144] C. David White, "Geology and Occurrences of Petroleum in the United States," *Petroleum Investigation Part II* (U. S. 73rd Congress H.R. Committee on Interstate and Foreign Commerce Hearings before a Subcommittee on H.R. 441), 1934, p. 899.

[145] Parker D. Trask, *et al., Origin and Environment of Source Sediments of Petroleum* (Gulf Publishing Co., Houston, Texas, 1932), p. 219.

[146] Parker D. Trask and H. Whitman Patnode, *Source Beds of Petroleum* (Am. Assoc. Petrol. Geol., Tulsa, Okla., 1942).

[147] L. C. Snider, "Current Ideas Regarding Source Beds for Petroleum," *Problems of Petroleum Geology* (Am. Assoc. Petrol. Geol., Tulsa, 1934), pp. 51–66.

or to the gathering of oil from leaner source rock over a much wider area. In Snider's opinion, the number one source rock is shale, usually, but not necessarily, dark gray, chocolate brown, blue, or black. However, other colors, especially red, may mask the dark coloration that denotes organic material. Limestones and sandstones may be source as well as reservoir rocks.

POSSIBLE FRESH-WATER SOURCE ROCKS. The traditional view that source materials must be deposited in marine environment was given earlier in this chapter. Recently, however, oil has been discovered in occurrences difficult to explain by migration from marine source rocks. In the Rocky Mountain province, oil and gas have been found in non-faulted, non-marine, Tertiary strata in both the Powder Wash [148] and the East Hiawatha [149] fields. A field in Shensi province in China has been described [150] in which both the reservoirs and the probable source rocks occur in a thick series of early Mesozoic continental rocks. Several recently discovered California fields are also producing from continental rocks, and the probable source rocks have similar origin. Noble [151] classifies the current belief that oil cannot come from a fresh-water source as one of the "prejudices" restricting the discovery of new oil fields.

GEOLOGIC AGE OF ALLEGED SOURCE ROCKS. No doubt potential source rocks were deposited somewhere during every geological period. As would be expected, the periods of greatest marine submergence contain the largest number of possible source rocks. Periods of benign climates with most luxuriant plant growths also have an unusual number of possible source rocks.

The better known of the alleged source rocks are organic shales of wide areal distribution. Among the most famous of these are the Utica and other Ordovician shales, the widespread Chattanooga shale, which is of Devonian-Mississippian age, the Cherokee shale of the Mid-Continent Pennsylvanian, the Eagle Ford shale of Texas, and the Monterey shale of the California oil fields.

148 W. T. Nightingale, "Petroleum and Natural Gas in Non-Marine Sediments of Powder Wash Field in Northwest Colorado," *Bull. Am. Assoc. Petrol. Geol.*, Vol. 22 (August, 1938), pp. 1020–1047.

149 C. E. Dobbin, "Exceptional Oil Fields in Rocky Mountain Region of United States," *Bull. Am. Assoc. Petrol. Geol.*, Vol. 31 (May, 1947), pp. 797–823.

150 C. H. Pan, "Non-Marine Origin of Petroleum in North Shensi, and the Cretaceous of Szechuen, China," *Bull. Am. Assoc. Petrol. Geol.*, Vol. 25 (November, 1941), pp. 2058–2068.

151 Earl B. Noble, "Geological Masks and Prejudices," *Bull. Am. Assoc. Petrol. Geol.*, Vol. 31 (July, 1947), pp. 1109–1117.

RELATIONSHIP BETWEEN PRESENCE OF POSSIBLE SOURCE BEDS AND DISTRIBUTION OF OIL FIELDS. The importance to be attached to the presence or absence of possible source beds in an area undergoing exploration depends to a considerable extent upon the distance through which one will concede that oil can migrate, a subject to be discussed in the following section. Those who believe that oil can migrate no great distance consider the nature and abundance of source material of utmost importance.[152]

The erratic distribution of oil can be most easily explained by variations in the amount of source material locally available. Heald [153] cites a number of examples of empty or near empty traps in the immediate vicinity of traps filled with oil. In the Conroe, Texas, field the trap is full of oil and gas, but near by are two equally good traps that contain but little oil in comparison to Conroe. The north flank of the regional anticline that overlies the Amarillo Mountains and crosses the Texas Panhandle from east to west is full of oil and gas. The south flank is empty; yet the geological conditions are the same on both sides. Similar relationships between full traps and empty traps exist in the Great Valley of California. Quoting Heald: "The absence of source must be responsible for the failure to discover oil in extensive areas where all other conditions exist." Also, "Recognition that source conditions are variable may justify the search for oil pools in areas where the other requisites are believed to be mediocre or poor, for if a great deal of oil has been formed it will accumulate if given any encouragement."

[152] Frank R. Clark, "Origin and Accumulation of Oil," *Problems of Petroleum Geology* (Am. Assoc. Petrol. Geol., Tulsa, 1934), p. 334.

[153] K. C. Heald, "Essentials for Oil Pools," *Elements of the Petroleum Industry* (Am. Inst. Min. and Met. Eng., 1940), Chapter IV, pp. 27–28.

Chapter 6

MIGRATION OF OIL AND GAS[1]

Because oil and gas ordinarily do not occur in commercial deposits in the same rocks in which they probably originated, *migration* of these hydrocarbons from source rock to reservoir rock is postulated. In addition, most students of petroleum geology subscribe to the belief that further migration can and does take place through the reservoir rock until the hydrocarbons either escape or are caught in some type of natural trap. Therefore migration is a probable chapter in the history of an oil or gas deposit, falling between generation and accumulation.

Owing to the extreme mobility of natural gas, there is little, if any, dissent to the concept of its migration. Gas under pressure will move through all but the tightest rocks in the direction of lesser pressure; usually, but not necessarily, this direction is upward. There is less agreement on the migratory habits of petroleum, and therefore most of the discussion that follows is concerned with the liquid hydrocarbons.

DOES OIL MIGRATE? Some years ago it was fashionable to attempt to solve the question of oil migration by means of laboratory experiments. Many of these used dry sand. Since the work of Schilthuis[2] on the presence of interstitial ("connate") water in oil and gas reservoir rocks, we have learned that such experiments are valueless. Even if water-wet sand is used the laboratory experimentation tends

[1] F. M. Van Tuyl, Ben H. Parker, and W. W. Skeeters, "The Migration and Accumulation of Petroleum and Natural Gas," *Quarterly Colo. School of Mines,* Vol. 40 (January, 1945), 111 pp. (112 titles in bibliography); William B. Heroy, "Petroleum Geology," *Geol. Soc. Am., 50th Anniversary Vol.* (1941), pp. 512–548; V. C. Illing, "The Migration of Oil," *Science of Petroleum* (Oxford Univ. Press, 1938), Vol. 1, pp. 209–215; James Frost, "Oil Migration," *Jour. Inst. Petrol. Technologists,* Vol. 31 (December, 1945), pp. 486–493.

[2] R. J. Schilthuis, "Connate Water in Oil and Gas Sands," *Transactions Am. Inst. Min. Met. Engineers,* Vol. 127 (1938), pp. 199–214.

to be inadequate because of the impossibility of duplicating natural conditions. The containers used are relatively small; the crude oil used has changed considerably from its original nature, owing to the escape of volatiles, especially methane, and to the action of sunlight and other agents; the time involved is not comparable; and most experiments have been carried on at atmospheric pressure and room temperature, which are quite different from those existing in the natural environment. As stated in Chapter 4, oil underground has mobility approaching that of water because of the presence of gas in solution and because of the higher temperatures that exist beneath the surface. A better approach to the problem of oil migration is to make a critical study of the natural occurrences of petroleum.

Evidence Opposed to Oil Migration. Actually no one is so extreme as to believe that each drop of oil in the reservoir rock is the relic of an organism that once occupied that exact spot. The disagreement is one of *degree* of migration; the opponents of migration believe that the oil came from the enclosing and immediately surrounding rocks so that it did not move any great distance.

Perhaps the best argument for relatively slight migration is the occurrence of oil in lenticular sand bodies completely surrounded by dense shale. As in every other instance, the origin of the oil in the sand is not known, but it probably was squeezed out of the enclosing shale during compaction. That it came from a more distant source is most unlikely. Another argument opposing migration, at least across stratification planes, is the presence in different superimposed reservoirs in a single field of different types of petroleum, showing that there has been no intermingling of crude oils. This is a general, but by no means universal, rule; exceptions that tend to prove migration will be cited subsequently. Additional arguments, advanced by Clark,[3] are that if oil accumulates by migration from far-flung source materials, then (1) every trap should contain oil, and (2) the water-filled reservoir rock below oil pools should contain traces of the oil that once passed through. However, there are other explanations for barren traps, and furthermore it is questionable that oil passing through a wet sand would leave any trace.

Evidence in Support of Oil Migration. Oil underground is a fluid with considerable mobility. To deny categorically that it can migrate, or that it can migrate through any great distance, is also to deny that underground water has migratory possibilities. Under the influence of

[3] Frank R. Clark, "Origin and Accumulation of Oil," *Problems of Petroleum Geology* (Am. Assoc. Petrol. Geol., 1934), pp. 309–335.

a pressure differential of considerable magnitude brought about by poking a well into a reservoir, the oil migrates with rapidity from surrounding rock into the bore hole. In the Oklahoma City field, a single 80-acre tract produced 2020 barrels per acre-foot, whereas the original oil content was at the most 1200 barrels per acre-foot as calculated by Brauchli.[4] The logical conclusion is that this surplus oil migrated during exploitation from an undrilled area one-half mile northwest.

But reasoning that oil can migrate is not in itself proof that it has migrated. Following are some points of evidence that oil has migrated in the geological past:

1. *The presence of oil seeps.* The mere existence of an oil seep is evidence of the natural movement of oil today. The petroleum that emerges at the surface has migrated from a buried reservoir.

2. *Accumulations in inorganic rocks.* Most commercial petroleum deposits occur in rocks that in all probability never contained the source organisms whence the oil came. Therefore the oil must have migrated from source to reservoir. The most common oil reservoir, sandstone, is deposited under strand-line conditions that are inimical to the growth and preservation of organisms. Carbonate rocks, second only to sandstone in importance as oil reservoirs, may be organic in origin, but in most cases, at least, it is very unlikely that the oil is indigenous. Much carbonate rock porosity (Chapter 7) is the result of solution-leaching, which does not take place until after lithifaction and emergence; it is difficult to picture indigenous oil waiting around until leaching has produced cavities. Even where the cavities are primary, as is common in a reef, the oil may have migrated into the porous zone from without.

For various reasons, the presence of oil in non-marine rocks has been cited as evidence of migration. McDermott[5] believes that chlorine in sea water is essential to the formation of oil. Hoots[6] notes several fields in California which produce from the up-dip non-marine and organically barren facies of formations that may be marine basinward. Here, however, migration is assumed because of the inorganic characteristics of the reservoir rock and not merely because

[4] R. W. Brauchli, "Migration of Oil in Oklahoma City Field," *Bull. Am. Assoc. Petrol. Geol.*, Vol. 19 (May, 1935), pp. 699–701.

[5] Eugene McDermott, "Concentrations of Hydrocarbons in the Earth," *Geophysics*, Vol. 4 (July, 1939), pp. 195–209.

[6] Harold W. Hoots, "Origin, Migration, and Accumulation of Oil in California," *Calif. Div. Mines, Bull.* 118 (August, 1941), pp. 261–262.

it is continental in origin. Noble[7] has pointed out the danger of ignoring continental deposits as sources of hydrocarbons simply because they were laid down in fresh water.

A strong argument for migration into reservoirs exists where oil deposits occur in intrusive and crystalline basement rocks. It is impossible to conceive of such oil as being indigenous. A similar situation exists where oil has accumulated in the porous tops of buried hills and ridges. This oil, like that in the crystalline rocks, must have migrated into place after the porosity had been developed, which was considerably later than the formation of the rock itself.

3. *Chemically similar oils in a series of superimposed reservoirs.* Although the general rule is to the contrary, there are examples of migration of oil from reservoir to reservoir in a multiple-zone field. At Garber, Oklahoma, the same type of oil has been obtained in 14 distinct reservoirs, lying one above the other and ranging in age from Ordovician to Permian. Obviously trans-formational channelways have permitted migration between reservoirs at Garber. At Oklahoma City the oils in Ordovician reservoirs are alike, but the opportunities for transverse migration do not extend upward across the unconformity into the Pennsylvanian rocks, for there the oil is different. Other examples of migration between reservoirs could be cited, but they are much less common than examples of no migration between superimposed reservoirs.

4. *Structural adjustment of hydrocarbons in a reservoir.* The crust of the earth is constantly yielding to diastrophic forces which fold and tilt the rock strata, and yet, regardless of the lateness of such activity, the gas, oil, and water are almost always in adjustment with the structure. Regional tilting will change markedly the contour pattern of a dome, but not only the highly mobile gas of a gas cap but also the oil and underlying water migrate relatively quickly into the new positions called for by the structural change. In the great oil districts in the San Joaquin Valley and in the Los Angeles Basin in California, no traps with adequate sedimentary section have been found barren as yet, in spite of their extreme youth.[8]

5. *Quantitative considerations.* Probably the strongest argument for large-scale migration is the presence of oil in such enormous quantities in fields like those of the salt domes of the Gulf Coast, East

[7] Earl Noble, "Geological Masks and Prejudices," *Bull. Am. Assoc. Petrol. Geol.*, Vol. 31 (July, 1947), pp. 1109–1117.

[8] Harold W. Hoots, *op. cit.*

Texas, and Leduc, Alberta, that it is quantitatively inconceivable that a local, or even near local, accumulation of organic debris would have been great enough to yield all the oil.

The conclusion would seem to be that even though migration of oil may have been minor in some fields, such as the "shoestring sand" pools, still, in the great majority of fields, large-scale migration is not only possible but also probable.

CAUSES OF MOVEMENT OF OIL.[9] The first migration that oil experiences after generation is from fine-grained source rock into porous and permeable reservoir rock. Except where the reservoir rock is an isolated lens, the primary migration is followed by a secondary migration through the reservoir rock until the oil either escapes or is trapped. The same forces operate in both primary and secondary migration, but their relative importance differs greatly. To a considerable extent, these forces are also responsible for reservoir pressures, which were discussed in Chapter 3.

Compaction[10] is the outstanding cause for the expulsion of oil from the source rock. Initially, the source rock is a clay, mud, or calcareous ooze with porosity as high as 90 per cent. As it is squeezed by the weight of overlying sediment, or by lateral pressures accompanying diastrophism, the fine-grained material is compacted, with a reduction in porosity down to 35 per cent or less. Obviously the fluids occupying the pore space that is obliterated by the compaction will be driven out. They will move in the direction of least resistance into non-compacting porous formations such as sandstones and permeable limestones. Water is always the more abundant fluid, but if any oil is present in the interstices between the water-wet grains of the source rock, its expulsion during compaction will be virtually complete, whereas some of the water will be left behind in the diminished pore space. This may explain why oil is not found in suspected source rocks.

[9] E. DeGolyer and Harold Vance, "Bibliography of the Petroleum Industry," *Bull. A. and M. Coll. Texas,* 83 (1944), pp. 343–345 (57 titles).

[10] Hollis D. Hedberg, "Gravitational Compaction of Clays and Shales," *Am. Jour. Sci.,* 5th Ser., Vol. 31 (April, 1936), pp. 241–287; L. F. Athy, "Density, Porosity and Compaction of Sedimentary Rocks" and "Compaction and Oil Migration," *Bull. Am. Assoc. Petrol. Geol.,* Vol. 14 (January, 1930), pp. 1–36; R. C. Beckstrom and F. M. Van Tuyl, "Compaction as a Cause of the Migration of Petroleum," *Bull. Am. Assoc. Petrol. Geol.,* Vol. 12 (November, 1928), pp. 1049–1055; H. D. Hedberg, L. C. Sass, and H. J. Funkhouser, "Oil Fields of Greater Oficina Area, Central Anzoategui, Venezuela," *Bull. Am. Assoc. Petrol. Geol.,* Vol. 31 (December, 1947), p. 2137 and footnote, p. 2138.

Even sandstones are not completely incompressible, and the compaction of such a rock may be a contributing force to the migration of oil through sandstone reservoirs.[11]

Although there have been many attempts to minimize and even deny[12] its importance, *gravity* (sometimes called "buoyancy" or "flotation") remains the primary cause for movement of oil through reservoir rocks. The fluids in readily permeable rocks obey the law of gravity; both water and oil move down as far as possible, but of the two oil is the lighter, and so, when it is present, it overlies the water. When oil is injected into a water-filled reservoir (by expulsion from a compacting source rock), it rises to the top of the water. If the reservoir is an inclined stratum overlain by a relatively impervious cap rock, the oil first rises vertically to the roof and then up the incline to the highest point on the water column. This may be the water table, in which event the oil can escape by seepage, volatilization, or other means, or it may be a trap (Chapter 8), such as an anticline, unconformity, or fault plane, which will permit the oil to accumulate.

Because of its early application to oil-finding, the gravity theory was first called the "anticlinal" theory. However, since gravity explains the presence and position of oil in all other types of traps as well, the more restrictive term has been dropped.

Every oil pool is evidence of migration caused by the action of gravity. Almost invariably (1) the oil is underlain by water or is in contact with water at the down-dip edge, and (2) the oil occupies the highest point beneath an impervious roof or beneath a cap of still lighter natural gas. Even if other means are advanced to move the oil great distances through the reservoir rock, it is necessary to use gravity for the final arrangement of gas, oil, and water.

One of the reasons for the search for substitute theories has been the failure of many experiments to verify gravity as a sufficient migration force. But these experiments themselves were inadequate, as has been pointed out. There is, however, a lower limit in pore dimension below which the forces that tend to impede oil movement are greater than the gravitative force that causes oil to rise through water to the top. There is also a minimum pore size which limits the permeability of a rock to the gravitative flow of water. The usual source rock is so fine of grain that gravity cannot operate for either oil or

11 David Donoghue, "Elasticity of Reservoir Rocks and Fluids with Special Reference to East Texas Oil Field," *Bull. Am. Assoc. of Petrol. Geol.*, Vol. 28 (July, 1944), pp. 1032–1035.

12 F. B. Plummer, "Migration of Oil and Origin of Oil Pools," *Oil and Gas Jour.*, Vol. 43 (Oct. 21, 1944), pp. 139–140.

water movement; compaction pressures are necessary to move fluids from such rocks, and water-oil stratification within the rock is impossible. On the other hand, reservoir rocks are, by definition, rocks of permeability, as well as porosity, and both fluid movement and gravitative adjustment are possible within.

The usual substitute suggested for the gravity theory is the hydraulic[13] theory. According to this view, the cause of migration is the flow of underground water which carries the hydrocarbons along with it; accumulation is brought about by the gravitative stratification of water and the hydrocarbons when a trap is reached. A corollary to the hydraulic theory is the concept of the "flushing" of oil from traps, especially near the rim of artesian basins, by the force of moving ground water. This idea has been used by several writers to explain barren traps in the Rocky Mountain province, where artesian basins are plentiful.

To many, however, both the hydraulic theory and its corollary are unsatisfactory unless one is willing to concede a velocity to the groundwater circulation in excess of the speed of upward (vertical or up-dip) movement of oil through water. If the circulating ground water travels more slowly, the hydrocarbons will move ahead of it into the trap, and, once in the trap, the water could not dislodge ("flush") it. The movement of underground water, even with ideal artesian conditions, is very slow, of the order of magnitude of a foot or two a day. The movement of oil through water in the reservoir rock is probably faster than this. However, it is conceivable that oil migration could be aided or hindered, depending upon the direction of flow, by the movement of underground water.

A frequently listed cause of oil migration is *capillarity,* but it also has been pointed out that this force may serve more to retard than to promote oil movement through rock.[14] Capillarity may assist in expelling oil from source rocks, but this force cannot be considered to be of major importance. The confinement of oil to the coarser zones in thick sandstones is probably due to the fact that the envelopes

[13] Malcolm J. Munn, "Studies in the Application of the Anticlinal Theory of Oil and Gas Accumulation," *Econ. Geol.,* Vol. 4 (1909), pp. 141–157; John L. Rich, "Problems of the Origin, Migration, and Accumulation of Oil," *Problems of Petroleum Geology* (Am. Assoc. Petrol. Geol., 1934), pp. 337–345, "Moving Underground Water as a Primary Cause of the Migration and Accumulation of Oil and Gas," *Econ. Geol.,* Vol. 16 (September–October, 1921), pp. 347–371, "Further Notes on the Hydraulic Theory of Oil Migration and Accumulation," *Bull. Am. Assoc. Petrol. Geol.,* Vol. 7 (May–June, 1923), pp. 213–225.

[14] R. Van A. Mills, "Experimental Studies of Subsurface Relationships in Oil and Gas Fields," *Econ. Geol.,* Vol. 15 (July–August, 1920), pp. 398–421.

of "connate" water surrounding the grains of finer sediment impinge upon each other to such an extent that oil simply cannot enter rocks of this type, rather than to differential capillarity between oil and water as was once thought.[15]

Miscellaneous possible causes for oil migration include the expansion of associated water, gas streaming ("effervescence") upon release of pressure, and pressures created by the precipitation of mineral cements within the reservoir. Since these were discussed under causes of reservoir pressure in Chapter 3, further elaboration here is not necessary.

Disposal of Displaced Water. Oil entering a water-filled reservoir can make room for itself only by displacing a like volume of water. In an open system this does not create a problem, for the volume is kept constant by outflow at the outcrop. But in a closed reservoir the additional volume can be accommodated only by (1) compression of the reservoir fluids, or (2) forcible penetration of the overlying strata by the displaced water. Water has greater penetrability than oil, and a cap may permit the passage of water and yet retain the oil.

A greater mystery is the phenomenon of oil sands that contain little or no free (other than "connate") water. Some sandstone lenses, including "shoestring" sands, are of this type. They are subaqueous deposits and obviously were filled with water initially. Several explanations have been attempted for the disappearance of this water. Perhaps the best one is that the water was forcibly displaced by oil but the subsequent shrinkage of the oil due to escape of gas has left some void space unoccupied by either liquid hydrocarbon or water. Other suggested explanations are that the water has been absorbed by hydrating minerals in the surrounding rocks or that the water has been evaporated by natural gas.

DIRECTION OF OIL MIGRATION.[16] Migration directions are considered in terms of the stratification planes; the oil migrates either *parallel* or *transverse* to the stratification. Parallel migration is ordinarily referred to as "lateral" and transverse as "vertical," but these

[15] Alex W. McCoy and W. Ross Keyte, "Present Interpretations of the Structural Theory for Oil and Gas Migration and Accumulation," *Problems of Petroleum Geology* (Am. Assoc. Petrol. Geol., 1934), pp. 253–307.

[16] F. H. Lahee, "A Study of the Evidences for Lateral and Vertical Migration of Oil," *Problems of Petroleum Geology* (Am. Assoc. Petrol. Geol., 1934), pp. 399–427; F. M. Van Tuyl and Ben H. Parker, "The Time of Origin and Accumulation of Petroleum," *Quarterly Colo. School of Mines,* Vol. 36 (April, 1941), Chapter 17, pp. 116–123.

terms are unfortunate, especially where the sedimentary layers are steeply inclined. Parallel migration ordinarily takes place through the reservoir rock; transverse migration requires the presence of permeable zones that cross the stratification planes. As a general, but not invariable, rule, the primary migration from source rock to reservoir rock is transverse, and the secondary migration through the reservoir to the trap is parallel.

Transverse Migration. Transverse migration can be downward or upward. If movement is taking place because of differences in specific gravity of oil and water, the migration direction of the oil will obviously be upward. But if the oil is being squeezed from a compacting rock, it will move in the direction of least resistance, whether that direction is downward, upward, or sideways. Oil from different parts of a compacting rock probably moves in different directions, like water from a squeezed sponge. The sole prerequisite is that a receptive layer be present to receive the fluids. A receptive rock is one with porosity and permeability and with a fluid pressure less than that of the liquids being driven from the compacting rock. The latter pressure is due to the weight of a column of mud; it is greater than the hydrostatic pressures existing even in the subjacent rock, so oil can be squeezed into underlying as well as overlying reservoirs.

The channelways that are used by fluids squeezed from a compacting rock are the interconnecting pores between the grains, which become closed to further migration when compaction is complete. Subsequent transverse migration must be by way of secondary channelways that cut across the bedding. Outstanding examples are joint fractures, which are especially prevalent in brittle rocks such as limestone. Fault fractures play a most important role as channelways for ascending ore-depositing hydrothermal solutions, but examples of oil migration along fault planes are very scarce. On the contrary, most oil field faults are "tight," serving as dams to trap oil rather than as conduits for its transverse migration. Two reasons are suggested for this difference in permeability along fault planes: (1) ore-filled faults are in regions of much more intense diastrophism where the displacement has been great and the resulting fracture zone wide, and (2) most oil field faults are in sections containing thick shales which tend to bend rather than break so the fault planes are not continuous vertically. Sandstone dikes have been suggested as channelways for the transverse migration of oil through shales in California,[17] Rumania,[18] and elsewhere.

One excellent example of transverse migration is the previously cited Garber, Oklahoma, field, where like oil occurs in superimposed reservoirs.[19] Bailey [20] suggests that the oil in the Sespe red beds in California got there by migrating upward from Eocene shales through "several hundred to a few thousand feet" of intervening strata that consist of sandstones with shaly interbeds cut by "countless minor joints and cracks." Where the usual dense Arbuckle "cap rock" is absent at Chetopa, Kansas, Arbuckle oil has migrated upward into the overlying Chattanooga shale.[21] Some wells at Salt Creek, Wyoming, produced commercially from fracture zones in the shale overlying the major sandstone reservoir; it is logically concluded that this oil migrated upward across the lithologic boundary. Near Toyah in Reeves County of trans-Pecos Texas, wells produced "from a few gallons to a few barrels per day" at depths of less than 100 feet in Pleistocene or Recent alluvium.[22] Obviously this oil rose from beneath through vertical channelways that cross the nearly horizontal bed-rock strata. Transformational seeps, as on the island of Trinidad, illustrate transverse migration, but seeps can also result from parallel migration through an inclined reservoir rock.

Examples of transverse migration downward from source rock to reservoir rock are some of the occurrences of oil in crystalline basement rocks (Chapter 7) and in buried hills. Possible examples are oil accumulations beneath unconformities and especially those in the leached upper surfaces of thick limestones.[23] Some of the movement

[17] Olaf P. Jenkins, "Sandstone Dikes as Conduits for Oil Migration through Shales," *Bull. Am. Assoc. Petrol. Geol.,* Vol. 14 (April, 1930), pp. 411–421.

[18] W. A. J. M. van Waterschoot van der Gracht, "The Stratigraphical Distribution of Petroleum," *Science of Petroleum* (Oxford Univ. Press, 1938), Vol. 1, p. 60.

[19] James H. Gardner, "Vertical Source in Oil and Gas Accumulation," *Bull. Am. Assoc. Petrol. Geol.,* Vol. 29 (September, 1945), pp. 1349–1351.

[20] Thomas L. Bailey, "Origin and Migration of Oil into Sespe Redbeds, California," *Bull. Am. Assoc. Petrol. Geol.,* Vol. 31 (November, 1947), pp. 1913–1935.

[21] G. E. Abernathy, "Migration of Oil from Arbuckle Limestone into Chattanooga Shale in Chetopa Oil Pool, Labette County, Kansas," *Bull. Am. Assoc. Petrol. Geol.,* Vol. 25 (October, 1941), pp. 1934–1937.

[22] Ronald K. DeFord, *in* F. M. Van Tuyl and Ben H. Parker, "The Time of Origin and Accumulation of Petroleum," *Quarterly Colo. School of Mines,* Vol. 36 (April, 1941), Chapter 17, p. 120.

[23] Roy L. Ginter, "Exercise on Amount of Source Bed Required to Furnish Oklahoma City Oil Pool," *Bull. Am. Assoc. Petrol. Geol.,* Vol. 25 (September, 1941), pp. 1706–1712; Robert F. Walters and Arthur S. Price, "Kraft-Prusa Oil Field, Barton County, Kansas," *Structure of Typical American Oil Fields* (Am. Assoc. Petrol. Geol., 1948), Vol. 3, p. 268.

of oil from source shales into lenticular sandstones is probably transverse also.

Parallel Migration. Migration parallel to the stratification is possible where a porous and permeable rock layer occurs in the sedimentary section. Most numerous examples are sandstones and porous carbonate rocks. These are called reservoir rocks, and they are discussed in some detail in the following chapter. Needless to say, a rock that qualifies may be considered a reservoir rock even though it does not contain oil or gas; it is a potential hydrocarbon reservoir rock, and its voids are filled with water.

Parallel migration is by no means confined to widespread ("sheet") sandstones or regional porous limestones. Sand-filled channels and bars in thick shale sections also may be utilized as conduits for migrating hydrocarbons.[24] Before compaction makes the muds and oozes impervious, parallel movement is the preferred direction for fluids passing through these materials because of the lamellar characteristics of the minerals and their orientation parallel to the sea floor on which they were deposited.[25]

Parallel migration is so common as to be almost universal. Only a relatively insignificant part of each reservoir contains hydrocarbons; unless it is assumed that by strange coincidence oil entered the reservoir only where there were traps, it must be concluded that oil entering where traps were absent must have migrated laterally until trapped. The confinement of oil accumulations to the highest levels in the reservoir rock is presumptive evidence that oil moved through the rock until those levels were attained. The presence of extensive deposits in a given formation and none in higher potential reservoirs is also evidence that oil travels and accumulates parallel to the bedding far more often than across the bedding. This conclusion is supported by the fact that like oils may occur in a single reservoir formation in fields scattered over an area extending for scores of miles, whereas other formations, separated vertically by but a few feet, will have unlike oils.

Practically any oil field could be used to illustrate parallel migration. The enormous accumulation at East Texas (Fig. 76) has been at the upper end of a great sheet sand body where it has been truncated by erosion and overlapped by younger, impervious forma-

[24] W. C. Krumbein and L. T. Caldwell, "Areal Variation of Organic Carbon Content of Barataria Bay Sediments, Louisiana," *Bull. Am. Assoc. Petrol. Geol.*, Vol. 23 (April, 1939), pp. 582–594.

[25] D. A. Greig, memorandum dated Dec. 14, 1948.

tions. The best explanation for this great concentration of oil is that it entered the sandstone at an infinite number of points down the flank of the East Texas (Tyler) basin, whence it drained upward through the waterfilled pores of the reservoir until it was impounded below the tightly sealed unconformity where the sandstone wedges out. Lateral migration in a radial direction away from the center of the Eastern Venezuela basin is indicated by the fact that practically all accumulations of oil "are found on the basinward side of the barriers to such migration." [26]

Some seeps occur at the outcrop of reservoir rocks, which is evidence of parallel migration from a deeper, down-dip source. The Bartlesville sandstone, reservoir rock for many rich, relatively shallow, oil fields in southeastern Kansas and northeastern Oklahoma, is quarried at its outcrop in southwestern Missouri because of the presence of seep oil, which makes the crushed rock valuable as a road dressing.

Parallel migration is also a strong possibility for the primary movement from source rock to reservoir in the "shoestring" sand fields (Fig. 69). The belief has been expressed that the source material is the organic accumulations which were being deposited in the adjacent lagoons at the same time that the sand bars were being built.[27] The oil, as it formed, migrated laterally into the sand; some transverse movement from younger, overlying organic muds is also a possibility.

Without doubt, much of the migration from younger to older rocks is actually parallel rather than transverse. For example, the accumulation of oil in the basement rock schists in the Edison field of California has probably taken place through movements up-dip through sedimentary reservoirs into the fractured crystalline rock against which the sedimentaries abut: "The oil originated in the westerly extending Tertiary sedimentary basin and migrated into the pore and fracture spaces of the structurally higher schist." [28]

It can be concluded that parallel and transverse migration are not mutually exclusive and that many if not most oils, in journeying from source to trap, traveled both transverse and parallel to the

[26] H. D. Hedberg, L. C. Sass, and H. J. Funkhouser, "Oil Fields of Greater Oficina Area, Central Anzoategui, Venezuela," *Bull. Am. Assoc. Petrol. Geol.*, Vol. 31 (December, 1947), p. 2138.

[27] L. M. Neumann *et al.* (Research Committee, Tulsa Geological Society), "Relationship of Crude Oils and Stratigraphy in Parts of Oklahoma and Kansas," *Bull. Am. Assoc. Petrol. Geol.*, Vol. 31 (January, 1947), pp. 92–148.

[28] J. C. May and R. L. Hewitt, "The Nature of the Basement Complex Oil Reservoir, Edison Oil Field, California," *Bull. Am. Assoc. Petrol. Geol.*, Vol. 31 (December, 1947), p. 2240.

stratification planes. The direction of travel is a question of permeability. At the beginning of compaction, the permeability in the source mud or ooze is such that oil can migrate in any direction; after compaction, permeability parallel to the bedding is the rule and transverse to the bedding the exception. For this reason alone most later migrations are parallel.

DISTANCE OF OIL MIGRATION. The distance through which oil can migrate, and has migrated in the geological past, is a function of time, assuming continuity of permeability and gradient. If oil can migrate an inch, it can migrate a mile. A movement of but a foot a year becomes 190 miles in a million years.

Obviously the opportunities for migration over long distances are much greater by parallel than by transverse migration. In the second, the distance is limited to the thickness of the sedimentary column (or a somewhat greater distance where migration is on the bias), whereas the potential migration range for parallel movement is the distance from bottom to rim of a structural basin. The "gathering area" for a trap is considered to be the down-dip extension of the reservoir rock; if the trap is high on the flank of a basin and the reservoir rock has sheet porosity, the trap can impound the upward drainage from over an enormous area. This may explain why some of the greatest accumulations have just such a setting. Examples are the oil fields of Lake Maracaibo in Venezuela, the San Joaquin Valley fields of California, East Texas, Oklahoma City, and many others.

Definite figures of distance of migration are difficult to obtain. Brauchli [29] believes that the original accumulation at Oklahoma City may well be the result of drainage from far out in the Anadarko basin, a potential distance of more than 100 miles. Hoots [30] states that it is a matter of "several miles" between some of the California accumulations in non-marine and inorganic sediments and their down-dip marine organic facies whence the oil probably came. From "a few" to 15 miles is the range of migration given for some of the oil that subsequently devolatilized to form the asphalt deposits of western Kentucky.[31]

Examples of minimum distance of migration are the often-cited accumulations of oil in sand bodies completely surrounded by shale.

[29] R. W. Brauchli, "Migration of Oil in Oklahoma City Field," *Bull. Am. Assoc. Petrol. Geol.,* Vol. 19 (May, 1935), pp. 699–701.

[30] H. W. Hoots, "Origin, Migration, and Accumulation of Oil in California," *Calif. Div. Mines Bull.* 108 (August, 1941), pp. 261–262.

[31] W. L. Russell, "Origin of the Asphalt Deposits of Western Kentucky," *Econ. Geol.,* Vol. 28 (September–October, 1933), pp. 571–586.

The main input probably takes place during the compaction of the enclosing shale; it is difficult to visualize further migration after compaction and lithifaction are complete unless the shale is extensively fractured.

Carrier Beds. Rich, the foremost exponent of migration of oil over great distances, has coined the term "carrier beds" [32] for deep, highly porous, and permeable rocks through which oil can migrate. He cites as a possible example of the use of carrier beds the movement of oil from the geosynclinal basins of southern Oklahoma to the anticlinal traps of the central Kansas uplift. Possible carrier beds include sheet sandstones, cavernous limestones, and weathered surfaces beneath widespread unconformities. The oil works its way upward at every opportunity from the carrier beds to the reservoir rocks by means of joint fissures. Once the reservoir bed is reached, the oil may be immediately trapped, as in a "shoestring" sand, or it may continue parallel migration until a trap is found. Rich confines the term "reservoir rock" to the stratum or strata in which accumulation occurs.

CHANGES IN OIL DURING MIGRATION. As the oil moves from places of higher pressure to lower (*never* the reverse), some change in character may take place owing to the escape of a part of the dissolved gas. Temperature changes occurring en route may also affect the amount of gas held in solution. Contamination of the oil by minerals forming the pore walls is no longer considered possible because of the intervening water film now believed to be universally present. However, chemical changes due to contact with water through which the migrating oil passes are decidedly possible. Many believe that asphaltization of crude oil near the surface is due to chemical interaction between the upward migrating oil and downward percolating surface waters.

It is a well-known fact, utilized in refining both petroleum and vegetable oils, that some clays (such as fuller's earth) can be used as filters to remove discoloring or foul-smelling compounds from oils or to separate the heavy viscous asphaltic hydrocarbons from the lighter, more mobile compounds. Without doubt, the passage of crude oil underground through rocks of varying permeability also has a filtering effect that results, at the end of the migration, in an oil somewhat different from what it was when it started on its journeys.

[32] John L. Rich, "Function of Carrier Beds in Long-Distance Migration of Oil," *Bull. Am. Assoc. of Petrol. Geol.*, Vol. 15 (August, 1931), pp. 911–924; "Distribution of Oil Pools in Kansas in Relation to Pre-Mississippian Structure and Areal Geology, *ibid.*, Vol. 17 (July, 1933), pp. 798–815.

A light oil occurring in relatively minor amounts across the Whittier fault from the Brea-Olinda field may possibly be due to the filtering effect of the fault gouge, which allowed only the lightest of the liquid hydrocarbons to pass through.

If the oil and water are migrating together, intimately intermixed, the ability of the water, but not the oil, to enter the finer pores (already water-wet) of an argillaceous zone would result in a gradual enrichment of oil in the rock in front of the barrier.[33]

[33] V. C. Illing, "The Migration of Oil," *Science of Petroleum* (Oxford Univ. Press, 1938), Vol. 1, pp. 209–215.

Chapter 7

ACCUMULATION: RESERVOIR ROCKS[1]

The accumulation of oil or gas into a commercial deposit requires a combination of reservoir rock and trap. The reservoir rock is the container; it is usually much more extensive than the hydrocarbon deposit that has been localized by a trap. Beyond the confines of the oil or gas pool, the reservoir rock is almost always filled with water.

Reservoir rocks will be considered in this chapter, and oil and gas traps in Chapter 8.

GENERAL QUALIFICATIONS FOR RESERVOIR ROCKS. The qualifications of a reservoir rock are simple: it must have room enough to store a worthwhile volume of hydrocarbons, and the storage facilities must be such that the contained oil or gas will discharge readily when the reservoir is penetrated by a well. Any buried rock, whether it is igneous, sedimentary, or metamorphic, that meets these specifications may be utilized by migrating hydrocarbons as a reservoir. Actually, however, most of the world's oil and gas occur in sandstones or carbonate rocks simply because these are by far the most common rocks that qualify as reservoirs in those segments of the earth's crust containing generating or migrating hydrocarbons.

In order to contain enough oil or gas to make extraction profitable, a reservoir rock must exceed a minimum porosity and a minimum thickness. The value of these minima depend upon local conditions. Most producing reservoir rocks have porosities above 10 per cent and thicknesses greater than 10 feet. However, a rock with lesser porosity may be exploitable if the thickness is great, or a thinner rock may be

[1] David Donaghue, "Fundamental Data on Subsurface Reservoirs," *Bull. Am. Assoc. Petrol. Geol.,* Vol. 28 (December, 1944), pp. 1754–1755; P. G. Nutting, "Some Physical and Chemical Properties of Reservoir Rocks Bearing on the Accumulation and Discharge of Oil," *Problems of Petroleum Geology* (Am. Assoc. Petrol. Geol., 1934), pp. 825–832; G. E. Archie, "Introduction to Petrophysics of Reservoir Rocks," *Bull. Am. Assoc. Petrol. Geol.,* Vol. 34 (May, 1950), pp. 943–961.

developed successfully if the porosity is unusually large. The value of the oil, and the production cost, also enter into the question of whether a reservoir may be exploitable.

In addition to adequate porosity and thickness, a reservoir rock must have a certain degree of lateral continuity, or the volume of oil stored will not be adequate. In some areas lateral persistence of porosity cannot be taken for granted. Many wildcat wells have failed to become discovery wells because the reservoir rock was locally "tight." The first well drilled on the Eldorado dome in Butler County, Kansas, was a dry hole, but it was later completely surrounded by producing wells. On the other hand, other wildcatters have discovered oil only to find subsequently that they had a one-well pool with dry offsets owing to a decrease in porosity in the reservoir rock north, south, east, and west of the discovery well.

Some sheet sandstones and some porous carbonate rocks are true regional reservoir rocks, containing water or hydrocarbons everywhere in the subsurface. At the other extreme are porous zones of such limited lateral extent that they are, in themselves, traps for oil or gas accumulation. Many carbonate rock formations are notorious for their erratic porosities, and in some areas sandstones are equally unreliable. In districts too numerous to mention, not only must the oil-seeker locate a trap but also the trap must be baited with a porous zone in which hydrocarbons can accumulate.

The ability of a rock to discharge its hydrocarbon content is dependent upon its permeability.[2] There are three requisites to permeability: (1) porosity, (2) interconnecting pores, and (3) pores of supercapillary size. Although a permeable rock also must be porous, a porous rock does not have to be permeable. Pumice is porous, but not permeable, because the voids are not interconnecting; shale may be quite porous but impermeable because the pores are capillary or subcapillary in size, thereby preventing free movement of the contained fluids.

Porosity [3] is both created and destroyed by natural geological processes. Primary porosity in sedimentary rocks is that resulting from the accumulation of detrital or organic material in such a manner that openings or voids are left between grains of sand or fragments

[2] Gerald L. Hassler, "The Measurement of the Permeability of Reservoir Rocks and Its Application," *Science of Petroleum* (Oxford Univ. Press, 1938), Vol. 1, pp. 198–208.

[3] S. E. Coomber, "The Porosity of Reservoir Rocks," *Science of Petroleum* (Oxford Univ. Press, 1938), Vol. 1, pp. 220–223.

of shells. As a matter of fact, it is impossible to pack such material, especially spheroidal grains, without leaving considerable interconnecting void space. Primary porosity is of greatest importance in sandstone reservoirs. Secondary porosity is the result of some type of geological activity after the sediment has been converted into rock. It is of great importance in carbonate rock reservoirs. The most common types are solution cavities, which range in size from that of a pinhead to the Carlsbad Caverns, and fissures or fractures produced mainly by rock jointing. The fracture type of rock opening is never visible in well cuttings and is rarely discernible in cores; therefore, its quantitative significance has been largely ignored. Porosity determinations made on rock samples are always *minimum* figures because of the difficulty of evaluating the void space present in fractures.

The geological activities that tend to destroy porosity are cementation,[4] recrystallization, and granulation. Loose sand grains become sandstone by the deposition of cementing minerals in the interstices between the grains. If the cementation is carried to completion the porosity is destroyed. Fortunately, this rarely occurs; most sandstones are left with enough primary porosity to store large quantities of water, oil, or gas. Recrystallization tends to destroy any pre-existing porosity by changing the rock into a dense interlocking aggregate of crystals. It is a common feature of metamorphism, and that is one of the reasons why metamorphic rocks are characteristically impermeable. However, recrystallization can and does take place in limestone without metamorphism, destroying whatever primary porosity may have been present. Granulation or crushing will lower the porosity and destroy the permeability by squeezing the rock. The rocks that have been deeply buried in the geologic past, and those that have been strongly compressed by lateral diastrophic forces, have suffered granulation to varying degrees. A recent study of five sandstones, ranging in depth from 2885 to 8343 feet, in two Wyoming wells, shows a progressive change with depth from the original loose random packing to a tighter packing resulting from pressure.[5] Pressure effects included crushing and yielding of the mineral grains. With the exploration for oil extending to depths below 20,000 feet, the persistence of porosity with depth becomes a subject of utmost impor-

[4] Charles M. Gilbert, "Cementation of Some California Tertiary Reservoir Sands," *Jour. Geol.,* Vol. 57 (January, 1949), pp. 1–17.

[5] Jane M. Taylor, "Pore Space Reduction in Sandstones," *Bull. Am. Assoc. Petrol. Geol.,* Vol. 34 (April, 1949), pp. 701–716.

tance.[6] It is possible that sufficient intergrain void space in sandstone reservoirs carries downward as far as sedimentary basins extend into the earth's crust. It is less likely that limestone solution cavities have comparable persistence with depth, and it is highly improbable that fractures and fissures retain much permeability at even those levels now being explored. Some relatively deep mines in crystalline rocks which have a water problem in the upper levels are dry in the lower levels because of the drawing together of the fissure walls with depth. It can be concluded that the reservoir opportunities diminish in the deeper parts of the sedimentary basins as far as the variety of openings possible is concerned. This situation may be more than offset, however, by an increase in the percentage of sandstones in the section with depth.

Further details regarding reservoir rock porosities are included in the following sections describing the different types.

SANDSTONE RESERVOIRS.[7] Throughout the world, sandstone is by far the most important reservoir rock. Locally it may be exceeded in the volume of oil produced by carbonate rock, but in many great oil districts limestones and dolomites are entirely absent from the stratigraphic section. Sandstones possess the properties of porosity and permeability to a greater and more consistent extent than any other abundant rock. Furthermore, they may be thick—in some places several hundred feet thick—and they may (or may not) have great lateral continuity.

Sandstone porosity is of two types, intergranular and fracture. The intergranular porosity is the net void space remaining after the initial porosity has been decreased by cementation. The initial porosity depends mainly upon the extent to which the sand is graded (sorted).[8] Moderately rounded sand grains, such as commonly compose sandstones, which are all approximately the same size, will settle in water into an aggregate having a porosity of 35 to 40 per cent. With a mixture of sizes the porosity becomes less, for the smaller grains will partially fill the interstices between the larger grains, which otherwise

[6] James S. Cloninger, "How Deep Oil or Gas May Be Expected." *World Oil*, Vol. 130 (May, 1950), pp. 57–62.

[7] S. E. Coomber, "The Porosity of Reservoir Rocks," *Science of Petroleum* (Oxford Univ. Press, 1938), Vol. 1, pp. 220–223; P. G. Nutting, "Some Physical and Chemical Properties of Reservoir Rocks Bearing on the Accumulation and Discharge of Oil," *Problems of Petroleum Geology* (Am. Assoc. Petrol. Geol., 1934), pp. 825–832; Harry M. Ryder, "Character of Pores in Oil Sand," *World Oil*, Vol. 127 (April, 1948), pp. 129–134.

[8] Wilbur F. Cloud, "Effects of Sand Grain Size Distribution upon Porosity and Permeability," *Oil Weekly*, Vol. 103 (Oct. 27, 1941), pp. 26–32.

would be left open. Ill-sorted sands have porosities of 30 per cent and less. As a general rule, cementation lowers the porosity percentage from an initial 30 to 40 down to 10 to 20. Not even all this reduced space is available, however, for hydrocarbon storage. The interstitial ("connate") water has to be accommodated first. Bartle [9] has calculated the effective porosity of a gas sandstone reservoir in northwestern Missouri at 7 per cent.

Casts made of sandstone pores have shown that, although some sandstones have suffered no post-depositional activity other than cementation, others have been leached so that the pores may be even larger than the largest grains. Some of the pores in the Bradford "sand," Bradford, Pennsylvania, could hold from 10 to 100 of the surrounding sand grains.[10] Although solution cavities are commonly thought of for carbonate reservoirs, they obviously can be important in sandstone reservoirs.

"Tight" sandstones, or tight zones within a sandstone, may be due to nearly complete cementation, but more often they are the result of inadequate sorting of the detrital material at time of deposition. Intermixed clay or silt, or flakes of mica, will make a sandstone virtually impermeable.

Some apparently tight sandstones carry water or oil in fractures, in which event the actual porosity is many times the measurable porosity of a core sample. Sandstone is a competent and brittle rock, and it is just as subject to fissuring as any other rock of comparable competence. Where the sandstone is not tight but has a normal porosity of 10 to 20 per cent, it too may have a greater actual porosity due to fractures, but their existence will be less obvious. Finn [11] believes that the permeability of the Oriskany sandstone in Pennsylvania and New York has been "augmented in many producing areas by the presence of small open fractures, some of which have the character of open joint planes which are partly sealed by projecting quartz crystals. The presence of these fractures or slightly open joint planes has been the chief reason for the very large open flows in some Oriskany sand wells, and has caused the Oriskany to have a generally

[9] Glenn G. Bartle, "Effective Porosity of Gas Fields in Jackson County, Missouri," *Bull. Am. Assoc. Petrol. Geol.*, Vol. 25 (July, 1941), pp. 1405–1409.

[10] P. G. Nutting, "Some Physical and Chemical Properties of Reservoir Rocks Bearing on the Accumulation and Discharge of Oil," *Problems of Petroleum Geology* (Am. Assoc. Petrol. Geol., 1934), p. 827.

[11] Fenton H. Finn, "Geology and Occurrence of Natural Gas in Oriskany Sandstone in Pennsylvania and New York," *Bull. Am. Assoc. Petrol. Geol.*, Vol. 33 (March, 1949), pp. 303–335.

higher productive capacity than the average producing sand in the Appalachian area."

The dimensions of a sandstone body depend upon the conditions of its sedimentation. The most extensive sheet sandstones are deposited by a transgressing sea. They are continuous bodies throughout the area of overlap even though the sand deposited at the end of the transgression is younger than the sand deposited when transgression started. Some of the major reservoirs of the Gulf Coast are of this type. Malkin and Jung [12] point out that, as the sand was being deposited along the strand line, organic muds were being deposited to the seaward; oil generated in the organic sediments could migrate into the laterally adjacent sand or sandstone with the greatest ease.

Most sandstones are not sheet sands. They are lenticular; at one extreme are lenses many miles across and at the other extreme are the "shoestring" sands, which may measure but a few feet in width. The latter are so small as to constitute traps as well as reservoirs. Lenticular sands are deposited in regressing seas, along stagnant strand lines,[13] in offshore bars or shallow "banks," [14] in deltas and river floodplains, and on lake floors.

The original source of most sand grains is granite or granite gneiss. Heald [15] points out that the first sand to result from the wasting of granitic rock is not clean quartz sand but a mixture of quartz grains, clay particles, and accessory minerals in various stages of decomposition. A much better reservoir rock is produced after the sand has been reworked one or more times. Probably most sandstones, except those overlapping the crystalline basement rocks, consist of sand grains derived from older sandstones that are undergoing erosion.

CARBONATE ROCK RESERVOIRS. By carbonate rock is meant limestone, dolomite, and rocks intermediate between these two. In a few areas, notably the Lima-Indiana district and the Michigan basin, carbonate rocks are practically the sole reservoirs. In some other

[12] Doris S. Malkin and Dorothy A. Jung, "Marine Sedimentation and Oil Accumulation on Gulf Coast. I. Progressive Marine Overlap," *Bull. Am. Assoc. Petrol. Geol.,* Vol. 25 (November, 1941), pp. 2010–2020.

[13] George V. Cohee, "Lateral Variation in Chester Sandstones Producing Oil and Gas in Lower Wabash River Area, with Special Reference to New Harmony Field, Illinois and Indiana," *Bull. Am. Assoc. Petrol. Geol.,* Vol. 26 (October, 1942), pp. 1594–1607.

[14] John L. Rich, "Submarine Sedimentary Features on Bahama Banks and Their Bearing on Distribution Patterns of Lenticular Oil Sands," *Bull. Am. Assoc. Petrol. Geol.,* Vol. 32 (May, 1948), pp. 767–779.

[15] K. C. Heald, "Essentials for Oil Pools," *Elements of the Petroleum Industry* (Am. Inst. Min. Met. Engineers, 1940), p. 30.

regions, as in the eastern United States and the Mid-Continent, both limestones and sandstones contain prolific quantities of oil and gas. Mexico and the Middle East are outstanding examples among the foreign fields of production from carbonate rocks.

Carbonate reservoirs differ in several respects from sandstone reservoirs. Porosity is more likely to be localized, both laterally and vertically, within the rock layer. Although sheet porosity is possessed by a few carbonate rocks, this condition is decidedly exceptional. Within a given carbonate formation, even if several hundred feet in thickness, the porosity is in many places confined to the uppermost 25 to 50 feet. On the other hand, the pores may be much larger than in sandstone reservoirs, giving the rock an unusual permeability. For this reason, wells drilled into carbonate reservoirs hold the records for high initial yields, and limestone pools tend to be shorter-lived than sandstone pools.

Origin and Character of Carbonate Rock Porosity.[16] The porosity of carbonate rocks is the net result after pore-producing and pore-reducing processes have completed their work. Positive porosity is either primary or secondary; the negative, or pore-reducing, processes include cementation (or other precipitation) and recrystallization.

Primary porosity is that resulting from the original deposition of carbonate rock. In all probability, much limestone and dolomite is clastic, the result of the accumulation of "sand" grains derived from older carbonate rocks. Theoretically such rock should have the same interstitial voids as those possessed by sandstone, but actual examples are hard to find. Invariably the original porosity has been greatly reduced by infilling through the precipitation of calcite or dolomite by circulating solutions. Recrystallization is another cause for the virtual obliteration of primary porosity. There are, however, two types of primary porosity in limestones that may survive the subsequent activities and processes that tend to eliminate such porosity. These are shell and reef accumulations, which are discussed in the paragraphs following, and oölitic limestones.[17] The individual oölites

[16] W. V. Howard and Max W. David, "Development of Porosity in Limestones," *Bull. Am. Assoc. Petrol. Geol.,* Vol. 20 (November, 1936), pp. 1389–1412; W. V. Howard, "Accumulation of Oil and Gas in Limestone," *Problems of Petroleum Geology* (Am. Assoc. Petrol. Geol., 1934), pp. 365–376; W. V. Howard, "A Classification of Limestone Reservoirs," *Bull. Am. Assoc. Petrol. Geol,* Vol. 12 (December, 1928), pp. 1153–1161; Richard B. Hohlt, "The Nature and Origin of Limestone Porosity," *Quarterly Colo. School of Mines,* Vol. 43 (October, 1948), pp. 1–51.

[17] F. B. Plummer, "Pore Systems in Reservoir Rocks," *Oil and Gas Jour.,* Vol. 43 (Nov. 18, 1944), p. 245.

ordinarily range from 0.1 to 0.5 millimeter and are ellipsoidal. They are cemented together by calcium carbonate, and since, as a general rule, the degree of cementation is greater than it is for sandstones, the porosity and permeability are lower. In many places the oölites occur in discontinuous zones or lenses completely surrounded by relatively dense limestone.

A limestone reef is a deposit, mainly of organic origin, that "has been built upward at a more rapid rate than the contemporaneous sediments deposited about its margins." [18] Although modern reefs are mostly coral reefs, many other types of organisms contributed to reef development in the geologic past. Exploration for hydrocarbons has led to the discovery of many ancient buried reefs, some containing phenomenal quantities of oil. The recent discoveries at Leduc (Fig. 68) and elsewhere in Alberta are of this type.

Reefs are characteristically porous, but it is probable that the initial porosity resulting from the loose intergrowth of shell-producing marine organisms has been augmented by secondary processes, especially solution of calcite.[19] The principal reef producer at Leduc has been entirely converted to dolomite.[20] In the Marine Pool (Fig. 43) of Illinois the principal reservoir is not the reef rock itself but the "coquina-like detrital limestone which forms the mantling deposit of a Niagaran reef." [21]

The most striking feature about some of the reefs is the great thickness of the porous zones. The thickest section of the prolific D-3 reef zone at Leduc, which had been explored by April, 1949, was 165 feet. The discovery well of the nearby Golden Spike pool was brought into production in the same month with a rated initial production of 10,000 barrels per day after having cored 544 feet of porous reef material. The maximum thickness of porous reef rock reported for the Scurry County, west Texas, fields first discovered in mid-1948 is "approximately" 600 feet.[22]

[18] W. H. Twenhofel, "Characteristics and Geologic Distribution of Coral and Other Organic Reefs," *World Oil,* Vol. 129 (July 1, 1949), pp. 61–64.

[19] K. C. Heald, "Essentials for Oil Pools," *Elements of the Petroleum Industry* (Am. Inst. Min. Met. Engineers, 1940), p. 31.

[20] D. B. Layer, *et al.,* "Leduc Oil Field, Alberta, a Devonian Coral Reef Discovery," *Bull. Am. Assoc. Petrol. Geol.,* Vol. 33 (April, 1949), pp. 572–602.

[21] Heinz A Lowenstam, "Marine Pool, Madison County, Illinois, Silurian Reef Producer," *Ill. Geol. Survey, Rept. Investigations* 131 (1948).

[22] D. H. Stormont, "Scurry County, West Texas, Limestone Reef Development," *Oil and Gas Jour.,* Vol. 48 (July 7, 1949), pp. 54 *et seq.*

Older reef fields include the Hendrick pool of Winkler County, Texas,[23] the Southern Field of Mexico,[24] and others.

With the exception of reef porosities, which are in part, at least, primary, the porosity in carbonate rock reservoirs is largely secondary. Processes which produce subsequent porosity include solution, dolomitization, and fracturing. The greatest of these is solution. Calcite, or dolomite, is leached by percolating ground waters, especially above the water table. The resultant solution cavities range in size from minute pores to gigantic caverns. Regardless of size, the openings are interconnecting and extremely irregular. A reversal from dissolving to precipitating will produce dripstone deposits in caves and comparable deposits in the smaller pores, all of which tends to reduce the pore space available. Infiltration of the overlying sediment may also lessen or even obliterate carbonate rock porosity. The red shale of the Molas (Pennsylvanian) formation has penetrated the solution cavities of the underlying Ouray (Mississippian) limestone in the Rattlesnake (Fig. 40), New Mexico, field to such an extent that only the lowest 5 feet of a weathered zone 35 to 55 feet thick has adequate porosity and permeability to function as reservoir rock.[25]

In most carbonate reservoirs the solution cavities are of modest size, little larger than the interstices between grains of sand, but they range from this size upward to actual caverns. The Dollarhide field in Andrews County, west Texas, is an example of cavern accumulation. In drilling the Fusselman pay zone, the drill dropped as much as 16 feet into oil-filled openings in the limestone.[26] Other west Texas[27] fields have also been developed in truly cavernous zones, as well as some fields in Kentucky. Such accumulations come close to the usual layman's concept of an underground "lake" of oil.

Where the openings are large, it is obviously impossible to determine the porosity percentage by the usual core analysis methods.

23 K. C. Heald, "Essentials for Oil Pools," Elements of the Petroleum Industry (Am. Inst. Min. Met. Engineers, 1940), p. 31.

24 John M. Muir, "Limestone Reservoir Rocks in the Mexican Oil Fields," *Problems of Petroleum Geology* (Am. Assoc. Petrol. Geol., 1934), pp. 377–398.

25 H. H. Hinson, "Reservoir Characteristics of Rattlesnake Oil and Gas Field, San Juan County, New Mexico," *Bull. Am. Assoc. Petrol. Geol.,* Vol. 31 (April, 1947), pp. 731–771.

26 D. H. Stormont, "Huge Caverns Encountered in Dollarhide Field Make for Unusual Drilling Conditions," *Oil and Gas Jour.,* Vol. 47 (April 7, 1949), pp. 66 *et seq.*

27 H. P. Bybee, "Possible Nature of Limestone Reservoirs in the Permian Basin," *Bull. Am. Assoc. Petrol. Geol.,* Vol. 22 (August, 1938), pp. 915–924.

Where it is possible to measure the porosity of actual reservoir limestones and dolomites, it ranges from 5 to 20 per cent.[28]

Solution porosity is carried out by circulating meteoric waters. These waters take advantage of any primary porosity by enlarging the already existing pores.[29] They also follow and enlarge joints and bedding planes.[30] It can readily be observed at the outcrop that fossil shells are exceptionally vulnerable to solution so that fossiliferous carbonate rocks develop a pitted appearance.

Because most solution porosity is developed above the water table,[31] a carbonate rock must be not only emergent but also exposed, or nearly so, to subareal erosion. Therefore an unconformity should overlie every limestone with solution porosity. This explains why carbonate rock porous zones tend to lie near the top of the formation. They do not, however, have to lie at the very top; in the present cycle of erosion, solution leaching by circulating ground waters has taken place in exceptionally vulnerable layers several hundred feet below the surface.[32]

A list of fields producing from solution cavities in carbonate rocks would include most of the limestone and dolomite fields of the world. The development of solution porosity in Mississippian limestone at Turner Valley, Alberta, has been described recently.[33]

Because dolomites are comparable in solubility to limestones, they are subject to the same leaching by percolating meteoric waters. However, there are some places where limestones have been locally dolomitized, and the dolomite zones are porous and permeable, whereas the non-dolomitized limestone is dense and impervious. Such porous zones make both oil reservoirs and traps (Chapter 8). Obviously the development of this particular porosity is tied up with the process of dolomitization. The traditional theory that the porosity is due to volume shrinkage accompanying replacement of calcite

[28] S. E. Coomber, "The Porosity of Reservoir Rocks," *Science of Petroleum* (Oxford Univ. Press, 1938), Vol. 1, pp. 220–223.

[29] John Emery Adams, "Origin, Migration, and Accumulation of Petroleum in Limestone Reservoirs in the Western United States and Canada," *Problems of Petroleum Geology* (Am. Assoc. of Petrol. Geol., 1934), pp. 347–363.

[30] Jean M. Berdan, "Hydrology of Limestone Terrane in Schoharie County, New York," *Trans. Am. Geophys. Union,* Vol. 29 (April, 1948), pp. 251–253.

[31] Jean M. Berdan, *op. cit.*

[32] B. C. Moneymaker, "Some Broad Aspects of Limestone Solution in the Tennessee Valley," *Trans. Am. Geophys. Union,* Vol. 29 (February, 1948), pp. 93–96.

[33] A. J. Goodman, "Limestone Reservoir Conditions in Turner Valley Oil Field, Alberta, Canada," *Bull. Am. Assoc. Petrol. Geol.,* Vol. 29 (August, 1945), pp. 1156–1168.

by dolomite, molecule by molecule, is untenable for at least four reasons:[34] (1) replacement is always volume for volume and not molecule for molecule; (2) many dolomitized zones are not porous; (3) the porosity, where present, varies widely from the calculated 12.3 per cent; and (4) the cavities are not like any other shrinkage openings in shape but are much more like solution cavities. It has been suggested that in this instance, at least, the dolomitization was brought about by circulating ground waters, and the porosity was the result of an excess of solution over precipitation during the replacement process.[35] Bybee[36] cites an instance where dolomitization of an initially porous and permeable oölitic limestone has completely destroyed the porosity.

Carbonate rocks are brittle and in many places are extensively fractured. In some fields the fractures augment the cavity porosity of the carbonate reservoir rock, but in others the limestone or dolomite is internally quite impervious so that all the hydrocarbon deposit is stored in joint cracks and other types of crevices. An example of the former is the Marine Pool of Illinois. "The average daily production and the cumulative production . . . demonstrate that none of the discontinuous porous streaks appears thick enough to have the storage capacity correlative with the amount of fluid produced. It is the writer's opinion that the network of secondary porosity zones lining the fissure system and a crevice system connect the discontinuous producing streaks with each other and with the main reef core underneath, forming one common reservoir."[37] Boyd[38] has noted a gas reserve in excess of the calculated capacity of the Silurian dolomite in the Howell gas field, Michigan, and ascribes this discrepancy to the presence of fissures in the reservoir rock which add to its storage capacity. The best examples of accumulation exclusively in fissures cutting carbonate rocks are some of the foreign fields. Muir states the following regarding the Tamaulipas limestone in the northern fields of Mexico: "Due to the dense nature of the limestone, the oil (12.5° A.P.I.) does not penetrate it, but is found in joint planes or

[34] A. N. Murray, "Limestone Oil Reservoirs of the Northeastern United States and of Ontario, Canada," *Econ. Geol.*, Vol. 25 (August, 1930), pp. 452–469.

[35] Kenneth K. Landes, "Porosity through Dolomitization," *Bull. Am. Assoc. Petrol. Geol.*, Vol. 30 (March, 1946), pp. 305–318.

[36] H. H. Bybee, "Hitesville Consolidated Field, Union County, Kentucky," *Bull. Am. Assoc. Petrol. Geol.*, Vol. 32 (November, 1948), pp. 2063–2082.

[37] Heinz A. Lowenstam, "Marine Pool, Madison County, Illinois, Silurian Reef Producer," *Ill. Geol. Survey, Rept. Investigations* 131 (1948).

[38] Harold E. Boyd, informal communication.

other openings of induced character. . . . According to the lack, or presence, of 'induced porosity,' wells drilled into the Tamaulipas limestone vary in size from a mere showing of oil to gushers of 30,000 barrels per day, or larger. This variation occurs between wells which may be only 200 feet apart, horizontally." [39] Coomber [40] has noted that the Asmari limestone, the reservoir rock in the Iranian oil fields, is similarly lacking in obvious porosity but produces great quantities of oil from cracks and fissures. A somewhat different impression of the reservoir properties of the Asmari limestone is given by Lane: "The intense folding and flexing of this rock mass has cracked and fissured it extensively and this fissure system is responsible for the very free fluid connection throughout the reservoir which is the feature of these fields. The late Lord Cadman in one of his addresses referred to it as 'the transport organization of the underground reservoir system.' These fissures are, however, small, being normally less than 0.1 in. in width and they do not contribute a large proportion of the storage space in spite of the fact that when a well is drilled no appreciable production is obtained until a fissure is penetrated, even though the drill may pass through bands of highly porous rock. Though opinions vary, it is generally estimated that at least 80 per cent of the recoverable oil is stored in the porous limestone while only 20 per cent exists in the fissures." [41]

Nuss and Whiting [42] succeeded in obtaining a plastic model of fracture porosity enlarged by solution, in the Devonian limestone reservoir rock of the South Fullerton field, Texas.

MISCELLANEOUS RESERVOIRS. Although most of the world's oil and gas comes from sandstones and carbonate rocks, mainly from disseminated pores but in part from fractures, various other types of rock contain enough porosity to be locally important as reservoirs. In some places the porosity is interstitial, but in most it is due to the presence of fissures. *Conglomerate* has all the qualifications for a reservoir rock, but this variety of sedimentary rock is rare, especially out in the great sedimentary basins. However, some basal sandstones

[39] John M. Muir, "Limestone Reservoir Rocks in the Mexican Oil Fields," *Problems of Petroleum Geology* (Am. Assoc. Petrol. Geol., 1934), p. 382.

[40] S. E. Coomber, "The Porosity of Reservoir Rocks," *Science of Petroleum* (Oxford Univ. Press, 1938), Vol. 1, p. 221.

[41] H. W. Lane, "Oil Production in Iran," *Oil and Gas Jour.,* Vol. 48 (Aug. 18, 1949), p. 128.

[42] W. F. Nuss and R. L. Whiting, "Technique for Reproducing Rock Pore Space," *Bull. Am. Assoc. Petrol. Geol.,* Vol. 31 (November, 1947), pp. 2044–2049.

may be coarse enough to be termed conglomerates; the oil-bearing Sooey conglomerate of central Kansas is of this type. A conglomerate consisting of schist detritus from the underlying crystalline basement rock is a reservoir rock in two fields in the Los Angeles Basin.[43]

Fractured shales produce oil commercially in the Florence and Canon City fields of eastern Colorado, in the Rangely shallow field (Fig. 38) of western Colorado, and in three fields on the west side of the San Joaquin Valley, California.[44] The occurrence of oil in fissured shales overlying sandstone reservoir rock at Salt Creek, Wyoming, was mentioned previously as an example of migration.

Fractured shales and *fractured cherts* have been the reservoir rocks for three-fourths of the quarter-billion-barrel cumulative production of the Santa Maria district, California.[45] Some of the California fields discovered as far back as 1903 have produced most or all of their oil from fractured Monterey (Miocene) cherts. Eggleston[46] has noted that the best wells have been found in areas of faulting or intense folding. Some poor wells may be due to porosity reduction by secondary deposition of calcite in the fractures. As could be anticipated, it is impossible, at present at least, to make more than an intelligent guess of the oil reserves in a fracture-type reservoir.

Fractured basement rocks, which may be igneous, metamorphic, or ancient sedimentary, produce oil commercially in western Kansas[47] and in California.[48] Over a million barrels of oil have been produced from the fractured top of the basement pre-Cambrian quartzite by 15 wells in Rice County, Kansas. Scattered wells in three other pools in this district also produce from quartzite, and three wells in one pool and one in another produce from fractured pre-Cambrian

[43] Harold W. Hoots, "Origin, Migration, and Accumulation of Oil in California," *Calif. Div. of Mines, Bull.* 118 (August, 1941), p. 267.

[44] S. M. Reynolds, "Oil Production from Fractured Rocks on the West Side of the San Joaquin Valley," *Bull. Am. Assoc. Petrol. Geol.,* Vol. 31 (December, 1947), pp. 22–39.

[45] Louis J. Regan and A. W. Hughes, "Fractured Reservoirs of Santa Maria District, California," *Bull. Am. Assoc. Petrol. Geol.,* Vol. 33 (January, 1949), pp. 32–51.

[46] W. S. Eggleston, "Summary of Oil Production from Fractured Rock Reservoirs in California," *Bull. Am. Assoc. Petrol. Geol.,* Vol. 32 (July, 1948), pp. 1352–1355.

[47] Kenneth K. Landes, "Oil Production from pre-Cambrian Rocks in Kansas" (abstract), *Oil Weekly,* Vol. 93 (March 27, 1939), p. 74.

[48] Richard G. Reese, "El Segundo Oil Field," *Calif. Div. of Mines, Bull.* 118 (March, 1943), pp. 295–296; John H. Beach and Arthur S. Huey, "Geology of Basement Complex, Edison Field, California," *Am. Assoc. Petrol. Geol., Program Annual Meeting,* Los Angeles, 1947; J. C. May and R. L. Hewitt, "The Nature of the Basement Complex Oil Reservoir, Edison Oil Field, California," *Bull. Am. Assoc. Petrol. Geol.,* Vol. 31 (December, 1947), pp. 2239–2240.

granite.[49] A part of the production in the El Segundo, California, field comes from fractured schist. The "schist" discovery well in the Edison field of California, completed in 1945, was drilled 83 feet into the basement crystallines for an initial potential production of 528 barrels per day. Within the next two years 106 producers were completed in the fractured metamorphics in this field, with reservoir thicknesses ranging up to 1350 feet. According to Eggleston,[50] the Santa Maria Valley and Wilmington fields also produce from fractured basement rocks; at the time his paper was written, Eggleston estimated that 15,000 barrels per day, nearly 2 per cent of the total for California, was coming from basement reservoirs, a source of oil formerly considered to be entirely impossible.

Even *igneous rocks,* in addition to those underlying sedimentary sections, may be valuable oil reservoir rocks. Although the total of known occurrences of hydrocarbons in igneous rocks is large,[51] the number of commercial occurrences is much smaller. Sellards [52] lists two in Cuba, one in Mexico, and fourteen in Texas. Production from the Cuban fields is obtained from fractures in serpentine. The igneous rock field of Mexico is the Furbero in Vera Cruz. A sill of gabbro has been intruded into shale, metamorphosing the shale both above and below the sill. Oil occurs in porous zones in both the gabbro and the metamorphosed shale.

Four Texas counties in the Coastal Plain—Bishop (six fields), Caldwell (four fields), Travis (one field), and Williamson (three fields)—contain oil reservoir rocks that were originally igneous (Fig. 29). In every instance, the volcanic activity that produced the igneous material took place during the Cretaceous period, and the volcanic rocks are embedded in Cretaceous sediments. "In some instances apparently the lava was erupted in the Cretaceous sea and formed a submarine volcanic cone. Some of the volcanic cones projected above sea-level or were subsequently so elevated as to be exposed and subjected to erosion. Some possibly were entirely submarine. A part of the igneous rock did not reach the surface and is found in the formations in

[49] Robert F. Walters, "Oil Production from Pre-Cambrian Basement Rocks in Central Kansas" (abstract), *Bull. Am. Assoc. Petrol. Geol.,* Vol. 34 (March, 1950), p. 622.

[50] W. S. Eggleston, "Summary of Oil Production from Fractured Rock Reservoirs in California," *Bull. Am. Assoc. Petrol. Geol.,* Vol. 2 (July, 1948), p. 1353.

[51] Sidney Powers *et al.,* "Symposium on Occurrence of Petroleum in Igneous and Metamorphic Rocks," *Bull. Am. Assoc. Petrol. Geol.,* Vol. 16 (August, 1932), pp. 717–858.

[52] E. H. Sellards, "Oil Accumulation in Igneous Rocks," *Science of Petroleum* (Oxford Univ. Press, 1938), Vol. 1, pp. 261–265.

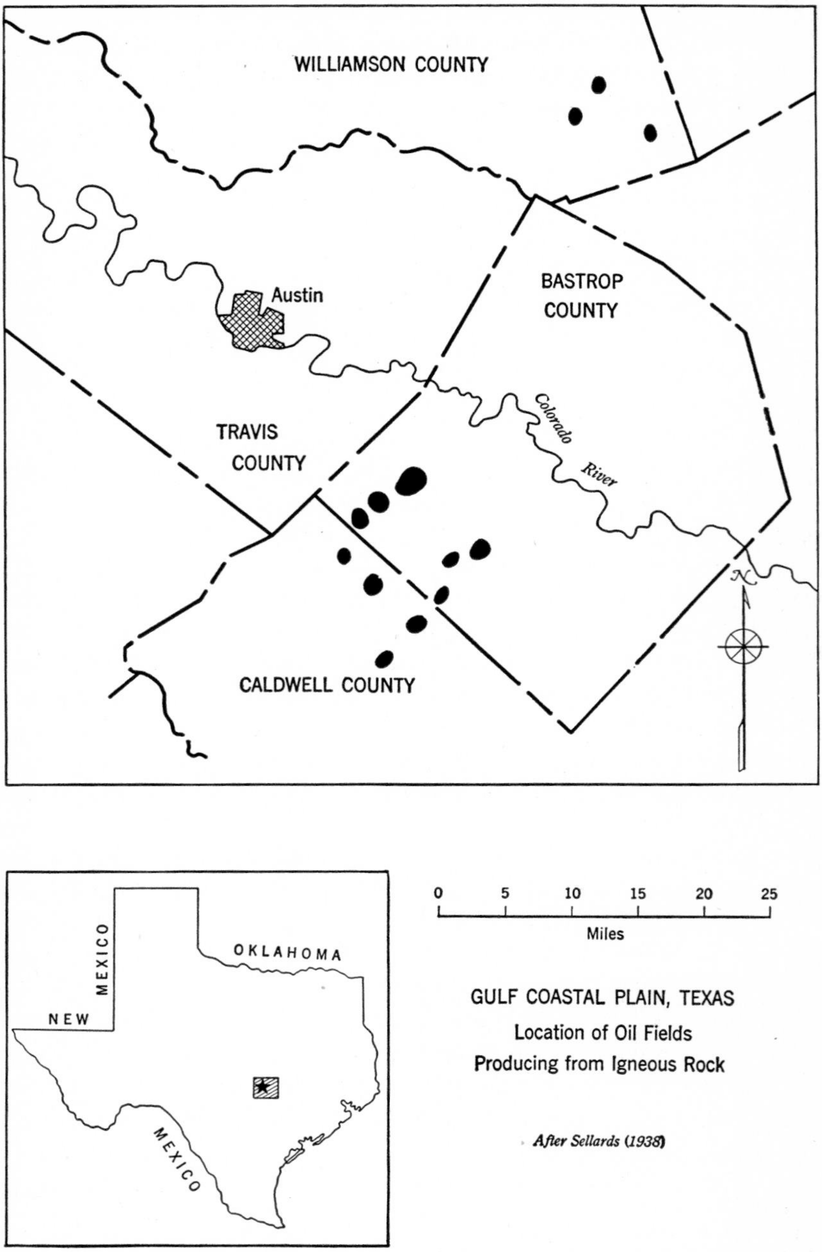

WILLIAMSON COUNTY
Austin
BASTROP COUNTY
TRAVIS COUNTY
Colorado River
CALDWELL COUNTY
N

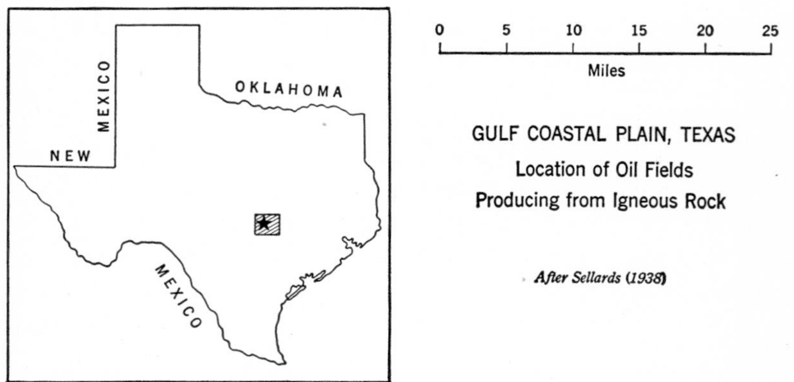

FIG. 29. Oil fields of Texas with igneous rock reservoirs. *Courtesy Texas Bureau of Mines and Geology.*

the form of laccoliths, dykes, or sills. Many of the igneous masses in this region, originally embedded in the Cretaceous strata, are now exposed. None of the exposed igneous rock produces oil, and of the embedded igneous masses many are likewise non-productive." [53] The porosity is apparently in part primary, due to the vesicular character of the flow rocks, and in part secondary due to the alteration of the volcanic material. Over 17 million barrels of oil have been produced from igneous rock reservoirs in Texas.

CAP ROCKS. To be effective, a reservoir rock must be overlain by relatively impervious material which is called "cap rock." The same term is also used in a completely different sense for the cap lying at the top of a prism of salt in a salt dome, which is described in Chapter 8. The function of the reservoir cap rock is to prevent further upward migration of oil or gas. It plays an essential role in oil accumulation, but ordinarily rocks of this type are sufficiently abundant in the stratigraphic section so that their presence can be assumed.

The sole qualification of a cap rock is that it be impervious to the passage of hydrocarbons in any volume. Shale is by far the most common cap rock because it is almost invariably impervious and at the same time is the most abundant sedimentary rock in the earth's crust. The majority of sandstone reservoirs, and many limestone reservoirs, are capped by shale. Other common caps are dense limestones and tight sandstones. Sandstones may be impervious because of thorough cementation or because of the presence of fine particles of clay or silt in the interstitial openings. Much less common barriers to further upward migration of oil and gas include anhydrite or gypsum, fault gouge, and (very rarely) igneous rocks.

AGE OF RESERVOIR ROCKS.[54] The geologic age of reservoir rocks is but one of several ages or times that the petroleum geologist must consider. Of comparable importance is the age of the source materials and the time of hydrocarbon generation; of greater import is the time at which accumulation takes place (Chapter 8). But reservoir rock age has one outstanding advantage: it is the only one that can be determined consistently with some degree of exactness.

[53] E. H. Sellards, *op. cit.*, p. 261.

[54] W. A. J. M. van Waterschoot van der Gracht, "The Stratigraphical Distribution of Petroleum," *Science of Petroleum* (Oxford Univ. Press, 1938), Vol. 1, pp. 58–62; "Oil Zones of the United States," in various issues of *Oil and Gas Jour.* between March 8, 1943 (Cambrian and Lower Ordovician) and Oct. 28, 1943 (Miocene and Pliocene); L. B. Kellum, "Petroleum Stratigraphy" (privately published, 1944).

Actually the age of an oil- or gas-filled reservoir rock is more or less accidental. The presence of the hydrocarbons is due to a combination of reservoir rock and trap which afforded sanctuary to the oil or gas. Inasmuch as one or both of these conditions may be the result of geological activities taking place long after deposition, the age of the host rock is not too significant. The source organisms may or may not have been deposited during the same geological period.

In the past the age of the reservoir rock was considered to be much more important than it is today. As a matter of fact, too great attention to geologic age of producing formations led to the development of a series of prejudices that impeded the search for new deposits. It was categorically stated in practically every oil district that there was "no oil below the blank formation," the blank being the name of whatever the stratigraphically deepest reservoir for that area happened to be at the moment. The discovery of oil in commercial quantities in pre-Cambrian rocks should bring an end to the game of limiting reservoir rocks to certain favored periods.

Reservoirs range in age from pre-Cambrian to Pleistocene. Some periods are, however, much more important than others as a time of reservoir rock deposition. The greatest production comes from rocks deposited during periods of thick and widespread sedimentation, with a considerable volume of porous and permeable rock present in the section. Benign climates are not essential to the deposition of reservoir rock, but they are essential to the accumulation of source organic material. The greatest periods of reservoir rock deposition were also times of widespread flourishing life, but the time involved in a geologic period is great and the two were not necessarily contemporaneous.

Throughout the world, the Tertiary is the outstanding period of reservoir rock deposition. Other important periods, mainly in the United States, are the Cretaceous, Pennsylvanian, Mississippian, Devonian, and Ordovician. The following review of the age of reservoir rocks has been summarized from van der Gracht,[55] with some newer information added. The names of the reservoir formations, and other stratigraphic details, are given in the regional discussions (Part III).

Cenozoic Reservoirs. The Tertiary, mainly Miocene and Pliocene formations, is almost the sole source of oil in California. It is the only oil-producing period along the Gulf Coast margin in Texas and Louisiana. There, as a general rule, the reservoir-containing epochs

[55] W. A. J. M. van Waterschoot van der Gracht, *op. cit.*, pp. 61–62.

progress from Pliocene to Eocene from the coast inland. Non-marine strata of Tertiary age yield oil in commercial quantities in the Powder Wash field of Colorado.[56]

To list the foreign fields that produce from Tertiary reservoirs is to call the roll of almost all the major oil districts outside the United States. In South America the oil fields of Trinidad, Venezuela, Colombia, and Peru are in Tertiary rocks; in Europe the fields of Rumania and southern Russia; all the Middle Eastern production, including the prolific fields in Arabia, Iraq, and Iran; as well as the oil in India, Burma, and the Netherlands East Indies comes from the Tertiary.

In southeastern Europe and elsewhere the oil-producing section may extend upward from the Tertiary into the Quaternary.

Mesozoic Reservoirs. The Cretaceous is a prolific source of oil in the United States in the Gulf Coast interior and in the Rocky Mountains. It is also of great importance in Mexico; South America and Europe, however, have minor Cretaceous production.

Jurassic and Triassic reservoirs are relatively unimportant in North America, but some production is obtained in the Rocky Mountain province especially from sandstones of Jurassic age. Some flank production in the north German salt domes comes from Jurassic strata, and the Emba district in Russia northeast of the Caspian produces mainly from Jurassic rocks.

Paleozoic Reservoirs. North America does not have a complete monopoly on Paleozoic oil fields, but it does have the only great fields so far discovered in rocks of this era. The Permian produces in the Texas Panhandle and in the salt basin of western Texas and southeastern New Mexico. Reservoir rocks of Pennsylvanian age are of relatively minor importance in the state of Pennsylvania, but they have yielded enormous quantities of oil and gas in the Mid-Continent, especially in Oklahoma and Kansas. The Rocky Mountain province produces some oil from Pennsylvanian rocks, and southeastern New Mexico and western Texas have both had discoveries in the rocks of that period. Relatively insignificant quantities of oil are obtained in Europe from Carboniferous and Permian reservoirs.

The Mississippian is outstanding in Illinois. Rocks of this period are also productive in other parts of the eastern United States, in the northern Mid-Continent, and in the northern Rocky Mountain prov-

[56] W. T. Nightingale, "Petroleum and Natural Gas in Non-Marine Sediments of Powder Wash Field in Northwest Colorado," *Bull. Am. Assoc. Petrol. Geol.,* Vol. 22 (August, 1938), pp. 1020–1047.

ince, including especially Wyoming, Montana, and Alberta. Devonian reservoirs produce most of the oil in the Appalachian fields and in Michigan. One Siluro-Devonian formation in the Mid-Continent is an important reservoir. The new prolific fields of Alberta produce from Devonian reefs. Silurian reservoirs containing oil or gas occur on the west side of the Appalachian district and across southwestern Ontario i- to Michigan. Texas became a Silurian producer in 1940 when a successful wildcat in Ward County was completed in limestone of that age.[57]

Ordovician reservoirs, several in number, have superseded Pennsylvanian as the leading source of oil in the Mid-Continent. The once great Lima-Indiana district of Ohio and Indiana produces from Ordovician dolomites. Other reservoirs of this age occur in Kentucky and Tennessee. Several isolated cases of Cambrian production are on record. Gas has been obtained from Cambrian reservoir rocks in New York for many years. Basal Paleozoic sandstone, tentatively referred to the Cambrian, produces oil in the Mid-Continent. In mid-1948, oil was discovered in considerable volume in a Cambrian reservoir rock in the Lost Soldier field, Wyoming.[58]

Oil is produced commercially from the pre-Cambrian in Russell County, Kansas.

[57] C. D. Cordry and M. E. Upson, "Silurian Production, Shipley Field, Ward County, Texas," *Bull. Am. Assoc. Petrol. Geol.,* Vol. 25 (March, 1941), pp. 425–427.

[58] E. W. Krampert, "Commercial Oil from Cambrian Beds in Lost Soldier Field, Wyoming" (abstract), *Am. Assoc. Petrol. Geol., Program Annual Meeting,* St. Louis, 1949, pp. 12–13; Gilbert M. Wilson, "Cambrian Production at Lost Soldier is Significant Wyoming Discovery," *World Oil,* Vol. 128 (November, 1948), pp. 76–77.

Chapter 8

ACCUMULATION: TRAPS

The final stage in the natural history of an oil or gas field is the trapping of the hydrocarbons into an accumulation of exploitable size. The first prerequisite to accumulation, a reservoir rock, was discussed in the preceding chapter. The second prerequisite is that the reservoir be *closed* so that the hydrocarbons will be trapped within. A closed reservoir, hereafter referred to as the *trap*, is a body of reservoir rock completely surrounded above a certain level by impervious rock. The amount of *closure* is the vertical distance between the "certain level" and the highest point reached by the reservoir rock. All traps must have closure, but the concept is best illustrated in elliptical anticlines and domes, which can be mapped readily by structure contours. Closure begins at the level of the lowest *possible* closed contour and extends upward to the apex of the structure. The approximate amount of closure can be calculated by multiplying the number of closed contours by the contour interval; the actual closure lies within one contour interval of this figure.

The amount of closure is also the *maximum* vertical distance through which hydrocarbons can accumulate in the reservoir rock; any additional oil would flow out of the structure beneath the inverted lip of the trap. Rarely are traps completely filled with oil. More commonly the oil-water contact lies well above the lowest closed contour.

The structural *relief* is the maximum vertical distance between the top of a fold and the bottom of the deepest neighboring syncline. It is always greater than the closure. The structural relief gives some idea of the extent of the local "gathering area" down-dip from the trap.

CLASSIFICATION OF TRAPS

Several classifications of traps have been proposed. Wilson,[1] before presenting his own classification in a paper published in 1934, re-

[1] W. B. Wilson, "Proposed Classification of Oil and Gas Reservoirs," *Problems of Petroleum Geology* (Am. Assoc. Petrol. Geol., 1934), pp. 433–445.

viewed those put forth by others. Since then several other classifications have appeared.[2] The classification used in this book is a simplification of that originally submitted by Wilson [3] and modified by Heald.[4] It follows:

Classification of Oil and Gas Traps

- I. Structural traps.
  - *a.* Folds.
  - *b.* Faults.
  - *c.* Fissures.
- II. Varying permeability traps.
  - *a.* Varying permeability caused by sedimentation.
  - *b.* Varying permeability caused by ground water.
  - *c.* Varying permeability caused by truncation and sealing.
- III. Combined structural and permeability traps.

Structural traps are the result of movements of the earth's crust. The second class (II) contains all traps in which closure is due to more or less abrupt termination of permeability in a direction parallel to the bedding without the intervention of a fault. The term most often used for this class is "stratigraphic" trap, but Wilson [5] points out that it is not exactly applicable, for the strata may continue even though the permeability does not.

Oil accumulations may result from *single traps, multiple traps,* or *combination traps.* A single trap is illustrated by the accumulation of oil in a reservoir rock across the top of a structural dome. An example of multiple trapping is the occurrence of oil beneath an asphalt seal in one part of a field and beneath an anticlinal axis in another part. Another example is presented by traps all of the same nature, as a series of small domes superimposed upon a large anticline. Combination trapping is very common. It differs from multiple

[2] William B. Heroy, "Petroleum Geology," *Geol. Soc. Am. 50th Anniversary Vol.* (1941), pp. 512–548; C. W. Sanders, "Stratigraphic Type Oil Fields and Proposed New Classification of Reservoir Traps," *Bull. Am. Assoc. Petrol. Geol.,* Vol. 27 (April, 1943), pp. 539–550; O. Wilhelm, "Classification of Petroleum Reservoirs," *Bull. Am. Assoc. Petrol. Geol.,* Vol. 29 (November, 1945), pp. 1537–1580; I. O. Brod, "Geological Terminology in Classification of Oil and Gas Accumulation," *Bull. Am. Assoc. Petrol. Geol.,* Vol. 29 (December, 1945), pp. 1738–1755; Sylvain J. Pirson, "Genetic and Morphologic Classification of Reservoirs," *Oil Weekly,* Vol. 118 (June 18, 1945), pp. 54–59.

[3] W. B. Wilson, *op. cit.,* p. 442.

[4] K. C. Heald, "Essentials for Oil Pools," *Elements of the Petroleum Industry* (Am. Inst. Min. Met. Engineers, 1940), pp. 26–62.

[5] W. B. Wilson, "Classification of Oil Reservoirs," *Bull. Am. Assoc. Petrol. Geol.,* Vol. 26 (July, 1942), pp. 1291–1292; H. R. Lovely, "Classification of Oil Reservoirs," *ibid.,* Vol. 27 (February, 1943), p. 224.

trapping in that the traps are mutually dependent in closing the reservoir. *Most of the accumulations credited to varying permeability are actually due to a combination of erratic permeability and structural position.* Some of the fields so credited are entirely structurally controlled, as pointed out by Sanders.[6] Examples are accumulations lying across anticlines and containing local barren spots due to erratic permeability. In these places the trapping is entirely anticlinal, but the distribution within the trap is controlled by the local porosity.

Some great oil fields are due to structural trapping; others are the result, in part at least, of varying permeability. Several attempts have been made to evaluate the relative importance of these two types of accumulation. According to Levorsen: "Of the 22 largest oil pools in the United States, according to the *Oil and Gas Journal's* list, over half of the oil production was obtained from pools in which the dominant trap-making element was a change from porosity to non-porosity." [7] Wilson [8] and Hornbaker [9] each made a census of the published descriptions of oil fields. Wilson studied the articles in Volumes 1 and 2 of *Typical American Oil Fields* (Am. Assoc. Petrol. Geol., 1929) and found that approximately half the fields that were described produced from anticlines or domes without complications. Hornbaker surveyed all the publications of the American Association of Petroleum Geologists and other sources and found that 57 per cent of the descriptions covered fields with structural trapping and the remaining 43 per cent fields with varying permeability an important factor in the accumulation. Of course a census of published descriptions tends to minimize the importance of the commonplace, in this case anticlinal accumulation, because of the greater interest in the unusual. On the other hand, structural traps are much more readily discovered than the varying permeability type, and therefore it is highly probable that a greater proportion of the total number of varying-permeability traps remains to be discovered than of structural traps.

The conclusion appears justified that structural position or attitude is of utmost importance, being the sole factor in many accumulations

[6] C. W. Sanders, "Stratigraphic Type Oil Fields and Proposed New Classification of Reservoir Traps," *Bull. Am. Assoc. Petrol. Geol.*, Vol. 27 (April, 1943), p. 540.

[7] A. I. Levorsen, "Stratigraphic versus Structural Accumulation," *Oil and Gas Jour.*, Vol. 34 (March 26, 1936), p. 42.

[8] W. B. Wilson, "Proposed Classification of Oil and Gas Reservoirs," *Problems of Petroleum Geology* (Am. Assoc. Petrol. Geol., 1934), p. 445.

[9] A. L. Hornbaker, "Structural and Stratigraphic Oil Traps," *unpublished thesis* (Univ. Michigan, 1947), pp. 57–58.

and a contributing factor in most others, and that varying porosity has played an important role in oil trapping in many fields and its *relative* importance is likely to increase in the future.

STRUCTURAL TRAPS

Folds, faults, and fissures are structural features that may cause oil and gas to accumulate in exploitable deposits. They result from diastrophic movements in the earth's crust. Of the three, folds are by far the most important in the quantity of hydrocarbons impounded.

In the following discussion, the traps that result from, or are accompanied by, the flowage of salt are described separately from the folds.

FOLDS. Folds originate through vertical and horizontal movements; pseudofolds can result from initial dips. Vertical forces are of greatest importance in the non-mountainous provinces such as the Mid-Continent, although horizontal stresses create most of the folds in the orogenic belts.

There are two types of vertical movement: (1) movement up or down due to diastrophic and perhaps even igneous activity in the earth's crust, and (2) settling due either to compaction or to leaching. As a general rule, the locus of the geologic activity that causes vertical movement is in the unexplored crystalline basement rocks. Consequently, the nature of the deep-seated activity that results in folds in the sedimentary rock veneer is not known. Faulting,[10] igneous intrusion, isostatic adjustment, and rock flowage are possibilities that have been suggested at one time or another. There is abundant seismological evidence of deep-seated faulting, and there are many examples in the visible parts of the earth's crust of faults damping out upward into folds. That igneous intrusions also may arch overlying rock is well known from the occurrences in Utah,[11] around the periphery of the Black Hills, and elsewhere.[12] An unusually symmetrical dome (Fig. 30), thought to be the result of laccolithic intrusion, contains oil in Gallatin County, Illinois.[13] Evidence favor-

[10] Alex. W. McCoy, "An Interpretation of Local Structural Development in Mid-Continent Areas Associated with Deposits of Petroleum," *Problems of Petroleum Geology* (Am. Assoc. Petrol. Geol., 1934), pp. 581–627.

[11] Charles B. Hunt, "New Interpretation of Some Laccolithic Mountains and Its Possible Bearing on Structural Traps for Oil and Gas," *Bull. Am. Assoc. Petrol. Geol.*, Vol. 26 (February, 1942), pp. 197–203.

[12] G. L. Knight and Kenneth K. Landes, "Kansas Laccoliths," *Jour. Geol.*, Vol. 40 (January–February, 1932), pp. 1–15.

[13] R. M. English and R. M. Grogan, "Omaha Pool and Mica-Peridotite Intrusives, Gallatin County, Illinois," *Structure Typical American Oil Fields* (Am. Assoc. Petrol. Geol., 1948), Vol. 3, pp. 189–212.

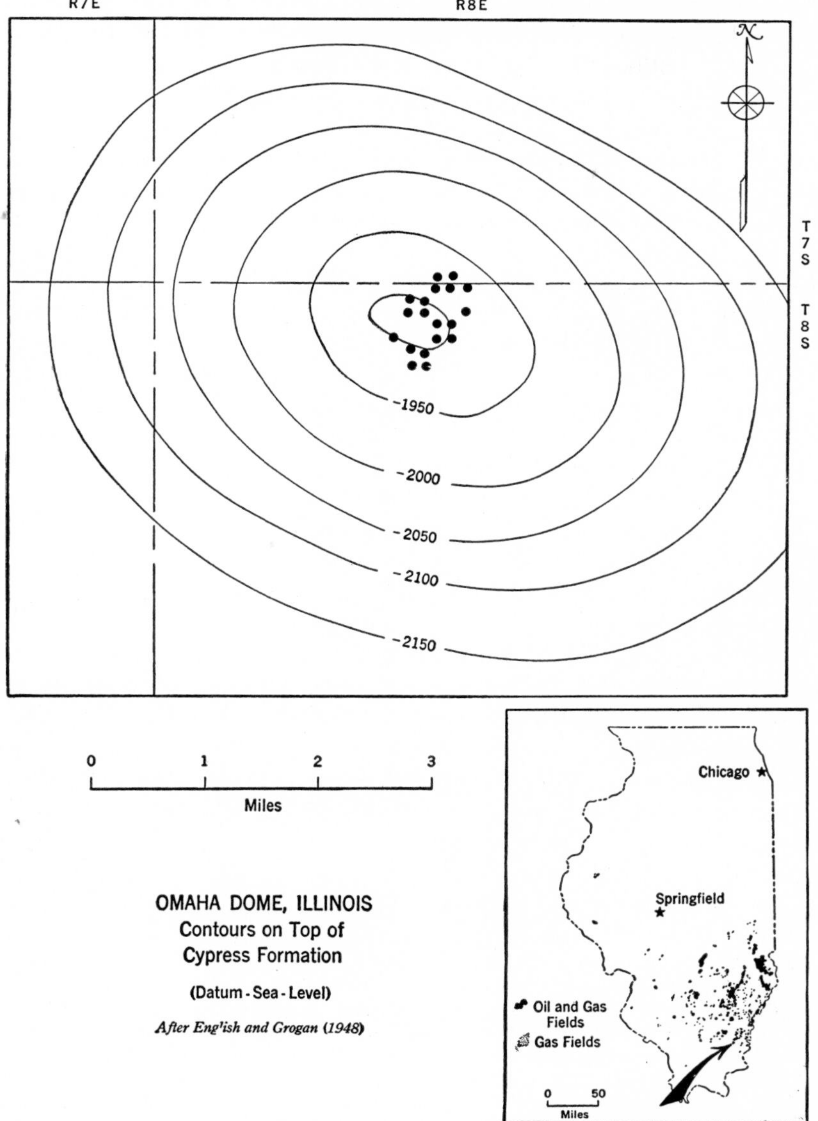

FIG. 30. Producing dome possibly formed by laccolithic intrusion. Omaha field, Illinois. *Courtesy American Association of Petroleum Geologists.*

ing the hypothesis of an underlying intrusive is the presence of dikes and sills of peridotite up to 50 feet in thickness cutting the sedimentary section, including the reservoir strata. It is of course not necessary that the laccolithic-like intrusions reach the sedimentary shell; they can be quite effective in producing differential vertical movements even though they stop in the crystalline basement rocks.

The vertical movements that produce folds in the sedimentary rocks do not have to be upward movements. Lockett [14] and others favor differential subsidence as the means by which the folds in sedimentary basins are formed.

Whatever the cause for the vertical movement, it must be, in most instances, an activity that is subject to repeat performances, for recurrent folding [15] is the rule rather than the exception in the Mid-Continent and similar areas. Subsurface isopach mapping has shown that most structures are the result of several periods of folding. "Once an anticline, always an anticline" [16] is a maxim with wide applicability.

Settling, like subsidence, will not produce folding unless it is differential. Areas of lesser settling, if the sedimentary rocks bend and do not break, will become anticlinal in structure; the greater settling will produce synclines. The most common cause for settling is compaction.[17] Clay and mud, as originally deposited on the sea floor, have porosities as high as 90 per cent. With the piling on of younger sediment, the weight of the overlying rock will squeeze and compact this material until it eventually becomes shale. The possible significance of the liquids escaping during this squeezing was discussed in previous chapters. If the compacting material overlies a smooth floor, and is homogeneous throughout, the settling will not be differential and no folds will result. But if the floor contains hills or monadnocks

[14] J. R. Lockett, "Development of Structures in Basin Areas of Northeastern United States," *Bull. Am. Assoc. Petrol. Geol.*, Vol. 31 (March, 1947), pp. 429–446.

[15] F. M. Van Tuyl and Ben H. Parker, "The Time of Origin and Accumulation of Petroleum," *Quarterly Colo. School of Mines*, Vol. 36 (April, 1941), Chapter 11 (Recurrent Folding and Accumulation), pp. 83–89.

[16] Credited to E. O. Ulrich by G. M. Ehlers.

[17] Hollis D. Hedberg, "The Effect of Gravitational Compaction on the Structure of Sedimentary Rocks," *Bull. Am. Assoc. Petrol. Geol.*, Vol. 10 (November, 1926), pp. 1035–1072; L. F. Athy, "Density, Porosity, and Compaction of Sedimentary Rocks," *Bull. Am. Assoc. Petrol. Geol.*, Vol. 14 (January, 1930), pp. 1–24; L. F. Athy, "Compaction and Its Effect on Local Structure," *Problems of Petroleum Geology* (Am. Assoc. Petrol. Geol., 1934), pp. 811–823; John L. Rich, "Application of Principle of Differential Settling to Tracing of Lenticular Sand Bodies," *Bull. Am. Assoc. Petrol. Geol.*, Vol. 22 (July, 1938), pp. 823–833; G. D. Hobson, "Compaction and Some Oil Field Features," *Jour. Inst. Petrol.*, Vol. 29 (February, 1943), pp. 37–54.

or reefs [18] of older rock which were surrounded by clay or mud before being covered by the same material, there will be less settling over these topographic features, and so the structure of the overlying rock will reflect to some extent the buried topography (Fig. 31). The "draping" of sediments over reefs by differential compaction is an

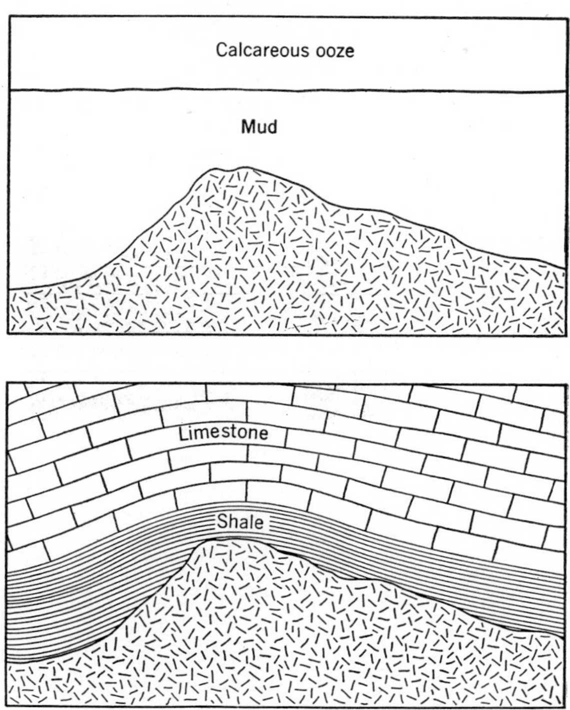

FIG. 31. Differential compaction over hill. Upper: mud deposited around and over hill of crystalline rock. Lower and later: mud has compacted into shale; both the shale and overlying rock are draped over unyielding hill as a result of greater compaction where the mud was thicker. *Drawing by John Jesse Hayes.*

important clue in finding buried reefs today. Likewise, if the compacting material contains lenses of sand, which is relatively noncompactible, the rocks above such lenses will settle through a lower vertical interval and low structural bulges will result (Fig. 32).

Where soluble rocks occur in the section, leaching followed by slumping may produce sagging in the overlying strata, with arching

[18] Gerson H. Brodie, "Structure Forming Role of Limestone Reefs in Eastern Platform Area of West Texas," *Am. Assoc. Petrol. Geol., Program Annual Meeting* (1950), p. 14.

over the blocks that have not collapsed. These folds do not, of course, extend below the soluble rock zone; if the potential reservoir rocks are below this zone, the structure maps based on higher datum planes are valueless. The soluble rocks are limestone and dolomite, salt,

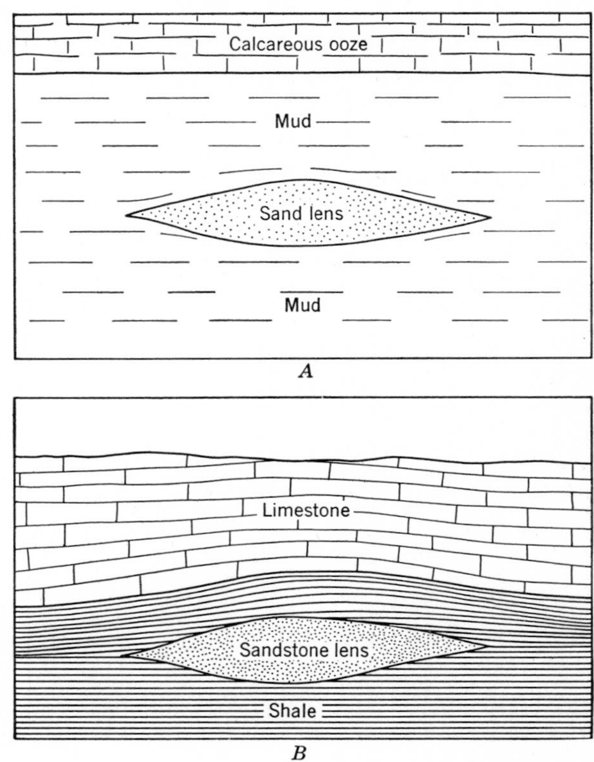

FIG. 32. Compaction over sand lens. Upper: lens of sand surrounded by mud. Lower and later: mud has compacted into shale; strata are arched over sand lens because of its relative incompressibility. *Drawing by John Jesse Hayes.*

and gypsum. Salt collapse structures are especially prevalent around the leached edges of evaporite deposits, as in the Michigan Basin.[19] They can be recognized by (1) their position in respect to the periphery of the salt deposit; (2) the presence of small faults, slickensides, and breccia; (3) the prominence of depression contours; and (4) the irregularity of slope and lack of parallelism of the structures.

[19] Kenneth K. Landes, G. M. Ehlers, and George M. Stanley, "Geology of Mackinac Straits Area," *Mich. Geol. Survey, Pub.* 44 (1945), pp. 123–153.

Residual structural highs may also possibly result from the plastic flow of salt. As will be described later, some salt columns are surrounded by so-called rim synclines, which are most easily explained as downwarps of beds above the salt due to the flow of the salt into domes. Presumably an area surrounded by these synclines would be structurally higher than the immediate surroundings. It has been suggested that the presence of such an isolated body of undisturbed sedimentary salt may be responsible for the doming of the younger sediments and the trapping of oil in the Katy field of Texas.[20]

Horizontal movements are at their maximum in orogenic belts where the earth's crust is under compression. The rock strata are buckled into folds and may even be broken and overthrust. The result is a shortening of the earth's crust, by a matter of several miles in some folded mountain belts. The time-honored explanation for this shortening is the adjustment of the crust to a cooling and shrinking interior.

Some geologists have credited horizontal movements for the folds occurring in plains areas far beyond the mountain fronts. These folds have relatively low dips and are never accompanied by thrust faulting, but otherwise they have the same appearance as compressional folds. As a general rule, however, they do not conform in either age or orientation with the folds produced by tangential forces in any of contiguous mountain systems.[21] It is more likely that these folds result from vertical movements of one type or another.

Oil can be and is trapped in upfolds, whether they be formed by horizontal or by vertical forces. In the Rocky Mountain and Pacific oil provinces, and in most of the foreign fields, the folds have resulted from tangential movements. Oil is even found in regions of overthrust faulting. The recently discovered Rose Hill field in Virginia is an example of this, as is the older Turner Valley, Alberta, field, and the Polish oil fields in front of the Carpathian Mountains.[22]

Pseudo-folds, so called because they look like folds but are not the result of any movement, are formed by deposition parallel to an irregular ocean floor. If the deposition is from suspension, and the slopes are not steeper than the angle of repose of the unconsolidated

[20] A. P. Allison, *et al.*, "Geology of the Katy Field, Waller, Harris, and Fort Bend Counties, Texas," *Bull. Am. Assoc. Petrol. Geol.*, Vol. 30 (February, 1946), p. 169.

[21] Alex. W. McCoy, "An Interpretation of Local Structural Development in Mid-Continent Areas Associated with Deposits of Petroleum," *Problems of Petroleum Geology* (Am. Assoc. Petrol. Geol., 1934).

[22] W. A. J. M. van Waterschoot van der Gracht, "Oil Fields in Folded Rocks," *Science of Petroleum* (Oxford Univ. Press, 1938), pp. 247–251.

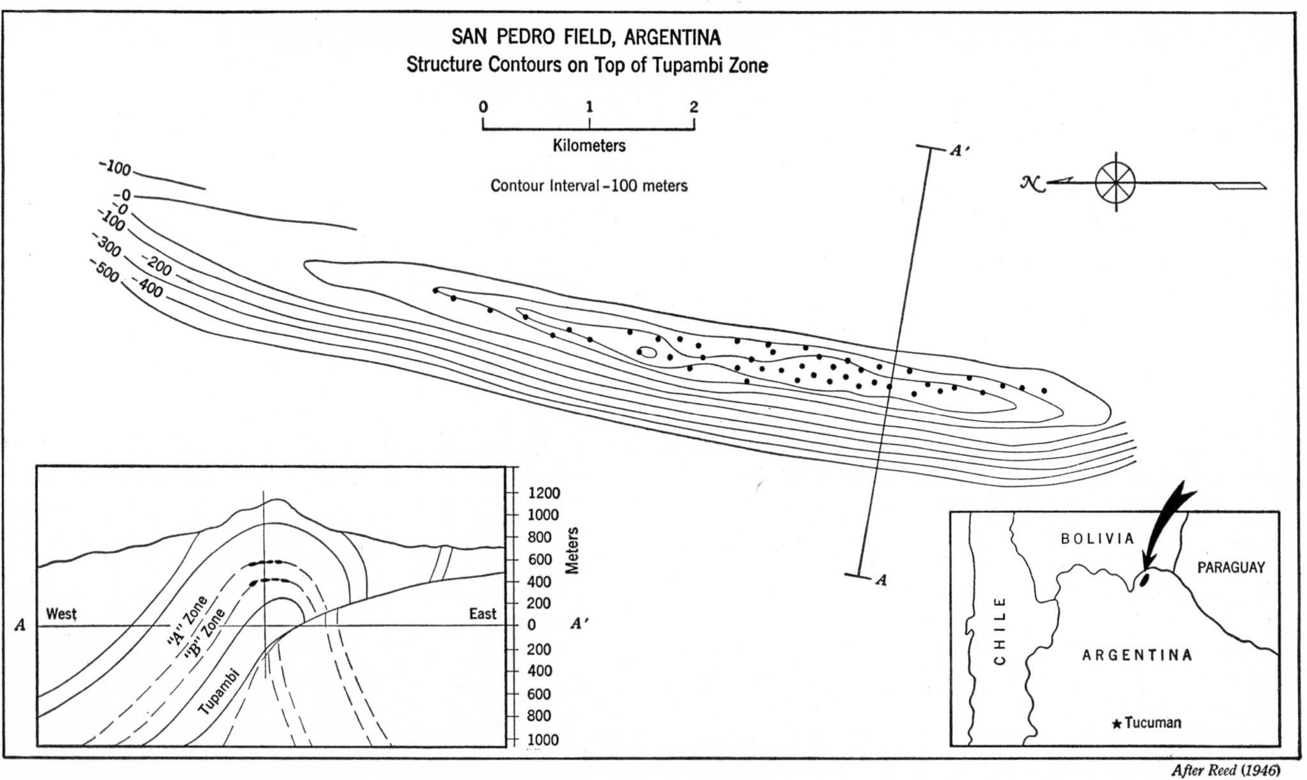

After Reed (1946)

FIG. 34. San Pedro Field, Argentina.

Elongate Anticline. The San Pedro oil field * is in Salta province in northern Argentina. It is the most important of the seven fields that lie in the Tarija sedimentary basin. The San Pedro field occurs along the crest of a partly eroded, tightly folded anticline which makes a ridge in the San Antonio range. The structure was mapped by several oil company geologists beginning as early as 1921. The discovery well for this particular field was completed in 1928, but the first commercial production in the district had been obtained two years earlier.

The structure of the San Pedro anticline as mapped at the top of the main producing sand is shown on the opposite page. The anticline is many times longer than wide, and the production is confined to the uppermost 300 feet of a total closure far in excess of that figure. This anticline is a more or less superficial wrinkle on a great overriding thrust sheet.

Oil occurs in the San Pedro anticline in three zones, of which the upper two are relatively unimportant. These are sandstones in a thick "clay grit" section in the Tarija formation of Permo-Triassic age. The major oil producing zone is the *C* zone in the underlying Tupambi formation, which is also of Permo-Triassic age. The actual reservoirs are sandstones occurring in lenses and layers in a siltstone section 300 feet thick. Apparently enough oil was available at San Pedro to fill only the very top of the trap. The major overthrust was a deep low-angle thrust from the west; the San Pedro anticline, and the relatively shallow fault shown in the cross section on the opposite page, were formed during that eastward push. San Pedro is but one of five or more parallel thrust-faulted anticlinal ranges in the Tarija basin, but it is the only field in which the oil occurs at the highest point of the anticline. The other Salta fields produce from lenticular sands along the axis but down the plunge a considerable distance from the highest point.

The Tarija basin is filled with sediments which may exceed 32,000 feet in thickness. They consist mostly of Devonian shales, Permo-Carboniferous clastics of glacial origin, and Pliocene and Pleistocene continental sediments. The thrusting with concurrent folding did not take place until Pleistocene, an unusually recent date for a hydrocarbon trap. *Courtesy American Association of Petroleum Geologists.*

* Lyman C. Reed, "San Pedro Oil Field, Province of Salta, Northern Argentina," *Bull. Am. Assoc. Petrol. Geol.,* Vol. 30 (April, 1946), pp. 591–605.

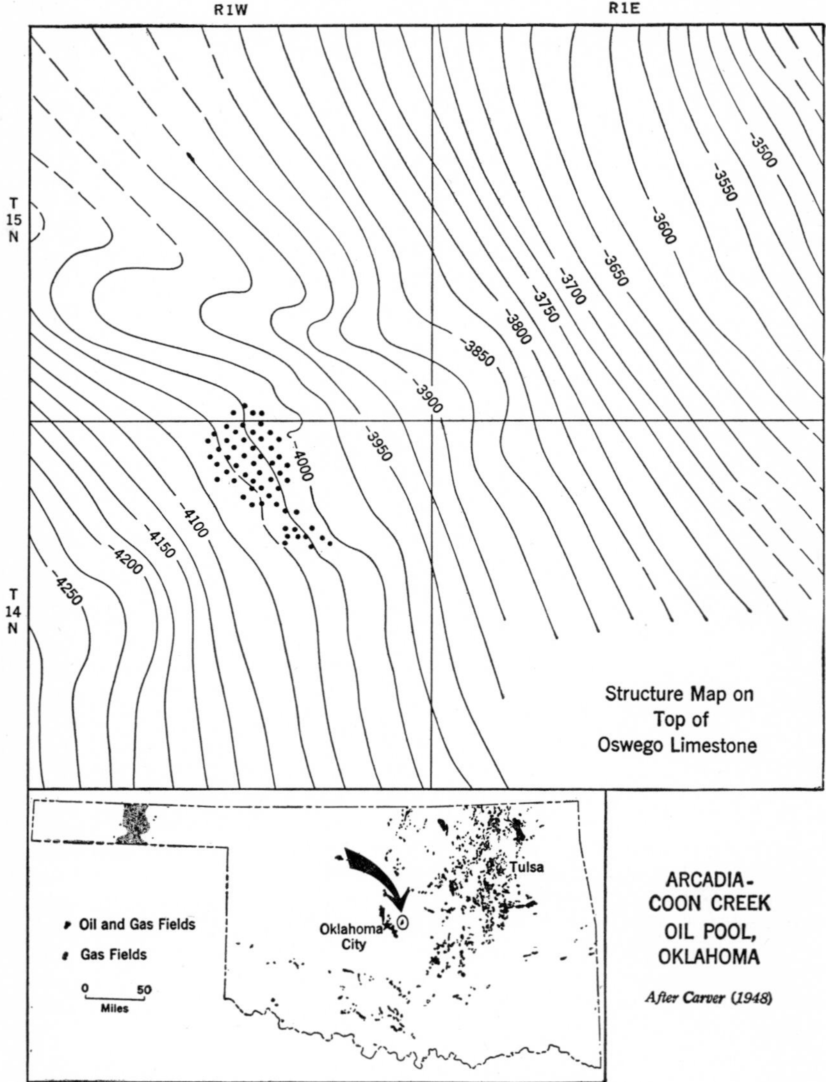

FIG. 35. Arcadia-Coon Creek Oil Pool, Oklahoma.*

Anticline. The left figure is the structure map of the Arcadia-Coon Creek oil field contoured on top of the Oswego limestone of Pennsylvanian age,

* G. E. Carver, Jr., "Arcadia-Coon Creek Oil Pool, Oklahoma and Logan Counties, Oklahoma," *Structure of Typical American Oil Fields* (Am. Assoc. Petrol. Geol., 1948), Vol. 3, pp. 319–340.

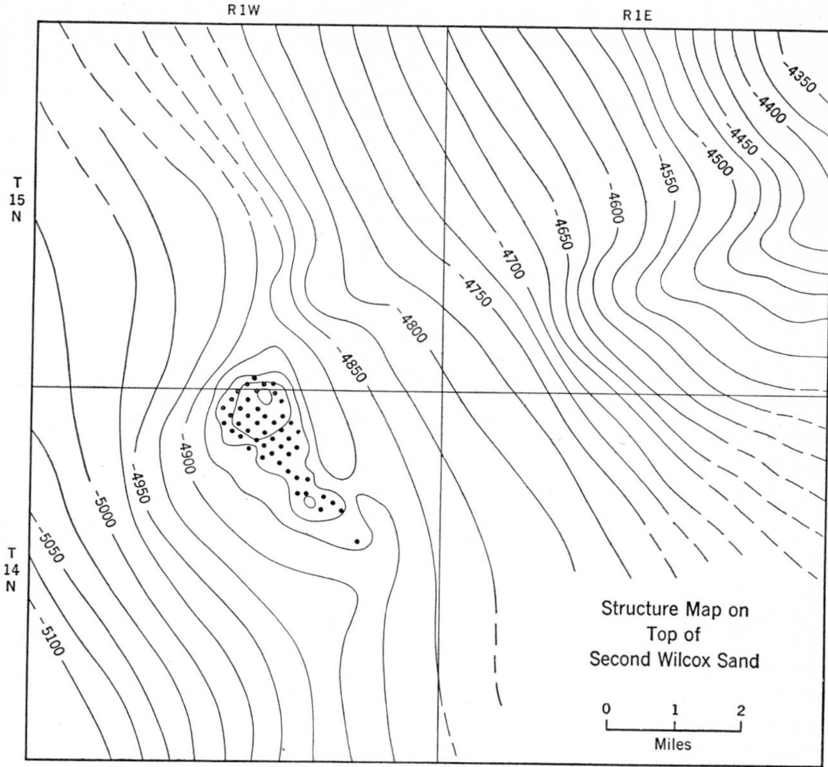

which lies at a depth of about 5000 feet. There is no suggestion of a closed structure at this stratigraphic level. The right drawing shows the structure as contoured on top of the "Second Wilcox" sandstone which is Ordovician in age and which lies at a depth of approximately 6000 feet. This is the producing formation in the Arcadia-Coon Creek pool and is a white sandstone consisting of rounded and frosted quartz grains with a total thickness of about 150 feet. At the producing level the structure is an anticline about 3 miles long by 1 to 1½ miles wide. It has two distinct domes, but the oil-water interface lies at an elevation of approximately 4850 feet below sea level, which is low enough to enclose both domes and the intervening saddle so that production is continuous the length of the anticline. The effective oil sand thickness from the water level to the top of the anticline is 58 feet, out of a total closure of 70 feet.

The dying-out upwards of the anticlinal structure is due to the thinning of the post-"Wilcox" formations across the crest of the anticline. The anticline disappears entirely above the unconformity at the base of the Pennsylvanian. The Mississippian sediments are missing completely across the crest of the anticline, owing to pre-Pennsylvanian erosion and truncation. *Courtesy American Association of Petroleum Geologists.*

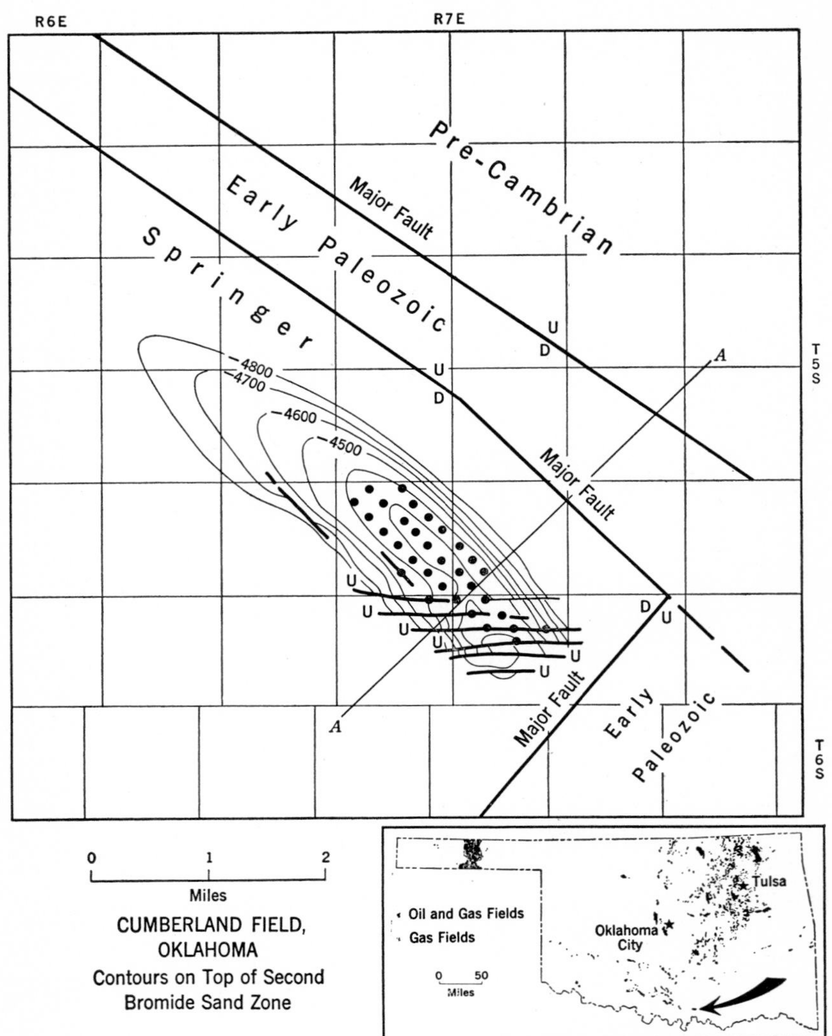

FIG. 36. Cumberland Oil Field, Oklahoma.

Anticline. The Cumberland oil field * lies on the south flank of the Arbuckle Mountain system in southern Oklahoma. The pre-Cambrian core of the Arbuckles is exposed only 12 miles to the northwest. Previous to the drilling of the discovery well in 1940 the Cumberland area had been

* Ira H. Cram, "Cumberland Oil Field, Bryan and Marshall Counties, Oklahoma," *Structure of Typical American Oil Fields* (Am. Assoc. Petrol. Geol., 1948), Vol. 3, pp. 341–358.

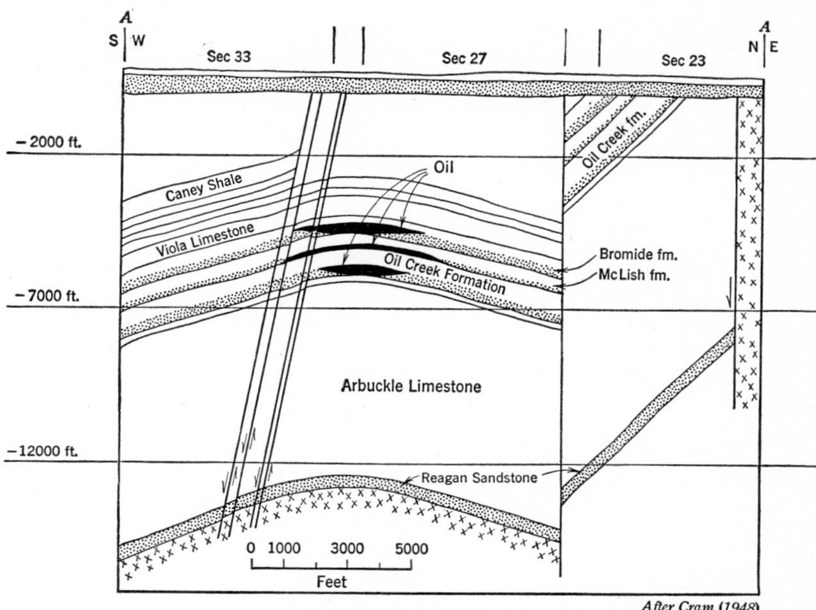

After Cram (1948)

Cross-Section across Axis of CUMBERLAND ANTICLINE

covered by surface, subsurface, magnetic, and seismograph surveys, each one of which increased the interest in the possibilities of the area.

The Cumberland structure is a closed faulted anticline which lies within a down-faulted block of sedimentary rock. The structure map is contoured on top of the second Bromide (Ordovician) sand zone. The contour interval is 100 feet. The map indicates a closure of approximately 550 feet, but it may actually be as much as 1000 feet. The faults that cross the southeast end of the anticline have displacements as great as 300 feet. The major faults at the sides of the graben which contains the Cumberland anticline have displacements somewhere between 7000 and 13,000 feet.

The right figure shows a cross section along line *AA′* drawn from southwest to northeast across the Cumberland anticline in the left drawing. The dips are of such magnitude that no exaggeration of the vertical scale is necessary. The section shows the graben character of the block containing the Cumberland anticline, the Comanchean Trinity sand blanketing everything, and the anticlinal control on the trapping of the oil.

The reservoirs are sandstones belonging to the Bromide, McLish, and Oil Creek formations of the Simpson group of Ordovician age. There are three producing sandstones in the lower part of the Bromide, each one over 100 feet in thickness. At the base of the underlying McLish formation is another 100-foot sandstone which is one of the main producing zones in the field. The still deeper First Oil Creek sand averages 185 feet in thickness, and the Second Oil Creek sand, a large producer, is 210 feet thick. *Courtesy American Association of Petroleum Geologists.*

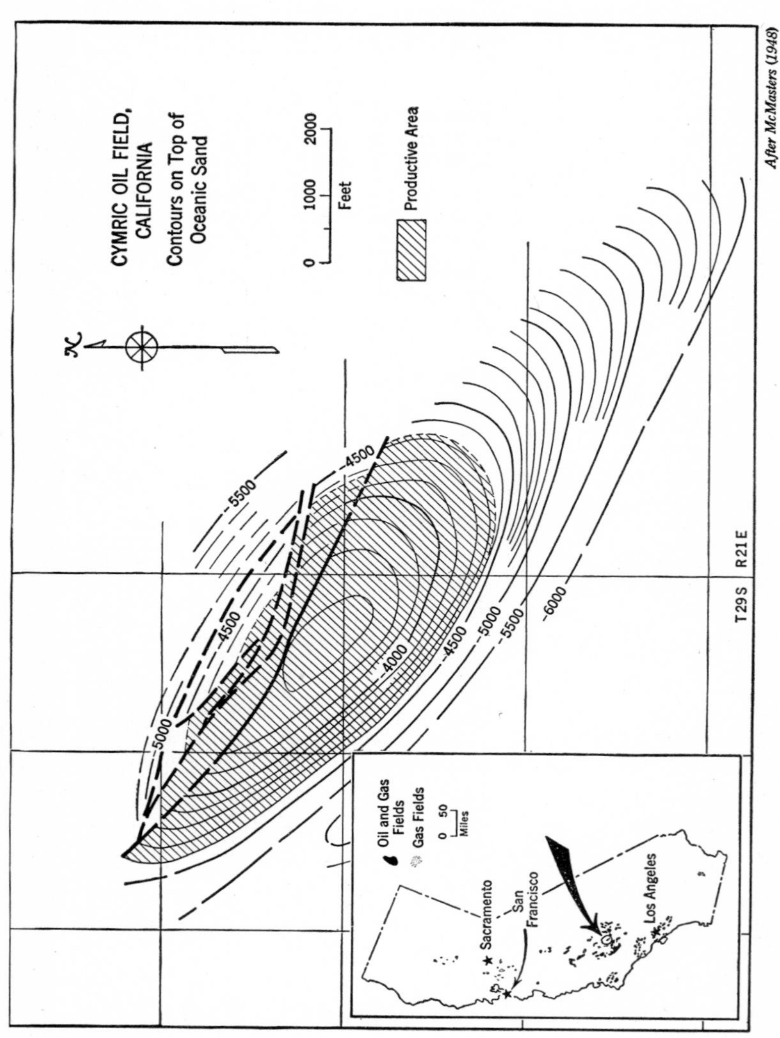
CYMRIC OIL FIELD, CALIFORNIA
Contours on Top of Oceanic Sand
0 1000 2000
Feet
Productive Area
-5500
-4500
-5000
-4500
-4000
-4500
-5000
-5500
-6000
T29S
R21E
Oil and Gas Fields
Gas Fields
0 50
Miles
Sacramento
San Francisco
Los Angeles
After McMasters (1948)

FIG. 37. Cymric Oil Field, California.

Anticline. The Cymric oil field * is in Kern County, California, on the west side of the San Joaquin Valley. The first discovery was made in 1916 in a shallow reservoir; the deeper zone was not discovered until 1945.

On the opposite page is shown the Cymric structure contoured on top of the Oligocene Oceanic sand, which is the leading producing formation out of eleven distinct superimposed reservoirs. The anticline is elliptical in plan and unusually symmetrical. The oil in the Oceanic sand lies above the −4400-foot contour. Faulting on the northeast flank does not contribute to the trapping, but it does limit production by dropping the down-dropped reservoir rock below the general level of the oil-water contact in the Oceanic formation.

The shallow reservoirs, which were the sole producers at Cymric between 1916 and 1945, are the Cymric sands and the Amnicola sand, both belonging in the Tulare formation of Pleistocene-Pliocene age. These sediments are of continental origin, and the reservoir sands disappear to the north and west. The oil is black and tarry with a gravity ranging from 11° to 13°. The deeper reservoirs include one in the Pliocene, six in the Miocene, one in the Oligocene, and one in the Upper Eocene. The Pliocene reservoir is a fine, silty sand. The six Miocene producers occur in four Lower Miocene formations. The prolific Oceanic reservoir of Oligocene age is a uniform, medium-grained, friable, and somewhat silty sandstone. The contained oil is very much lighter than that found in the shallow sands; the gravity varies between 37° and 38°. The eleventh and deepest reservoir is the Point of Rocks sand in the Upper Eocene. This is a hard, fine-grained sandstone containing primarily gas. Structurally high wells in this zone have tested as much as 30,000,000 cubic feet of gas per day with some 52° gravity condensate. Lower wells produce less gas and more oil; the deeper oil runs about 36° in gravity.

Accumulation in the Miocene and older sands is anticline controlled, but distribution of oil varies somewhat from one zone to the next owing to faulting, variable permeability, and truncation beneath unconformities. The anticline is not present in the post-Miocene reservoirs, and trapping there has been the result of wedging-out of the reservoir sands on the flanks of a monocline. *Courtesy American Association of Petroleum Geologists.*

* J. H. McMasters, "Cymric Oil Field, Kern County, California," *Structure of Typical American Oil Fields* (Am. Assoc. Petrol. Geol., 1948), Vol. 3, pp. 38–57.

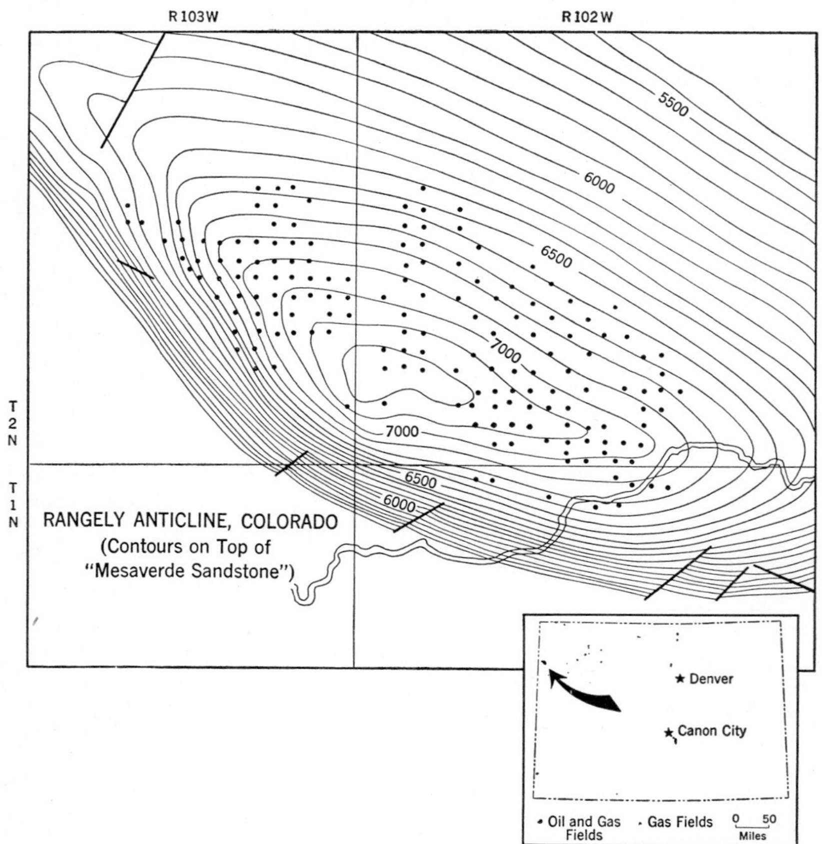

FIG. 38. Rangely Field, Colorado.

Anticline. The Rangely field * lies in northwestern Colorado on the northeastern edge of the Uinta basin. The Cretaceous Mesa Verde sandstone is exposed throughout this area and was used to construct the structure contour map shown on the left. The Rangely anticline at the surface has a closure of 1900 feet. It was recognized by federal geologists as early as 1878. Oil was discovered in shallow fissured shale belonging to the Mancos (Upper Cretaceous) formation in 1902. A large accumulation in the Weber sandstone of Pennsylvanian age was discovered by the drilling of a 7000-foot well in 1931. Exploitation of the field, however, did not become active until 1943, when the demand for oil overcame problems of inaccessibility.

The right map is the Rangely anticline contoured on the producing Weber formation. This anticline, both at the surface and in the subsurface,

* W. Y. Pickering and C. L. Dorn, "Rangely Oil Field, Rio Blanco County, Colorado," *Structure of Typical American Oil Fields* (Am. Assoc. Petrol. Geol., 1948), Vol. 3, pp. 132–152.

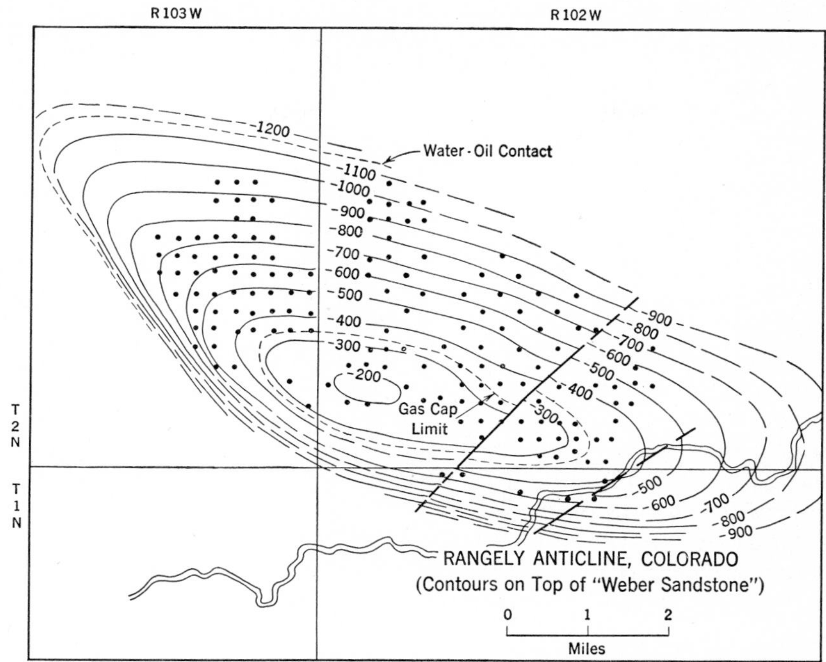

After Pickering and Dorn (1948)

is decidedly asymmetrical with the steeper dip on the southwest side. It is approximately 20 miles long and nearly 8 miles wide in the central part. The structure is crossed by faults toward the eastern end, but these have had little or no effect in the trapping of oil. The oil-water contact plane lies at an elevation of −1160 feet, about 1000 feet below the top of the anticline. However, a gas cap is present in the uppermost 170 feet of the structure, so that the thickness of the oil-bearing section is about 830 feet.

The Weber is a fine-grained, calcareous, and somewhat tight sandstone. The total thickness of the formation is about 550 feet, of which about 30 per cent is calculated to be effective oil sand. In spite of the relatively tight character of the sandstone, initial productions range up to 1000 barrels a day. Development and production procedures at Rangely are controlled by the Rangely Engineering Committee.

The Rangely field is notable for two reasons in addition to its size. It was the scene of one of the few authentic cases (popular opinion to the contrary notwithstanding) of the temporary capping of a successful wildcat because of remoteness from market. Secondly, its discovery was delayed because earlier tests stopped short of the Weber for the reason that it was popularly, but mistakenly, referred to as the Weber "quartzite," a most unlikely reservoir rock. *Courtesy American Association of Petroleum Geologists.*

sediment, the layers may be deposited with initial dips which conform to the topography of the submerged surface.[23] Submergence must be fairly rapid, so that deposition takes place concurrently on hilltop and valley floor. If the low areas fill with fine sediment while the hills are still emergent, the stage is set for compaction but not for initial dip; these two methods of obtaining a reflection of buried topography in the structure of the overlying rocks are mutually antagonistic. Initial dip structures tend to diminish in relief upward and to become lost by flattening a few hundred feet above the erosional unconformity.

Hills in the Permian surface appear to have been reflected upward by initial dips in the overlying Cretaceous sediments in western Kansas.[24] Limestone reefs may provide arched floors for the conformable deposition of overlying sediment.[25] Initial dip folds extend downward only to the unconformity, and considerable money has been spent in drilling wells on surface anticlines that were not anticlines at the depths of the potential reservoirs.

Anticlines. A large proportion of the world's oil has been trapped in upfolds, or anticlines. There are two types of anticlines in nature, but neither one has a horizontal axis like the ridgepole of a roof, for that structure exists only in textbook drawings. Invariably the axis is curved in vertical plane, commonly plunging in both directions from the highest point on the fold. As the axis reaches lower elevations at both ends, the structure contours loop around from one flank to the other. This is the closed anticline, hereinafter referred to merely as *anticline.* Oil and gas are trapped beneath the tops of such folds because they have reached that point by traveling up one flank or the other, owing to their inherent buoyancy; to continue down the other side would be to move in the direction of greater pressure, which is not possible.

The other type of anticline is superimposed upon the flank of a much larger monocline, with the anticlinal axis normal to the regional strike (parallel to the monoclinal dip). The axis of this type of anticline is also curved in the vertical plane, but because of the regional

[23] Josiah Bridge and C. L. Dake, "Initial Dips Peripheral to Resurrected Hills," *Mo. Bur. Geol. and Mines, Bienn. Repts. State Geologist 1927–1928* (1929), pp. 93–99; "Buried and Resurrected Hills of Central Ozarks," *Bull. Am. Assoc. Petrol. Geol.,* Vol. 16 (July, 1932), pp. 629–652.

[24] Kenneth K. Landes and J. W. Ockerman, "Origin of Domes in Lincoln and Mitchell Counties, Kansas," *Bull. Geol. Soc. Am.,* Vol. 44 (June 30, 1933), pp. 529–540.

[25] Heinz A. Lowenstam, "Marine Pool, Madison County, Illinois, Silurian Reef Producer," *Structure Typical American Oil Fields* (Am. Assoc. Petrol. Geol., 1948), Vol. 3, pp. 153–188.

dip, the up-dip plunge is relative rather than actual, and so the fold does not close in that direction. This structure will be referred to hereafter as *plunging anticline*. The structure contours express a plunging anticline by an outward bulge in the direction of the regional dip. The closest imitative topographic feature is a fan, or delta. Folds of this type are sometimes referred to as "structural noses," but this expression is incongruous for a feature that is usually over one hundred times wider than it is high.

The plunging anticline is of utmost importance in fault trap and combination trap accumulations. It supplies closure on three sides; the fourth side may be closed by strike fault (Fig. 65), up-dip facies change (Fig. 71), unconformity overlap (Fig. 76), or other type of permeability barrier. Without the presence of a plunging anticline, these local dams athwart the regional dip are valueless because the would-be trap lacks closure at the sides.

Anticlinal trapping could be illustrated by literally hundreds of oil and gas fields. The selected examples that follow are subdivided into three arbitrary classes: *elongate anticlines,* which are over four times as long as wide; *anticlines,* which are from two to four times longer than wide; and *domes,* which are less than twice as long as wide.

Elongate anticlines are illustrated by the Long Beach (Fig. 33), California, and the San Pedro (Fig. 34), Argentina, fields. Other well-known examples include Ventura Avenue,[26] California; Fairport (Fig. 7),[27] Kansas; Hendrick,[28] Texas; and Kirkuk (Fig. 209),[29] Iraq. Fields selected in this chapter to illustrate trapping in anitclines that are two to four times longer than wide are Arcadia-Coon Creek (Fig. 35), Oklahoma; Cumberland (Fig. 36), Oklahoma; Cymric (Fig. 37), California; Rangely (Fig. 38), Colorado; Augusta (Fig. 39), Kansas; Rattlesnake (Fig. 40), New Mexico; Porter (Fig. 41), Michigan; and Elk Basin (Fig. 42) in Wyoming and Montana. Famous anticlinal fields not illustrated here include Salt Creek,[30] Wyoming; Bradford (Fig.

[26] F. W. Hertel, "Ventura Avenue Oil Field, Ventura County, California," *Structure of Typical American Oil Fields* (Am. Assoc. Petrol. Geol., 1929), Vol. 2, pp. 23–24.

[27] Thomas H. Allan and M. M. Valerius, "Fairport Oil Field, Russell County, Kansas," *Structure of Typical American Oil Fields* (Am. Assoc. Petrol. Geol., 1929), Vol. 1, pp. 35–48.

[28] A. L. Ackers, R. DeChicchis, and R. H. Smith, "Hendrick Field, Winkler County, Texas," *Bull. Am. Assoc. Petrol. Geol.,* Vol. 14 (July, 1930), pp. 923–944.

[29] N. E. Baker, "The Structural Conditions of the Kirkuk Oil Field, Iraq," *Science of Petroleum* (Oxford Univ. Press, 1938), p. 149.

[30] Elfred Beck, "Salt Creek Oil Field, Natrona County, Wyoming," *Structure of Typical American Oil Fields* (Am. Assoc. Petrol. Geol., 1929), Vol. 2, pp. 589–603.

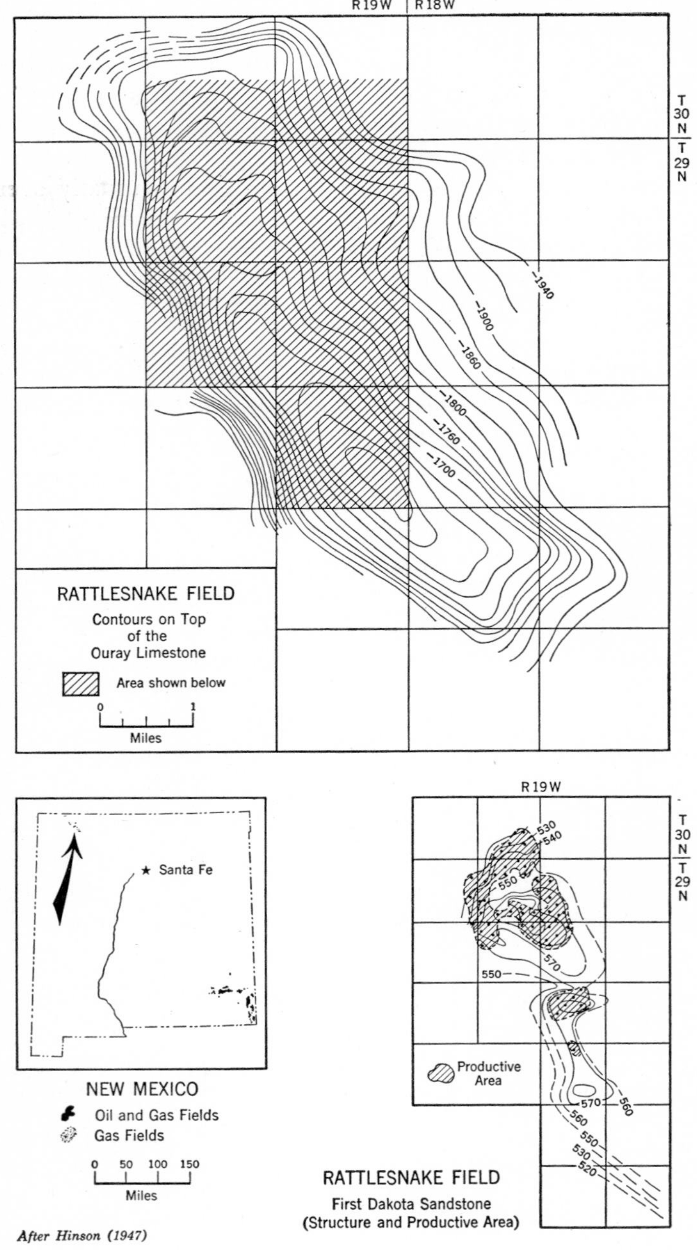
R19W
R18W
T 30 N
T 29 N
-1940
-1900
-1860
-1800
-1760
-1700
RATTLESNAKE FIELD
Contours on Top of the Ouray Limestone
Area shown below
0
1
Miles
Santa Fe
NEW MEXICO
Oil and Gas Fields
Gas Fields
0 50 100 150
Miles
R19W
T 30 N
T 29 N
530
540
550
570
550
Productive Area
570
560
560
550
530
520
RATTLESNAKE FIELD
First Dakota Sandstone
(Structure and Productive Area)

After Hinson (1947)

FIG. 40. Rattlesnake Field, New Mexico.

Anticline. The Rattlesnake field * lies in the Navajo Indian Reservation about 7 miles southwest of Shiprock in northwestern New Mexico. It is in, but near the northwest edge of, the San Juan basin. The Rattlesnake anticline was first mapped by surface observation using a sandstone member of the outcropping Mancos shale as a structure contour datum. The testing of this structure began in 1923, and the first well, which proved to be a small producer, was completed in February, 1924. Deeper reservoirs were found to be productive of oil or gas by tests drilled in 1929 and 1942.

The upper figure is a subsurface structure map of the Rattlesnake Field contoured on top of the deep Ouray limestone of Mississippian-Devonian age. The contouring is based on four wells and a seismograph survey. Helium-bearing natural gas occurs across the top of the anticline in four porous zones in the upper part of the Ouray limestone at depths in the neighborhood of 7000 feet. Porosity is of two types, solution porosity and porosity due to openings between crystals of dolomite. The Rattlesnake anticline is about 6 miles long and asymmetrical, with the steeper dip to the southwest. The apex at the Ouray level is near the southeast end of the axis.

The lower figure shows the structure contour map contoured on the shallow First Dakota sandstone. This sandstone lies more than 6100 feet above the Ouray limestone. In the intervening distance the axis of the anticline has shifted northeast approximately ⅝ mile, owing to the asymmetry of the fold, and the apex of the structure has shifted along the axis 2½ miles to the northwest.

The earlier production at Rattlesnake was entirely from the Dakota sandstones which lie at depths of 800 to 900 feet. Production has been obtained from three different sandstones within the Dakota formation. Accumulation in the Dakota has taken place in the highest parts of the anticline, but only where the sandstones have adequate porosity and permeability. The Hermosa formation of Pennsylvanian age, which lies at a depth of approximately 5700 feet, was exploited for its oil content by two wells over a period of eleven years, but production ceased in 1940. Three other wells have tested this formation but found no more than showings. *Courtesy American Association of Petroleum Geologists.*

* H. H. Hinson, "Reservoir Characteristics of Rattlesnake Oil and Gas Field, San Juan County, New Mexico," *Bull. Am. Assoc. Petrol. Geol.,* Vol. 31 (April, 1947), pp. 731–771.

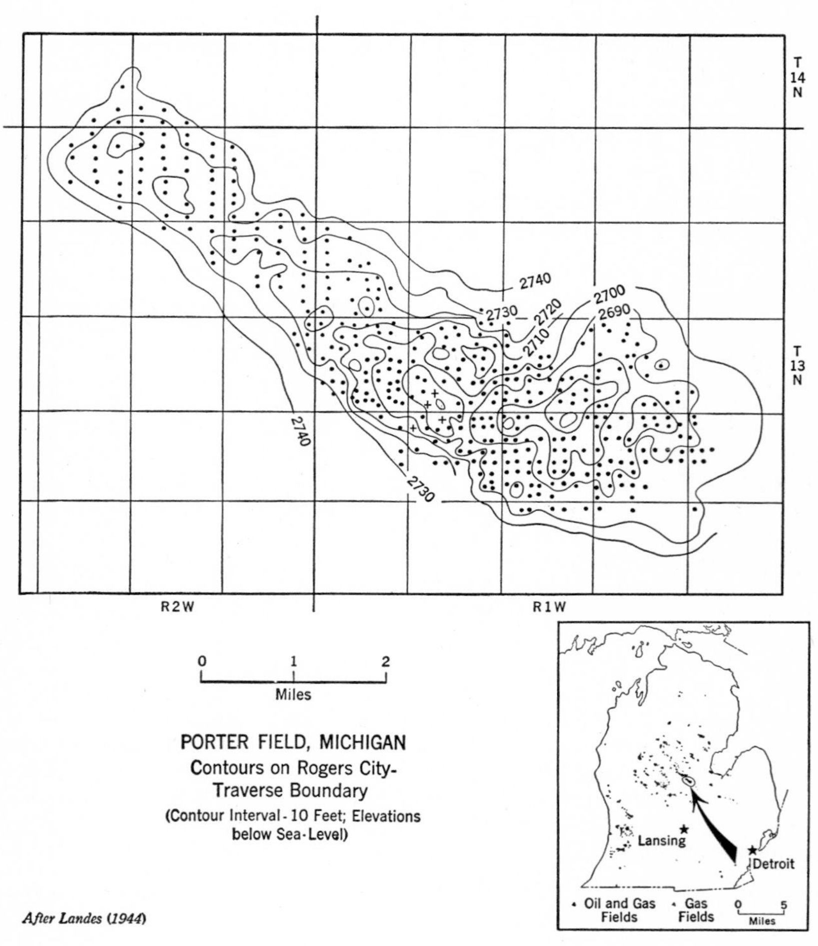

PORTER FIELD, MICHIGAN
Contours on Rogers City-Traverse Boundary
(Contour Interval - 10 Feet; Elevations below Sea-Level)

After Landes (1944)

Fig. 41. Porter Field, Michigan.

Anticline. The Porter lies in Midland County, Michigan, close to the center of both the southern peninsula of Michigan and the Michigan sedimentary basin.* The northwest-southeast trend of anticlines on which the Porter field lies was discovered in 1926 through the study of brine-well records. Subsurface methods were necessary from the start because of the cover of several hundreds of feet of glacial drift. The discovery well for the Porter field was drilled in 1931.

The structure map on the opposite page is contoured at the base of the Traverse formation of Devonian age. It shows an anticline with a node to the southeast and a long spur to the northwest. The closure on the dome is only about 50 feet, and the structural relief in the immediate vicinity is a little over 90 feet.

Beneath the Traverse formation is 4 to 35 feet of Rogers City limestone, a dark brown organic limestone which thins across the crest of the Porter anticline owing to pre-Traverse folding and erosion. The Dundee limestone, also of Devonian age, and the only formation to produce in any volume at Porter, underlies the Rogers City. It is porous toward the top, owing to pre-Rogers City emergence and leaching. It is possible that after the submergence of the leached Dundee the oil entered from above from the compacting Rogers City ooze.

Permeability in the Dundee is erratic laterally as well as vertically. Accumulation has been controlled by the anticlinal structure, but distribution on the anticline has been controlled by permeability. Dry holes (literally "dry") have been drilled high on the flank of this anticline where the limestone had not been leached sufficiently for commercial storage of oil. A group of four dry holes, completely surrounded by producing wells, can be seen on the map on the opposite page in sections 17 and 20.

The elevation of the oil-water interface is 35 feet lower at the northwest end of the Porter field than at the east end. One possible explanation of this not uncommon situation is that regional tilting has occurred after accumulation took place and recently enough so that readjustment has not yet been completed. *Courtesy American Association of Petroleum Geologists.*

* Kenneth K. Landes, "Porter Oil Field, Midland County, Michigan," *Bull. Am. Assoc. Petrol. Geol.,* Vol. 28 (February, 1944), pp. 173–196.

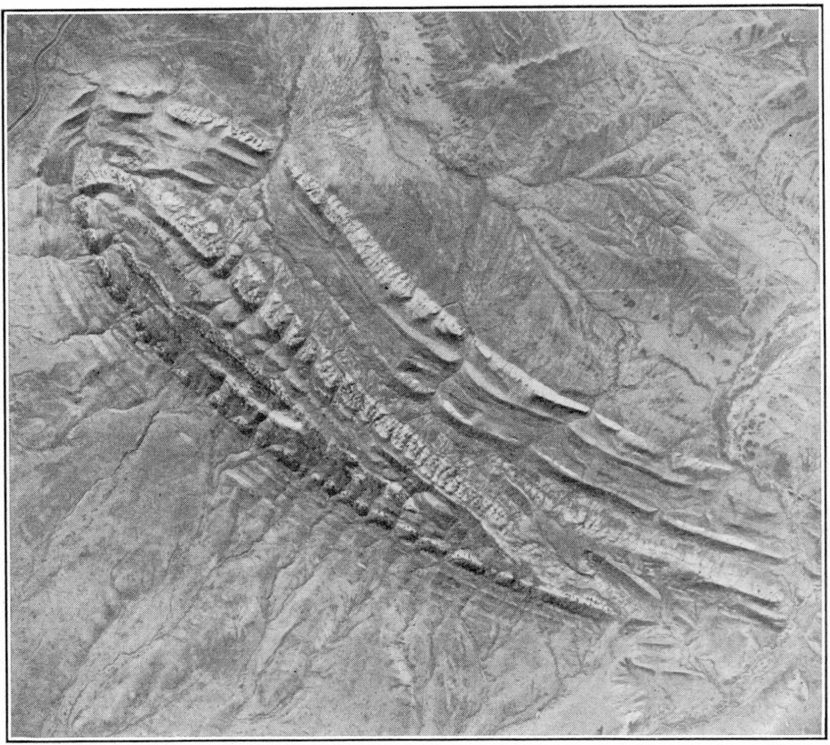

Fig. 42. Elk Basin Field, Wyoming-Montana.

Anticline. The Elk Basin anticline and oil field lies in the north end of the Big Horn Basin.* As can be seen in the air photograph of the Elk Basin, not only is this anticline obvious at the surface but actually a fair job of mapping can be done from air photos. The crest of the anticline is a topographic basin, the result of the cropping there of Cretaceous shales. Shown on the right page is a subsurface structure map contoured on top of the second Wall Creek sandstone. The anticline has 5000 feet of closure, but the oil occurs only in the upper part of the structure.

So far five zones have been found to be oil- or gas-bearing in the Elk Basin anticline. The youngest reservoirs are the First and Second Wall Creek sandstones of the Frontier (Cretaceous) formation, which lie at an average depth of 1500 feet. About 95 per cent of the Frontier oil has come from the Second Wall Creek, which is productive over an area of approximately 500 acres. The many normal faults shown on the structure contour map have affected the distribution of oil on the upthrown blocks, but the trapping has been anticlinal. These faults apparently die out in the formations

* W. S. McCabe, "Elk Basin Anticline, Park County, Wyoming, and Carbon County, Montana," *Bull. Am. Assoc. Petrol. Geol.*, Vol. 32 (January, 1948), pp. 52–67.

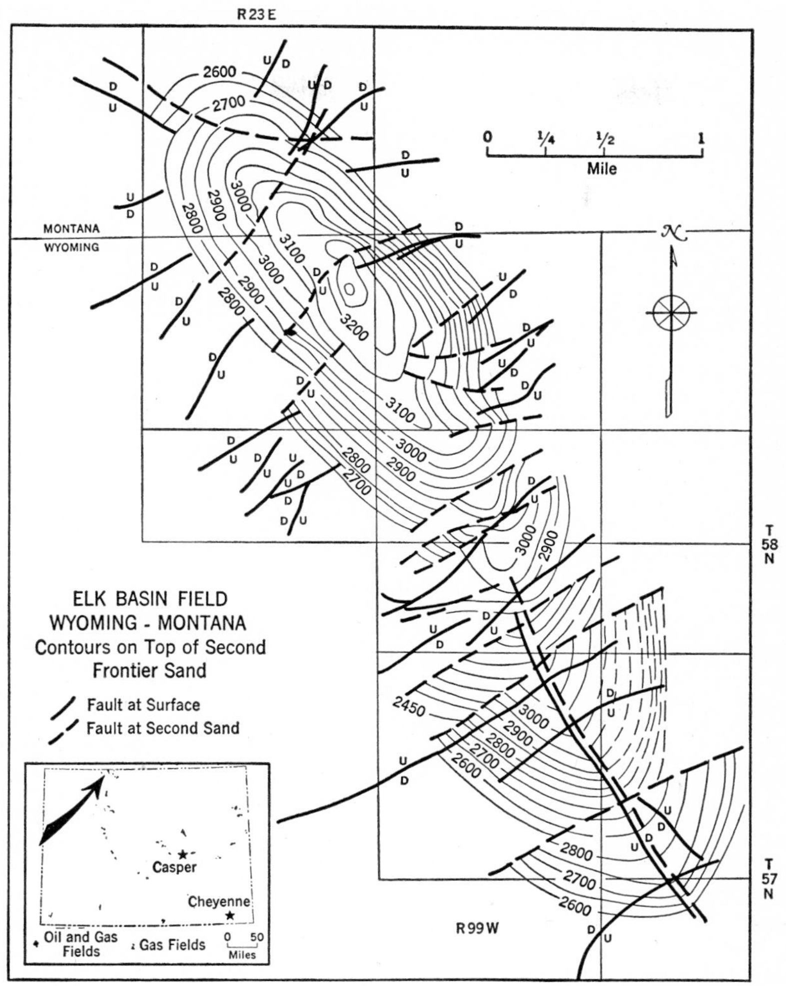

After Bartram (1929)

below the Frontier. The oil in the Wall Creek sandstones is noticeably lighter than the oil in the deeper and older formations.

Gas is produced from the Greybull (Cretaceous) sandstone reached at a depth of about 2600 feet. The Pennsylvanian Tensleep sandstone is the leading reservoir at Elk Basin. It lies at depths ranging between 3900 and 6000 feet. The producing section is about 100 feet thick, and the area is 5000 acres. About 1900 feet of the total closure is oil-bearing.

Oil was discovered in the Mississippian Madison formation between depths of 4350 and 5013 feet by a well completed in 1946. *Courtesy Aero Exploration Company and American Association of Petroleum Geologists.*

89),[31] Pennsylvania; Hobbs,[32] New Mexico; Kettleman Hills,[33] California; and Voshell Field,[34] Kansas. Of many possible domes, the following fields were selected to illustrate domal trapping: Marine (Fig. 43), Illinois; Santa Fe Springs (Fig. 44), California; Big Lake (Fig. 45), Texas; San Joaquin (Fig. 46), Venezuela; and Hitesville (Fig. 47), Kentucky. Other good examples are Bowlegs and Seminole City,[35] Oklahoma; Kevin-Sunburst,[36] Montana; Wilmington,[37] California; and Yates,[38] Texas.

More oil has been produced from simple anticlines than from any other single type of trap. The amount of closure varies from thousands of feet down to tens of feet. The size varies from a minimum length of under a mile to many miles. As a general rule, however, the larger anticlines do not carry oil the entire length; instead, the superimposed domes or nodes are oil-bearing and the intervening saddles contain only water.

Anticlines that are approximately circular in plan are sometimes referred to as *quaquaversal domes.* Salt domes (and probable salt domes) are discussed in the subsequent section. Many additional illustrations of anticlinal trapping can be found in Chapters 9 and 10, which are devoted to the geographic distribution of oil fields.

Other folds also illustrated, for the sake of completeness, are accumulations described as *terrace* traps and *synclinal traps.* They are quantitatively insignificant. The theory behind the terrace trap is that there is a minimum gradient below which oil will not migrate up-dip. Where the dip flattens to less than this minimum gradient, oil will accumulate; reversal of dip direction, as in an anticline, is therefore

[31] Charles R. Fettke, "Bradford Oil Field, Pennsylvania and New York," *Pennsylvania Geol. Survey,* 4th Series, Bull. M21, (1938).

[32] Basil B. Zavoico, "Geology and Economic Significance of Hobbs, New Mexico," *World Petroleum,* Vol. 6 (August, 1935), pp. 459–472.

[33] George C. Gester and John Galloway, "Geology of Kettleman Hills Oil Field, California," *Bull. Am. Assoc. Petrol. Geol.,* Vol. 17 (October, 1933), pp. 1161–1193.

[34] T. C. Hiestand, "Voshell Field, McPherson County, Kansas," *Bull. Am. Assoc. Petrol. Geol.,* Vol. 17 (February, 1933), pp. 169–191.

[35] A. I. Levorsen, "Greater Seminole District, Seminole and Pottawatomie Counties, Oklahoma," *Structure of Typical American Oil Fields* (Am. Assoc. Petrol. Geol., 1929), Vol. 2, pp. 315–361.

[36] W. F. Howell, "Kevin-Sunburst Field, Toole County, Montana," *ibid.,* pp. 254–268; A. J. Collier, "The Kevin-Sunburst Oil Field and Other Possibilities of Oil and Gas in the Sweetgrass Arch, Montana," *U. S. Geol. Survey, Bull.* 812 (1929), pp. 57–189.

[37] E. J. Bartosh, "Wilmington Oil Field, Los Angeles County, California," *Bull. Am. Assoc. Petrol. Geol.,* Vol. 22 (August, 1938), pp. 1048–1079.

[38] Ray V. Hennen and Roy J. Metcalf, "Yates Oil Pool, Pecos County, Texas," *Bull. Am. Assoc. Petrol. Geol.,* Vol. 13 (December, 1929), pp. 1509–1556.

not necessary. In earlier days of oil-finding, many pools were considered to be terrace, or "nose," accumulations because no closure was evident in the structure contours drawn on the outcropping formations. However, with the development of subsurface structure contouring it was found that practically all these structures were closed in the producing formations. This is strikingly illustrated in two maps published by W. B. Wilson [39] (Fig. 48). The Wheat, Texas, field, illustrated in Fig. 49, is the only oil pool described in recent years as being due to terrace accumulation. In a few places, the water table for the bottom water is below the top of the trap, and so the accumulation may be on the flanks of folds. Examples are some of the Miocene sandstone reservoirs of the Midway-Sunset district, California.[40]

As a trap, the closed syncline, or basin, is possible only in the absence of water, which is an unusual situation. Some geologists question the existence of an actual synclinal trap. According to Heald,[41] ". . . investigation of synclinal fields has failed to discover a single one in which both water and gas were absent." The Griffithsville, West Virginia, oil pool is illustrated in Fig. 50, as an example of synclinal accumulation. Because it has a large gas cap, it can be argued that the gas pushed the oil to the bottom of the structure and the oil pushed the water into the finer sediments adjacent to the reservoir rock, but it might also be possible that for some reason there was no water in the reservoir rock in the first place, and so the oil collected at the bottom of the fold and the gas at the top. Some alleged examples of synclinal trapping are in reality porosity traps; the only rock sufficiently permeable for use as a reservoir happened to be at or near the bottom of a syncline.

SALT-CORE STRUCTURES.[42] A salt-core structure is one in which pressures in the earth's crust have caused normally bedded salt

[39] W. B. Wilson, "Proposed Classification of Oil and Gas Reservoirs," *Problems of Petroleum Geology* (Am. Assoc. Petrol. Geol., 1934), pp. 438 and 439.

[40] Harold W. Hoots, "Origin, Migration, and Accumulation of Oil in California," *Calif. Div. Mines, Bull.* 118 (April, 1943), pp. 261–262.

[41] K. C. Heald, "Essentials for Oil Pools," *Elements of the Petroleum Industry* (Am. Inst. Min. Met. Engineers, 1940), p. 46.

[42] A voluminous bibliography has resulted from the widespread interest in structures cored (or probably cored) with salt. The DeGolyer and Vance *Petroleum Bibliography* (College Station, Texas, 1944) lists 94 titles on this subject. The American Association of Petroleum Geologists has published a symposium, *Gulf Coast Oil Fields* (Tulsa, 1936) containing 36 papers dealing with salt-cored and probable salt-cored structures; several of these papers include extensive bibliographies. There is also the older symposium, *Geology of Salt Dome Oil Fields* (Tulsa, 1926). Additional bibliographies are appended to the following articles on this subject: M. A. Hanna, "Geology of Gulf Coast Salt Domes," *Problems of Petroleum*

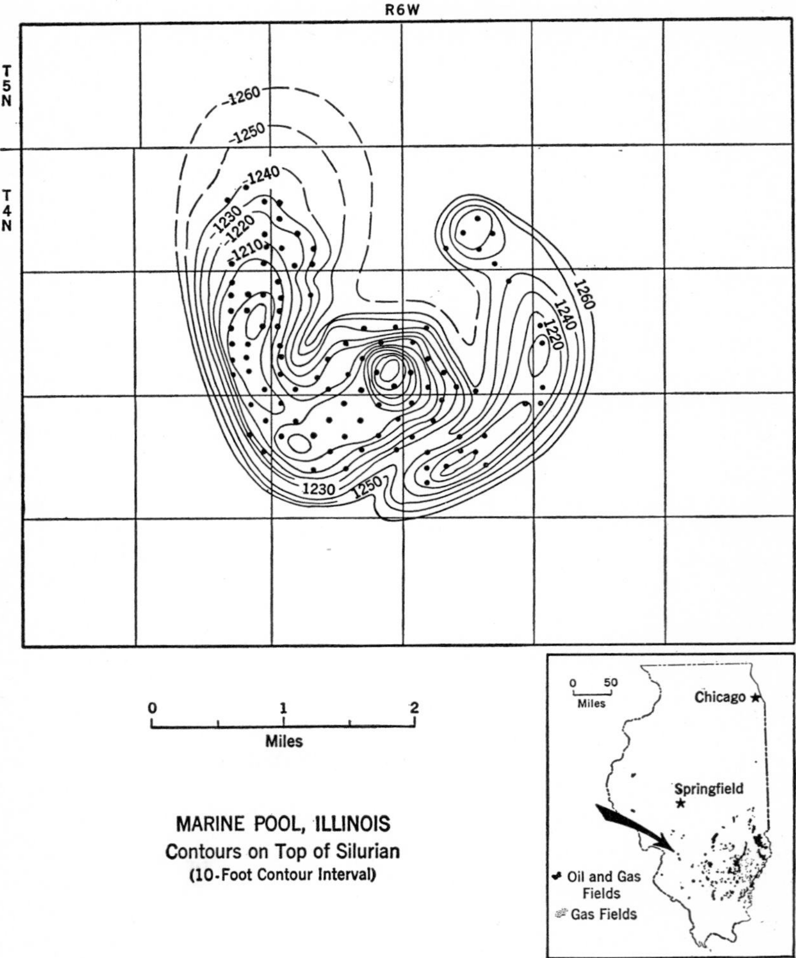

FIG. 43. Marine Pool, Illinois.

Dome. The Marine pool * is in Madison County, Illinois, about 25 miles northeast of St. Louis, Missouri. It lies near the western border of the eastern interior basin. The discovery of the Marine pool was based in part on geophysical exploration. The initial well was completed in 1943. This was the first production of oil from a Silurian reef in Illinois.

The left figure shows the structure of the Marine pool as contoured on top of the Silurian rocks, which at this point were deposited as a reef.

* Heinz A. Lowenstam, "Marine Pool, Madison County, Illinois, Silurian Reef Producer," *Structure of Typical American Oil Fields* (Am. Assoc. Petrol. Geol., 1948), Vol. 3, pp. 153–188.

The reef is horseshoe shaped, and the top has 120 feet of closure. The deeper rocks, belonging to the Ordovician system, conform to the regional dip which is to the east. The younger rocks reflect the reef structurally, but to a diminishing extent upward.

The right figure is a hypothetical cross section of the reef. In its broader aspects the buried Marine reef is similar to outcropping Niagaran reefs around the rim of the Michigan basin. It is, however, less dolomitized, and it has a well-developed detrital cap which is not present on the outcropping reefs.

The structure at the top of the Silurian (left figure) is also largely the topography at the beginning of Devonian deposition. The actual topography of the reef was modified to some degree by erosion, and deposition of reef detritus, before submergence beneath the Devonian sea. There is also the possibility of some slight modification due to later structural wrinkling. It is obvious, however, that in Niagaran time a horseshoe-shaped reef developed through the activity of various organisms in the Niagaran sea. A lagoon was partially enclosed on the northeast side, and a large and a small fore-reef grew on the southeast and east sides of the main reef.

The oil has accumulated in a coquina-like detrital limestone which mantles the reef. As many as four porous zones are present, and in addition some oil is obviously stored in a network of interconnecting fissures which extend not only through the reef limestone but also into the overlying Devonian limestone. Although Lowenstam refers to the Marine pool as a stratigraphic trap it is probable that the domal structure of the porous zone has been as responsible for the trapping as the varying permeability. *Courtesy American Association of Petroleum Geologists.*

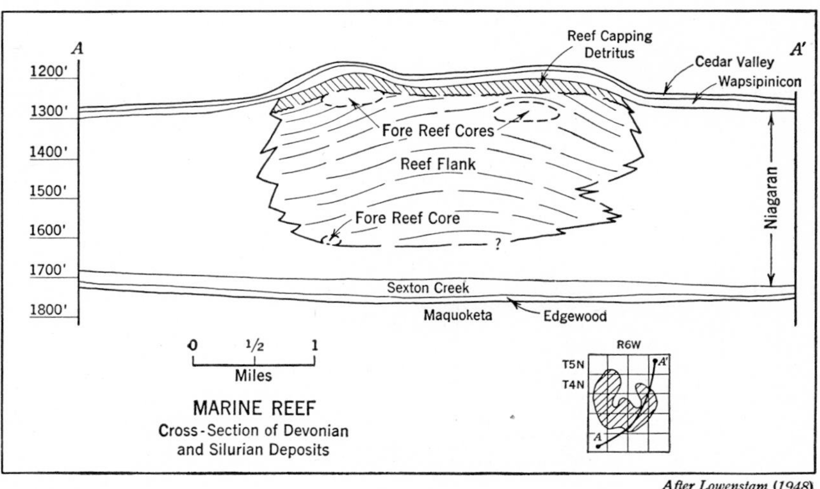

MARINE REEF
Cross-Section of Devonian and Silurian Deposits

After Lowenstam (1948)

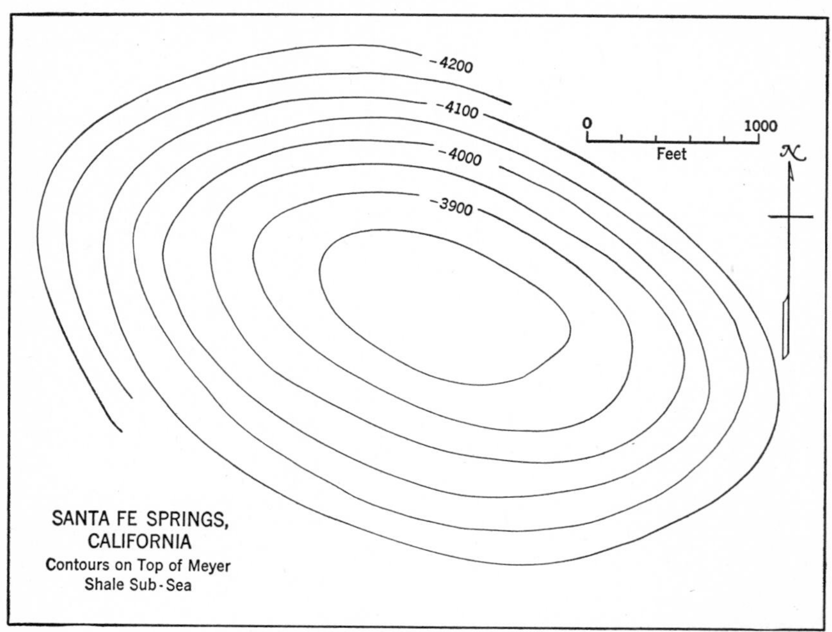

SANTA FE SPRINGS, CALIFORNIA
Contours on Top of Meyer Shale Sub-Sea

After Winter (1943)

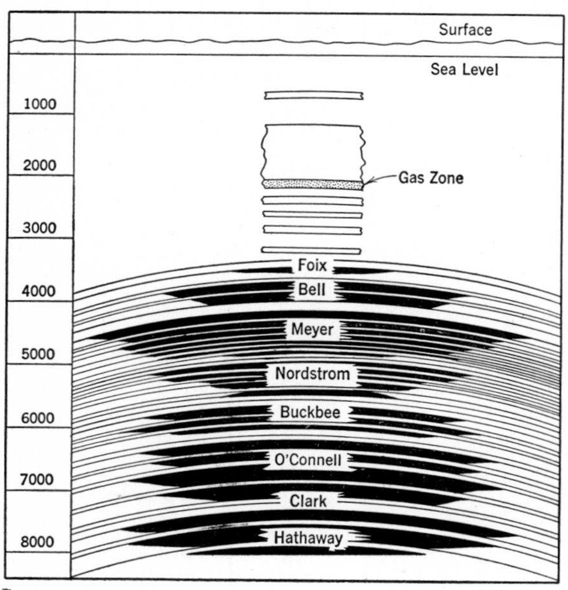

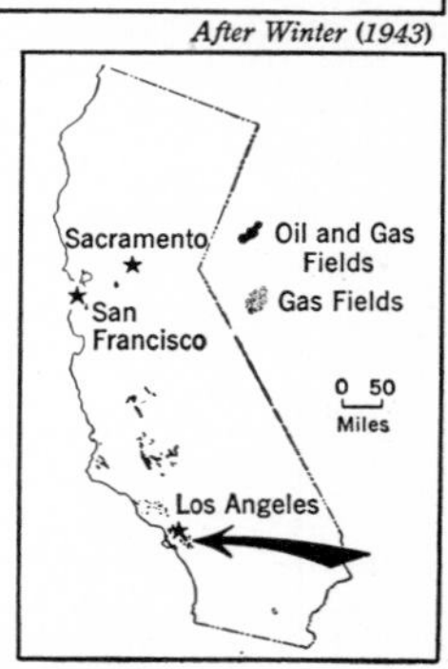

SANTA FE SPRINGS FIELD, CALIFORNIA
Diagrammatic Transverse Section (Original Condition)

FIG. 44. Santa Fe Springs Oil Field, California.

Dome. The Santa Fe Springs oil field * lies in Los Angeles County, about 12 miles southeast of the center of the city of Los Angeles. Although the productive area never exceeded 1500 acres, the total output of the field has been nearly a half billion barrels, making Santa Fe Springs one of the great oil fields of the world. Because of lack of outcrops the anticline could not be mapped by surface surveys, but its presence was suspected from the topography and the appearance of gas in water wells. The discovery well was drilled in 1919.

The subsurface structure map on the opposite page, contoured on one of the oil zones, shows the anticline to be an unusually symmetrical elliptical dome. The dip is quite uniform, and no faults have ever been discovered. The field was originally 2½ miles long and 1 mile wide at the widest point.

The reason for the prolific production at Santa Fe Springs is the presence of eight distinct superimposed oil zones, with from 100 to 550 feet of initially productive sand in each zone. In addition there is a shallow gas zone which lies above the oil sands in the upper part of the Pliocene section. Below are six Pliocene producing zones, of which the third one from the top, the Meyer, has yielded nearly half of the total production from the Santa Fe Springs field. It lies beneath a thick shale at a depth of 4150 feet. The zone consists of 650 feet of sediment, of which two-thirds was initially oil-filled sand. The original area over which this zone was productive was 1450 acres, three times larger than any other Pliocene productive zone.

The two lowest productive zones, the Clark and the Hathaway, are Miocene in age. They produce from depths between 7250 and 8000 feet. The Miocene sands are harder and less porous than the Pliocene sands. The Clark-Hathaway sands underlie 900 acres and contained initially 375 feet (out of twice that thickness) of oil-saturated sand, but they have only produced about 10 per cent of the field's total.

Many of the wells were completed as multiple-zone producers. Three of the Pliocene zones have had per acre recoveries in excess of 150,000 barrels. The initial productions per well ranged from 1000 to 10,000 barrels per day.

Trapping is entirely anticlinal at Santa Fe Springs, with water underlying the oil around the periphery of each zonal accumulation. *Courtesy California Division of Mines.*

* H. E. Winter, "Santa Fe Springs Oil Field," *Calif. Div. Mines, Bull.* 118 (March, 1943), pp. 343–346.

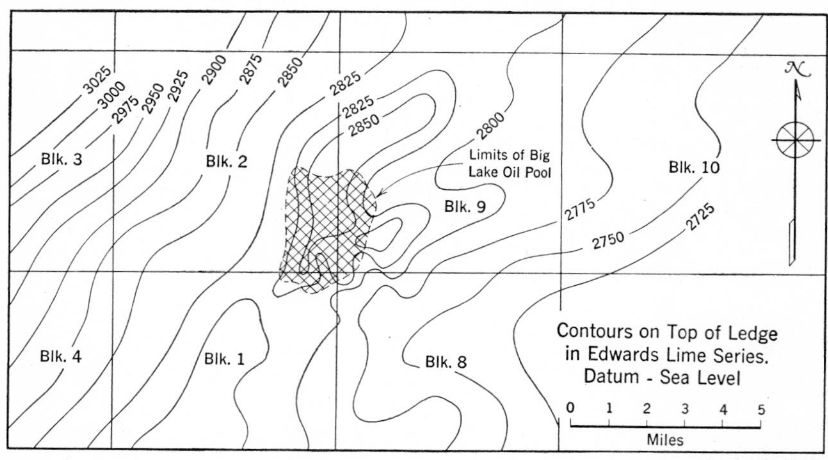

After Hennen (1948)

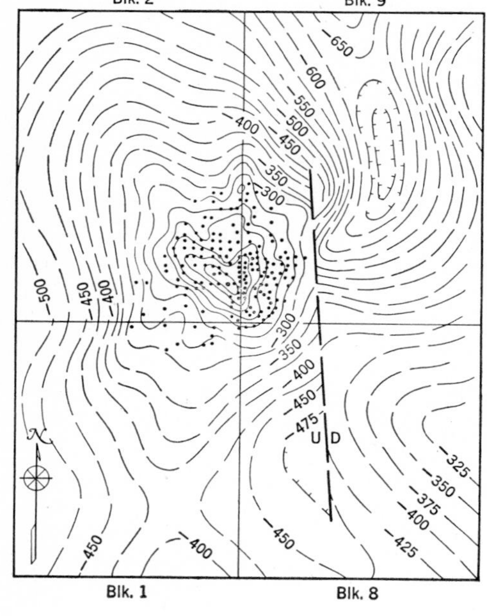

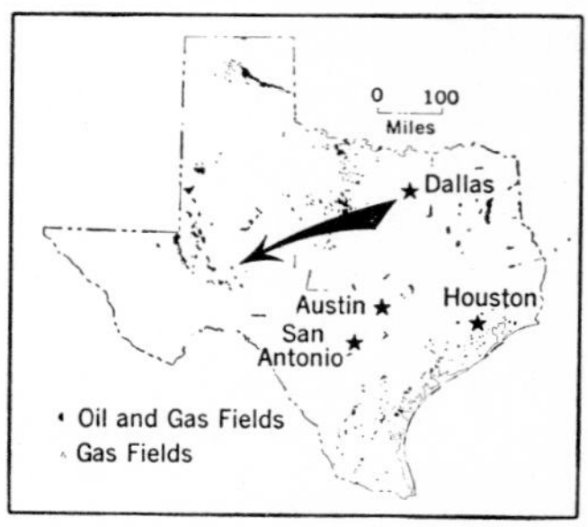

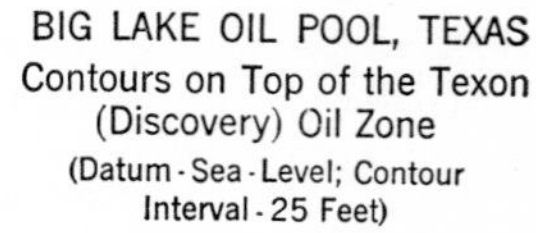

BIG LAKE OIL POOL, TEXAS
Contours on Top of the Texon (Discovery) Oil Zone
(Datum - Sea - Level; Contour Interval - 25 Feet)

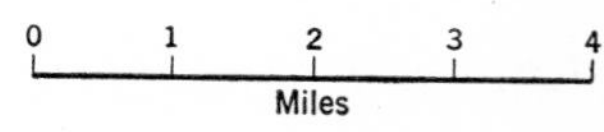

FIG. 45. Big Lake Pool, Texas.

Dome. The Big Lake oil pool * is in the southwestern corner of Reagan Couny, in west Texas. It was the first major oil field to be discovered in what is known now as the west Texas or Permian basin petroliferous province. The discovery well was completed in 1923. The exploration was based on surface geologic studies; the Edwards limestone and other Lower Cretaceous formations crop out in this area.

The upper figure shows the structure of the Big Lake area as contoured on top of a ledge within the Edwards limestone formation. The regional dip is to the northwest into the Permian basin, and the Big Lake fold is one of several anticlines which lie on the southeast flank of this basin. As can be seen from the figure, closure in the surface formations is only 30 feet and the anticline is decidedly elongate in a northeast-southwest direction. The lower figure shows the Big Lake dome as contoured on the producing Texon (Permian) zone. At this level the Big Lake structure is a quaquaversal dome with 250 feet of closure. This is more than eight times the closure in the surface rocks and double that present in the intervening salt measures. The fault shown on the east flank of the dome does not appear in the surface rocks and was probably formed before Cretaceous deposition. It has had no effect on trapping.

Four permeable zones—two in Permian rocks, one in the Pennsylvanian, and one in the Ordovician—carry oil. The two Permian producers are the Shallow and the Texon. The Shallow zone is a silty sand from 30 to 50 feet in thickness lying at a depth of about 2450 feet. Much more important in size and yield is the Texon zone, which lies between 2800 and 3100 feet below the surface. The Texon is a highly porous oölitic dolomite, averaging 22 feet in thickness. The third oil zone is 6300 feet deep. It is a sandstone, 15 feet thick, of probable Pennsylvanian age. The Ordovician reservoir is the deep, but prolific, Ellenberger dolomite. Oil accumulation has been brought about by oil rising through the water-filled reservoirs to the top of the anticline. The oil may have traveled a considerable distance up the flank of the Permian basin from the northwest. *Courtesy American Association of Petroleum Geologists.*

* Ray V. Hennen, "Big Lake Oil Pool, Reagan County, Texas," *Structure of Typical American Oil Fields* (Am. Assoc. Petrol. Geol., 1929), Vol. 2, pp. 500–541.

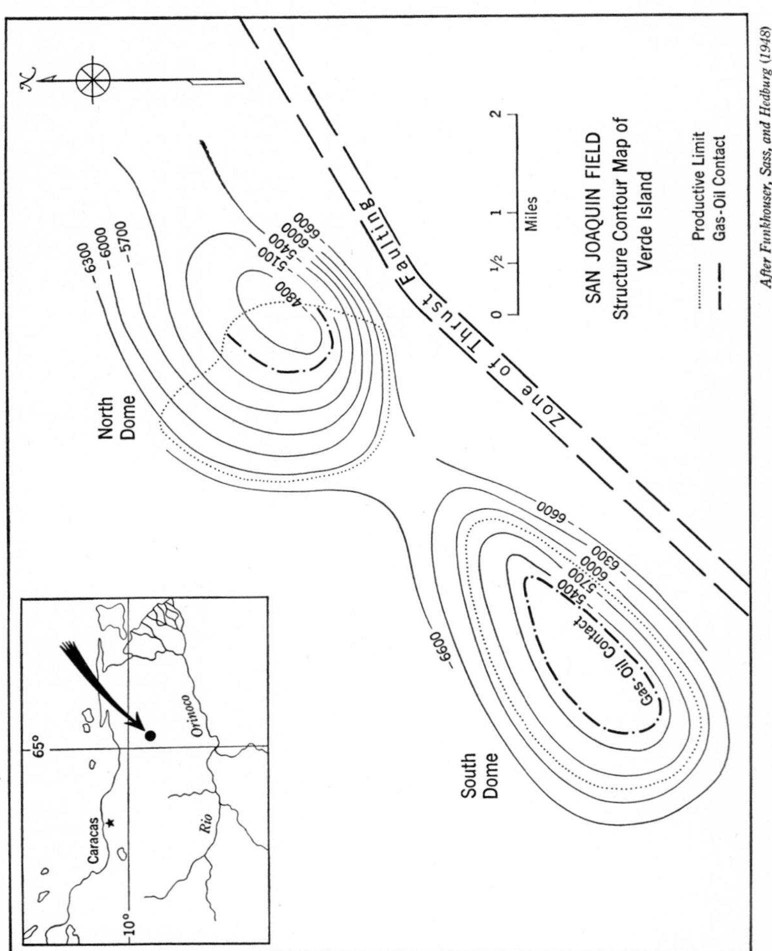

After Funkhouser, Sass, and Hedburg (1948)

FIG. 46. San Joaquin Field, Venezuela.

Domes. The San Joaquin field is one of a group of fields lying in the central part of the state of Anzoategui, in eastern Venezuela.* The San Joaquin and the neighboring Santa Ana domes were first outlined as the result of air-photograph study and surface geological reconnaisance in 1934. This was followed by a seismograph check and the drilling of the discovery well for the Santa Ana field in 1936. The discovery well for the San Joaquin field was completed in 1939.

The map on the opposite page shows by means of contours the structure of the two domes that constitute the San Joaquin field. The datum for the contours is the Verde I sand, one of many oil-bearing sandstones which lie within the Oficina formation of Oligocene-Miocene age. The domes are believed to be the result of drag over a northwest-dipping zone of thrust faulting; the fault planes crop out to the southeast as shown on the map.

The Oficina formation is from 7500 to 10,000 feet thick. It contains twenty-eight sands which have produced oil, and at least fifteen more are known to contain gas. Within the productive section of the Oficina, sandstone beds constitute but 8 per cent. Only the uppermost 1900 feet of the underlying Merecure formation (upper Eocene-lower Oligocene) have been explored as yet. This section is about 50 per cent sandstone and 50 per cent shale. Oil and gas have been found within the sandstones wherever tested. The sandstones are probably interconnecting and so constitute a single reservoir.

The south dome has a closure of about 1200 feet. In the Verde I sand the oil-water contact lies about 600 feet above the saddle between the north and the south domes. The top of the dome contains a gas cap. The oil-water contact is several hundred feet lower on the north dome; a gas cap is present there also. As the Verde I sand lenses out to the east and north, only the west end of the north dome is productive at this stratigraphic level.

The San Joaquin field illustrates almost perfectly the trapping of oil at the top of a dome-shaped structure where a pervious reservoir rock is present. Some gas has separated out from the oil and has accumulated below the very top of the trap. *Courtesy American Association of Petroleum Geologists.*

* H. J. Funkhouser, L. C. Sass, and H. D. Hedberg, "Santa Ana, San Joaquin, Guario, and Santa Rosa Oil Fields (Anaco Fields), Central Anzoátegui, Venezuela," *Bull. Am. Assoc. Petrol. Geol.,* Vol. 32 (October, 1948), pp. 1851–1908.

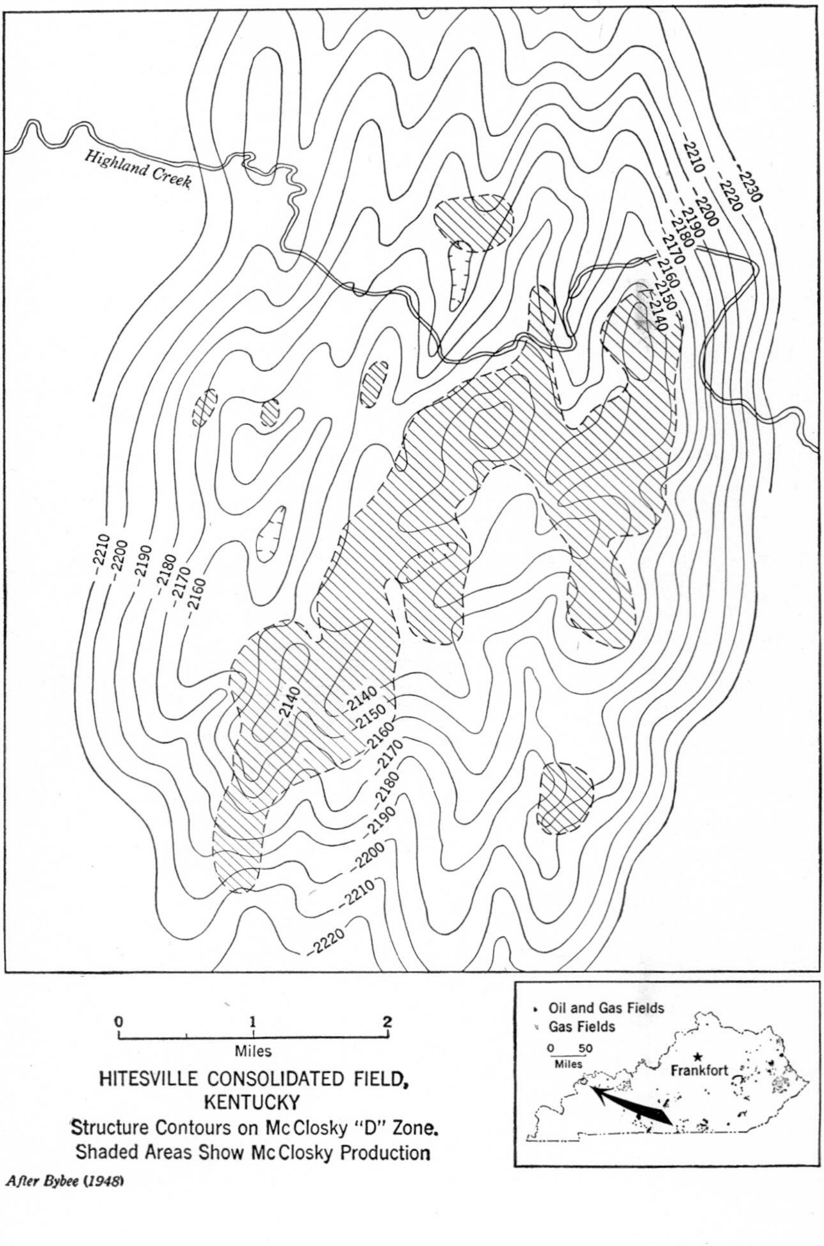

0 1 2
Miles

HITESVILLE CONSOLIDATED FIELD, KENTUCKY
Structure Contours on McClosky "D" Zone.
Shaded Areas Show McClosky Production

After Bybee (1948)

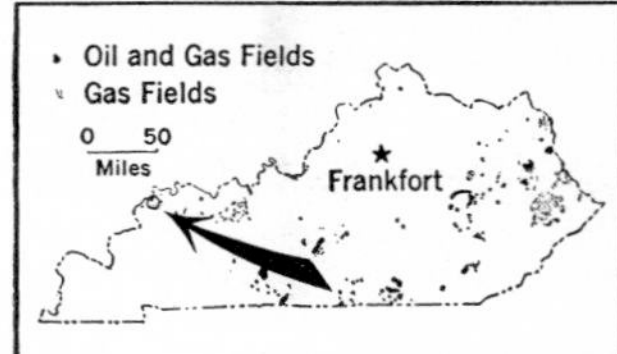

Fig. 47. Hitesville Consolidated Field, Kentucky.

Dome. The Hitesville * field is included in order to show that a dome has neither to be a perfectly symmetrical structure nor to have a closure measured in thousands of feet. As can be seen on the structure contour map the Hitesville dome is irregular in plan and has a closure of less than 100 feet. It is, however, the largest known anticline in western Kentucky as far as areal extent is concerned. The anticline measures 5 by 6 miles and the oil field about 2 by 5 miles.

The Hitesville field is in western Kentucky about 4½ miles north of the Shawneetown-Rough Creek fault system and at the extreme southern end of the Illinois basin. It was discovered in 1943 by the third well drilled to test a structure which had been explored previously by both core drill and seismograph. The structure map shown is contoured on the McCloskey *D* zone, which is the most important oil-producing unit in the section.

The most unusual feature at Hitesville in comparison with other Illinois basin fields is the multiple-zone production within the St. Genevieve limestone formation of Lower Mississippian age. Seven separate porous zones occur in the McCloskey member of the St. Genevieve. In addition the Chester of the Upper Mississippian contains five oil reservoirs, the Waltersburg, Tar Springs, upper and lower Cypress, and Aux Vases sands, and a little production has been obtained from a Pennsylvanian sandstone. The reservoirs at Hitesville are either large in area with the oil water-driven, or are discontinuous lenses with dissolved gas drive. Accumulations in the latter type of reservoir are erratically distributed across the Hitesville structure.

The McCloskey reservoirs are porous and permeable oölitic limestones. The prolific *D* zone is also the most widespread. The oil in this reservoir is everywhere underlain by water under enough pressure so that it has flowed. The elevation of the oil-water interface is at −2187 feet at the north end of the anticline and drops to −2225 feet in the southeast part of the field. The maximum productive thickness of the *D* oölitic zone is 20 feet.

The trapping at Hitesville has been due to the anticlinal structure, but in most of the reservoir formations the distribution of the oil across the large dome has been controlled by permeability. *Courtesy American Association of Petroleum Geologists.*

* H. H. Bybee, "Hitesville Consolidated Field, Union County, Kentucky," *Bull. Am. Assoc. Petrol. Geol.,* Vol. 32 (November, 1948), pp. 2063–2082.

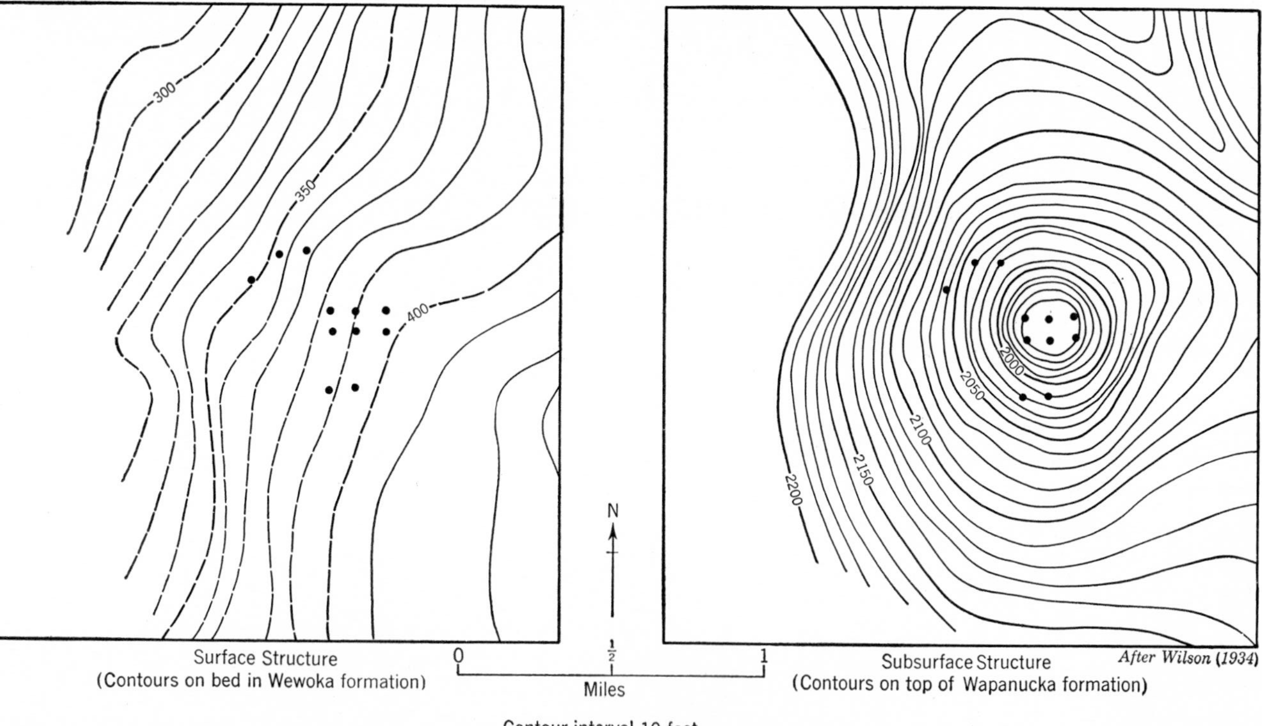

FIG. 48. Development of closure on terrace with depth. Left: structure at surface. Right: structure over same area at deeper level. *Courtesy American Association of Petroleum Geologists.*

deposits to flow plastically, first bulging and then in many places rupturing the overlying sediments.

Among the many types of oil and gas traps, those that result from the flowage of salt are the most bizarre. In spite of their odd nature and origin, however, a substantial percentage of the world's petroleum comes from salt-core structures. Outstanding in this regard is the Gulf Coast of Texas and Louisiana, where nearly 5 billion barrels of oil have come from such structures. Over one-half billion barrels of oil have been produced from salt-core traps in Rumania. Mexico, Germany, and Russia are other, but relatively minor, sources of oil that has accumulated in salt structures. In addition to oil and gas, the greater part of the annual world yield of sulfur, and some of the salt and potash production, come from salt deposits of this type.

Classification. Salt-core structures may be classified into two main types: non-piercement and piercement (Fig. 51). The first includes the *salt anticline,* a laccolith-like structure in which the bedded salt has thickened locally by flowage but has not ruptured the overlying strata. Salt anticlines occur in the Utah-Colorado salt basin and in Europe. To date no oil deposits have been found associated with these structures. The term non-piercement has also been applied, somewhat questionably, to deep-seated probable salt masses not yet reached by the drill. Under the piercement classification are all the salt intrusions which transect the stratification of the intruded sediments. A few of these injected salt masses followed fissures and so are dike-like in shape. Much more abundant are the vertical, or near-vertical, pipe-like intrusions, which are similar to igneous stocks, plugs, and necks. In some of these, the flowing salt has reached the surface through these conduits.

Examples of salt extrusion have been found in the Colorado-Utah district, on the Isthmus of Tehuantepec, and in the Middle East. Because of the extreme aridity on the high plateau of central Iran, the salt that has broken through the overlying sediments makes a dome-shaped hill, whence it flows down the flanks in tongues or "glaciers" for distances as great as three miles.[43] In the other two districts, leaching of the salt has been followed by surface collapse producing topographic depressions.

Geology (Am. Assoc. Petrol. Geol., 1934), pp. 629–678; G. D. Hobson, "Salt Structures; Their Form, Origin, and Relationship to Oil Accumulation," *Science of Petroleum* (Oxford Univ. Press, 1938), Vol. 1, pp. 255–260; P. I. Bediz, "Salt Core Structures and Their Importance in Petroleum Geology," *Mines Mag.,* Vol. 32 (May, 1942; June, 1942), pp. 215 *et seq.*

[43] P. I. Bediz, *op. cit.,* p. 288.

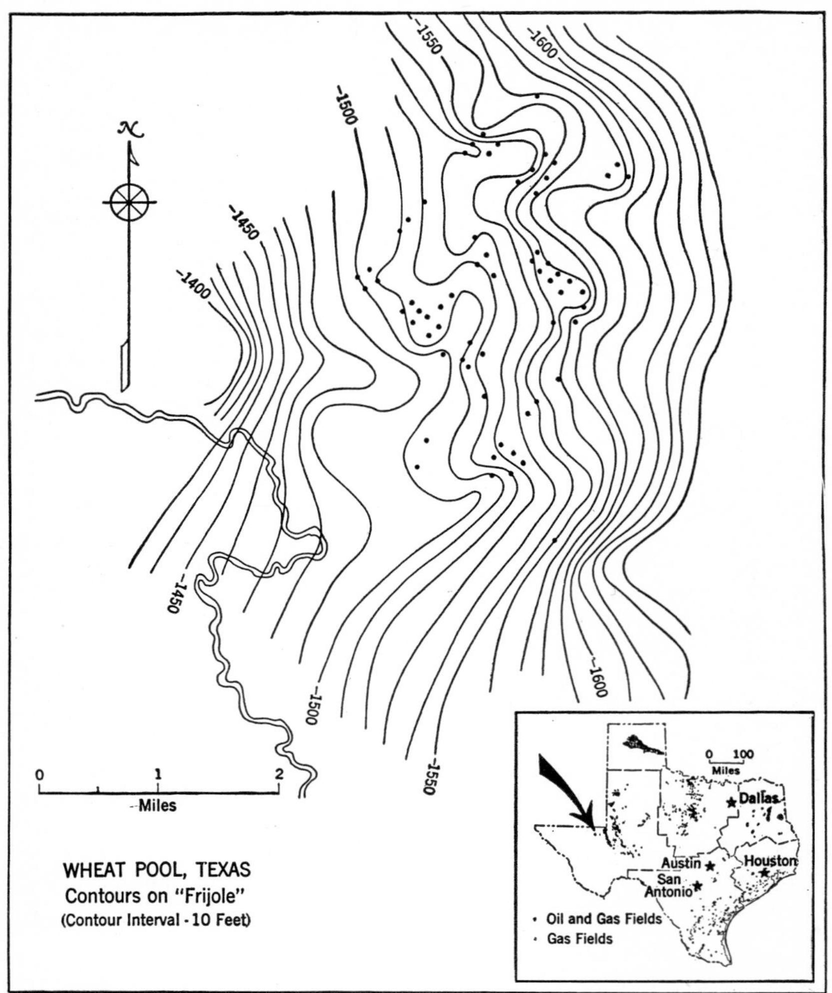

After Adams (1936)

Fig. 49. Wheat Pool, Texas.

Terrace Accumulation. The Wheat pool * lies near the center of the Delaware basin on the east side of Pecos River in Loving County, Texas. It began to produce commercially in 1925. There is no surface evidence of structure of any sort at Wheat, for the bed rock is buried beneath a thick veneer of caliche, alluvium, and sand.

The stratigraphic section so far explored at Wheat extends from the Cenozoic down into the Upper Permian. About 1500 feet of Upper Castile

* John Emery Adams, "Oil Pool of Open Reservoir Type," *Bull. Am. Assoc. Petrol. Geol.,* Vol. 20 (June, 1936), pp. 780–796.

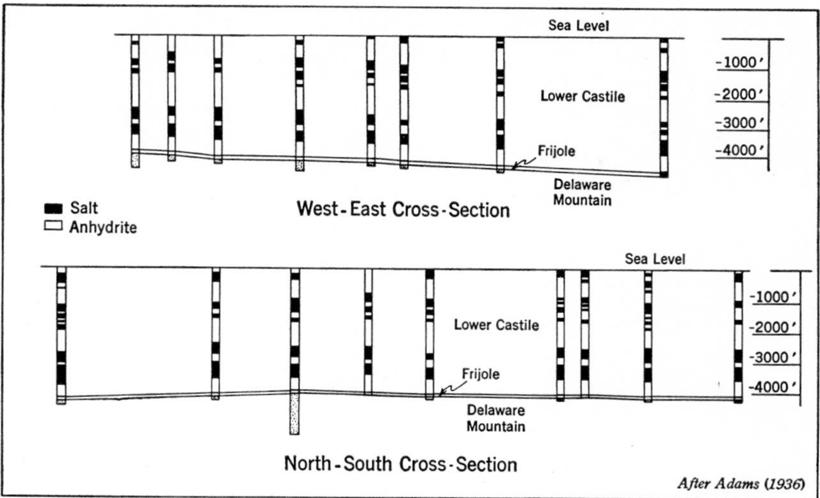

After Adams (1936)

(Permian) evaporites, including anhydrite, salt, and polyhalite (potash salt), are present in the wells drilled at Wheat. Below is about 2000 feet of Lower Castile, which likewise consists of anhydrite and salt, but no potash. The evaporites are underlain by the thin Frijole shale at the top of the Delaware Mountain group, also Permian in age. Below the Frijole is the reservoir sandstone, which actually consists of about 70 per cent very fine sand and 30 per cent silt.

The left figure shows the subsurface structure as contoured on the top of the Frijole formation which overlies the reservoir rock. The west-east cross section shown to the right, and the contour map itself, indicate a gentle dip to the east and a noticeable flattening in the middle, productive, part of the area. The north-south cross section, in conjunction with the structure contour map, shows a fairly consistent tendency for structural nosing in those parts of the area where the producing wells are indicated. The oil occurs in the zone of 50-feet-per-mile dip; to the west and east, above and below the oil accumulation, the dip is in the neighborhood of 100 feet per mile and the sandstone is water-bearing. Wilson † suggests that the oil may have been generated locally and have been unable to escape up-dip because of the lesser permeability of the fine sand. It is also interesting to note that as far as the north-south section is concerned accumulation is anticlinal. The oil appears to have migrated up-dip on the flanks of the structural noses and to have become trapped at the top, owing either to lesser dip or to lesser permeability. *Courtesy American Association of Petroleum Geologists.*

† W. B. Wilson, *ibid.*, p. 795.

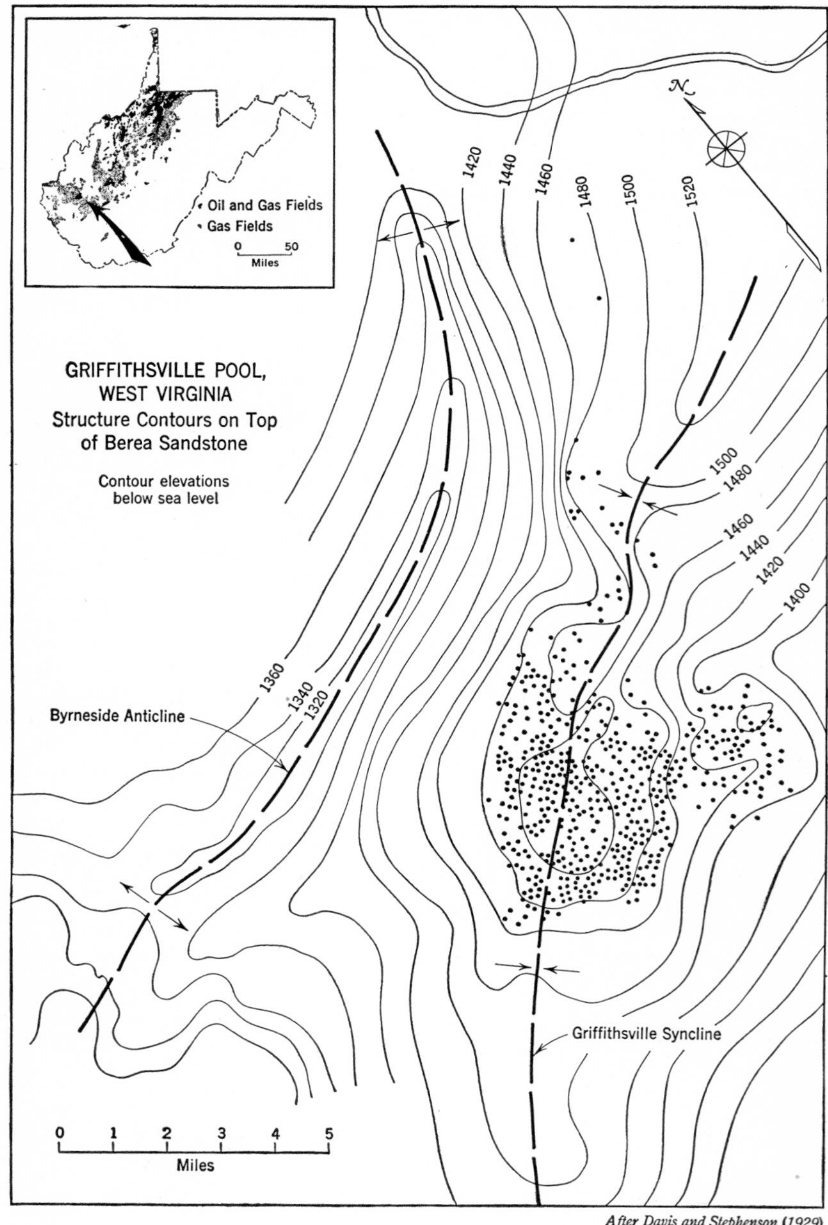

After Davis and Stephenson (1929)

FIG. 50. Griffithsville Pool, West Virginia.

Synclinal Accumulation. The Griffithsville oil field * is in Lincoln County, West Virginia, about 18 miles southwest of Charleston. It was discovered in 1908. Development was rapid, and before long the producing area had spread over 20 square miles. The Berea sandstone is the main oil-producing stratum. It is between 20 and 25 feet thick and is fine-grained, hard, and tightly cemented. All the oil wells have been small but remarkably long-lived.

The structure map on the opposite page is contoured on the Berea. The greatest accumulation of oil occurs across the axis of the northeastward-plunging Griffithsville syncline between elevations −1480 and −1400. Above the −1400 contour and surrounding the oil pool on three sides is one of the major gas fields of West Virginia. The gas accumulation extends to, or close to, the crests of the adjacent anticlines lying to the southeast and to the southwest. Practically no water has been produced in connection with the development of this field. The gas trapping in this field is anticlinal, but the oil gathered in local basins along the synclinal axis. Water may be present beneath the oil down the axis of the syncline to the north, but none has been found in wells drilled in the pool.

Similar synclinal accumulations in other parts of southern West Virginia are described by Davis and Stephenson in the same article. The Tanner Creek field in Gilmer County produces from the Maxon sand along the axis and up the flanks of the Robinson syncline. Oil is especially abundant in several small structural basins along the synclinal axis. No water has been found beneath the oil. The synclinal axis plunges downward both to the northeast and southwest from the Tanner Creek field. The Granny's Creek field of Clay County, West Virginia, is also cited as an illustration of synclinal accumulation. The structural map of this field, however, shows that not only is the synclinal axis much deeper to the northeast but also that the production is largely confined to one flank of the syncline, indicating probable erratic permeability which has controlled the distribution of the oil. *Courtesy American Association of Petroleum Geologists.*

* Ralph E. Davis and Eugene A. Stephenson, "Synclinal Oil Fields in Southern West Virginia," *Structure of Typical American Oil Fields* (Am. Assoc. Petrol. Geol., 1929), Vol. 2, pp. 571–576.

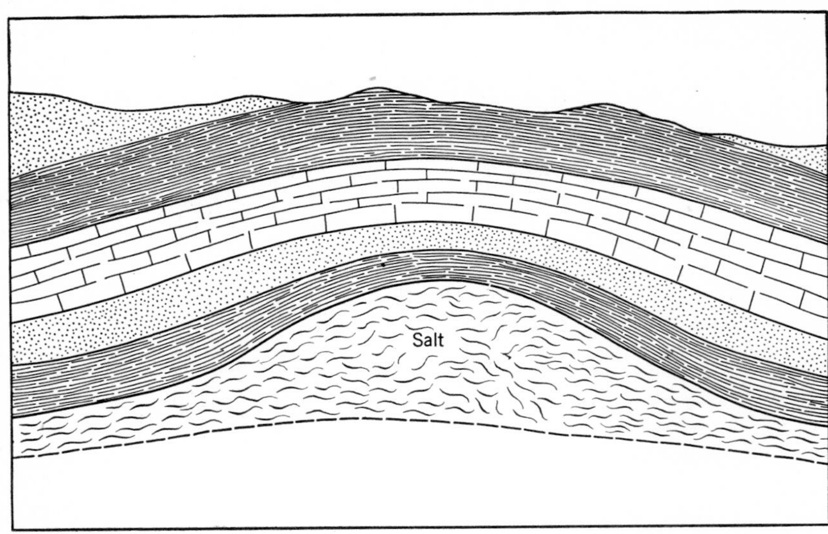

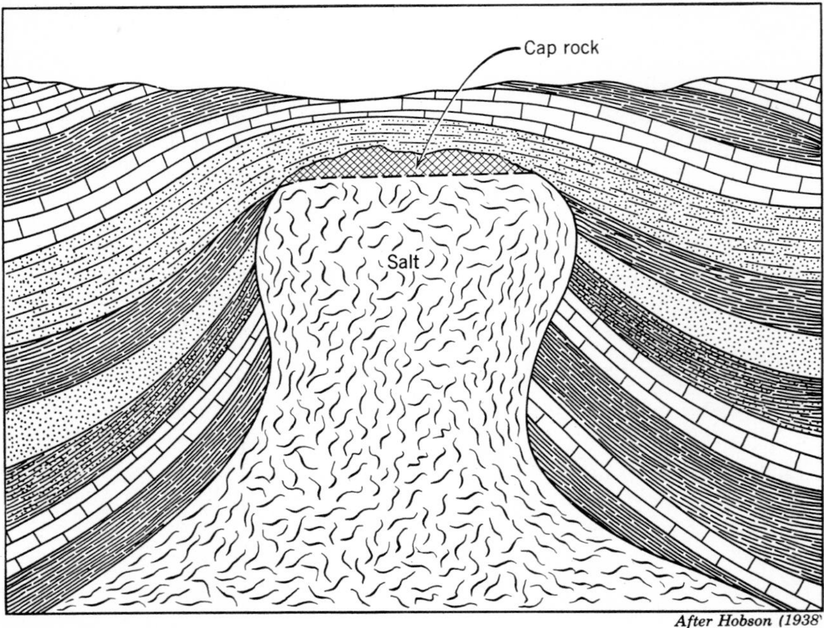

After Hobson (1938)

Fig. 51. Non-piercement and piercement salt domes. Upper: anticline produced by salt flowage. Lower: ruptured anticline or piercement salt dome. *From Science of Petroleum; permission to publish purchased from Oxford University Press.*

Salt-core structures of the piercement type are ordinarily referred to as salt domes in the United States and diapiric folds in Rumania. Wide variation exists between these structures in size, shape, and degree of tectonic disturbance of the associated sediments. In the north German salt basin, all stages are present between undisturbed salt layers, salt anticlines, and salt stocks extending upward into the overlying ruptured sediments. A moderate degree of diastrophism has taken place in this basin, as shown by the folding of the rock strata. The diastrophism in Rumania has been much more intense, and the salt has been "squirted" upward through the apices of the anticlines into bodies of irregular shape. Both the German and Rumanian salt intrusions are small compared with those of the Gulf Coast.

Non-Gulf Coast Salt Structures. The prolific Gulf Coast salt domes of Texas and Louisiana are not the only North American occurrences of salt-core structures. West and north of the "Four Corners," mainly in Utah and Colorado, is a second province of this type.[44] It covers about 6000 square miles (Fig. 52). The gypsiferous rock which caps the salt plugs is exposed at several places, and drilling has shown that the salt is not far beneath. So far, no important hydrocarbon deposits have been found associated with these salt-core structures. The third North American occurrence of salt structures is on the Isthmus of Tehuantepec in the state of Vera Cruz, Mexico (Fig. 53). Hanna [45] names eighteen domes which were known definitely at that time (1934) to have salt cores. This district has become one of the more important oil-producing areas in Mexico.

The German salt structure province is in the North German Zechstein Basin. All stages between undisturbed flat-lying sedimentary layers of salt and intrusive salt "stocks" are to be found there. The salt-core structures are in a triangular area with the three apices lying in the North Sea, the Baltic Sea, and the Harz Mountains. The Hannover, Bremen, and Hamburg districts lie within this triangular area.

Oil was produced by means of dug wells from salt-core traps in Rumania before the drilling of the Drake well in Pennsylvania.

[44] Thomas S. Harrison, "Colorado-Utah Salt Domes," *Bull. Am. Assoc. Petrol. Geol.,* Vol. 11 (February, 1927), pp. 111–133; H. W. C. Prommel and H. E. Crum, "Salt Domes of Permian and Pennsylvanian Age in Southeastern Utah and Their Influence on Oil Accumulation," *Bull. Am. Assoc. Petrol. Geol.,* Vol. 11 (April, 1927), pp. 373–393.

[45] Marcus A. Hanna, "Geology of Gulf Coast Salt Domes," *Problems of Petroleum Geology* (Am. Assoc. Petrol. Geol., 1934), p. 633.

Rumania has two salt-structure districts: (1) the outer edge of the Carpathians; and (2) the intermontane Transylvanian basin. Russia

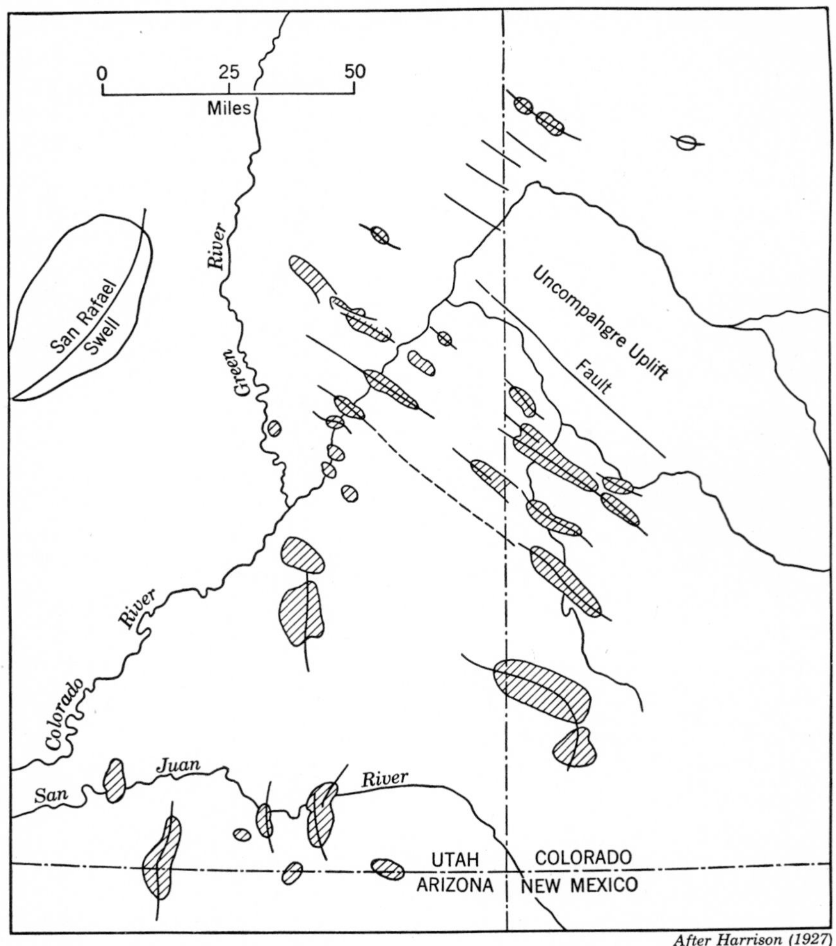

Fig. 52. Salt-cored structures in Utah and Colorado. *Courtesy American Association of Petroleum Geologists.*

also has oil-producing salt-core structures, in the Ural-Emba [46] district north of the Caspian. Many of these, like those in the Gulf Coast district of the United States, were discovered by geophysical methods.

[46] C. W. Sanders, "Emba Salt Dome District, U.S.S.R., and Some Comparisons with Other Salt Dome Regions," *Bull. Am. Assoc. Petrol. Geol.,* Vol. 23 (April, 1939), pp. 492–516.

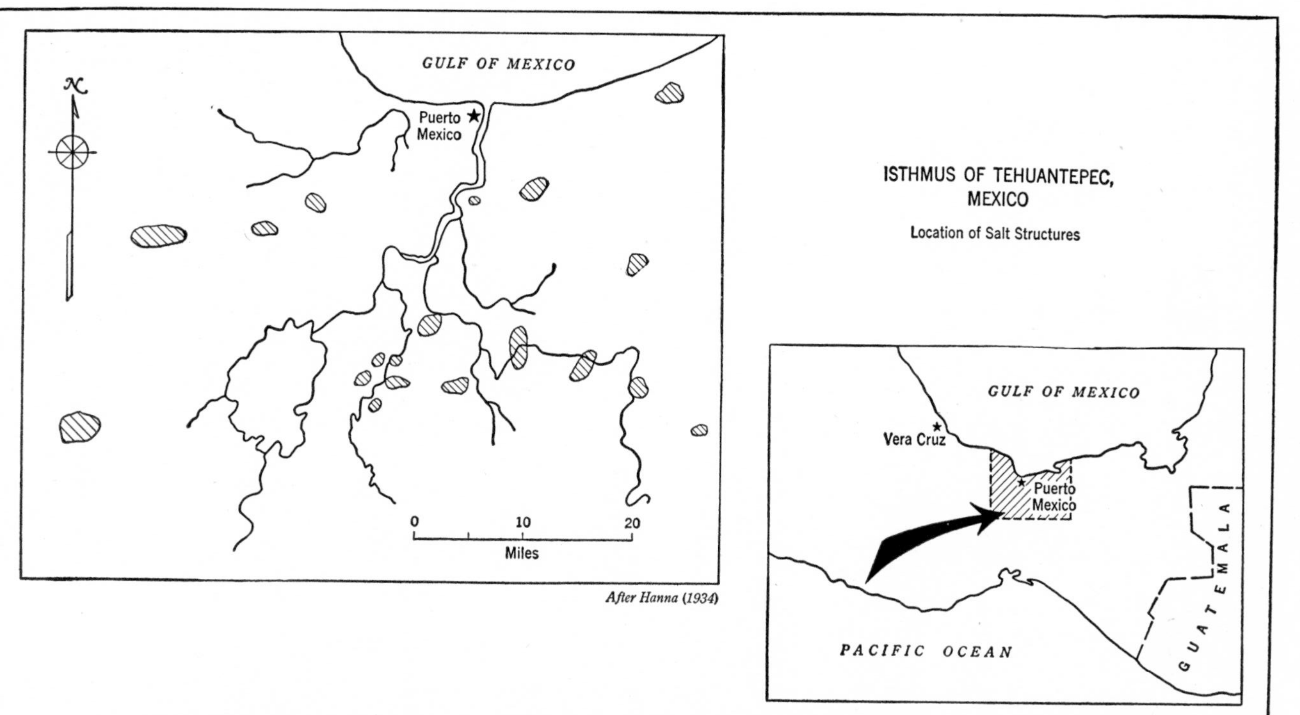

Fig. 53. Salt-cored structures on Isthmus of Tehuantepec. *Courtesy American Association of Petroleum Geologists.*

The Middle East has three salt-core districts. One is near Qum, south of Teheran and many miles north of the Iranian oil fields. Another is the Persian Gulf coast of Iran, Iraq, and Saudi Arabia. In this district, salt intrusives appear at the surface as hills on the mainland and islands offshore. The jumbled core material surrounded by concentric rings of younger formations makes these structures strikingly apparent from the air. Although some of the prolific Middle Eastern oil fields lie within the same district, the association appears to be solely geographic and not geologic. The third salt structure district of the Middle East is on the opposite side of Arabia along the Red Sea coast.

In addition, salt-core structures have been reported from Palestine and North Africa (Tunisia, Algeria, and Morocco). Other parts of the world have also been credited with salt structures, but the evidence is not yet conclusive. However, salt flows so readily under pressure that it is unlikely that deeply buried sedimentary layers of salt have not suffered some contortion and distortion. Closer spacing of wells drilled through the salt measures in such districts as the Michigan Basin and the Permian Basin may yet reveal some flowage. It appears improbable, however, that the degree of salt movement in these and other diastrophically quiescent salt basins has been of sufficient magnitude to produce large-scale trapping conditions like those that exist in the Gulf Coast and Rumania.

Distribution and Description of Gulf Coast Salt Domes. The salt-core structure province of the Gulf Coast of North America extends along the coast line, both onshore and offshore, from Mississippi to Mexico. The greatest concentration of salt intrusions occurs in a zone extending from about 200 miles east of the Louisiana-Texas line to a point about 200 miles west of this boundary (Fig. 54). There are also three inland groups of salt-core structures. One group lies in the Tyler Basin of northeast Texas, one on the east flank of the Sabine uplift in northern Louisiana, and the third in eastern Louisiana, south central Mississippi, and western Alabama.

The Gulf Coast salt-core structures are unique in their enormous per acre production of oil, in their size, and in the total absence, to the depths so far explored, of any appreciable diastrophic activity in the sediments not disturbed by the salt intrusion itself. These great bodies of salt are vertical cylinders, circular or elliptical in plan, with diameters varying from ½ mile to 4 miles and with maximum vertical dimension perhaps as great as 30,000 feet.[47] The more shallow domes are invariably covered by cap rock, to be described and discussed subsequently. At least eleven of the Gulf Coast salt plugs are known to overhang at the top to a varying degree.[48] As much as 2800 feet of

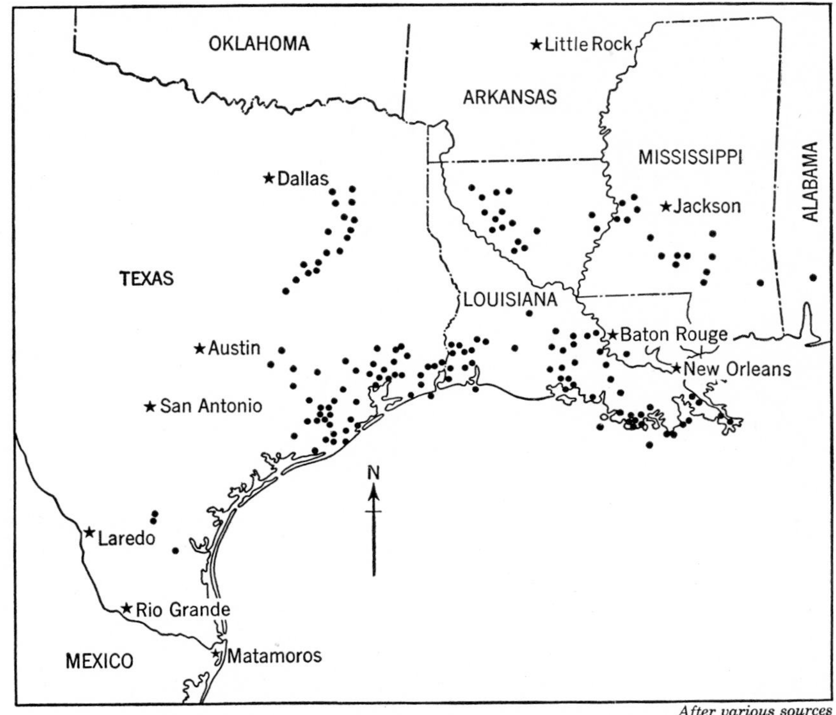

Fig. 54. Map of the Gulf Coast from Texas to Alabama, showing location of known salt domes.

salt has been penetrated between top and bottom of such overhangs (Fig. 55).

The Gulf Coast salt cores average from 5 to 10 per cent disseminated anhydrite, with the rest halite.[49] The Tehuantepec cores are similar in degree of purity, but the Colorado-Utah salt is much more impure,

[47] Marcus A. Hanna, "Geology of the Gulf Coast Salt Domes," *Problems of Petroleum Geology* (Am. Assoc. Petrol. Geol., 1934), p. 646.

[48] Sidney A. Judson and R. A. Stamey, "Overhanging Salt on Domes of Texas and Louisiana," *Gulf Coast Oil Fields* (Am. Assoc. Petrol. Geol., 1936), pp. 141–169.

[49] Marcus A. Hanna, *op. cit.*, p. 637.

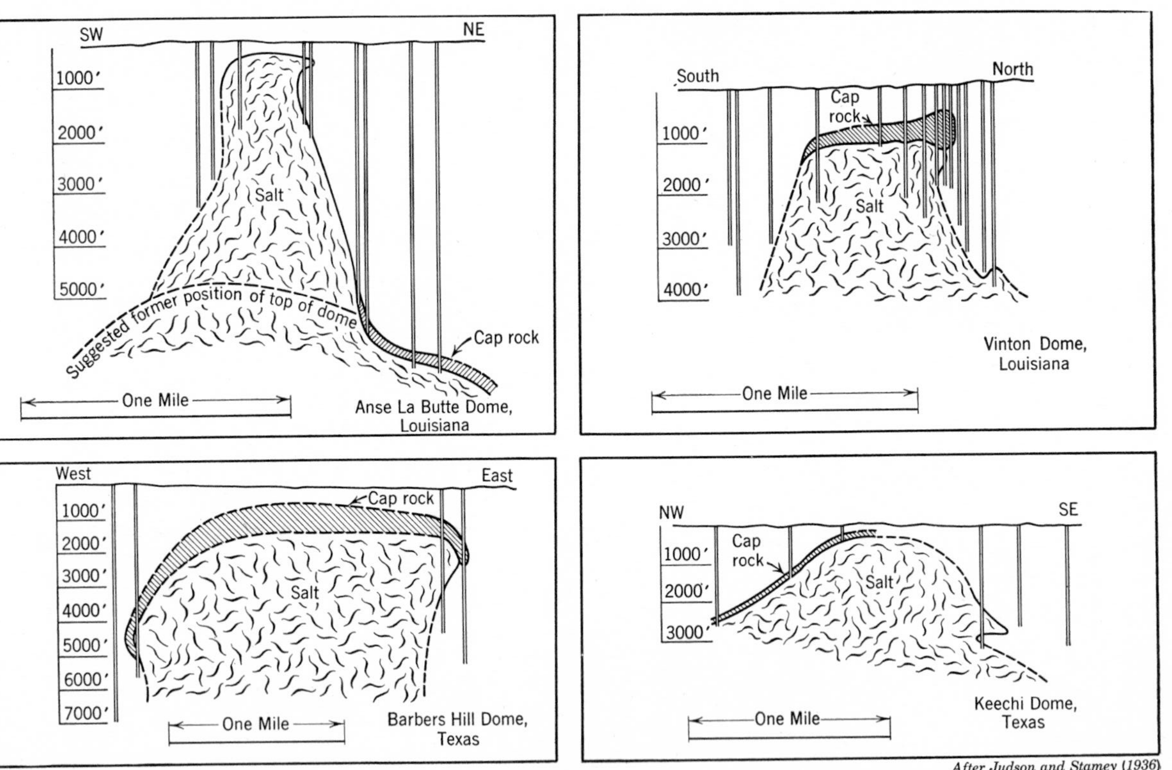

Fig. 55. Four examples of overhanging salt domes, Louisiana and Texas. *Courtesy American Association of Petroleum Geologists.*

and in Iran the injected material is a mixture of salt, gypsum, and red shale.[50]

The cap rock is a disclike body at the top of the salt cylinder which may extend for some distance down the flanks. Although cap rocks are best developed in the Gulf Coast, they are also found rather generally elsewhere, except in Rumania. They are exposed at the surface in some places, and often have been found by drilling. However, in the salt-dome district of the Gulf Coast there are a number of probable salt-cored structures where drilling to depths in excess of 15,000 feet has failed to reach either the salt core or its overlying cap. The caps so far explored have varied in thickness from a few feet to over 1100 feet, with an average of about 350 feet. Although twenty-eight minerals [51] and varieties have been described in the Gulf Coast cap rocks, the only ones of any abundance are anyhdrite, gypsum, and calcite, with sulfur present in important volume in a few places.

Anhydrite is invariably present immediately overlying the salt. It is massive and may be banded. Sand grains and other impurities may be present. The gypsum zone of the cap overlies the anhydrite and is gradational with it. Undoubtedly the gypsum is the result of hydration of anhydrite which originally occupied the gypsum zone level. The gypsum is usually coarsely crystalline selenite.[52] Above the gypsum zone, or immediately above the anhydrite where the gypsum zone is absent, is the so-called "limestone" cap rock. This rock is an aggregate of calcite crystals, but it is not a sedimentary stratum of limestone. It may be porous and even cavernous. Sulfur, where present, usually overlies the anhydrite in the calcite or gypsum zones.

Like all the piercement salt cores, those of the Gulf Coast have emplaced themselves by rupturing the overlying sediments. In this case, however, the overlying sediments were flat-lying previous to the intrusion. As a result of the forcible injection of the salt mass, the initially horizontal strata have been dragged upward from a few hundred to several thousand feet around the flanks of the intrusion before being truncated. Dips have been increased from an original zero to as much as 60° to 90° and even more than 90° in the case

[50] P. I. Bediz, "Salt Core Structures and Their Importance in Petroleum Geology," *Mines Mag.,* Vol. 32 (May, 1942; June, 1942), p. 288.

[51] Marcus A. Hanna and Albert G. Wolf, "Texas and Louisiana Salt-Dome Cap Rock Minerals," *Gulf Coast Oil Fields* (Am. Assoc. Petrol. Geol., 1936), pp. 119–132; F. W. Rolshausen, "Occurrence of Siderite in Cap Rock at Carlos Dome, Grimes County, Texas," *ibid.,* pp. 133–135.

[52] Marcus A. Hanna, *op. cit.,* p. 642.

of some of the overhangs. These strata also tend to thin toward the core, owing to attenuation by drag, or to lesser original sedimentation because of concurrent uplift, or to erosion and overlap.

The strata overlying the salt and its cap have been arched upward, producing, as a general rule, a quaquaversal dome. In many places, however, the overlying sediments are faulted as well as arched. A type of structure that is becoming increasingly common, owing to new discoveries, is the dome-with-graben, which overlies deep-seated salt cores. In this type, the arched sediments are crossed by a series of normal faults that create a keystone graben in the center of the domed area. These grabens are bordered by major faults which dip inward at angles ranging from 45° to 65°. The faults are normal, and the displacement varies from 100 feet to more than 900 feet. Subsidiary minor faults may parallel the major faults. Minor radial faults may also be present. Wallace [53] believes that the major faults bounding the grabens converge downward, meeting at the top of the salt core, and he suggests that the grabens are actually undisturbed areas surrounded by blocks lifted up and tilted by movement along the diagonal faults caused by the intrusion of the salt stock (Fig. 56).

Rim synclines may occur about the periphery of Gulf Coast salt domes. These are closed depressions with depths up to several hundred feet, and like the keystone grabens, they extend down to depths not yet explored by the drill. Possibly rim synclines are the result of the flowage of the adjacent bedded salt into the salt core, with subsequent sagging of the salt roof rock.

Some of the shallow zones have sunken tops, owing to leaching of salt followed by collapse of the cap and overlying sediments.

Origin of the Gulf Coast Salt Domes. There can be little doubt that the salt in salt-cored structures everywhere was originally stratified sedimentary salt. The age of the mother salt beds ranges from the Cambrian (Iran) to the Tertiary (Rumania). No wells in the Gulf Coast salt dome district have reached the source strata as yet. The only positive statement that can be made at this time is that the salt is pre-Upper Cretaceous. It has been variously ascribed to the Comanchean, Jurassic, Permian, and even the Silurian periods. The Comanchean is known to carry evaporites in the form of anhydrite in the Gulf embayment rocks, and the Permian and Silurian are salt-bearing to the northwest and northeast respectively. The age of the Gulf Coast salt-core salt is probably the same as the age of the thick

[53] W. E. Wallace, Jr., "Structure of South Louisiana Deep-Seated Domes," *Bull. Am. Assoc. Petrol. Geol.*, Vol. 28 (September, 1944), pp. 1249–1312.

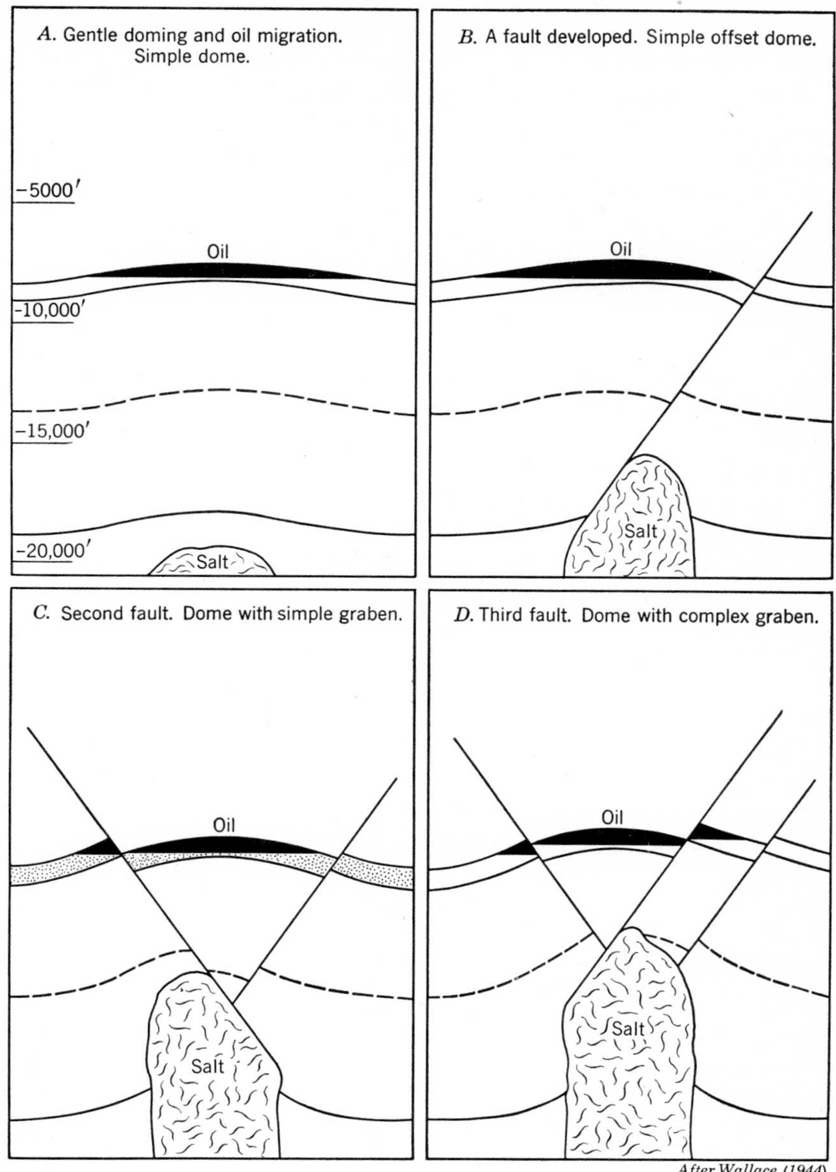

FIG. 56. Suggested origin for keystone grabens in salt domes. *Courtesy American Association of Petroleum Geologists.*

salt bed penetrated in exploring beneath the Smackover, Arkansas, oil field. This salt has been assigned to the Jurassic by some and to the Permian by others.[54]

The origin of salt-core structures has long been a subject of interest. Chief American investigators in recent years include Barton,[55] Hanna,[56] and Nettleton.[57] Older theories, including volcanic intrusion and salt crystallization,[58] are entirely untenable in the light of present knowledge of salt-core structures. Only the plastic flow theory is adequate to explain all the following observational features: (1) the injection of bedded salt into the ruptured roofs of anticlines in Germany and Rumania; (2) the uplift and truncation of sedimentary strata overlying the salt in the Gulf Coast district; (3) the presence of cap rocks; and (4) contorted banding within the salt masses. That salt can flow plastically has been demonstrated by numerous investigators in the laboratory and by witnessed natural flow of the salt "glaciers" in Iran.

Barton,[59] Nettleton,[60] and, more recently, Balk[61] have studied the mechanics of salt flowage, especially as applied to the genesis of the Gulf Coast domes. In all the other regions of salt-core structures, the local sedimentary section has been subjected to lateral pressures during one or more periods of diastrophism. In Rumania especially these tangential forces have been considerable, resulting in tight folding of the salt-bearing sedimentary rock series. Under such circumstances, the pressures needed to cause the relatively vulnerable salt to flow are obvious, and the salt will move in the direction of least

[54] Roy T. Hazzard, W. C. Spooner, B. W. Blanpied, "Notes on the Stratigraphy of the Formations Which Underlie the Smackover Limestone in South Arkansas, Northeast Texas and North Louisiana," *Shreveport Geol. Soc., Rept.* II (1945), pp. 483–503.

[55] Donald C. Barton, "Mechanics of Formation of Salt Domes with Special Reference to Gulf Coast Salt Domes of Texas and Louisiana," *Gulf Coast Oil Fields* (Am. Assoc. Petrol. Geol., 1936), pp. 20–78.

[56] Marcus A. Hanna, "Geology of Gulf Coast Salt Domes," *Problems of Petroleum Geology* (Am. Assoc. Petrol. Geol., 1934), pp. 629–678.

[57] L. L. Nettleton, "Fluid Mechanics of Salt Domes," *Gulf Coast Oil Fields* (Am. Assoc. Petrol. Geol., 1936), pp. 79–108; "Recent Experimental and Geophysical Evidence of Mechanics of Salt Dome Formation," *Bull. Am. Assoc. Petrol. Geol.*, Vol. 27 (January, 1943), pp. 51–63.

[58] Revived by Bailey Willis, "Artesian Salt Formations," *Bull. Am. Assoc. Petrol. Geol.*, Vol. 32 (July, 1948), pp. 1227–1264.

[59] Donald C. Barton, *op. cit.*

[60] L. L. Nettleton, *op. cit.*

[61] Robert Balk, "Structure of Grand Saline Salt Dome, Van Zandt County, Texas," *Bull. Am. Assoc. Petrol. Geol.*, Vol. 33 (November, 1949), pp. 1791–1829.

resistance, which is through the fractured anticlinal crests. However, in the Gulf Coast district there is no visible evidence of the existence in the past of any appreciable tangential pressure. It is quite possible, if not probable, that there is an angular unconformity at depth beneath which the salt measures are folded and in which the original piercement of the salt roof rock took place,[62] but all the later injection has been through strata which had been hitherto undisturbed. The authorities ascribe this movement to (1) the great weight of the thick body of sediment overlying the salt-bearing strata, and (2) the lesser density of the salt compared with that of the "country rock." The static weight of the overburden pressing upon the relatively incompetent salt caused it to flow plastically, moving upward through whatever openings it could find in the roof. Once the salt body became a vertical feature, its lighter weight, compared with the weight of the laterally adjacent rocks, would create an isostatic inequilibrium which might cause further vertical movement. Barton points out that both the coastal and the interior salt domes of the Gulf area are in regions of pronounced downsinking; he believes, therefore, that much of the injection of the salt cores into the sediments has been actually residual accumulation of salt stocks by "downbuilding."[63] As the mother salt beds and the associated sediments sank, the plastic, lighter salt drained into the base of the non-sinking (or even up-rising) salt prism.

The value of interstitial water as a lubricant in aiding salt flow is stressed by some investigators and seriously questioned by others.[64]

Most students of Gulf Coast salt domes agree that the upward (relative) movement of the salt cores has been intermittent rather than continuous.[65] This movement ceased at various times in the geologic past. Occasionally, post-Pleistocene movement has taken place, and some of these salt-core structures may be still growing. Various reasons that have been suggested for the cessation of upward movement of the salt include: (1) establishment of isostatic equilibrium; (2) reaching a balance between static pressure and frictional

[62] E. DeGolyer, "Origin of North American Salt Domes," *Bull. Am. Assoc. Petrol. Geol.,* Vol. 9 (August, 1925), pp. 831–874.

[63] Donald C. Barton, "Mechanics of Formation of Salt Domes with Special Reference to Gulf Coast Salt Domes of Texas and Louisiana," *Gulf Coast Oil Fields* (Am. Assoc. Petrol. Geol., 1936), pp. 54 *et seq.*

[64] L. L. Nettleton, "Fluid Mechanics of Salt Domes," *Bull. Am. Assoc. Petrol. Geol.,* Vol. 18 (September, 1934), p. 1180.

[65] F. M. Van Tuyl and Ben H. Parker, "The Time of Origin and Accumulation of Petroleum," *Quarterly Colo. School of Mines,* Vol. 36 (April, 1941), pp. 130–133.

resistance; (3) cessation of regional downwarping; (4) exhaustion of salt supply; (5) removal of peripheral salt accompanied by a drawing together of the underlying and overlying strata.

The origin of the cap rocks and of the cap-rock minerals has also led to a lot of observation, cerebration, and publication.[66] The dominant and sole essential mineral in cap rocks is anhydrite. Its presence and position have been explained in several ways, but chiefly by either (1) the residual accumulation, through differential leaching, of anhydrite originally disseminated through the salt mass, or (2) by the punching out, followed by a ride upward on the top of the salt stock, of a slab of sedimentary anhydrite country rock. The best arguments for the second theory appear to be the sharpness and horizontality of the anhydrite-salt contact exposed in digging a shaft to the salt in the Texas Gulf Coast, and the presence of horizontal bands of sandstone at one level in the 900-foot-thick anhydrite cap.[67] The arguments opposed to this concept are based mainly on improbability. So far as the writer knows, no 900-foot bed of sedimentary anhydrite has ever been noted. Furthermore, the question naturally rises as to why anhydrite, out of the many different types of rock passed through by the rising salt mass, should be the only one to be punched out and carried upward.

According to Hobson, "In Germany it has been widely accepted that if the salt rises into the zone of circulating subsurface waters the soluble materials at the top will be removed, leaving a more or less flat table of anhydrite, gypsum, and clay."[68] This has also become the more generally accepted theory for the origin of the Gulf Coast cap rocks. The presence of 5 to 10 per cent of anhydrite in the Gulf salt cores has already been mentioned. Although both minerals are relatively soluble compared with most other minerals, salt is much the more soluble of the two. *Any contact of the surface of an anhydrite-containing salt core with ground water would indubitably lead to an enrichment of that mineral in the contact zone.*

[66] Marcus A. Hanna, "Geology of Gulf Coast Salt Domes," *Problems of Petroleum Geology* (Am. Assoc. Petrol. Geol., 1934), pp. 648 *et seq.;* Ralph E. Taylor, "Origin of Cap Rock of Louisiana Salt Domes," *La. Geol. Survey, Bull.* 11 (1938); L. S. Brown, "Cap-Rock Petrography," *Bull. Am. Assoc. Petrol. Geol.,* Vol. 15 (May, 1931), pp. 509–529; M. I. Goldman, "Origin of the Anhydrite Cap Rock of American Salt Domes," *U. S. Geol. Survey, Prof. Paper* 175 (1933), pp. 83–114.

[67] L. P. Teas, "Hockley Salt Shaft, Harris County, Texas," *Gulf Coast Oil Fields* (Am. Assoc. Petrol. Geol., 1936), pp. 136–140.

[68] G. D. Hobson, "Salt Structures: Their Form, Origin, and Relationship to Oil Accumulation," *Science of Petroleum* (Oxford Univ. Press, 1938), Vol. 1, pp. 258–259.

Opinions also vary as to the genesis of some of the associated minerals in the cap rock. No doubt the gypsum that overlies the anhydrite is formed by hydration of the anhydrite. The sulfur that is present in a few caps is much more difficult to explain. The occurrence of native sulfur as a probable alteration product of anhydrite in Sicily and elsewhere supports the belief that the Gulf Coast sulfur is likewise derived from anyhdrite. Since the limestone part of the cap always overlies the anhydrite-gypsum zone, it could not be the result of residual accumulation of calcite crystals carried within the salt. It is more likely the result of interaction between carbonate waters and calcium sulfate which resulted in the precipitation of calcium carbonate. The limestone zone is characteristically cavernous, and in many places it consists of collapse breccia which contains intermingled fragments of sedimentary limestone, sandstone, and other types of rock from the overlying section. Some of the sandstone fragments found in the cap rock are thought to be "xenoliths" carried upward by the salt along with the anhydrite.[69]

Hanna [70] has divided the various stages in the evolution of the American salt-core structures into youth, maturity, and old age. Youth is the stage of earliest salt flowage, when the bedded, flat-lying salt flows into anticlines, arching the overlying sediments. In maturity the roof is breached, the salt stock starts upward and solution at the top of the stock becomes active, resulting in a concentration of anhydrite. During old age the stock continues upward and the cap increases in thickness. Solution activity spreads down the flanks of the salt core. Overhang of both cap and salt may be produced. Rim synclines are developed in the surrounding rocks. In extreme senility much salt is removed by circulating water, and collapse of the cap results in depressed tops. The cycle ends when upward movement and solution cease. There is some evidence that a few Gulf Coast domes have been actively eroded.[71]

Oil Trapping by Gulf Coast Salt Domes. Salt-core structures are important to the petroleum geologist because the intrusion of a salt stock creates local traps in which hydrocarbons can accumulate. There is no genetic relationship between salt and oil; the relationships are

[69] Marcus A. Hanna, "Geology of Gulf Coast Salt Domes," *Problems of Petroleum Geology* (Am. Assoc. Petrol. Geol., 1934), p. 643.

[70] Marcus A. Hanna, *op. cit.*, pp. 656 *et seq.*

[71] Marcus A. Hanna, "Evidence of Erosion of Salt Stock in Gulf Coast Salt Plug in Late Oligocene," *Bull. Am. Assoc. Petrol. Geol.*, Vol. 27 (January, 1943), pp. 85–89, and Vol. 23 (April, 1939), pp. 604–607.

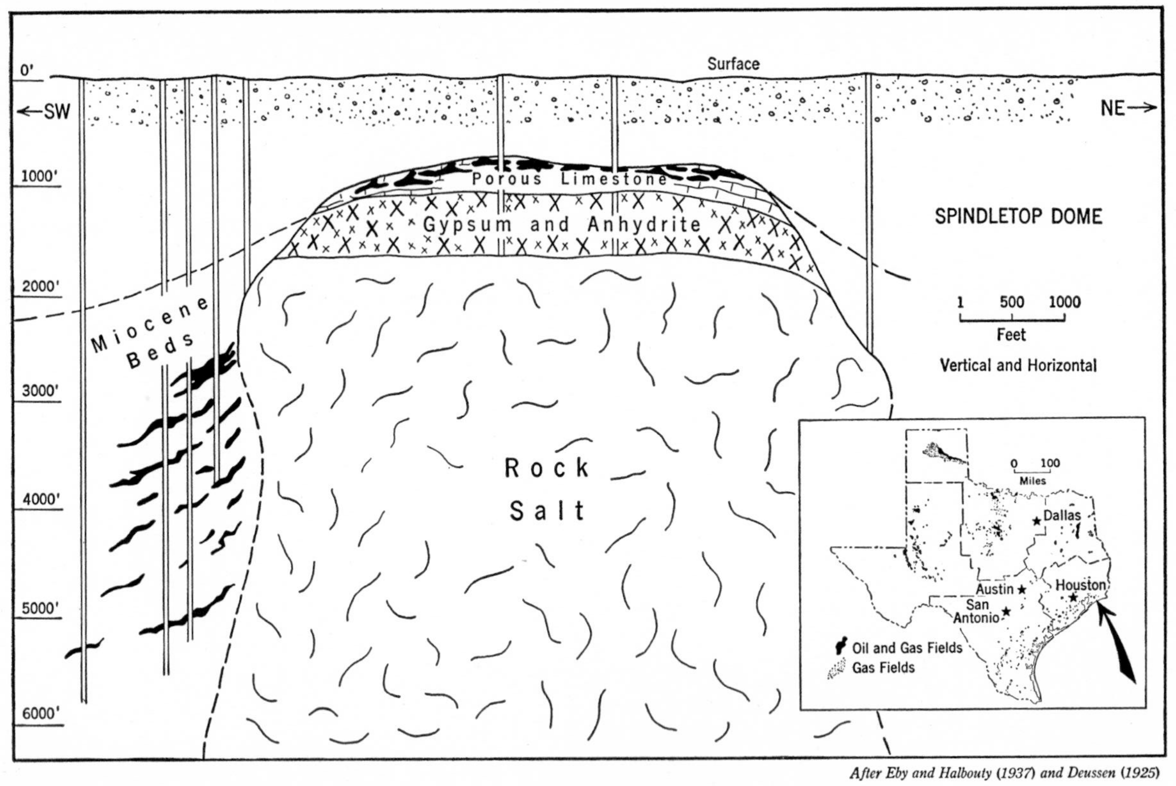

After Eby and Halbouty (1937) and Deussen (1925)

FIG. 57. Spindletop, Texas.

Cap and Flank Production. The discovery of oil by Captain Lucas at Spindletop in January, 1901, marked the beginning of the Gulf Coast oil industry. The discovery well, drilled on the top of a topographic mound, was a gusher, estimated to flow 75,000 barrels daily. Sixty-four gushers of equal capacity were completed during the following 9 months.

The illustration is a composite from cross sections published by Deussen,* Barton and Paxson,† and Eby and Halbouty.‡ The initial discovery was in "limestone" cap rock which in reality is a highly cavernous dolomite. Coupled with the phenomenal early production rate was the rapid exhaustion of the reservoir; by the end of 5 years the field was down to 4000 barrels daily, relatively a mere trickle. The Spindletop cap-rock discovery was followed between 1901 and 1905 by similar discoveries at Sour Lake, Batson, and Humble, but there have been no important finds of this nature in the Gulf Coast area since.

Above the productive cap rock at Spindletop and Humble are several shallow sands belonging in the Lissie-Reynosa (Pleistocene) group in which some oil had accumulated, probably the result of leakage from the underlying cap.

Production from reservoirs flanking the salt cores was discovered first at Sour Lake in 1914. The southwest flank at Spindletop was found to be productive in 1926. A second Spindletop "boom" followed, and during the following decade the flank produced 50 per cent more oil than the prolific cap rock had produced since discovery. The flank reservoirs are sands in the Fleming formation of Miocene age.

The trapping at Spindletop has been due to various situations brought about by the intrusion of a salt stock. Over 50 million barrels of oil accumulated in the cavernous dolomitic cap rock which is overlain by relatively impervious sediment. Even greater in volume is the oil caught in the flank sands which were dragged up and pinched off by the salt intrusion. A little oil appears to have worked upward into arched supercap sands. Originally the oil must have traveled laterally into the flank and cap traps. *Courtesy American Association of Petroleum Geologists.*

* Alexander Deussen, "Oil-Producing Horizons of Gulf Coast in Texas and Louisiana," *Gulf Coast Oil Fields* (Am. Assoc. Petrol. Geol., 1936), p. 3.

† Donald C. Barton and Roland B. Paxson, "The Spindletop Salt Dome and Oil Field, Jefferson County, Texas," *Bull. Am. Assoc. Petrol. Geol.*, Vol. 9 (May-June, 1925), p. 601.

‡ J. Brian Eby and Michel T. Halbouty, "Spindletop Oil Field, Jefferson County, Texas," *Bull. Am. Assoc. Petrol. Geol.*, Vol. 21 (April, 1937), p. 486.

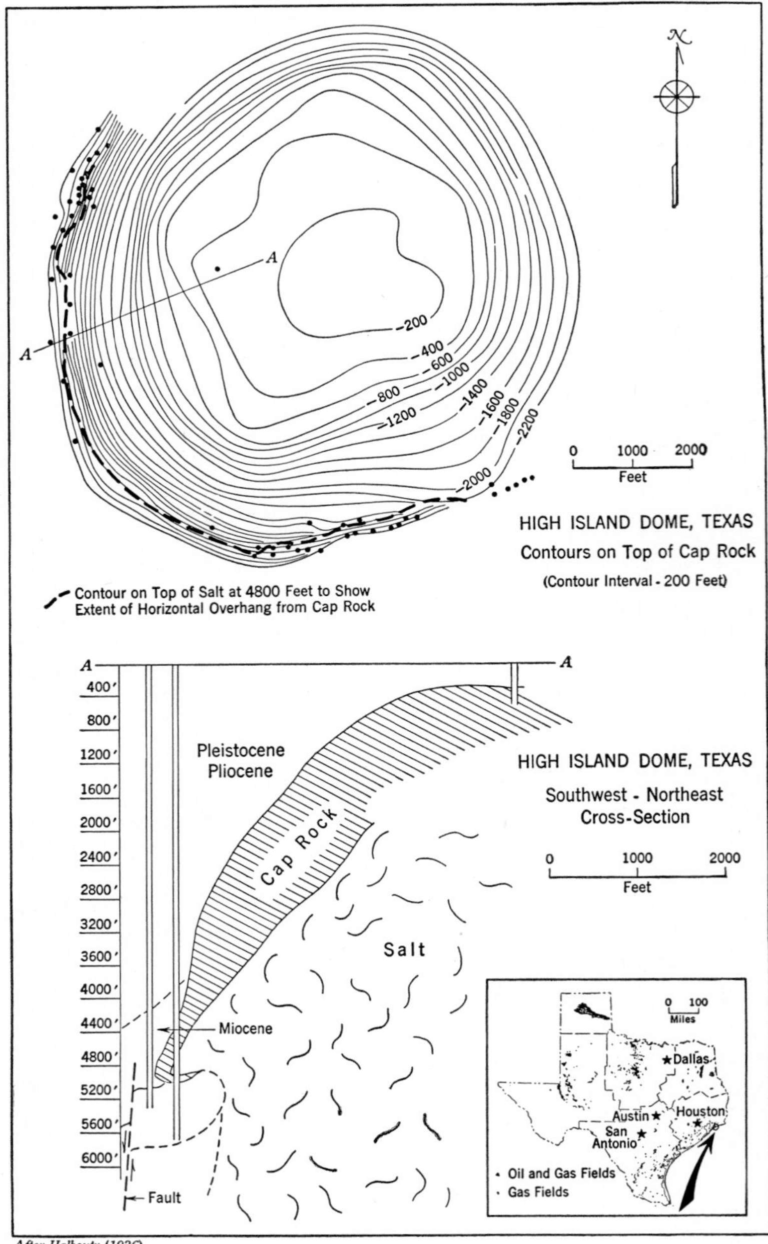
N
A
A
-200
-400
-600
-800
-1000
-1200
-1400
-1600
-1800
-2000
-2200
0 1000 2000
Feet
HIGH ISLAND DOME, TEXAS
Contours on Top of Cap Rock
(Contour Interval - 200 Feet)
Contour on Top of Salt at 4800 Feet to Show
Extent of Horizontal Overhang from Cap Rock
A
A
400'
800'
1200'
1600'
2000'
2400'
2800'
3200'
3600'
4000'
4400'
4800'
5200'
5600'
6000'
Pleistocene
Pliocene
Cap Rock
Salt
Miocene
Fault
HIGH ISLAND DOME, TEXAS
Southwest - Northeast
Cross-Section
0 1000 2000
Feet
0 100
Miles
Dallas
Austin
Houston
San
Antonio
Oil and Gas Fields
Gas Fields

After Halbouty (1936)

FIG. 58. High Island Dome, Texas.

Flank Production from beneath Overhang. The High Island salt dome * lies about a mile inland from the Gulf of Mexico in Galveston County, Texas. It is marked at the surface by a mound that rises above the surrounding marshes for a height of about 20 feet. The presence of this hill, so similar in appearance to that at Spindletop, plus abundant seeps of sulfurous inflammable gas, led to an oil test in 1901. This test, and many more in the succeeding years, were unsuccessful. It was not until 1922 that High Island became a commercial producer. The first successful wells were drilled into porous cap rock. In 1931 the discovery well for the deep and prolific flank reservoirs was drilled; this well also proved the presence of an overhang of cap rock and salt with producing sands beneath the overhang as shown in the cross section on the opposite page.

Above the High Island salt core is the "true" cap consisting of anhydrite grading upward into gypsum with calcite at the top. The maximum thickness of this cap is 675 feet. Above the true cap is the "false" cap, which ranges from 200 to 1300 feet in thickness. It consists of hard sandstone and "lime rock" which is actually calcareous sandstone. The initial production at High Island was from the calcite zone in the true cap.

According to Halbouty the overhang had been proved for all flanks drilled at that time, which included the northwest, west, south, and southeast, and probably continued completely around the salt core. The horizontal extent of the overhang is as much as 800 feet. Both the cap rock and the salt itself occur in the overhanging section, as shown on the opposite page. The sedimentary formations below the overhang are faulted, broken, and distorted. On the western flank much gouge material is present in this zone. A peripheral fault is assumed, and a well-developed graben was discovered off the south flank.

The most prolific of the flank sands are in the Lower Miocene (*MDv* zone) and Middle Oligocene (*Discorbis* zone). These sands are dragged up so that in some places they are vertical. The intrusion of the salt core also shattered and faulted the reservoir rocks. Apparently the oil migrated through the Tertiary sandstones up-dip toward the salt stock and were trapped in the broken zone beneath the salt and cap overhang. *Courtesy American Association of Petroleum Geologists.*

* Michel T. Halbouty, "Geology and Geophysics Showing Cap Rock and Salt Overhang of High Island Dome, Galveston County, Texas," *Gulf Coast Oil Fields* (Am. Assoc. Petrol. Geol., 1936), pp. 909–960.

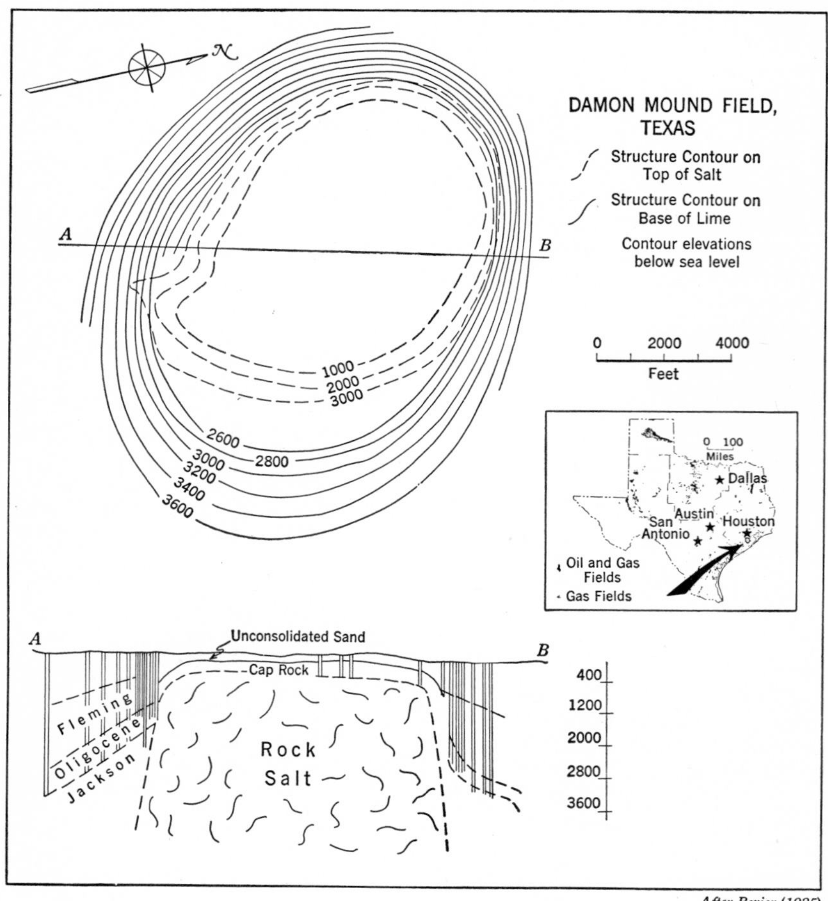
N
DAMON MOUND FIELD, TEXAS
Structure Contour on Top of Salt
Structure Contour on Base of Lime
Contour elevations below sea level
0 2000 4000
Feet
A
B
1000
2000
3000
2600
2800
3000
3200
3400
3600
0 100
Miles
Dallas
Austin
San Antonio
Houston
Oil and Gas Fields
Gas Fields
Unconsolidated Sand
Cap Rock
Fleming
Oligocene
Jackson
Rock Salt
400
1200
2000
2800
3600

After Bevier (1925)

FIG. 59. Damon Mound, Texas.

Salt-Core Flank Accumulation. The structure contour map and cross section on the opposite page are for the Damon Mound * oil field in northwestern Brazoria County, Texas. Damon Mound itself is a conspicuous topographic feature on the Texas Coastal plain, rising 83 feet above the surrounding countryside, and readily visible from points 5 and 6 miles away. Other criteria of a salt-core structure were noted by the early settlers. Many of their wells struck highly mineralized water, and a few produced a small amount of inflammable gas. The northern part of the hill contained isolated crystals of sulfur, the western flank a 1-acre deposit of sour dirt; and on the eastern slope the limestone cap rock cropped out and was quarried in the early days.

When Captain Lucas completed his famous gusher at Spindletop in January of 1901 attention was focused on salt domes, and before the year was out a test had been drilled at Damon Mound through the cap rock and into salt for a distance of nearly 600 feet. Neither this well nor any of four additional cap-rock tests found even a favorable show of oil or gas. Activity at Damon Mound was dormant between 1905 and early in 1915 when the second cycle of salt-dome exploration, the search for flank production, led to the drilling of a well on the west side of the hill which ran wild for a time, producing an estimated 5 million cubic feet of gas and 100 barrels of oil daily before it sanded up and was abandoned. Two years later the first commercial producer was drilled. The oil accumulations are two in number, one, the larger, on the southwestern side, the other on the northeastern side. About 15 per cent of the total acreage of the mound is classed as productive.

The structure contour map on the opposite page is based, for the flank structure, on a marker limestone bed within the *Heterostegina* zone of the Oligocene. The most prolific of the producing sands occur within the *Heterostegina* and another Oligocene zone, the *Marginulina*. The relative upward movement of the salt core has dragged up these sands, pinched them off, and faulted them. The dips within the producing areas are in the neighborhood of 40°; the sands in the non-productive segments of the salt dome flank are either considerably less or greater. Bevier believes that the adjacent bituminous strata in the stratigraphic section on the flanks of Damon Mound were the source beds and that the oil migrated into the sandy layers and became trapped up-dip, largely owing to peripheral faulting. *Courtesy American Association of Petroleum Geologists.*

* George M. Bevier, "The Damon Mound Oil Field, Texas," *Bull. Am. Assoc. Petrol. Geol.,* Vol. 9 (May–June, 1925), pp. 505–535.

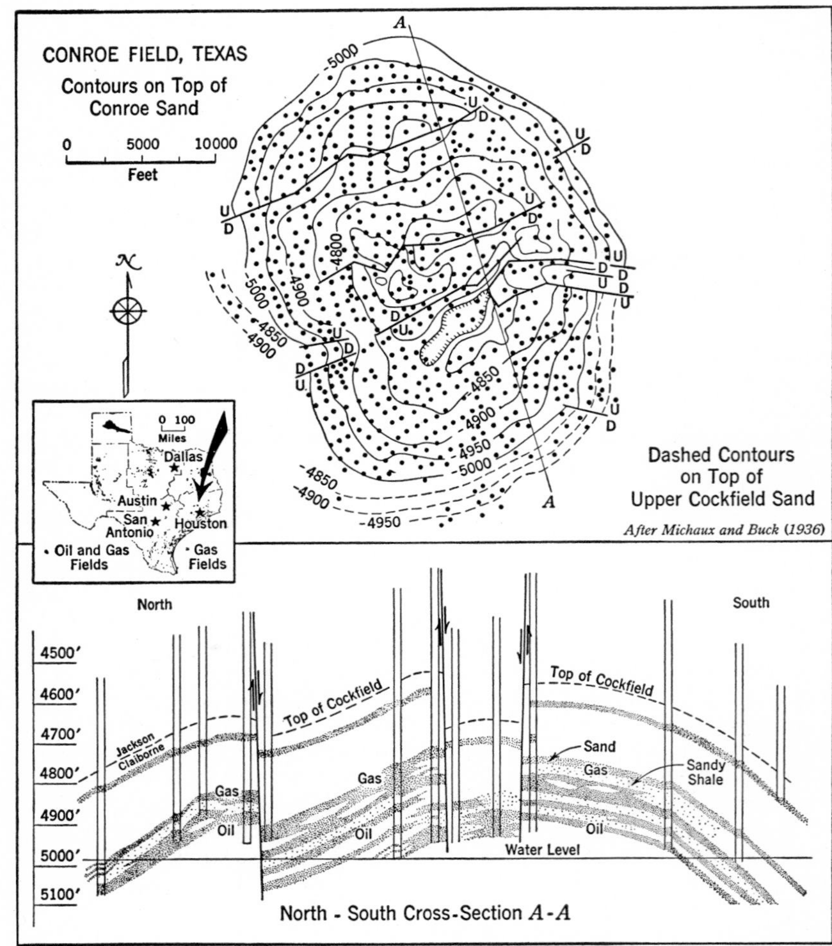

CONROE FIELD, TEXAS
Contours on Top of Conroe Sand
0 5000 10000
Feet
Dallas
Austin
San Antonio
Houston
0 100 Miles
• Oil and Gas Fields
◦ Gas Fields
Dashed Contours on Top of Upper Cockfield Sand
After Michaux and Buck (1936)
North
South
4500′
4600′
4700′
4800′
4900′
5000′
5100′
Jackson
Claiborne
Top of Cockfield
Gas
Oil
Sand
Sandy Shale
Water Level
North - South Cross-Section A-A

After Michaux and Buck (1936)

FIG. 60. Conroe, Texas.

Supercap Production. The Conroe oil field * is in Montgomery County, Texas, 40 miles north of Houston. Although preceded by Goose Creek and a few other fields the Conroe discovery in 1931 ushered in a new era in Gulf Coast history. Since Conroe most of the Gulf Coast oil has been produced from domes which are assumed to overlie a salt core, but the core is so deep-seated that it has not yet been penetrated by the drill. Today there are literally hundreds of fields of this type in Texas and Louisiana.

Although the arched sands above the cap produced some oil in the "piercement" type of structure at Spindletop and Jennings and perhaps other fields, the deep-seated supercap production at Conroe is analogous only in relative position and probable structural origin. At Conroe the assumed salt core is hundreds if not thousands of feet below the lowest "supercap" oil, and the field has 17,200 producing acres which at the time of discovery exceeded the total aggregate productive acreage of the entire Gulf Coast salt-dome province of Texas and Louisiana.

The prediscovery surface indications at Conroe consisted of gas seeps and springs of hydrogen sulfide-bearing water. Some unusual clay outcrops were thought (but never proved) to be inliers.

The upper figure shows the geologic structure of the Conroe field mapped on the top of the main producing sand. Below is a northwest to southeast cross section. The Conroe structure is an unusually symmetrical dome with a structural relief in the Cockfield (Eocene) of over 800 feet and closure of 360 feet. Crossing the dome are three parallel normal faults. The fault pair to the south creates a keystone graben, ¾ mile wide, which occupies the exact center of the dome. The displacements range from zero at the ends to a maximum of 165 feet.

Accumulation has occurred in three sand members of the Cockfield, of which the lowest ("Conroe") is most important. However, the fault planes are not tight within the Cockfield, so there is free communication between sand members and they constitute one reservoir with a gas cap above and bottom water below. The gas cap is 170 feet thick, and the oil occupies an interval 130 feet in thickness. The elevation of the oil-water contact is rather uniformly 4990 feet below sea level. *Courtesy American Association of Petroleum Geologists.*

* Frank W. Michaux, Jr. and E. O. Buck, "Conroe Oil Field, Montgomery County, Texas," *Gulf Coast Oil Fields* (Am. Assoc. Petrol. Geol., 1936), pp. 789–832.

entirely physical. Oil and gas deposits may occur in three positions in respect to the salt core, namely: (1) in the cap rock; (2) in the sedimentary rocks on the flanks of the salt intrusion; and (3) in the sedimentary rocks arched over the top of the stock. No commercial deposits have ever been found within the salt. Most fields in the Gulf Coast produce from only one of the three potential reservoirs, but some produce from two, and at least two (Spindletop, Texas, and Jennings, Louisiana) have produced from all three. By means of modern geophysical techniques, it is possible to discover and even "pin-point" salt-core structures. However, the area of accumulation may be so small, especially in the case of flank trapping, that the explorer may have to drill many failures before drilling the discovery. But the rewards are well worth the gamble; the Gulf Coast salt-core fields are noted for their prolific yields, especially for their enormous production-per-acre figures.

Cap-rock production is almost entirely confined to the limestone cap. The limestone may be brecciated, because of either salt thrust or collapse. Solution porosity is common, and some caps have been found to be truly cavernous. Phenomenal yields have been obtained at Spindletop, Texas, which is illustrated in Fig. 57, and at Humble (Harris County, Texas) from cavernous caps. All production to date from cap-rock reservoirs has been from relatively shallow depths; Hanna [72] points out that thick limestone caps are found only near the surface.

Flank production may be from pinched sands in the drag zone or from reservoirs abutting against the so-called "gouge" at the salt-country rock contact. Several cases are known where the oil is obtained from reservoirs immediately underlying an overhang in the salt stock. This is illustrated by High Island, Texas (Fig. 58). Wedge-outs of sandstones may occur on the flanks owing to drag or unconformities or both. Flank gouge is in reality a porous mixture of residually concentrated granules of anhydrite from the salt stock with country rock sand and shale. As a general rule, flank production from any one reservoir is confined to but a small segment of the total circumference of the salt dome. Spindletop (Fig. 57) illustrates flank as well as cap accumulation. Also shown to illustrate flank trapping is Damon Mound (Fig. 59). Other famous flank fields are Anse la

[72] Marcus A. Hanna, "Geology of the Gulf Coast Salt Domes," *Problems of Petroleum Geology* (Am. Assoc. Petrol. Geol., 1934), p. 669.

Butte[73] and Jennings[74] in Louisiana and Barbers Hill,[75] Humble, and Sour Lake in Texas.[76]

Super-cap accumulation is in normal reservoirs which have been arched upward into anticlinal traps by a salt intrusion. The usual laws of anticlinal accumulation apply, but the distribution of the hydrocarbons across the top of the structure may be complicated by the segmentation produced by faulting.[77] With a few relatively insignificant exceptions, all these salt stocks are so deeply buried that their actual existence has not been proved; the reservoirs are classified as super-cap because of the geographic location (in the case of Gulf Coast structures), the quaquaversal shape of the dome, minimum gravity readings in some instances, and, perhaps, the presence of central grabens or rim synclines. Super-cap accumulation is illustrated by the Conroe (Fig. 60) field, Texas. Most of the many fields discovered in the Gulf Coast district since 1931 are of this type. Some of these fields are described under Texas and Louisiana in Chapter 9.

Other oil-yielding structures that may owe their genesis to the plastic flow of deeply buried salt are the domes of the Gulf interior, illustrated by Hawkins (Fig. 61), and the accumulations which have taken place along the Gulf Coast in anticlines lying at the edges of downfaulted blocks. The latter type is known as the Tepetate structure and is illustrated in this chapter by the West Tepetate (Fig. 62) field, Louisiana, and in Chapter 9 by the La Rosa (Fig. 125) field in Refugio County, Texas.

FAULTS. The same earth forces that create folds may cause the rocks to break and fault. Normal faults result from vertical movements and horizontal tension; reverse faults are the product of lateral compressional forces in the earth's crust.

Faulting plays various roles in the accumulation of oil. For example, graben faulting may result in an adequate sedimentary section for oil occurrence in an area where the normal section is too thin. Over-

[73] F. W. Bates and Jay B. Wharton, Jr., "Anse la Butte Dome, St. Martin Parish, Louisiana," *Bull. Am. Assoc. Petrol. Geol.,* Vol. 27 (August, 1943), pp. 1123–1156.

[74] M. T. Halbouty, "Geology and Geophysics of Southeast Flank of Jennings Dome, Acadia Parish, Louisiana, with Special Reference to Overhang," *Bull. Am. Assoc. Petrol. Geol.,* Vol. 19 (September, 1935), pp. 1308–1329.

[75] M. T. Halbouty, "Geology and Economic Significance of Barbers Hill Salt Dome," *World Petrol.,* Vol. 10 (January, 1939), pp. 40–55.

[76] Alexander Deussen, "Oil-Producing Horizons of Gulf Coast in Texas and Louisiana," *Bull. Am. Assoc. Petrol. Geol.,* Vol. 18 (April, 1934), pp. 500–518.

[77] W. E. Wallace, Jr., "Structure of South Louisiana Deep-Seated Domes," *Bull. Am. Assoc. Petrol. Geol.,* Vol. 28 (September, 1944), pp. 1249–1312.

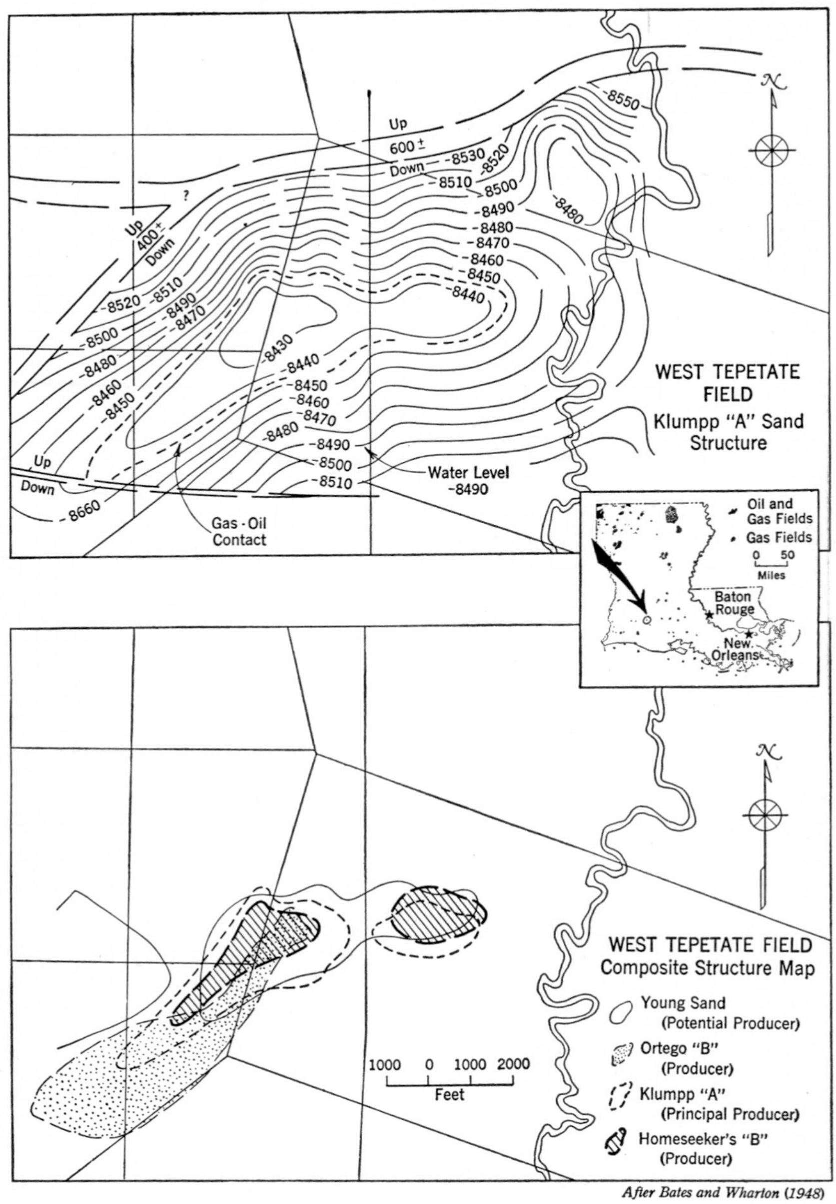

Up
600 ±
Down
Up
400 ±
Down
Up
Down
-8550
-8530
-8520
-8510
-8500
-8490
-8480
-8470
-8460
-8450
-8440
-8430
-8660
Water Level
-8490
Gas - Oil
Contact
WEST TEPETATE
FIELD
Klumpp "A" Sand
Structure
Oil and
Gas Fields
Gas Fields
0 50
Miles
Baton
Rouge
New
Orleans
WEST TEPETATE FIELD
Composite Structure Map
Young Sand
(Potential Producer)
Ortego "B"
(Producer)
Klumpp "A"
(Principal Producer)
Homeseeker's "B"
(Producer)
1000 0 1000 2000
Feet

After Bates and Wharton (1948)

FIG. 62. West Tepetate, Louisiana.

Gulf Coast Anticlinal Accumulation in Downblock. Second only to the salt dome in importance as a trap for hydrocarbons along the Gulf Coast of Louisiana and Texas is the elongate anticline in which accumulation is in the downblock of a fault. Elsewhere than in these coastal districts accumulation is almost always in the upblock. The Gulf Coast faults parallel the shoreline and the strike of the Gulfward-dipping sediments. The shore-side block has dropped; on this block next to the fault plane is an anticline with long axis parallel to the fault. Oil moving up-dip from the direction of the Gulf has been trapped in this anticline, and either the fault on the north flank or the oil-water interface limits production in that direction.

Sometimes called the "Tepetate type" structure, because of its occurrence at Tepetate, Louisiana, downblock anticlinal accumulation is illustrated here by the adjacent West Tepetate * field. This lies about 40 miles northeast of the town of Lake Charles in the northeastern corner of Jefferson Davis Parish.

The structure map contoured on the Klumpp *A* oil sand, which is the principal producer, is shown on the opposite page. The West Tepetate anticline is a low, gentle feature with only 60 to 70 feet of closure above the oil-water level. The dips range from about 100 to 200 feet per mile at the Klumpp level. The fault on the north side has a displacement of about 600 feet.

The lower figure is a composite structure map made by superimposing approximately equivalent contours from each of four structure maps. This composite shows that during the growth of the West Tepetate anticline the zone of greatest uplift shifted northward and lengthened in an east-west direction.

The producing section in the West Tepetate field lies below the Second Marginulina sand in a series of sandstones commonly considered to be Middle Miocene in age. The average depth of the Klumpp *A* reservoir is 8500 feet. Some oil and considerable gas distillate have been found in lower reservoirs.

The uplift is assumed to have been caused by the deep-seated intrusion of salt. After (or during) the arching of the strata above the salt core the hydrocarbons in the various permeable layers moved upward toward the structural crest, where they became trapped. *Courtesy American Association of Petroleum Geologists.*

* Fred W. Bates and Jay B. Wharton, Jr., "Geology of West Tepetate Oil Field, Jefferson Davis Parish, Louisiana," *Bull. Am. Assoc. Petrol. Geol.,* Vol. 32 (September, 1948), pp. 1712–1727.

thrust faults may produce anticlinal traps in the thrust sheet, or they may mask possible traps in the underlying block. Illing [78] calls attention to what he terms "contact enrichment," by which is meant the bringing together of source rocks and reservoir rocks on opposite sides of a fault plane. Obviously, however, for contact enrichment to be effective the faulting would have to take place before the source rock was through yielding oil. Without doubt, fault planes function in some areas as channels for vertical or transverse migration. This migration may be from deep-seated "carrier beds" upward into more shallow reservoirs, or it may be from reservoirs to the surface, producing seeps.

Oil-field faults, by which is meant faults passing through hydrocarbon-bearing reservoirs, are of two structural types: (1) along the crest or high on the flanks of anticlines, and (2) strike faults cutting plunging anticlines on monoclines. The first faults are *not* traps, for the oil would have accumulated in the structure whether the faults were present or not. However, such faults may control the distribution of oil on the anticline by placing a barrier across the path of the hydrocarbons migrating through the reservoir rock toward the top of the anticline. The continuation of the reservoir rock across the fault plane may have been dropped below the level of the oil-water interface so the reservoir rock contains only water. On the other hand, anticlinal faults may interconnect various reservoirs, uniting them into one continuous reservoir. On some domes the faulting has no effect on accumulation whatsoever, for the displacement has not been sufficient to offset completely the reservoir rock.

Faulted plunging anticlines on monoclines are true traps, for in these the oil would not have accumulated where it did were it not for the dam created by the faulting across the pathway of the hydrocarbons migrating up a dipping reservoir rock. Fault trap pools tend to be elongate parallel to the fault line, and the accumulation is bounded by the fault on the up-dip side and by water on the down-dip side. The greatest concentration of fault trap pools occurs in Texas along the Mexia fault zone, where such pools as Mexia, Powell (Fig. 63), Richland, Wortham, and Talco have made this zone a leading oil-producing district.[79] Oil was discovered in the Mexia district in

[78] V. C. Illing, "The Role of Faulting in the Accumulation of Oil and Gas," *Science of Petroleum* (Oxford Univ. Press, 1938), Vol. 1, pp. 252–254.

[79] F. H. Lahee, "Oil and Gas Fields of the Mexia and the Tehuacana Fault Zone, Texas," *Structure of Typical American Oil Fields* (Am. Assoc. Petrol. Geol., 1929), Vol. 1, pp. 304–388.

FIG. 63. Fault trap. Diorama of Powell oil field, Texas. *Courtesy Humble Oil Company and Texas Memorial Museum, Austin.*

the Woodbine sand in 1920. The zone is dominated by a series of closely related parallel en echelon faults. The displacement at the surface is as much as 150 feet, but it increases severalfold with depth. The fault planes dip 35° to 60° west, steepening in the limestone and lessening in shale. Owing to the dip of the fault plane, production may be found up to a half mile west of the fault outcrop. The older pools are from ½ to 1½ miles wide and up to 7 miles long; the newer Talco field is considerably larger. The Talco field is an example of fault trapping and is illustrated in Fig. 64.

Very similar in structural relationship to the fault trap pools of the Mexia zone are the Pickens, Mississippi, field and the Gilbertown field in Choctaw County, Alabama.[80] These are illustrated in Fig. 65. At Gilbertown the oil migrated updip through the sandy upper Eutaw formation and through a fracture system in the overlying Selma chalk until it reached the barrier formed by the fault. Fault trapping is also assumed for the Olinda end of the Brea Canyon-Olinda field, which lies along the Whittier fault in the Los Angeles basin. The greater part of the production at Olinda is obtained from inclined reservoirs that abut against this fault.[81] To the westward in the Brea Canyon part of the field is an elongate anticline the axis of which parallels the Whittier fault to the south, and the accumulation there is controlled by this anticline. Still another example of fault trapping is in the Greater Oficina area in eastern Venezuela, where "accumulation is controlled largely by normal faults constituting barriers to migration of oil southward and westward up the regional dip of the basin. Stratigraphic pinchouts are locally important adjuncts to accumulation." [82] Faulting has also been responsible for trapping in the Eocene rocks in the Mene Grande field in western Venezuela.[83]

Figure 66 is a drawing of a model of the Creole field [84] which lies 1¼ miles off the coast of Louisiana and was the first field discovered in the open waters of the Gulf of Mexico. Not only does this figure portray graphically the fault trapping in the Miocene sandstone

[80] A. N. Current, "Gilbertown Field, Choctaw County, Alabama," *Structure of Typical American Oil Fields* (Am. Assoc. Petrol. Geol., 1948), Vol. 3, pp. 1–4.

[81] Walter A. English, "Geology and Oil Resources of the Puente Hills Region, Southern California," *U. S. Geol. Survey, Bull.* 768 (1926), pp. 80–81.

[82] H. D. Hedberg, L. C. Sass, H. J. Funkhouser, "Oil Fields of Greater Oficina Area, Central Anzoategui, Venezuela," *Bull. Am. Assoc. Petrol. Geol.,* Vol. 31 (December, 1947), p. 2090.

[83] Staff of Caribbean Petroleum Company, "Oil Fields of Royal Dutch-Shell Group in Western Venezuela," *Bull. Am. Assoc. Petrol. Geol.,* Vol. 32 (April, 1948), p. 576.

[84] Theron Wasson, "Creole Field, Gulf of Mexico, Coast of Louisiana," *Structure of Typical American Oil Fields* (Am. Assoc. Petrol. Geol., 1948), Vol. 3, pp. 281–298.

reservoirs but it also shows how the field was exploited by drilling a series of slanted holes from one platform.

FISSURES. Fracturing without faulting is most common, especially in brittle rocks. Many different forces operating in the earth's crust may produce fissures. Contraction, which accompanies cooling (igneous rocks) or dehydration (sedimentary rocks), results in columnar jointing. Horizontal tension and diastrophism both produce fractures. The intrusion of an igneous magma, or a prism of salt, will cause fissuring in the country rock. Even the settling of a compactible sedimentary section over a topographically uneven floor will cause the more brittle layers to break.

The importance of fissures and fractures as reservoirs for hydrocarbons was emphasized in the preceding chapter. Almost always this type of opening is not in itself a trap, and the same laws of accumulation apply here as apply to interstitial openings in sandstones and solution cavities in carbonate reservoirs. In other words, the fissures and fractures that are filled with hydrocarbons either lie high on an anticline or occur immediately down-dip from a fault or other type of barrier. An example of this type of accumulation is the shallow oil production at Rangely [85] (Fig. 38), where wells drilled to depths of less than 500 feet have produced as much as 150 barrels a day from fractures in the Mancos (Cretaceous) shale. The oil in one of the productive zones in the Tupungato oil field in Argentina [86] occurs in fractures in the upper part of a thick series of volcanic tuffs. But here, as at Rangely, the producing fissures lie across the top of a pronounced anticline. Fissured reservoir rocks are also found at Salt Creek, Wyoming, in the Northern Field of Mexico, in Iran, and in other places noted in Chapter 7, but these likewise are structurally controlled accumulations.

Very few places are known where the fissures double as both reservoir rock and trap. Perhaps the best example of this is in the Florence pool in the Canon City embayment, Colorado.[87] This is the oldest field in Colorado, with enough production in 1887 to support a refinery. Over 1000 wells were drilled, and the field has produced

[85] W. Y. Pickering and C. L. Dorn, "Rangely Oil Field, Rio Blanco County, Colorado," *Structure of Typical American Oil Fields* (Am. Assoc. Petrol. Geol., 1948), Vol. 3, p. 134.

[86] H. L. Baldwin, "Tupungato Oil Field, Mendoza, Argentina," *Bull. Am. Assoc. Petrol. Geol.,* Vol. 28 (October, 1944), pp. 1455–1484.

[87] Ronald K. DeFord, "Surface Structure, Florence Oil Field, Fremont County, Colorado," *Structure of Typical American Oil Fields* (Am. Assoc. Petrol. Geol., 1929), Vol. 2, pp. 75–92.

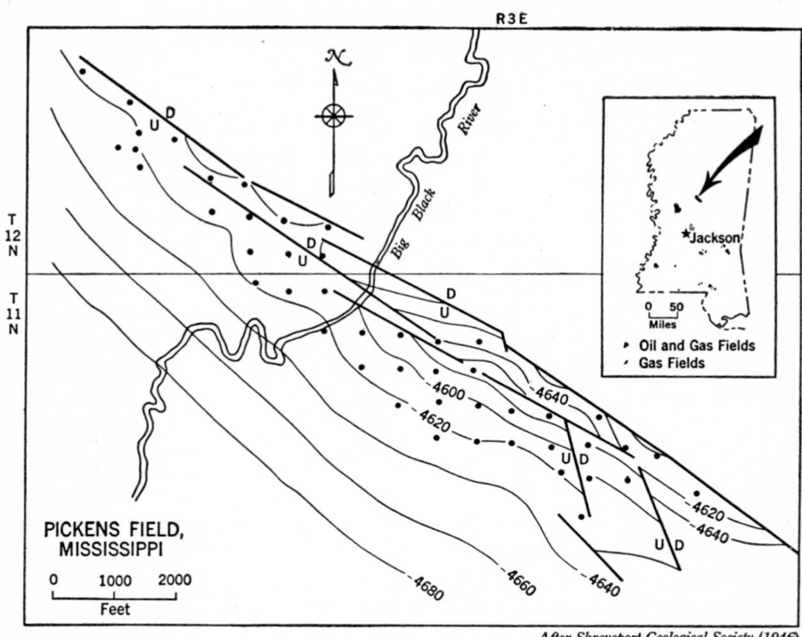

After Shreveport Geological Society (1946)

R4W R3W

Chalk Wells

Eutaw Wells

0 1 2 3

Miles

T 11 N

T 10 N

-3800 -3750 -3700 -3650 -3600 -3550 -3500

-3450 -3400 -3350 -3300

-2150 -2200 -2250

Montgomery

Mobile

0 50 Miles

Oil and Gas Fields

Gas Fields

GILBERTOWN FIELD, ALABAMA

Structure Contours on Top of Eutaw Formation

After Current (1948)

FIG. 65. Pickens, Mississippi, and Gilbertown, Alabama.

Fault Traps. Both figures on the opposite page illustrate fault trapping in the "interior" Gulf Coast district of Mississippi and Alabama. This type of accumulation is fairly common both here and to the westward in northern Louisiana and southern Arkansas. The upper figure is the Pickens field * in central Mississippi, and the lower figure is Alabama's first oil field, the Gilbertown,† on the west edge of southern Alabama.

In both fields the fault line is parallel to the strike. At Gilbertown it is also parallel to the shoreline, but the swing of the strike into the Mississippi embayment gives the Pickens fault a northwest trend. At both Pickens and Gilbertown and in the other interior fault fields the accumulation is on the "up" side of the fault which is on the side down the regional dip. Accumulation is on the same side in the Gulf Coast (Tepetate) type (Fig. 62) of fault structure, but there the down-dip side of the fault is also the down block.

Both the fields on the opposite page illustrate accumulation of oil in plunging anticlines dammed up the regional dip by faults. At Pickens a single plunging anticline nearly 6 miles long carries oil in its highest parts, adjacent to the fault zone. The trap is closed laterally by the turning of the flanks of the fold into the faults. The Gilbertown structure shows three plunging anticlines, with two intervening synclines, abutting the fault zone. Dry holes have been drilled in the synclines, and the producers are found only above the oil-water interface level on the plunging anticlines.

The discovery at Pickens was the result of surface mapping followed by a detailed geophysical survey. The reservoir rock is a sandstone (Wilburn) member of the Austin formation of Upper Cretaceous age. The average producing depth is about 4800 feet.

The Gilbertown field was discovered in 1944 as a result of surface geological studies. Oil is produced from two reservoir rocks. The upper one is a fractured zone in the Selma chalk (Upper Cretaceous) which lies at depths ranging from 2300 to 2800 feet. The other is a sandstone lying about 900 feet deeper in the Upper Cretaceous Eutaw formation. So far attempts to obtain Tuscaloosa production have not been successful. *Courtesy Shreveport Geological Society and American Association of Petroleum Geologists.*

* Shreveport Geol. Soc., "Pickens Field, Madison and Yazoo Counties, Mississippi," *1945 Reference Rept.,* Vol. 1 (1946), pp. 295–298.

† A. M. Current, "Gilbertown Field, Choctaw County, Alabama," *Structure of Typical American Oil Fields* (Am. Assoc. Petrol. Geol., 1948), Vol. 3, pp. 1–4.

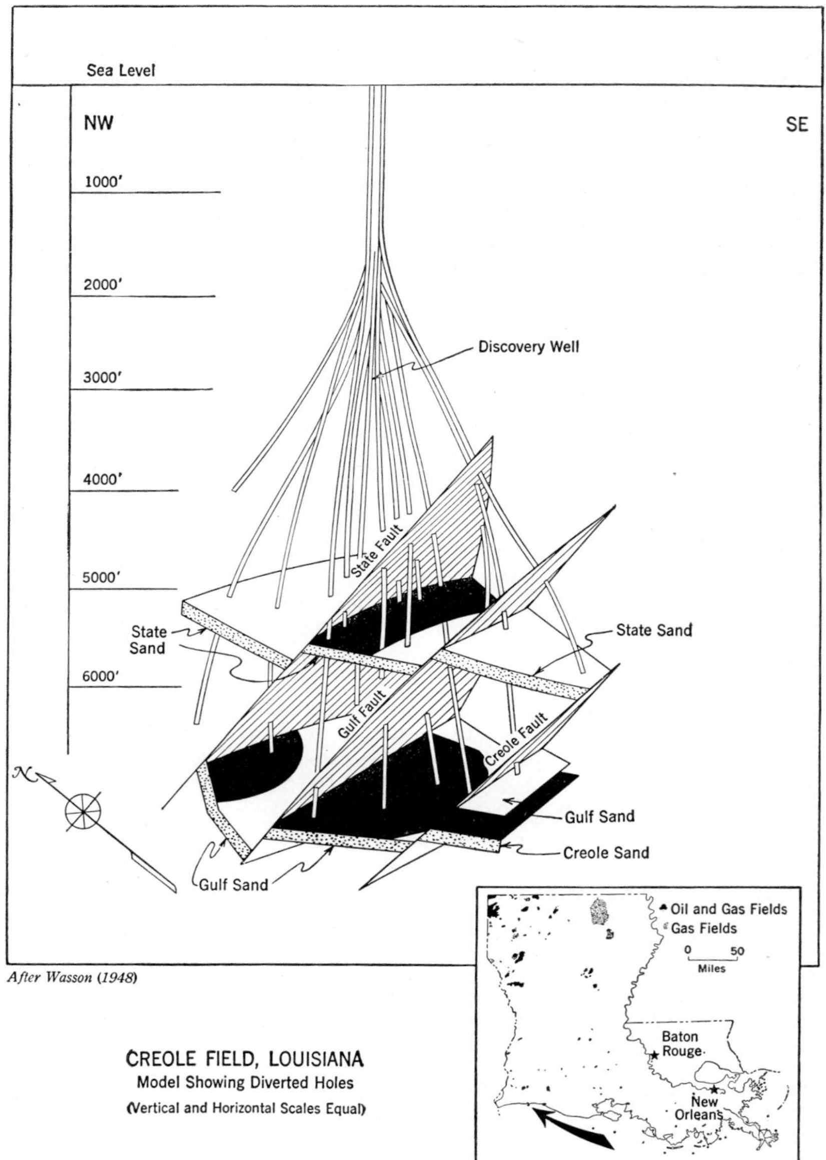

FIG. 66. Multiple-fault trap. Model of Creole field, offshore Louisiana, showing both fault-controlled accumulation and slanted bore holes drilled from one platform. *Courtesy American Association of Petroleum Geologists.*

about 14 million barrels of oil. The oil occurs in near vertical fissures in the black, organic Pierre (Cretaceous) shale in a belt about 3 miles wide along the eastern side of a regional syncline. The fissures apparently failed to reach the surface, and because the fissure walls pinch together with depth, neither surface water nor water from an underlying aquifer can penetrate to these openings. As a result they are water free. Therefore, the oil lies in the lower part of the fissures, and as it is pumped, the fluid level in the fissures is lowered. Obviously these cracks are much younger in age than the Pierre shale. Because of its rich organic content and the manner in which it completely envelops the oil-bearing fractures, the Pierre shale is the most logical source rock. If so, one wonders when and how the connate water in the shale disappeared and where the oil (if present then) was stored before the shale became fractured.

It appears probable that fractures in the Trenton limestone function both as reservoir and trap in the relatively new Rose Hill oil field in Lee County, Virginia.[88] This unusual field, the only oil field so far discovered in Virginia, is in a sedimentary section that has been overridden for several miles by an overthrust block of considerable size. The wells are drilled in fensters, or windows, which expose the stationary block. The relatively brittle Trenton limestone has been fractured, and the oil occurs in these fractures without any as yet apparent anticlinal control on its accumulation. In a part of the oil field the Trenton formation appears to be practically horizontal.

STRUCTURAL TRAP FINDING. Almost all the oil-finding techniques have been developed for the purpose of, and are most effective in, finding traps of the structural type. Thus, anticlines and faults have been, and can be, found by the use of surface geologic methods, core drilling, geophysical instruments where the rocks vary sufficiently in gravity or shock-wave velocity, and by subsurface studies. Salt domes have been discovered by surface geology and especially by the use of three geophysical instruments, the seismograph, the torsion balance, and the gravity meter. The fissure trap fields have been discovered by luck rather than by geologic method, but once they are discovered, geologic method can be used in further development of them. After the pattern of the fissuring had been determined at Florence, the new wells were drilled according to that pattern. If a well missed the near vertical fissure for which it was aiming, the rig was skidded a few feet and a new hole was drilled.

88 Ralph L. Miller, "Rose Hill Oil Field, Lee County, Virginia," *Structure of Typical American Oil Fields* (Am. Assoc. Petrol. Geol., 1948), Vol. 3, pp. 452–479.

VARYING PERMEABILITY TRAPS

The disappearance upward in a reservoir rock of permeability adequate for the movement of oil or gas creates just as effective a trap for the accumulation of hydrocarbons as that created by an anticline or a fault. This upward eclipse of adequate permeability may be abrupt, as where an inclined reservoir rock has been truncated and subsequently sealed, or it may be gradual, as in a facies change. The trapping is more closely connected with stratigraphy than with diastrophism, and so accumulations caused by varying permeability are generally referred to as "stratigraphic" traps. However, in most places, tilting of the sedimentary layers has been an essential event in the natural history of traps of this type.

A large number of oil and gas pools, described in the literature as stratigraphic trap accumulations, actually do not merit this classification. These are the pools in which varying permeability merely limits the *distribution* of hydrocarbons across the top of an anticline or other type of structural trap. If the answer to the question "Would hydrocarbons have accumulated here had the reservoir rock been consistently permeable?" is "Yes," the pool should not be classified as a varying-permeability or stratigraphic trap.

In the following discussion, varying-permeability traps are classified genetically into three types: (1) those in which the permeability differences are acquired initially, during the depositional or sedimentation stage; (2) those in which circulating ground waters have been responsible for locally increasing or decreasing the porosity; and (3) those in which an inclined permeable stratum has been truncated and the eroded edge sealed by a covering of relatively impervious material. The last of these categories is most important in terms of oil-production figures.

VARYING PERMEABILITY CAUSED BY SEDIMENTATION. Sedimentation traps are of three types: (1) reefs, (2) lenticular sandstone, and (3) facies change.

Reefs.[89] Reefs have been defined by Wilson as follows: "A reef is a sedimentary rock aggregate, large or small, composed of the remains of colonial type organisms that lived near or below the surface of water bodies, mainly marine, and developed relatively large vertical

[89] Seismograph Service Corp., *Bibliography of Organic Reefs, Bioherms, and Biostromes* (Tulsa, 1950).

dimensions as compared with the proportions of adjacent sedimentary rocks. The organisms, generally corals and algae and less commonly crinoids and bryozoa, creating the essential features of a reef lived their mature lives on it, and their hard parts remain in place there after death. Reefs tend to develop as mounds or ridges but also grow in irregular, asymmetrical forms. In all, however, a rigid framework is developed that does not compact under weight of overburden. This framework enables a reef margin to grow upward and outward at much steeper angles (even vertical) than is the case with sedimentary clastic rocks. Reefs are commonly characterized by lack of well-developed stratification. Differential settling in rocks adjacent to them usually causes draping of strata over reefs. The extra weight of reefs may cause downward bending of strata under them. Clastic materials or chemically precipitated sediments may be substantial constituents of reefs but are not distinctive parts of them." [90]

Reefs are also known as bioherms. Although colonial corals are common modern reef builders, corals were but one of several types of organisms that were responsible for the reefs in the geologic past. Many of these ancient reefs, originally composed of calcite, have been completely dolomitized. A wide variation exists in the height and area of reefs. Some are barely noticeable nodes on the upper surface of a limestone stratum, but others are abrupt vertical features rising hundreds of feet into younger sediments. Reefs vary in area from protuberances no greater than a washtub in diameter to massive features underlying many square miles. Link [91] believes that a series of interconnecting reefs may be deposited by a transgressing sea, with each succeeding reef a little higher and offset landward until the point of maximum submergence is reached, and then regression starts and a second continuous series of reefs, extending outward from the now rising land mass, is formed, resulting in a recumbent V with the apex at the point of maximum submergence (Fig. 67). Evaporites might be deposited on the shoreward side of the regressive reefs. If the reef building in the transgressing and regressing sea took place on the same vertical plane, a well could be drilled through both legs

[90] W. B. Wilson, "Reef Definition," *Bull. Am. Assoc. Petrol. Geol.,* Vol. 34 (February, 1950), p. 181.

[91] T. A. Link, "Leduc Oil Field, Alberta, Canada," *Bull. Geol. Soc. Am.,* Vol. 60 (March, 1949), pp. 318–402; "Theory of Transgressive and Regressive Reef (Bioherm) Development and Origin of Oil," *Bull. Am. Assoc. Petrol. Geol.,* Vol. 34 (February, 1950), pp. 263–294.

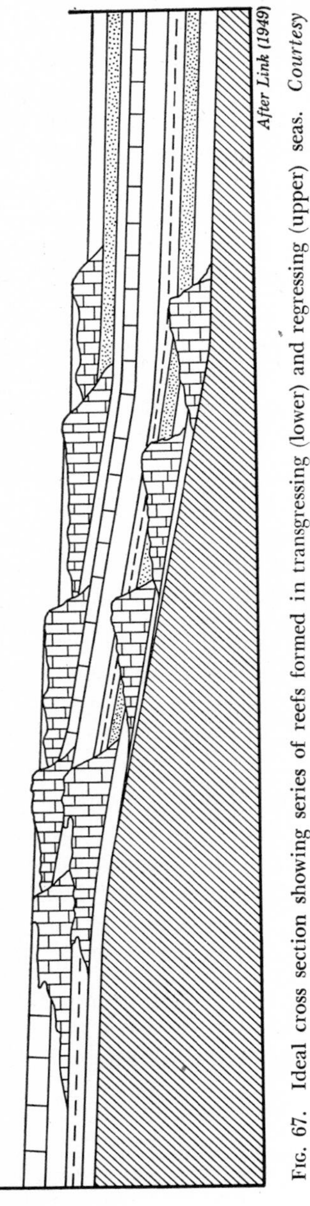

Fig. 67. Ideal cross section showing series of reefs formed in transgressing (lower) and regressing (upper) seas. *After Link (1949)* *Courtesy Geological Society of America.*

of the V, penetrating first the regressive bioherm with associated evaporites and at a lower level reaching the zone of transgressive bioherms with associated clastics.

Reefs are widely distributed both in space and time. Modern coral reefs are limited geographically by water temperatures, being largely confined to seas in which the minimum temperature is rarely lower than about 68° Fahrenheit. Some of the reefs of the past may also have been controlled by temperature, but the geographic distribution was greater because of the greater poleward spread of warm waters during certain periods of geologic time. Furthermore, some reef-building organisms, such as algae, do not have the temperature restrictions possessed by corals and so could probably form reefs in the higher latitudes during times of less benign climate.

Twenhofel [92] describes reefs of algae in the pre-Cambrian, reefs built of algae and sponges in the Cambrian, with coral-containing reefs appearing in the Ordovician. Corals and algae were both very important in building Silurian and Devonian reefs. Crinoids also aided during these periods, and were mainly responsible for large reefs occurring in the Mississippian rocks. Enormous reefs were built during the Permian, especially in western Texas and southeastern Russia. Reefs are relatively scarce in the Mesozoic and Ter-

[92] W. H. Twenhofel, "Characteristics and Geologic Distribution of Coral and Other Organic Reefs," *World Oil,* Vol. 129 (July 1, 1949), pp. 61–64; "Coral and

tiary rocks of North America, but the Middle East contains reefs of both Cretaceous and Tertiary age.[93]

The principal reason for the prolific oil production of some reefs lies in the extreme porosity and permeability of the reservoir rock. This porosity may be initial or it may be induced. As a matter of fact, it is highly probable that the great reef reservoirs had considerable original porosity which expedited the development of secondary openings, so the extreme porosity is actually a combination of both types. Initial porosity is due to both the presence of the abandoned chambers in which the animals lived and the inevitable empty spaces between the outer walls of the shells in a motley assemblage of organisms. The porosity produced by random shell arrangement is combined from the start with permeability. The living chambers, on the other hand, may be sealed off from the outside and be unavailable for the storage of oil unless boring organisms have riddled the framework of shell material, creating connections from room to room and from room to intershell void.

Induced porosity is that which results from: (1) the leaching of a reef mass by circulating waters when the reef lies close to the surface; (2) an excess of solution over precipitation during dolomitization; [94] and (3) the fracturing of the rigid reef rock due to subsequent earth movements. Some oil-producing reefs have been at or near the surface in the geologic past and have developed a honeycomb porosity due to the dissolving activity of circulating waters, and have also been fractured to such an extent that a considerable volume of oil can be stored in the fracture fissures alone. The completely dolomitized reefs of Alberta have extensive porosity and permeability which have been described by Link [95] as primary, but which appear from the published pictures [96] to have undergone considerable enlargement by

Other Organic Reefs in Geologic Column," *Bull. Am. Assoc. Petrol. Geol.,* Vol. 34 (February, 1950), pp. 182–202.

[93] F. R. S. Henson, "Cretaceous and Tertiary Reef Formation and Associated Sediments in Middle East," *Bull. Am. Assoc. Petrol. Geol.,* Vol. 34 (February, 1950), pp. 215–238.

[94] Kenneth K. Landes, "Porosity through Dolomitization," *Bull. Am. Assoc. Petrol. Geol.,* Vol. 30 (March, 1946), pp. 305–318.

[95] T. A. Link, "Leduc Oil Field, Alberta, Canada," *Bull. Geol. Soc. Am.,* Vol. 60 (March, 1949), pp. 389–390.

[96] D. B. Layer *et al.,* "Leduc Oil Field, Alberta, A Devonian Coral Reef Discovery," *Bull. Am. Assoc. Petrol. Geol.,* Vol. 33 (April, 1949), p. 586, Plate 2, middle picture. Also W. W. Waring and D. B. Layer, "Devonian Dolomitized Reef, D-3 Reservoir, Leduc Field, Alberta, Canada," *Bull. Am. Assoc. Petrol. Geol.,* Vol. 34 (February, 1950), pp. 301–307.

leaching. Many of the vugs are lined with dolomite crystals, which suggests that the leaching may have accompanied dolomitization.

In addition to the porosity within the reef rock itself some reefs have been elevated above the sea and have been eroded and blanketed with a veneer of clastic reef material. In the Marine, Illinois, oil pool (Fig. 43) such reef "sand" is the principal oil reservoir rather than the underlying solid reef rock.[97]

The origin of the oil within the reefs is a matter of controversy. Some, like Link,[98] believe that the oil is indigenous to the reef; others suspect that the reef was merely a convenient body of porous rock which afforded storage space to the oil in the same manner as did the serpentine rock reservoirs in the Gulf Coastal Plain of Texas which are described in the next section. It is obviously true that the reefs were once scenes of teeming life. It is not so obvious that any appreciable percentage of the soft body parts of the reef-building organisms were trapped and preserved within the reefs, later to become oil which accumulated beneath the reef cover.

The trapping of oil and gas in reefs is the most easily understood part of the natural history of a bioherm oil deposit. All oil-producing reefs are highly porous and permeable bodies of rock completely surrounded, at least above the water level, by fine sediment impervious to the passage of hydrocarbons in any volume. Ordinarily the pores in a bioherm are filled with water just as are the pores in any other type of buried reservoir rock. Oil in the reef rock, whether indigenous or migrant, will rise through the waterfilled pores until the impervious cap of overlying shale is reached. Many reefs have the same succession below the cap of gas, oil, and water as found in anticlinal accumulations.

Oil has been produced for many years from reefs in several regions, especially the Southern Field of Mexico, and in western and northern Texas.[99] The Norman Wells reef limestone field in Northwest Territory, Canada, was discovered in 1920.[100] This field lies less than 100 miles south of the Arctic Circle. It was not until the advent of war created demand in 1942 that Norman Wells was fully developed.

[97] Heinz A. Lowenstam, "Marine Pool, Madison County, Illinois, Silurian Reef Producer," *Structure of Typical American Oil Fields* (Am. Assoc. Petrol. Geol., 1948), Vol. 3, pp. 153–188.

[98] T. A. Link, *op. cit.*

[99] Carl B. Richardson, "Regional Discussion of Pennsylvanian Reefs of Texas," *Am. Assoc. Petrol. Geol., Program Annual Meeting* (1950), p. 14.

[100] J. S. Stewart, "Norman Wells Oil Field, Northwest Territory, Canada," *Structure of Typical American Oil Fields* (Am. Assoc. Petrol. Geol., 1948), Vol. 3, pp. 86–109.

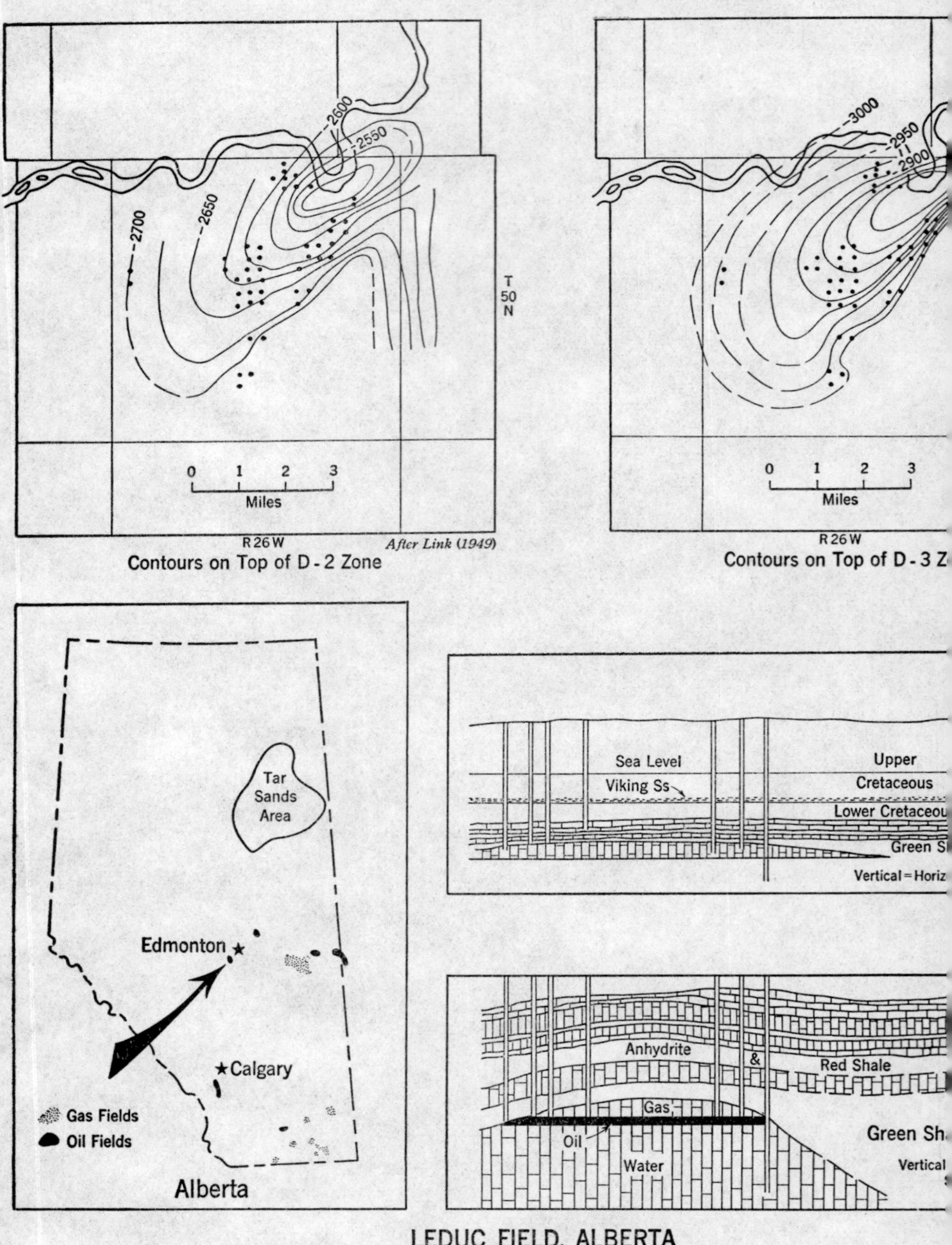

2600
2550
2650
2700
T
50
N
0 1 2 3
Miles
R 26 W
After Link (1949)
Contours on Top of D - 2 Zone
3000
2950
2900
0 1 2 3
Miles
R 26 W
Contours on Top of D - 3 Z
Tar
Sands
Area
Edmonton
Calgary
Gas Fields
Oil Fields
Alberta
Sea Level
Upper
Viking Ss
Cretaceous
Lower Cretaceou
Green S
Vertical = Horiz
Anhydrite
&
Red Shale
Gas
Oil
Water
Green Sh
Vertical

LEDUC FIELD, ALBERTA

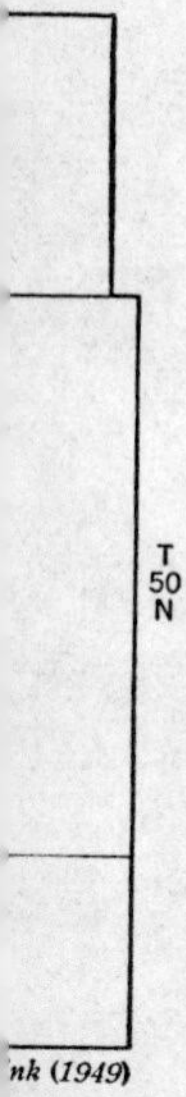

Fig. 68. Leduc Field, Alberta.

Reef Trap. The Leduc field * is 15 miles southwest of Edmonton, Alberta, about 300 miles north of the international border (see index map).

The general vicinity of Leduc was chosen for a stratigraphic test after a regional geologic study. The actual site for the first test and discovery well was based upon seismic surveys. On Feb. 13, 1947, this well was completed with an initial production rate of 1000 barrels a day.

The basic structural feature at Leduc is a reef or bioherm. This is shown in the cross sections at the lower right. The upper section shows the reef and the overlying strata without any exaggeration of vertical scale. In the lower section the vertical scale has been exaggerated 5 to 1. The two contour maps are subsurface structure contour maps. One of these shows the subsea structure contours based on the top of the bioherm, which has been named the *D*-3 zone. The other contour map shows the structure of the *D*-2 zone, which is a blanket limestone separated from the reef by green shale of variable thickness. The *D*-2 limestone is in part "draped" over the reef reflecting, in a subdued manner, its upward bulge. The overlying formations also reflect this structure, but to a lessening degree.

The outcropping rocks in the Leduc area belong to the Upper Cretaceous. Upper Devonian rocks directly underlie the Lower Cretaceous. The uppermost Devonian formation, called the *D*-1, is a porous, highly fractured, and brecciated dolomite and limestone containing "shows" of relatively heavy oil, but no commercial accumulations as yet. The *D*-2 formation, which was the reservoir rock for the Leduc discovery well, is a porous dolomite containing abundant corals and Bryozoa. Below is a greenish gray shale overlying the *D*-3 bioherm, which has become the main producing oil formation. This is a porous, fossiliferous dolomite with both granular and vuggy porosity. As can be seen in the cross section this reservoir has a thick gas cap underlain by a thinner oil-bearing section with water everywhere beneath.

Accumulation in the *D*-3 zone is entirely stratigraphic, controlled by the presence of a highly porous reef limestone completely surrounded by impervious shale. The accumulation of oil in the *D*-2 zone, however, is anticlinal. *Courtesy Geological Society of America and American Association of Petroleum Geologists.*

* D. B. Layer *et al.*, "Leduc Oil Field, Alberta, A Devonian Coral Reef Discovery," *Bull. Am. Assoc. Petrol. Geol.*, Vol. 33 (April, 1949), pp. 572–602; T. A. Link, "Leduc Oil Field, Alberta, Canada," *Bull. Geol. Soc. Am.*, Vol. 60 (March, 1949), pp. 381–402.

However, it was the discovery of the Leduc field of Alberta, a prolific reef producer, in 1947 that really started the intensive search for the bioherm type of accumulation. This field has been chosen to illustrate reef traps (Fig. 68). The Leduc discovery was followed shortly by Redwater, Golden Spike, and other new strikes in the Edmonton district, and within a few months the estimate of the reserve in reef oil accumulation in Alberta had risen to 1 billion barrels.

At the same time, limestone reef fields were being discovered in Scurry County in west Texas. The first strike was made in July, 1948, and within the year five areas in the western part of the county had been found to be underlain by oil pools trapped in reefs. Subsequent drilling may connect some of these separate fields. Several wells have penetrated nearly 700 feet of oil-producing reef rock.[101] Another Texas producing reef is a crinoidal limestone of Pennsylvanian age in the Todd field of Crockett County.[102] The accumulation of oil in the detrital zone lapping up on a reef at Marine, Illinois, was described and illustrated (Fig. 43) in the section on anticlinal traps.

Lenticular Sandstones. A considerable volume of oil is produced each year from lenticular sands. Classified in this group are those sandstones which, owing to local conditions of sedimentation, were deposited as separate and distinct bodies of sand completely surrounded by finer sediment which subsequently became shale. Not included in this classification are the sandstone reservoirs with lenticular porosity due to lateral facies change during sedimentation. These are discussed in a subsequent paragraph.

Lenticular sands vary in shape from extremely elongate "shoestring" sands to highly irregular-shaped bodies. They are more likely, however, to have a definite "trend" than to be equidimensional in plan. It should also be noted that even the shoestring sands are not continuous but are broken every few miles by a shale-filled gap.

The origin of the lenticular sands, especially those of decided elongation, has been a subject of considerable investigation.[103] Among the

[101] D. H. Stormont, "Scurry County, West Texas, Limestone Reef Development," *Oil and Gas Jour.,* Vol. 48 (July 7, 1949), pp. 54 *et seq.*

[102] Robert F. Imbt and S. V. McCollum, "Todd Deep Field, Crockett County, Texas," *Bull. Am. Assoc. Petrol. Geol.,* Vol. 34 (February, 1950), pp. 239–262.

[103] N. Wood Bass, Constance Leatherock, W. Reese Dillard, and Luther E. Kennedy, "Origin and Distribution of Bartlesville and Burbank Shoestring Oil Sands in parts of Oklahoma and Kansas," *Bull. Am. Assoc. Petrol. Geol.,* Vol. 21 (January, 1937), pp. 30–66; N. Wood Bass, "Origin of Shoestring Sands of Greenwood and Butler Counties, Kansas," *State Geol. Survey Kans., Bull.* 23 (1936); Homer H. Charles, "Oil and Gas Resources of Kansas, Anderson County," *State Geol. Survey Kans., Bull.* 6, part 7 (1927); John L. Rich, "Shorelines and Lenticular Sands as Factors in

various environments of deposition which have been postulated as causing the development of lenticular sand bodies are: stream channel fillings; channel fillings in the distributaries of deltas; beaches, hooks, and spits; offshore bars separated from the mainland by shallow brackish-water lagoons which may be replete with plant and animal life; and sea-bottom sand accumulations which have the appearance of giant ripples on the present sea floor and which may be the result of currents or storm waves or a combination of both.[104]

Examples of lenticular sands which have been chosen for illustration are the famous shoestring sands of Greenwood and adjacent counties, Kansas (Fig. 69), and the sand "trends" in the Venango district, northwestern Pennsylvania (Fig. 70). Other occurrences of shoestring sands include sands considerably younger than those in Greenwood County which produce at shallow depths in Anderson County in northeastern Kansas; [105] gas-producing "stray" sands in Michigan; [106] the Gay-Spencer-Richardson trend in West Virginia; [107] and the Music Mountain pool in Pennsylvania.[108]

Less elongate in outline, but nevertheless lenticular, is the Bradford sand, the reservoir rock for the Bradford pool of Pennsylvania and New York.[109] Lenticular sands are oil reservoirs in many other parts of the Appalachian province also, but some accumulations so credited may be due to facies change rather than depositional lenticularity.[110] Furthermore, much of the Appalachian accumulation is actually anti-

Oil Accumulation," *Science of Petroleum* (Oxford Univ. Press, 1938), Vol. 1, pp. 230–239; John L. Rich, "Submarine Sedimentary Features on Bahama Banks and Their Bearing on Distribution Patterns of Lenticular Oil Sands," *Bull. Am. Assoc. Petrol. Geol.,* Vol. 32 (May, 1948), pp. 767–779; R. E. Sherrill, P. A. Dickey, and L. S. Matteson, "Types of Stratigraphic Oil Pools in Venango Sands of Northwestern Pennsylvania," *Stratigraphic Type Oil Fields* (Am. Assoc. Petrol. Geol., 1941), pp. 507–538; Oren F. Evans, "Internal Structure of Shoestring Sands," *World Oil,* Vol. 131 (July 1, 1950), pp. 66–70; and others.

104 John L. Rich, *op. cit.*

105 Homer H. Charles, *op. cit.*

106 Max W. Ball, T. J. Weaver, H. D. Crider, Douglas S. Ball, "Shoestring Sand Gas Fields of Michigan," *Stratigraphic Type Oil Fields* (Am. Assoc. Petrol. Geol., 1941), pp. 237–266.

107 E. T. Heck, "Gay-Spencer-Richardson Oil and Gas Trend, Jackson, Roane, and Calhoun Counties, West Virginia," *Stratigraphic Type Oil Fields* (Am. Assoc. Petrol. Geol., 1941), pp. 806–829.

108 Charles R. Fettke, "Music Mountain Oil Pool, McKean County, Pennsylvania," *Stratigraphic Type Oil Fields* (Am. Assoc. Petrol. Geol., 1941), pp. 492–506.

109 Wallace W. Wilson, "Practical Application of Geology to Reservoir Analysis," *Petrol. Engineer,* Vol. 17 (September, 1946), pp. 152 *et seq.*

110 A. H. McClain, "Stratigraphic Accumulation in Jackson-Kanawha Counties Area of West Virginia," *Bull. Am. Assoc. Petrol. Geol.,* Vol. 33 (March, 1949), pp. 336–345.

cline controlled, but with varying permeability responsible for the distribution of hydrocarbons across the tops of the structures.

Accumulation along old strand lines where the sands pinch out up-dip in Jim Hogg County, Texas,[111] has been described. The Osage field in eastern Wyoming produces mainly from "locally thick discontinuous sandy bodies enclosed by marine shale" which constitute the Newcastle sandstone member of the Graneros (Cretaceous) shale along the east flank of the Powder River basin.[112] The Sunburst and Moulton production at Cut Bank, Montana, is from lenticular sandstone beds, but the main production is from the Cut Bank sand, in which trapping is due to facies change.[113] Sand lenticularity and facies changes are also responsible for much of the accumulation in the Maracaibo basin oil fields of western Venezuela.[114]

The trapping of hydrocarbons in lenticular sands is due to the presence of a porous and permeable reservoir completely surrounded by impervious material. The best guess as to the source of the oil is that it has been squeezed out of the surrounding shale into the relatively incompactible and permeable sandstone. A very local (vertically) source for the oil in the shoestring sands of southeastern Kansas and northeastern Oklahoma is indicated by the fact that the crude oils from thirty-three pools in the Burbank sand distributed through an area 150 miles long are alike but quite dissimilar from that found in other sands separated vertically from the Burbank by but a few feet of shale.[115]

Facies Change. Trapping due to facies change is usually brought about by up-dip "shaling" of sandstone or limestone; more rarely it is created by the merging of sandstone into limestone. Facies change traps are due to environmental differences at the time of deposition. They occur (1) where coarser sediment merges with finer sediment which was deposited in quieter water or at a greater distance from

[111] James E. Freeman, "Strand Line Accumulation of Petroleum, Jim Hogg County, Texas," *Bull. Am. Assoc. Petrol. Geol.,* Vol. 33 (July, 1949), pp. 1260–1270.

[112] C. E. Dobbin, "Exceptional Oil Fields in Rocky Mountain Region of the United States," *Am. Assoc. Petrol. Geol.,* Vol. 31 (May, 1947), p. 801.

[113] John E. Blixt, "Cut Bank Oil and Gas Field, Glacier County, Montana," *Stratigraphic Type Oil Fields* (Am. Assoc. Petrol. Geol., 1941), pp. 327–381.

[114] Staff of Caribbean Petroleum Company, "Oil Fields of Royal Dutch-Shell Group in Western Venezuela," *Bull. Am. Assoc. Petrol. Geol.,* Vol. 32 (April, 1948), pp. 517–628.

[115] Tulsa Geological Society Research Committee, "Relationship of Crude Oils and Stratigraphy in Parts of Oklahoma and Kansas," *Bull. Am. Assoc. Petrol. Geol.,* Vol. 30 (May, 1946), pp. 747–748; L. M. Neumann, *et al.,* "Relationship of Crude Oil and Stratigraphy in Parts of Oklahoma and Kansas," *Bull. Am. Petrol. Geol.,* Vol. 25 (September, 1941), pp. 1801–1809.

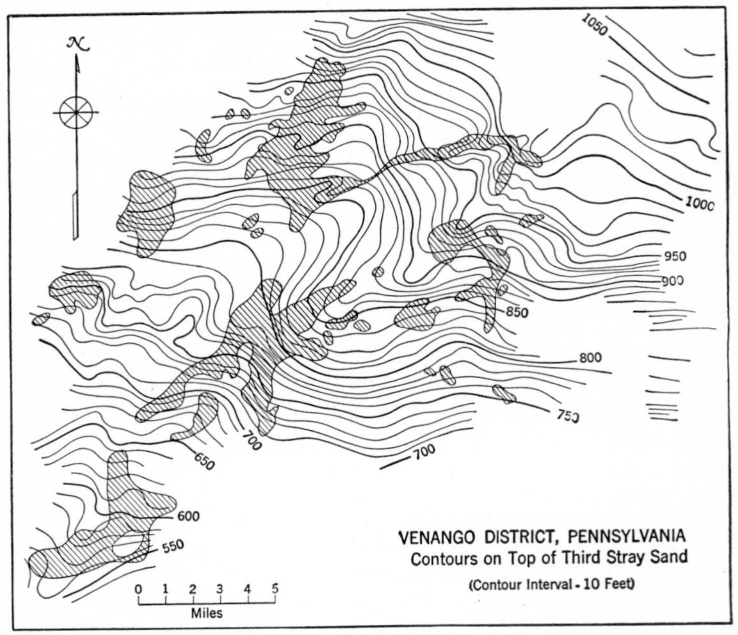
N
1050
1000
950
900
850
800
750
700
700
650
600
550
0 1 2 3 4 5
Miles
VENANGO DISTRICT, PENNSYLVANIA
Contours on Top of Third Stray Sand
(Contour Interval - 10 Feet)

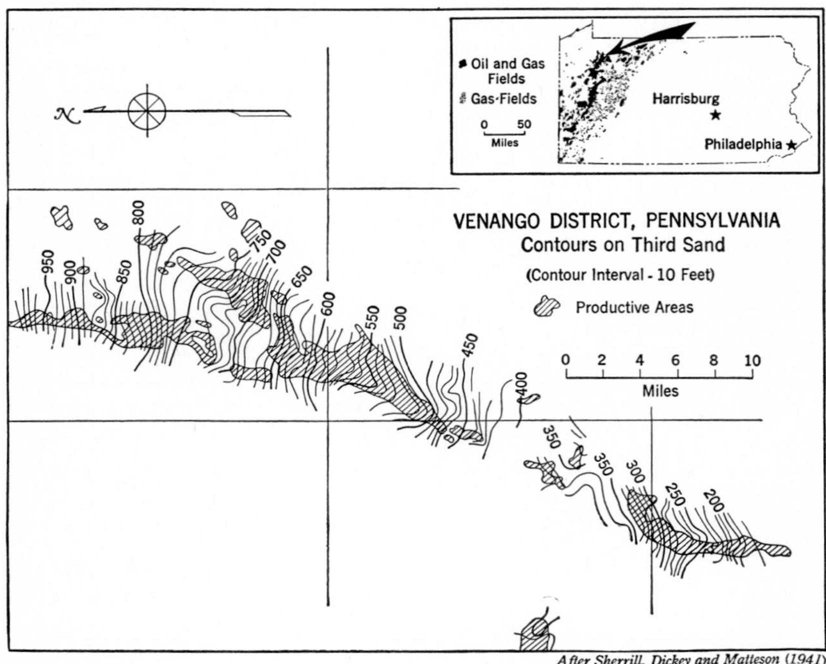
Oil and Gas Fields
Gas-Fields
0 50
Miles
Harrisburg
Philadelphia
N
VENANGO DISTRICT, PENNSYLVANIA
Contours on Third Sand
(Contour Interval - 10 Feet)
Productive Areas
0 2 4 6 8 10
Miles
950
900
850
800
750
700
650
600
550
500
450
400
350
350
300
250
200

After Sherrill, Dickey and Matteson (1941)

FIG. 70. Northwestern Pennsylvania.

Accumulation in Lenticular Sands. All the production in the Venango district * in northwestern Pennsylvania comes from lenticular sands which are generally less than 1000 feet below the surface. This area includes the site of the Drake well, the birthplace of the American oil industry. The Venango district fields were discovered between 1859 and about 1900. They were found by prospecting near oil seeps, or by following trends, or merely through random drilling.

The Venango group of sands lies within the uppermost series of the Devonian system. The group is about 350 feet in thickness and consists of alternating sands and shales. No single sand stratum can be traced throughout the district, but three persistent sand zones separated by sections of shale can be mapped. These sands are designated in descending order, the First, Second, and Third. Although the sands within each of these members are lenticular, appearing and disappearing across the district, the intervening shales are continuous. The Third sand consists of interbedded fine to coarse-grained and even pebbly sandstones and shales. It contains two principal sands, the Third Stray, above, and the Third sand itself, below.

The trapping in the Venango district is entirely stratigraphic. The lenticularity of the sand bodies is due to original depositon, and the three sand members differ not only in stratigraphic position but also in the environment during sedimentation. The small, irregular sand bodies of the First sand trend perpendicular to the old shoreline and may be channel sands in delta distributaries. The producing sands in the Second sand formation are more sheetlike but pinch out abruptly on the northwest along a line parallel to the ancient shoreline. These sands were probably distributed by longshore currents. The Third type consists of long, narrow, and sometimes pebbly sandbars parallel to the shoreline, which are perhaps buried offshore bars.

The upper drawing shows the oil pools producing from the Third Stray sand and the structure as contoured on top of that sand. Locally the rocks dip to the southwest, and the pools occur along this monoclinal slope without any apparent regard for the rock structure. A similar situation is obvious in the lower drawing, which shows the structure and distribution of oil fields in the Third sand. *Courtesy American Association of Petroleum Geologists.*

* R. E. Sherrill, P. A. Dickey, L. S. Matteson, "Types of Stratigraphic Oil Pools in Venango Sands of Northwestern Pennsylvania," *Stratigraphic Type Oil Fields* (Am. Assoc. Petrol. Geol., 1941), pp. 507–538.

the source of supply, or (2) where porous carbonate rock merges with fine clastic material in what was the landward direction at time of deposition. In addition to this environmental situation, it is necessary in order to create a trap that the sedimentary beds be subsequently tilted in such a direction as to place the impervious facies up-dip from the porous rock. Hydrocarbons entering the reservoir rock move up the inclined layer until impounded by the increasing imperviousness of the reservoir in the zone of facies change.

An outstanding example of the up-dip shaling of carbonate rock reservoirs is illustrated by the Hugoton field of southwestern Kansas (Fig. 71). Gas has accumulated below the facies barrier in this area for many miles down-dip. Another possible illustration of trapping by up-dip shaling, this time of a sandstone reservoir rock, is the Clinton gas field of central Ohio. Accumulation here has been along the western edge of the reservoir rock on the east flank of the Cincinnati arch. The pools, mostly gas but some oil, occur in a belt extending from Lake Erie southward to the Ohio River (Fig. 72). The "Clinton" sandstone reservoir is in reality a white sandstone belonging to the Medina (Silurian) rather than the Clinton. This sandstone thins rapidly westward and is absent or "very indefinite" before reaching the central part of eastern Ohio.[116] There is some doubt whether the western boundary of the Clinton sand is actually a change in facies from sand to shale. The westward thinning of the sandstone, with the source of supply to the east, makes the concept of a change to finer sediment, deposited contemporaneously, appear logical. However, some have interpreted the meager subsurface data available to indicate the deposition of discontinuous lenses of sand as offshore bars in a regressive Medina Sea.

The sandstone reservoir rocks in the Bryson field, Texas, grade up-dip into shale and siltstone with the oil trapped down-dip below the zone of facies change.[117] The Cut Bank sand, previously mentioned as the chief oil reservoir rock in the Cut Bank field, Montana, is a cherty, conglomeratic, pervious sand where it contains oil, but it merges up-dip and laterally into tight, chert-free, sandstone and siltstone. This facies change may be due to irregular sedimentation in a

[116] W. Stout, R. E. Lamborn, D. T. Ring, J. S. Gillespie, and J. R. Lockett, "Natural Gas in Central and Eastern Ohio," *Geology of Natural Gas* (Am. Assoc. Petrol. Geol., 1935), p. 908; Richard H. Denman, "The Clinton Gas Field of Ohio," *The Compass,* Vol. 22 (March, 1942), pp. 164–170.

[117] T. C. Hiestand, "Bryson Oil Field, Jack County, Texas," *Stratigraphic Type Oil Fields* (Am. Assoc. Petrol. Geol., 1941), pp. 539–547.

floodplain and delta environment.[118] The possible role of facies change in oil accumulation in the Jackson-Kanawha district of West

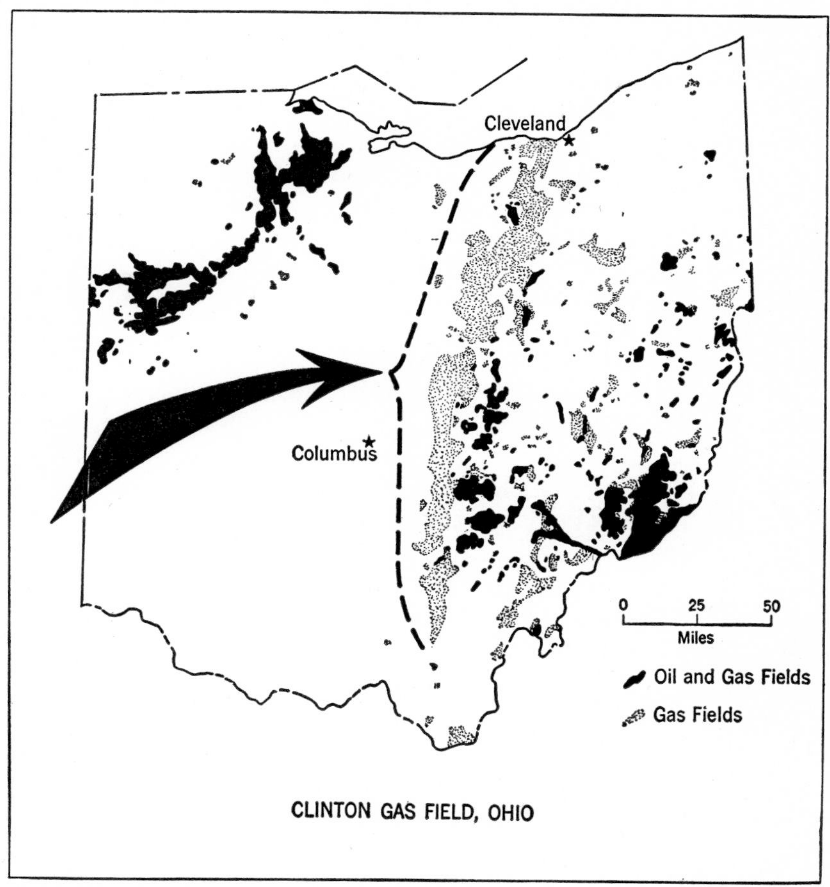

FIG. 72. Clinton gas field, Ohio. Trapping due to up-dip termination of porosity in reservoir rock. *United States Geological Survey.*

Virginia [119] has also been mentioned previously, as well as the impounding of hydrocarbons below facies barriers in the Maracaibo

[118] John E. Blixt, "Cut Bank Oil and Gas Field, Glacier County, Montana," *Stratigraphic Type Oil Fields* (Am. Assoc. Petrol. Geol., 1941).

[119] A. H. McClain, "Stratigraphic Accumulation in Jackson-Kanawha Counties Area of West Virginia," *Bull. Am. Assoc. Petrol. Geol.,* Vol. 33 (March, 1949), pp. 336–345.

basin, Venezuela.[120] Although the principal cause for trapping in the Benton field of Illinois is an anticline, a facies change from sandstone into shale in the northeast part of the field completes the closure needed for oil accumulation.[121]

VARYING PERMEABILITY DUE TO GROUND-WATER ACTIVITY. Circulating underground waters have the ability both of increasing rock porosity by solution and of diminishing porosity by precipitation of mineral matter in the pre-existing voids. Fortunately for mankind, more reservoirs have been created by solution than have been destroyed by precipitation. Although solution may occur in any type of rock, even sandstone (Chapter 7), the reservoirs most commonly aided by solution activity are carbonate rocks. In many carbonate rock reservoirs the oil is stored in cavities created or at least enlarged by the dissolving action of circulating ground waters. This leaching is selective, being most pronounced in the more susceptible layers and perhaps absent altogether in strata less vulnerable to this type of attack. Within a given stratigraphic zone, however, the extent of the permeability created by ground-water solution has a fair degree of lateral consistency, even though some zones are notoriously erratic in the degree of permeability across short distances. Because of the usual widespread character of solution porosity it is difficult to find examples of pools in which the trapping has been due solely to local solution porosity in carbonate rock. An exception is dolomitization porosity, which is discussed in a subsequent paragraph. Accumulation in solution porosity reservoirs is either anticlinal or is due to faulting, or truncation and overlap, or some other conventional type of trap. Locally erratic porosity may result in the drilling of many dry holes inside the periphery of oil pools of this sort, however. Variations in permeability therefore may control the *distribution* of oil within a trap.

A quite different situation is the porosity which is produced by and during dolomitization and which may be local in extent and without any structural relationship. An example of this type of accumulation is the Deep River pool of Michigan, in which the oil has accumulated without regard to rock structure in a long, narrow

[120] Staff of Caribbean Petroleum Company, "Oil Fields of Royal Dutch-Shell Group in Western Venezuela," *Bull. Am. Assoc. Petrol. Geol.*, Vol. 32 (April, 1948), p. 543.

[121] J. V. Howell, "Geology of Benton Field, Franklin County, Illinois," *Bull. Am. Assoc. Petrol. Geol.*, Vol. 32 (May, 1948), pp. 745–766.

porous zone where the rock has been locally dolomitized. Accumulation at Deep River is illustrated in Fig. 73. Similar in the manner of trapping are the many oil and gas pools which form the Lima-Indiana district (Fig. 101).[122] Although these fields lie either on the flanks or across the top of the broad Findlay arch, their localization at any one point is not due to the structural situation but to the fact that there and there only the Trenton limestone has been dolomitized and has sufficient porosity to function as a reservoir rock. The oil has accumulated in the dolomitized zone because that is the only place in a considerable stratigraphic section where there is enough porosity and permeability for the rock to be a reservoir. As in the case of the lenticular sands the trapping is due to the presence of a reservoir of limited extent completely surrounded by impermeable limestones and shales.

An unusual condition exists in the Gulf Coastal Plain of Texas and elsewhere where igneous rock bodies (Fig. 29) of limited extent have been altered, leached, and weathered into porous and permeable serpentines, as at Chapman, shown in Fig. 74. These porous rock masses are likewise surrounded by material impervious to the movement of hydrocarbons and have afforded a haven to migrating hydrocarbons, functioning in exactly the same way as the previously described dolomitized zones, lenticular sandstones, and isolated reefs.

It is theoretically conceivable that thorough cementation of the reservoir rock might create an up-dip barrier to further migration, trapping the oil below. Actually, cementation to such a degree that the permeability is completely destroyed is rare. It is difficult to find accumulations of oil in which up-dip cementation has been responsible for trapping. In the Tri-County oil field of southwestern Indiana differential cementation has been effective in limiting the distribution of oil, but accumulation at that particular spot has been due primarily to structure.[123] The same is true in the New Harmony field[124] in Illinois and Indiana. Accumulation of oil has been influenced by eccentric cementation of the reservoir rock in other fields, including

[122] J. Ernest Carman and Wilber Stout, "Relationship of Accumulation of Oil to Structure and Porosity in the Lima-Indiana Field," *Problems of Petroleum Geology* (Am. Assoc. Petrol. Geol., 1934), pp. 521–529.

[123] Joseph M. Wanenmacher and Wendell B. Gealy, "Surface and Subsurface Structure of the Tri-County Oil Field of Southwestern Indiana," *Bull. Am. Assoc. Petrol. Geol.*, Vol. 14 (April, 1930), pp. 423–431.

[124] George V. Cohee, "Lateral Variation in Chester Sandstones Producing Oil and Gas in Lower Wabash River Area," *Bull. Am. Assoc. Petrol. Geol.*, Vol. 26 (October, 1942), p. 1606.

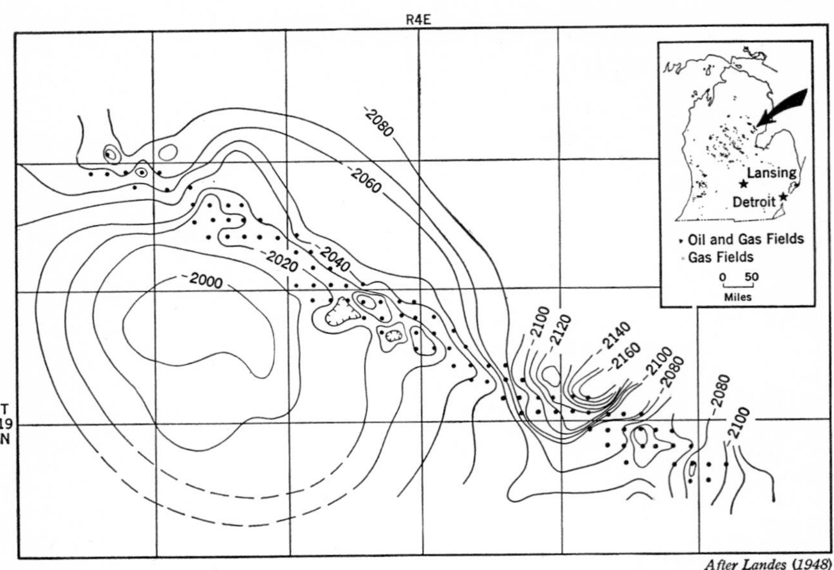

After Landes (1948)

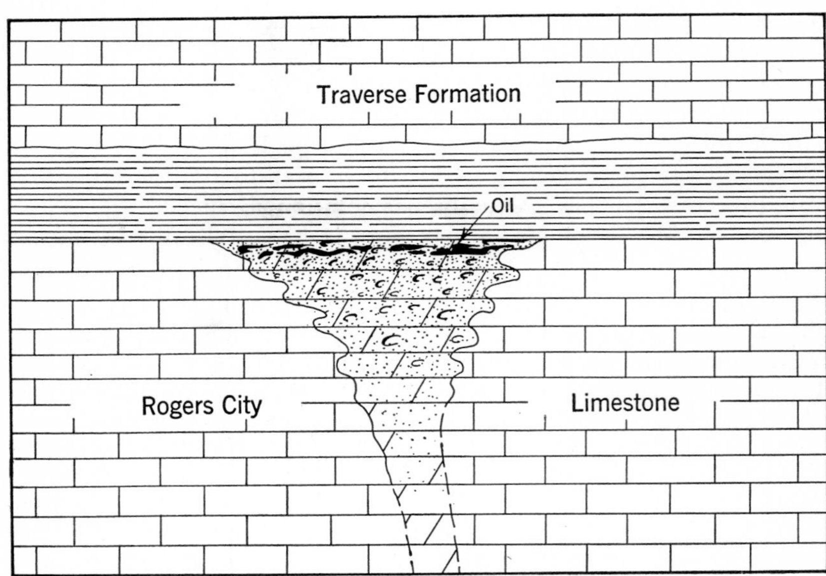

Hypothetical Cross-Section

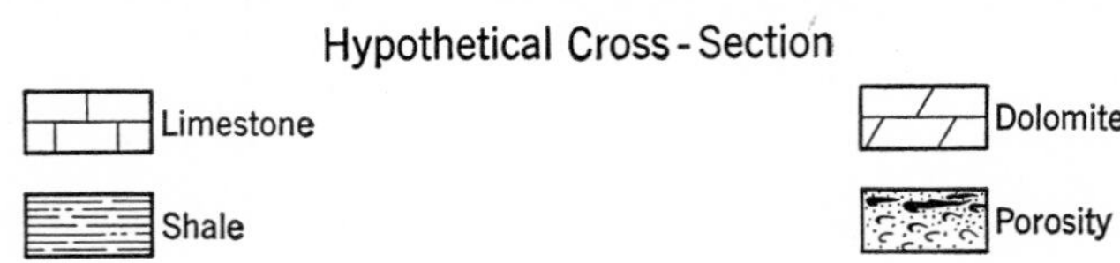

FIG. 73. Deep River, Michigan.

Localized Dolomite Porosity. A relatively new field illustrating the accumulation of oil in a patch of locally dolomitized limestone is the Deep River pool in Arenac County, Michigan.* This pool was discovered on Dec. 30, 1943. Subsequently about 150 wells were drilled, of which over one-third were failures. This abnormal percentage of dry holes after the discovery of a pool was due to the extremely narrow width of the producing zone, as can be seen in the upper figure on the opposite page.

The upper figure is a subsurface structure map contoured on the base of the Devonian Traverse formation which immediately overlies the reservoir rock. The structure is that of a dome, but the Deep River oil field, where on the dome at all, is far down on the northeast flank, and there is absolutely no relationship between accumulation and structure. The Deep River gas field, producing from the Mississippian Berea sandstone, occupies the highest part of the dome.

The oil reservoir rock at Deep River is the Rogers City formation of Devonian age. Normally the Rogers City formation is limestone, but at Deep River, *where productive of oil,* it is a porous dolomite. The unsuccessful wells failed to find oil, porosity, or dolomite. Conversely, where the limestone has been dolomitized it is both porous and oil-bearing in this general vicinity.

The lower figure is a hypothetical cross section of the Deep River producing zone. The areal distribution of the dolomitized zone beneath the Traverse can be accurately mapped, owing to the presence of some 57 dry holes surrounding the Deep River oil pool. However, the third dimension is entirely unknown; it is assumed that the dolomitized zone is vertical or nearly so, because none of the dry holes, regardless of depth drilled, have passed through this zone. It has been suggested that the localized porosity has been the result of an excess of solution over precipitation by dolomitizing solutions passing along a vertical fissure through the Rogers City formation. Apparently this dolomitized porous zone afforded sanctuary for oil which moved in after dolomitization had taken place. Presumably, but yet to be proved, the oil is underlain by water and has been impounded at the top of the porous zone by the presence of impervious shale at the base of the overlying Traverse formation. *Courtesy American Association of Petroleum Geologists.*

* Kenneth K. Landes, "Deep River Oil Field, Arenac County, Michigan," *Structure of Typical American Oil Fields* (Am. Assoc. Petrol. Geol., 1948), Vol. 3, pp. 299–304.

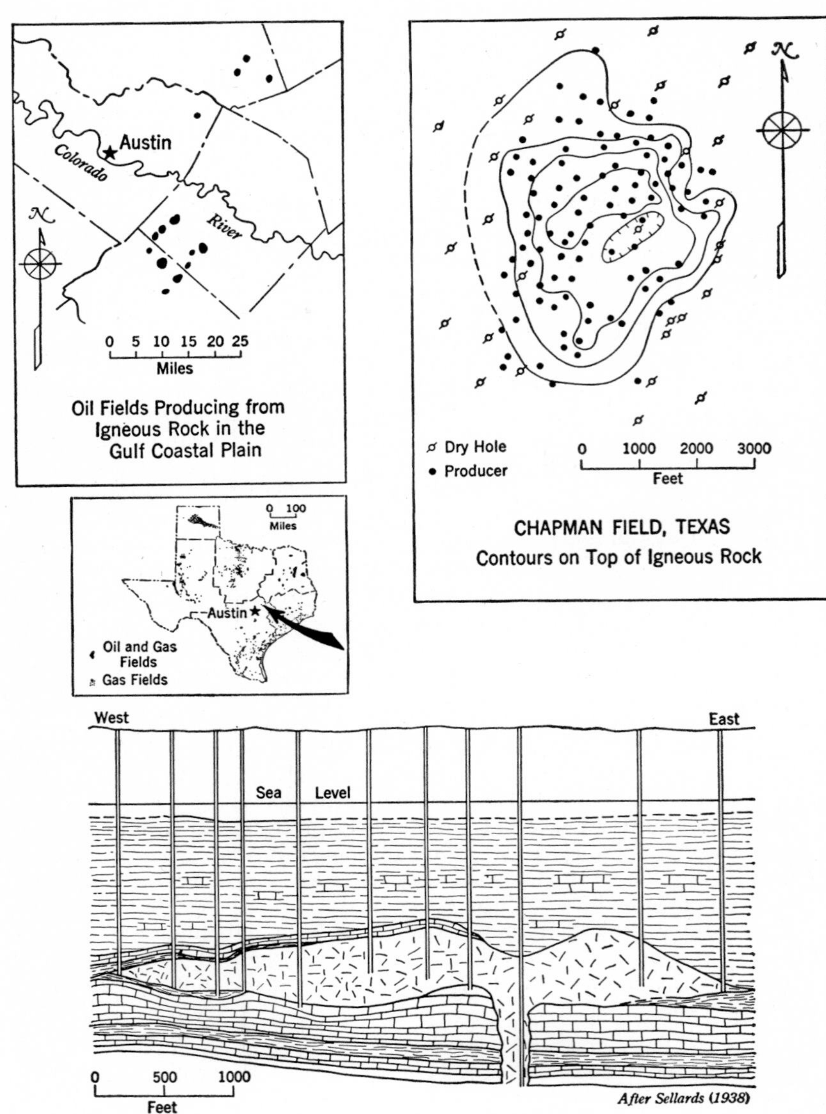
Austin
Colorado
River
0 5 10 15 20 25
Miles
Oil Fields Producing from
Igneous Rock in the
Gulf Coastal Plain
Dry Hole
Producer
0 1000 2000 3000
Feet
CHAPMAN FIELD, TEXAS
Contours on Top of Igneous Rock
0 100
Miles
Austin
Oil and Gas
Fields
Gas Fields
West
East
Sea Level
0 500 1000
Feet
After Sellards (1938)
Section through CHAPMAN FIELD

FIG. 74. Chapman Field, Texas.

Altered Igneous Rock Reservoir. The picture on the upper left on the opposite page shows the location of oil fields producing from altered igneous rock in the Gulf Coastal Plain of Texas. Both intrusion and extrusion of igneous rock occurred over a large area during Upper Cretaceous time in the Gulf province. The igneous activity continued through a considerable span of time, but the igneous rocks which subsequently became oil reservoirs were formed immediately after Austin time and were overlain and surrounded by clays and marls belonging to the Cretaceous Taylor formation. These igneous rocks, which may have had some initial porosity due to vesicularity, were altered to serpentine and allied rocks with considerable increase in permeability in pre-Taylor time. Oil is stored both in the igneous rock and in reworked igneous material deposited on the flanks of the serpentine masses. The depths to the igneous reservoir depend upon the position in respect to the monocline.

In all the serpentine fields the oil is believed to have moved into the porous igneous rock long after alteration and weathering took place and after the igneous rock had become submerged beneath the Taylor sea and covered with a thick blanket of sediment.

The figure on the upper right * is a map of the Chapman oil field in Williamson County contoured on top of the igneous rock with contour interval of 100 feet. This field produced over 3.7 million barrels of oil between the time of its discovery in 1930 and the end of 1934. The total producing area is 476 acres. Initial productions were highly variable, running as high as over 5000 barrels. The large lower figure * is a hypothetical cross section through the Chapman oil field. The igneous rock body is somewhat bulbous upward with a probable feeder vent at the point indicated in the cross section, where a well penetrated 954 feet of igneous rock without passing through this material. The rock beneath the igneous rock is Austin chalk, and the overlying rock is Taylor. Most, but not all, of the oil is produced from wells drilled varying distances into the igneous rock itself. However, some oil has been obtained from the cap limestone shown immediately overlying the west flank of the serpentine body. Apparently the oil was squeezed out of the compacting Taylor clay and obtained sanctuary in any porous rock it could find. *Courtesy Texas Bureau of Economic Geology and the American Association of Petroleum Geologists. Upper left figure after Lonsdale (1927).*

* E. H. Sellards, "Oil Accumulation in Igneous Rocks," *Science of Petroleum* (Oxford Univ. Press, 1938), pp. 261–265.

East Tuskegee,[125] Oklahoma; Greasewood,[126] Colorado; and Stephens,[127] Arkansas.

Many have noted the confinement of oil to zones of coarse, loosely cemented sandstone surrounded by fine and tightly cemented sandstone. The general tendency is to ascribe this situation to cementation *after* oil accumulation has taken place.[128] The oil entered the coarser sands initially because of the greater room in the interstices between the water-coated grains of sand. Then came the cementation, which was confined largely to the non-oil-bearing rocks because oil where present in the voids prevents cementation. Evidence of precementation oil in a limestone reservoir has been described by Wegemann: "Fragments of limestone thrown out of wild wells in the South Fields of Mexico and kept for years will, when struck with a hammer, break with explosive force due to confined gases cemented off in the pores of the limestone, proving cementation after accumulation." [129]

If the cementation is post-accumulation then the trap must be precementation in order for the accumulation to have taken place, and unless there has been subsequent tilting the tightly cemented rock would not be a factor in the capturing of the oil.

Sherrill, Dickey, and Matteson noted the presence of oil in Pennsylvania in comparatively unconsolidated gravel beds surrounded by fine, thoroughly cemented sands, and they conclude likewise that the lack of cementation in the coarser clastics was due to the early entrance of oil into them.[130]

VARYING PERMEABILITY DUE TO TRUNCATION AND SEALING. This type of trap has been responsible for the accumulation of enormous deposits of oil. The first step in the natural history of such accumulations is the emergence, folding and tilting, and beveling by erosion of a sedimentary section including reservoir rocks. The second step is the sealing of the edges of the reservoir layers, where folded into a plunging anticline, by impervious material. In rare

[125] J. L. Borden and R. A. Brant, "East Tuskegee Pool, Creek County, Oklahoma," *Stratigraphic Type Oil Fields* (Am. Assoc. Petrol. Geol., 1941), pp. 436–455.

[126] C. S. Lavington, "Greasewood Oil Field, Weld County, Colorado," *ibid.*, pp. 19–42.

[127] William C. Spooner, "Stephens Oil Field, Columbia and Ouachita Counties, Arkansas," *Structure of Typical American Oil Fields* (Am. Assoc. Petrol. Geol., 1929), Vol. 2, pp. 1–17.

[128] F. M. Van Tuyl and Ben H. Parker, "The Time of Origin and Accumulation of Petroleum," *Quarterly Colo. School of Mines,* Vol. 36 (April, 1941), Chapter 8, pp. 62–66.

[129] Carrol H. Wegemann, *in* F. M. Van Tuyl and Ben H. Parker, *op. cit.,* p. 63.

[130] *Op. cit.,* p. 538.

instances this impervious material has been asphalt formed from the seeping oil itself, but most accumulations of this type have been beneath beds of shale or dense limestone which were deposited on top of the truncated, beveled strata during a subsequent submergence —a type of trap referred to as an overlap seal.

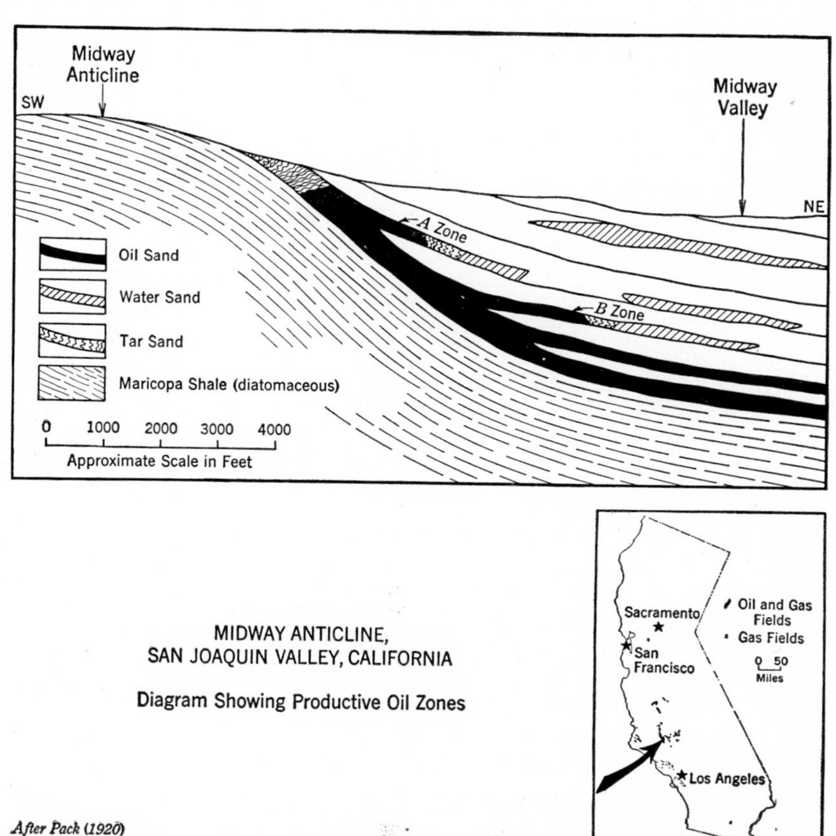

Fig. 75. Solid hydrocarbon (asphalt) seal, Midway anticline, California. *United States Geological Survey.*

Solid Hydrocarbon Seal. One of the relatively few examples of sealing by solid hydrocarbons is along the southwest edge of the Midway field in California [131] (Fig. 75). Oil moving to the southwest up the flank of the Midway syncline has been trapped just below the

[131] R. W. Pack, "The Sunset-Midway Oil Field, California," *U. S. Geol. Survey, Prof. Paper* 116 (1920), Fig. 13, p. 115.

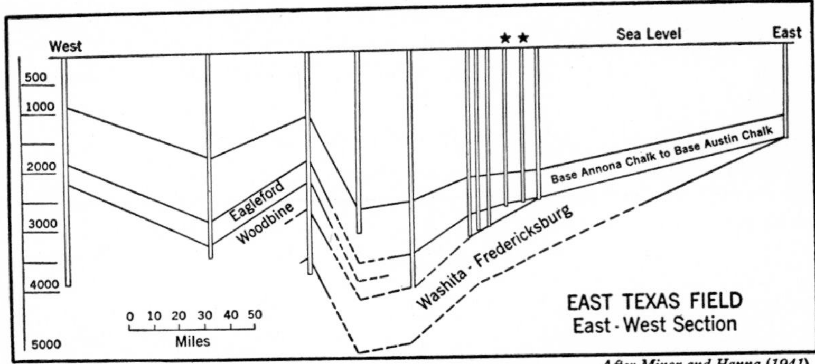
West
Sea Level
East
500
1000
2000
3000
4000
5000
Eagleford
Woodbine
Base Annona Chalk to Base Austin Chalk
Washita - Fredericksburg
0 10 20 30 40 50
Miles
EAST TEXAS FIELD
East - West Section

After Minor and Hanna (1941)

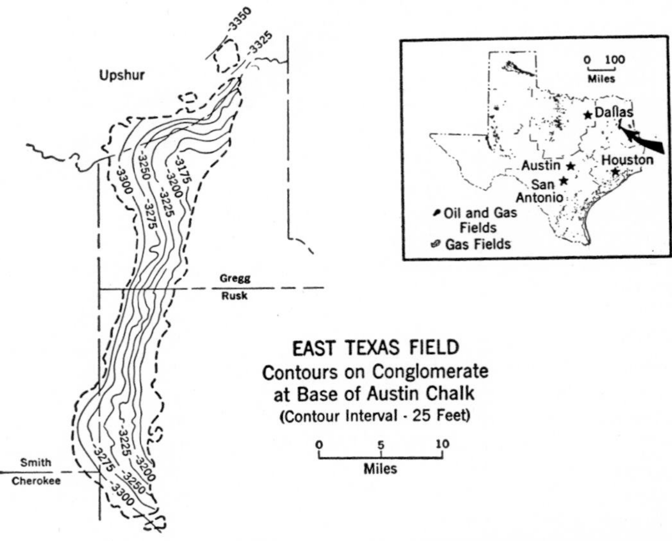
Upshur
Gregg
Rusk
Smith
Cherokee
-3350
-3325
-3300
-3275
-3250
-3225
-3200
-3175
EAST TEXAS FIELD
Contours on Conglomerate
at Base of Austin Chalk
(Contour Interval - 25 Feet)
0 5 10
Miles
0 100
Miles
Dallas
Austin
Houston
San Antonio
Oil and Gas Fields
Gas Fields

FIG. 76. East Texas Field.

Overlapped Sand Wedge. The East Texas field * is in northeastern Texas about 50 miles southwest of the northwestern corner of Louisiana and the southwestern corner of Arkansas. The field is over 40 miles long and is nearly 5 miles in average width. The discovery well was completed on Oct. 3, 1930. Within a few years after discovery the East Texas field had produced more oil than the total production of any other field in the United States. It has been estimated that the amount of oil originally present which can be successfully recovered from drilled wells is in excess of 4 billion barrels, or 30,000 barrels per acre.

Geologically the East Texas field lies along the wedgeout zone of the westward-dipping Woodbine sand of Upper Cretaceous age. To the west is the Tyler basin, and to the east is the Sabine uplift with its highest point in northwestern Louisiana. The uppermost figure on the opposite page is a cross section drawn from Powell, a fault trap field in Navarro County, northeastward and eastward across the northern end of the East Texas pool to the Louisiana line. The two wells in the cross section marked by stars are producing wells in the East Texas field. Accumulation is due to the pinching out of the Woodbine sand in a plunging anticline on the flank of the Sabine uplift. Wells drilled north, west, and south of the field boundary enter the Woodbine below the level of the oil-water interface.

The middle figure is a structure contour map of the base of the Austin chalk which blankets the truncated edges of the Woodbine and Eagle Ford formations. It is, therefore, a contour map showing the present configuration of an old erosion surface. No doubt a contour map of the structure of the Woodbine sandstone would show even greater dip to the west.

The Woodbine sand in the East Texas field consists of a series of thin, lenticular, but nevertheless interconnecting, sands interstratified with shales and silts. The average reservoir thickness is about 30 feet, and the maximum amount of sand which has been observed in cores is 75 feet.

Oil entering the Woodbine sand on the east flank of the Tyler basin has migrated up-dip until impounded below the overlapping Austin chalk.

The lower figure is a picture of a diorama of the East Texas field. *Courtesy American Association of Petroleum Geologists, Humble Oil and Refining Company, and Texas Memorial Museum.*

* H. E. Minor and Marcus A. Hanna, "East Texas Oil Field, Rusk, Cherokee, Smith, Gregg, and Upshur Counties, Texas," *Stratigraphic Type Oil Fields* (Am. Assoc. Petrol. Geol., 1941), pp. 600–640.

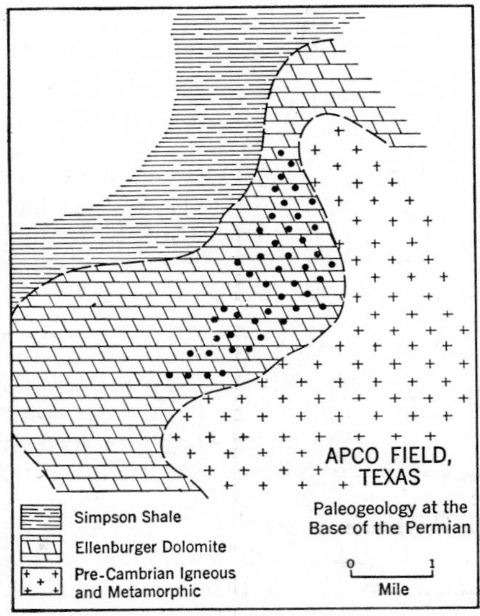
APCO FIELD, TEXAS
Paleogeology at the Base of the Permian
Simpson Shale
Ellenburger Dolomite
Pre-Cambrian Igneous and Metamorphic
0 1
Mile

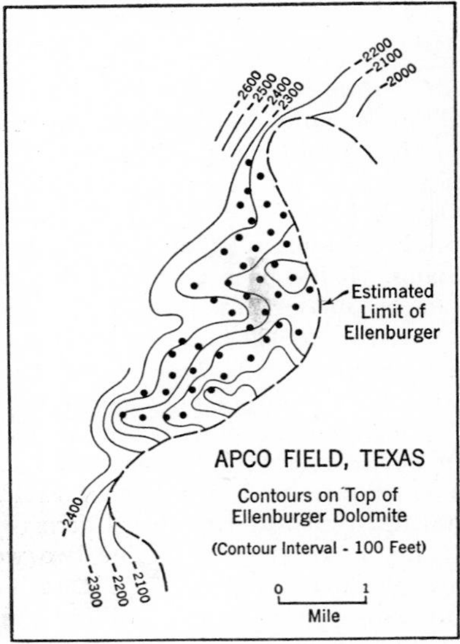
Estimated Limit of Ellenburger
APCO FIELD, TEXAS
Contours on Top of Ellenburger Dolomite
(Contour Interval - 100 Feet)
0 1
Mile

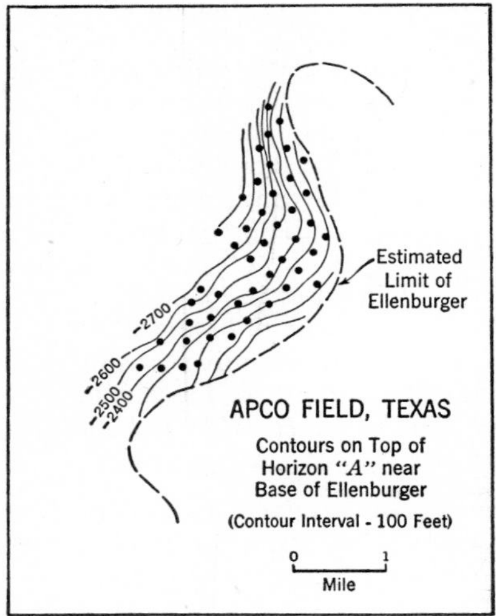
-2700
-2600
-2500
-2400
Estimated Limit of Ellenburger
APCO FIELD, TEXAS
Contours on Top of Horizon "A" near Base of Ellenburger
(Contour Interval - 100 Feet)
0 1
Mile

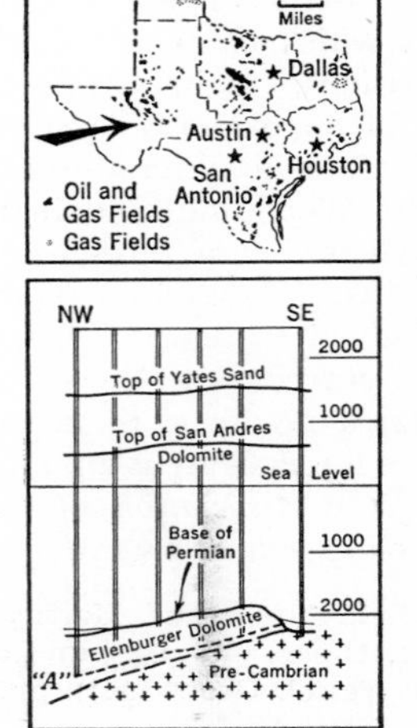
0 100
Miles
Dallas
Austin
San Antonio
Houston
Oil and Gas Fields
Gas Fields
NW
SE
2000
Top of Yates Sand
1000
Top of San Andres Dolomite
Sea Level
Base of Permian
1000
2000
Ellenburger Dolomite
"A"
Pre-Cambrian

After Ellison (1948)

FIG. 77. Apco Field, Texas.

Overlapped Dolomite Wedge. The Apco field * is south of the Pecos River in southwestern Texas. Although shallow oil had been produced in this area since 1929 the deep pay was not discovered until 1939.

The surface rocks in the vicinity of the Apco field are Quaternary and Recent alluvial sediments, ancient deposits of the Pecos River. The subsurface section includes Cretaceous, Triassic, Permian, Ordovician, and pre-Cambrian rocks. The greater part of the stratigraphic section between the thin veneer of surficial deposits and the oil reservoir rock consists of Permian dolomites.

The main producing zone of the Apco field lies within the Ellenburger formation of Lower Ordovician age. The Ellenburger is about 800 feet thick at Apco and consists primarily of gray to buff siliceous dolomite. It apparently underwent considerable weathering and leaching during pre-Permian emergence with the result that vuggy porosity has been developed in three persistent zones lying from 150 to 300 feet above the base. The interstitial porosity has been augmented by fractures. Exposure to weathering also produced an enrichment of siliceous material at the Ellenburger surface by differential leaching.

Accumulation in the Apco field is in a buried hogback of Ellenburger dolomite which laps up on the flank of a hill of pre-Cambrian rock. Trapping is due to the blanket of Permian shale which overlies not only the dip slope of the hogback but also the scarp face and the pre-Cambrian hill. Oil traveling up through porous zones in the tilted Ellenburger dolomite was impounded by this seal.

The upper left figure on the opposite page shows the paleogeology at the base of the Permian. The regional dip is to the northwest, and pre-Permian erosion beveled the Ordovician Simpson shale, the underlying Ellenburger dolomite, and the pre-Cambrian complex. The figure to the right shows, by means of contour lines, the topography of the top of the Ellenburger where it is in contact with the unconformable overlying Permian shale. Fairly consistent dips to the west show the dip slope of the hogback. Also shown is the rim of the hogback and the eroded scarp face. The drawing at the lower left shows the actual rock structure, a fairly consistent westward-dipping monocline. The cross section from northwest to southeast through the Apco field shows the Ellenburger hogback. *Courtesy American Association of Petroleum Geologists.*

* Samuel P. Ellison, Jr., "Apco Field, Pecos County, Texas," *Structure of Typical American Oil Fields* (Am. Assoc. Petrol. Geol., 1948), Vol. 3, pp. 399–418.

reservoir rock outcrop by the accumulation of asphalt there. It has been suggested that this tar was formed by the interaction between mineralized ground waters and petroleum hydrocarbons. Solid hydrocarbon seals also play a role in the trapping of oil in other California fields, especially East Coalinga and McKittrick. Yet another example is the Cacheuta field in Argentina.[132] Although some of the oil in the Whittier field in California has been trapped by the termination of the reservoir rock against the Whittier fault, there has also been trapping due to the presence of asphaltic residue at the outcrop of the reservoir.[133]

Overlap Seal. The overlap seals can be divided into two types: (1) the strata overlap a truncated plunging anticline on the flank of a monocline; (2) the overlapping sediments overlie a truncated closed anticline, which has been aptly referred to as a "baldheaded structure."

Angular unconformities are a well-known type of trap and the most prolific of those falling within the varying-permeability classification.[134] The outstanding example of sealing by overlap of monoclinal sediments is the East Texas field, in which the beveled Woodbine sandstone has been effectively sealed by overlapping Austin chalk. Accumulation in this field is illustrated in Fig. 76. If the pre-overlap tilted sediments are of unequal hardness, differential erosion may scallop the surface into hogback ridges and strike valleys. In the Apco field in Pecos County, Texas, a hogback of permeable Ellenburger dolomite was submerged and buried beneath impervious Permian sediments, forming an ideal trap for oil accumulation (Fig. 77). Very similar in its structural pattern to East Texas is the West Edmond oil field of central Oklahoma which was discovered in 1943.[135] At West Edmond the tilted, truncated, and overlapped reservoir rock is the Bois d'Arc limestone of Hunton (Siluro-Devonian age), sealed by unconformably overlying lower Pennsylvanian shale. At both

[132] Anon., "YPF Holds Leading Place in Argentine Oil Development," *World Petrol.,* Vol. 12 (September, 1941), pp. 72–79.

[133] W. H. Holman, "Whittier Oil Field," *Oil and Gas Fields of California* (*Calif. Div. Mines, Bull.* 118, 1943), p. 290.

[134] Frank J. Gardner, "Relationship of Unconformities to Oil and Gas Accumulation," *Bull. Am. Assoc. Petrol Geol.,* Vol. 24 (November, 1940), pp. 2022–2031; A. I. Levorsen, "Relation of Oil and Gas Pools to Unconformities in the Mid-Continent Region," *Problems of Petroleum Geology* (Am. Assoc. Petrol. Geol., 1934), pp. 761–784.

[135] D. A. McGee and H. D. Jenkins, "West Edmond Oil Field, Central Oklahoma," *Bull. Am. Assoc. Petrol. Geol.,* Vol. 30 (November, 1946), pp. 1797–1829; Robert M. Swesnik, "Geology of West Edmond Oil Field, Oklahoma, Logan, Canadian and Kingfisher Counties, Oklahoma," *Structure of Typical American Oil Fields* (Am. Assoc. Petrol. Geol., 1948), Vol. 3, pp. 359–398.

West Edmond and East Texas the reservoir rock extends down-dip westward into a large basin which supplies gathering area of considerable magnitude. To the south of West Edmond, along the eastern margin of the Anadarko basin, are additional unconformity accumulations including Oklahoma City, a baldheaded structure described in a subsequent paragraph. Similar traps are found in various other parts of the world; examples include many fields in California, especially in the San Joaquin Valley,[136] and in the west Buchivacoa district in Venezuela.[137]

Overlap across baldheaded structures may also be complicated by pre-overlap topography. If the strata in the anticlinal fold are similar in their degree of resistance to erosion, the plane of the unconformity will be flat and the picture the same as for an overlapped beveled monocline except that the reservoirs may be repeated, in reverse order, on the opposite side of the buried anticline. Many times, however, the rocks in the anticlinal fold prove to be of unequal resistance, and if the core is harder than the younger flanking rocks, the buried eroded anticline will also be a hill. Sometimes later folding along the same line of weakness sharpens the relief of the hill by further upward arching of the plane of unconformity. It is also possible for a hill containing flat-lying permeable strata to be submerged and covered by impervious overlapping rock, thus becoming a trap for oil accumulation, but such situations are uncommon.

Sealing on a baldheaded structure is usually brought about by the blanketing effect of the overlapping younger sediments as illustrated by the Kraft-Prusa field (Fig. 78). Another example of this type of trap is the Oklahoma City field,[138] one of the great oil fields of the world. There the "baldhead," the core of the truncated dome, is Arbuckle limestone of Cambro-Ordovician age. Arranged in semicircular pattern (Fig. 79), on the west are successively younger Ordovician strata, including various sandstones, whereas to the east, cutting across the side of the dome, is a major fault which has dropped the Mississippian rocks down to the level of the Arbuckle, and buried the Ordovician reservoirs to great depth. This eroded faulted dome is overlain un-

[136] George M. Cunningham and W. D. Kleinpell, "Importance of Unconformities to Oil Production in the San Joaquin Valley, California," *Problems of Petroleum Geology* (Am. Assoc. Petrol. Geol., 1934), pp. 785–805.

[137] G. W. Halse, "Oil Fields of West Buchivacoa, Venezuela," *Bull. Am. Assoc. Petrol. Geol.,* Vol. 31 (December, 1947), pp. 2170–2192.

[138] D. A. McGee and W. W. Clawson, Jr., "Geology and Development of Oklahoma City Field, Oklahoma County, Oklahoma," *Bull. Am. Assoc. Petrol. Geol.,* Vol. 16 (October, 1932), pp. 957–1020.

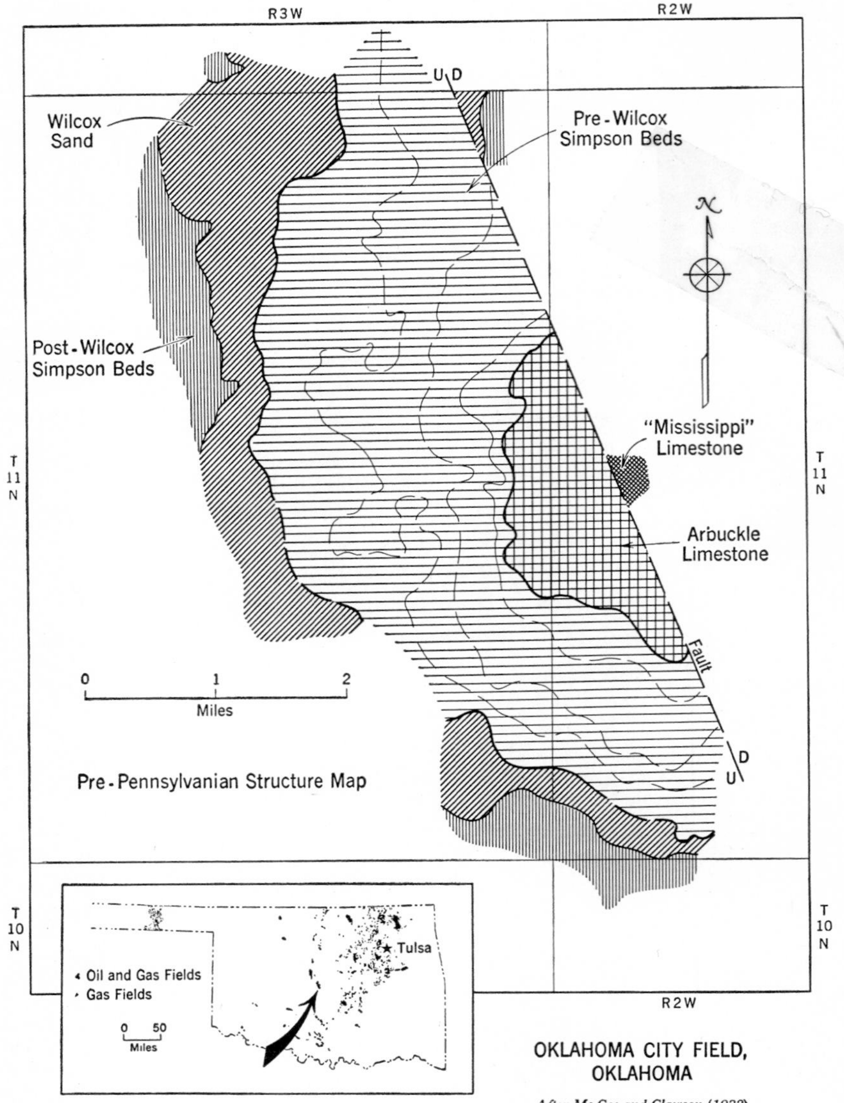

FIG. 79. The Oklahoma City oil field, an example of sealing by overlap across a truncated (baldheaded) faulted dome. *Courtesy American Association of Petroleum Geologists.*

conformably by Pennsylvanian formations. The principal reservoir rocks are the Arbuckle limestone at the top of the dome beneath the unconformity, and various truncated sandstone formations belonging to the Simpson group of Ordovician age.

Baldheaded structures buried beneath unconformities have been important producers of oil in many other localities.[139] At El Dorado,[140] Kansas, the core of the truncated anticline is the completely buried Nemaha granite ridge. In the Texas Panhandle the conditions are somewhat similar, but here the core rock is the east-west trending Amarillo Mountain range. At Healdton, Oklahoma, complexly folded sediments, instead of granite, underlie the unconformity. The Golden Lane pool of Mexico, south of Tampico, produces oil from a great buried anticlinal ridge of porous limestone. Other fields which illustrate this situation are Cushing and Seminole, Oklahoma; Gorham and Fairport (Fig. 7), Kansas; and Yates, Texas.[141]

Sealing at unconformities by the abutting of the reservoir rock against impervious older rock is also possible. This is an offlap, rather than an overlap, relationship, and it results from regression of the ancient sea in which reservoir rock deposition took place. The trapping of hydrocarbons in some of the producing sands in the Amarillo district of the Texas Panhandle has been a result of the deposition of granite wash material on the flanks of the now buried Amarillo Mountains. These arkosic sediments wedge out against the granite surface and have been covered by younger impervious rock.[142] At the southeast edge of the Oklahoma Anadarko basin in Garvin and McClain Counties, northwest of the Arbuckle Mountains, the late Pennsylvania sea lapped up upon the truncated edges of various older Pennsylvanian formations after the Paul's Valley uplift [143] had tilted the plane of the eroded surface to the west. During a regressive phase of the late Pennsylvania sea, the Deese sands were deposited in sheet

[139] John L. Ferguson and Jess Vernon, "The Relationship of Buried Hills to Petroleum Accumulation," *Science of Petroleum* (Oxford Univ. Press, 1938), Vol. 1, pp. 240–243; Joseph A. Kornfeld, "Stratigraphic Traps, Source of Major Production over Central Kansas Uplift," *Oil Weekly,* Vol. 100 (Jan. 15, 1941), pp. 13–19; A. I. Levorsen, "Stratigraphic versus Structural Accumulation," *Oil and Gas Jour.,* Vol. 34 (March 26, 1936), pp. 41 *et seq.*

[140] John R. Reeves, "El Dorado Oil Field, Butler County, Kansas," *Structure of Typical American Oil Fields* (Am. Assoc. Petrol. Geol., 1929), Vol. 2, pp. 160–167.

[141] John L. Ferguson and Jess Vernon, *op. cit.*

[142] Henry Rogatz, "Geology of Texas Panhandle Oil and Gas Field," *Bull. Am. Assoc. Petrol. Geol.,* Vol. 19 (August, 1935), pp. 1089–1109; Vol. 23 (July, 1939), pp. 983–1053.

[143] Anon., "Anadarko Basin Discoveries," *The Link,* Vol. 12 (May, 1947), pp. 1–5.

form extending out into the basin in one direction and abutting against the plane of angular unconformity in the other (Fig. 80). In both the Texas Panhandle and Deese sand fields, accumulation is the result of the impounding of oil moving up-dip and reaching an impervious barrier where the reservoir rocks terminate against the steeper surface of uplifted impervious older rocks.

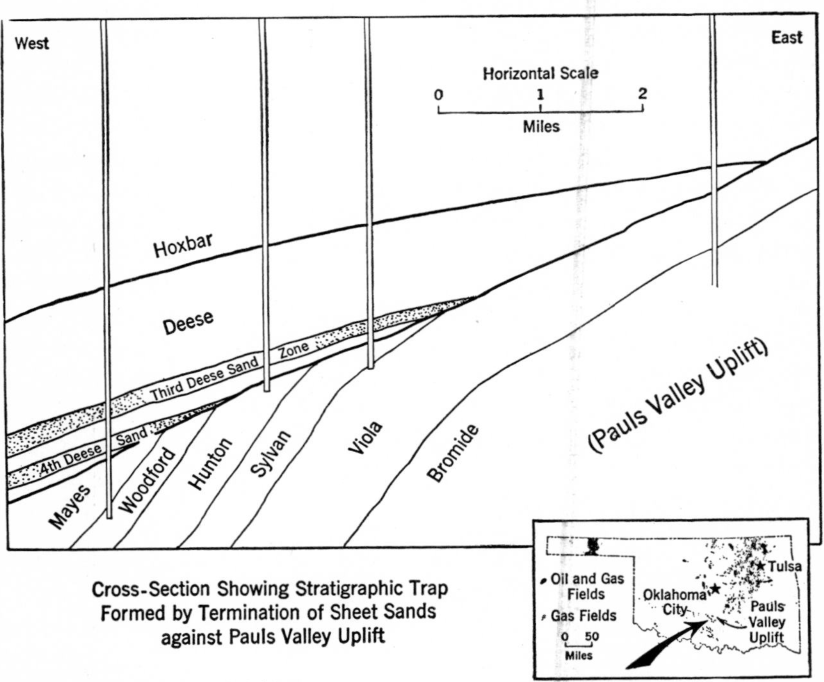

FIG. 80. Unconformity seal caused by offlap. Pauls Valley area, Oklahoma. *Courtesy The Link and the Carter Oil Company.*

STRATIGRAPHIC TRAP FINDING. As a rule, stratigraphic traps, unlike structural traps, give no surface indication of their presence. There are, however, two possible exceptions to this generalization. Differential compaction of shale above a shoestring sand may result in a slight arching of the higher strata.[144] Obviously it is necessary in order to determine the presence of buried sandstones of this type to employ extreme accuracy and detail in mapping the structure

[144] John L. Rich, "Application of Principle of Differential Settling to Tracing of Lenticular Sand Bodies," *Bull. Am. Assoc. Petrol. Geol.*, Vol. 22 (July, 1938), pp. 823–833.

in the surface bed-rock formations. The other possible exception is that resulting from the draping and differential compaction of the sediments overlying limestone reefs. If the reef is of sufficient magnitude, its presence may be reflected clear to the surface by the configuration of the younger strata. That is the situation in the Marine pool of Illinois, where a Pennsylvanian limestone only 250 feet below the surface has 60 feet of closure; the much deeper reef has double that closure.[145]

In addition to the general absence of criteria of the probable existence of varying-permeability traps in the surface formations the traditional techniques of geophysical exploration are similarly impotent, for they, too, are based on finding structural rather than stratigraphic features.[146] Again, some exception must be made for reefs. If the overlying sediments roughly parallel the upper topographic surface of the reef, the occurrence of this structural situation can be determined in the same way as that of any other anticline.[147] The Leduc field in Alberta was discovered in this way.[148] It has likewise been claimed that reefs could be discovered by determining the existence of arched overlying shales through their radioactivity.[149] Theoretically the reef itself, if of any magnitude, should be discoverable by geophysical methods, but geophysical techniques have not progressed to the point where their application has had any spectacular success. Gravity surveys tend to be complicated by unevenness on the crystalline rock basement floor, and seismic surveys tend to draw a blank above reef-containing areas. The latter, a negative criterion, may prove to be useful in reef-finding, however.

With these exceptions and possible exceptions, the sole technique for finding stratigraphic traps is the use of subsurface geology.[150] Only by detailed, accurate, and intelligently interpretive studies of paleogeology, paleogeography, and sedimentology can the presence and

145 Heinz A. Lowenstam, "Marine Pool, Madison County, Illinois, Silurian Reef Producer," *Structure of Typical American Oil Fields* (Am. Assoc. Petrol. Geol., 1948), Vol. 3, pp. 153–188.

146 J. L. Adler, "Geophysical Exploration for Stratigraphic Traps," *Geophysics,* Vol. 8 (October, 1943), pp. 337–347; Neal Clayton, "Seismic Problems in Reef Shooting," *World Oil,* Vol. 130 (Feb. 1, 1950), pp. 69–72.

147 E. O. Alcock, "Prospecting for Reefs with the Seismograph," *World Oil,* Vol. 130 (April, 1950), pp. 74 *et seq.*

148 T. A. Link, "Leduc Oil Field, Alberta, Canada," *Bull. Geol. Soc. Am.,* Vol. 60 (March, 1949), pp. 381–402.

149 R. A. Stothart, "Reef Surveying with Radioactivity," *World Oil,* Vol. 130 (January, 1950), pp. 61–63.

150 V. E. Monnett, "Stratigraphic Exploration and Future Discoveries," *Oil Weekly,* Vol. 101 (March 31, 1941), pp. 26 *et seq.*

position of unconformities, shorelines, and other types of wedgeouts be determined.[151] In addition to the information already available, it may be necessary to drill "stratigraphic tests" before selecting the location for exploratory wells.

It is obvious that the search for new stratigraphic traps is more expensive than the search for structural traps. But as the undiscovered traps become fewer and fewer the emphasis on the search for stratigraphic or varying-permeability traps will increase. It is equally apparent that this search is possible only by the employment of the finest type of scientific geology.

TIME OF ACCUMULATION

The time of accumulation [152] of hydrocarbons in traps in the earth's crust is a matter not only of considerable interest but also of great practical importance in oil-finding. Unfortunately our knowledge is rarely sufficient to permit the exact dating of accumulation. However, one can alway start with the general rule that the accumulation is later than the establishment of the trap.

Post-dating accumulation until after trap formation does not mean that a long period of time between the two is necessary. There are many examples of probable early accumulation, the word early being used in a relative sense. For example, it is quite likely that the oil trapped in the shoestring bodies entered those bodies shortly after deposition during the compacting of the surrounding shale. It is also possible that some anticlinal accumulations may have taken place long before the last folding. Subsurface studies show that most of the folds in the older rocks in the earth's crust have been formed through a series of recurrent movements, and adequate closure for

[151] W. C. Krumbein, "Recent Sedimentation in the Search for Petroleum," *Bull. Am. Assoc. Petrol. Geol.,* Vol. 29 (September, 1945), pp. 1233–1261; "Principles of Sedimentation and the Search for Stratigraphic Traps," *Econ. Geol.,* Vol. 36 (December, 1941), pp. 786–810.

[152] F. M. Van Tuyl and Ben H. Parker, "Time of Origin and Accumulation of Petroleum," *Quarterly Colo. School of Mines,* Vol. 36 (April, 1941); Alex. W. McCoy and W. Ross Keyte, "Present Interpretations of the Structural Theory for Oil and Gas Migration and Accumulation," *Problems of Petroleum Geology* (Am. Assoc. Petrol. Geol., 1934), pp. 296–303; William B. Heroy, "Petroleum Geology," *Geol. Soc. Am. 50th Anniversary Vol.* (1941), pp. 512–548; Stanley C. Herold, "Criteria for Determining the Time of Accumulation under Special Circumstances," *Bull. Am. Assoc. Petrol. Geol.,* Vol. 22 (July, 1938), pp. 834–851; A. I. Levorsen, "Time of Oil and Gas Accumulation," *Bull. Am. Assoc. Petrol. Geol.,* Vol. 29 (August, 1945), pp. 1189–1194; F. F. Hintze, "Oil Accumulation in Relation to Periods of Folding," *Bull. Am. Assoc. Petrol. Geol.,* Vol. 7 (January–February, 1923), pp. 58–65.

the trapping of oil may have existed several periods previous to the major diastrophism ordinarily credited with the creation of the present picture. To some degree, the same situation exists in regard to faulting. Many faults have been recurrent, and the offset may have been sufficient, after the initial movement, to create a subsurface dam for the impounding of oil. Therefore, some structural accumulations may have occurred at a relatively early date and subsequent earth movements may merely have accentuated the traps.

We do know, however, of anticlines containing oil which were formed by a single, relatively late, period of diastrophism, and many faults have had but one period of movement of any magnitude. Furthermore, in the unconformity traps a relatively late date of the accumulation can scarcely be denied. Examples of late accumulation are many. Bartram [153] finds no evidence of incipient folding in the Rocky Mountain fields producing from the Embar and Tensleep sands and so does not believe that the oil found in these Pennsylvanian and Permian reservoirs could have accumulated until the end of the Cretaceous or early Eocene when folding took place. Hoots [154] notes that the Ventura anticline in California, which produces from Pliocene and Pleistocene sediments, was not folded until middle Pleistocene time. The tilted and truncated Ordovician reservoirs at Oklahoma City contain great deposits of hydrocarbons immediately beneath a seal of Cherokee shale which was not deposited until into Pennsylvanian time. Furthermore, Levorsen,[155] from a study of reservoir pressures at Oklahoma City, believes that the accumulation did not reach its maximum until after the overburden above the truncated edges of the reservoirs had reached somewhere near its present thickness. Walters and Price [156] state their belief that migration of oil into the Arbuckle below the Pennsylvanian unconformity at Kraft-Prusa, Kansas, took place in late or post-Pennsylvanian time. Reasons follow: (1) solution porosity in the Arbuckle was not developed until the early Pennsylvanian; (2) Arbuckle dolomites probably would not have retained indigenous oil during exposure on early Pennsylvanian surface; (3) overlying and oil-bearing Pennsylvanian sediments constitute an adequate source; (4) probably no closure on this unconformity until after Lansing-Kansas City time; (5) reservoir struc-

[153] John G. Bartram, in F. M. Van Tuyl and Ben H. Parker, *op. cit.*, p. 153.

[154] H. W. Hoots, *ibid.*, p. 153.

[155] A. I. Levorsen, *op. cit.*, pp. 1192–1194.

[156] Robert F. Walters and Arthur S. Price, "Kraft-Prusa Oil Field, Barton County, Kansas," *Structure of Typical American Oil Fields* (Am. Assoc. Petrol. Geol., 1948), Vol. 3, p. 268.

ture is completely filled, indicating late adjustment to reservoir capacity.

The principal faulting which caused the accumulation in the Oficina area in Venezuela did not take place until after the beginning of Las Piedras (Miocene-Pliocene) time, whereas the reservoirs are of Oligocene-Miocene age.[157] An extreme situation has been noted by Reed [158] in the San Pedro and other oil fields in northern Argentina. There the only possible source rock is Devonian, and the structure-forming movement which created the trap in which the oil is found did not take place until the Pleistocene. In the fractured shale pools, such as the Florence field of Colorado, it is obvious that the oil could not have accumulated until after the fissures were formed, and these could not appear until the shale had attained some degree of lithifaction. It is also true that the oil which has accumulated in leached and porous zones in limestone could not have done so until after the period of emergence and subareal erosion that created the cavernous situation, and this may not have taken place until long after the original deposition of the carbonate rock. The ultimate in late accumulation is illustrated by the occurrence of oil beneath surficial asphalt deposits formed during the present cycle of erosion. The seeps that occur along the outcrop of some monoclinal reservoir rocks at the present time point to the possibility that accumulation is going on today where traps lie across the pathway of ascending oil.

Every great unconformity creates an almost infinite number of varying-permeability traps over many thousands of square miles beneath the plane of the unconformity. However, the magnificent opportunity during the long time of emergence and erosion for the escape of hydrocarbons from the older rocks should also be noted. Heald [159] points out that in pre-Pennsylvanian time erosion across the Barton arch in Kansas stripped off a great volume of Mississippian, Devonian, Silurian, and Ordovician rocks, exposing the pre-Cambrian complex along the arch axis. During that period any oil within those rocks must have had ample opportunity to escape. Yet today many great oil pools occur immediately beneath this unconformity, sealed there by the overlapping Pennsylvanian sediments, with accumulation in

[157] H. D. Hedberg, L. C. Sass, and H. J. Funkhouser, "Oil Fields of Greater Oficina Area, Central Anzoategui, Venezuela," *Bull. Am. Assoc. Petrol. Geol.*, Vol. 31 (December, 1947), p. 2138.

[158] Lyman C. Reed, "San Pedro Oil Field, Province of Salta, Northern Argentina," *Bull. Am. Assoc. Petrol. Geol.*, Vol. 30 (April, 1946), p. 605.

[159] K. C. Heald, "Essentials for Oil Pools," *Elements of the Petroleum Industry* (Am. Inst. Min. Met. Engineers, 1940), pp. 38–39.

porous rocks which must have been at or very close to the surface before being covered by the Pennsylvanian sea. A similar situation exists at Oklahoma City, but there some asphalt has been found at the top of the truncated sands, implying the presence of a seep when this surface was exposed. The presence of asphaltic material here can be taken as evidence that Ordovician oil was escaping during the pre-Pennsylvanian emergence, but the quantity of asphaltic material is too insignificant to warrant the postulation of a tar seal adequate to contain beneath it the great oil deposits now found there. Howard describes a similar problem in the northern Rockies: "The Madison limestone of Wyoming and Alberta contains oil but this formation is overlain directly by deposits which were laid down in the Jurassic, possibly 100,000,000 years later. It is difficult to conceive of oil forming in the Madison, staying there for that length of time and then rising into the reservoir only after a seal was laid down over it." [160]

At least six possible solutions of the enigma of "old" oil caught in "young" traps have been suggested. One obvious possible explanation is that the oil found beneath unconformities came from the overlying strata which functioned both as seal and source rock. The overlying material must then have been a highly organic mud or calcareous ooze. The compaction which it underwent while lithifying into shale or limestone would cause some of the contained fluids to be squeezed downward into porous carbonate rock or sandstones immediately underlying the unconformity. Though this simple explanation appears applicable in many areas, it is difficult to apply at Oklahoma City, because there the oil in the Ordovician reservoirs is quite dissimilar to that found in the Pennsylvanian reservoirs. The two oils are more nearly similar in the Barton arch area of Kansas, but there the Pennsylvanian reservoirs contain considerably more gas.

Another suggested explanation is that the oil was generated by and during the same diastrophism that produced the trap. This is the geologic distillation hypothesis [161] which is discussed in Chapter 5.

A third possible explanation is the recurrent generation hypothesis advocated by White and Stadnichenko and likewise described in Chapter 5. According to this concept, the Oklahoma City oil was being generated from source materials in pre-Pennsylvanian times;

[160] W. V. Howard, "The Derivation of Reservoir Rocks," *Oil and Gas Jour.*, Vol. 42 (June 24, 1943), part 1, p. 158.

[161] John L. Rich, "Source and Date of Accumulation of Oil in Granite Ridge Pools of Kansas and Oklahoma," *Bull. Am. Assoc. Petrol. Geol.* Vol. 15 (December, 1931), pp. 1431–1452.

this oil migrated up the inclined strata and escaped at the surface, occasionally leaving some asphaltic residue. Subsequently, after sealing by overlapping Pennsylvanian sediments, elevated earth temperatures and pressures due to deep burial brought about the harvesting of later crops from the same source material; this time the oil accumulated beneath the plane of the unconformity. However, the previously discussed studies of Brooks and others cast a doubt upon the validity of any process of oil generation that involves appreciable increase in temperature.

A fourth idea, advanced by Dorsey,[162] is that the oil accumulated in whatever traps were in existence before the uplift and truncation. With the uplift the water table was lowered and the oil followed the water down the dip, withdrawing from the near-surface zone where it was in greatest danger of escape or destruction. Subsequently, after resubmergence and the deposition of younger sediments above the unconformity, the water table rose to levels above the unconformity, permitting the oil to move back up-dip and become impounded below the plane of the unconformity. A major objection to this hypothesis is that the upper surface of the oil accumulation, perched on top of the water table during the time of uplift and erosion, was in constant contact with the atmosphere, even though the water table may have been several hundred feet below the topographic surface, so the more volatile petroleum compounds would escape and the remaining hydrocarbons would tend to combine with oxygen. Both of these activities produce a tarry or asphaltic residue which would in all probability not be able to move up to the plane of the unconformity after the overlying sediments were deposited.

Van Tuyl and Parker [163] suggest that perhaps the oil "may be stored for considerable periods after generation, either in a disseminated condition or as pools, which may undergo renewed migration as a result of changes in geologic structure." A somewhat similar concept has been expressed by Hedberg, Sass, and Funkhouser: "Since the principal faulting causing the accumulation did not occur until after the beginning of Las Piedras time, it is evident that while oil migration may have been taking place previously, it must have continued well into the time of Las Piedras deposition. It may be that the extensive migration could not proceed until a certain dip gradient

[162] George Edwin Dorsey, "Preservation of Oil During Erosion of Reservoir Rocks," *Bull. Am. Assoc. Petrol. Geol.,* Vol. 17 (July, 1933), pp. 827–842.

[163] F. M. Van Tuyl and Ben H. Parker, "Time of Origin and Accumulation of Petroleum," *Quarterly Colo. School of Mines,* Vol. 36 (April, 1941), p. 164.

had been established in the Oficina formation by the combined results of compaction and basin subsidence." [164] Davies [165] believes that the Mesozoic oil of the Rocky Mountain province was lying dormant in the deeper parts of the sedimentary basins until Laramide orogeny produced traps for its concentration.

The sixth suggestion, which is to a considerable extent an elaboration of the Van Tuyl-Parker-Hedberg *et al.* idea, is that the oil was formed early and was temporarily stored in "transient traps," which are very minor irregularities in the structure of the reservoir rock. These minor wrinkles, which are rather universally present in stratified rocks, would yield oil by spillage with every slight tilt. Therefore, the sinking of a regional basin, which takes place intermittently, would release oil from time to time which would drain up the flanks of the basin. The oil stored beneath the unconformities in the Mid-Continent and elsewhere could have accumulated after basinward tilting, which took place after (perhaps long after) the deposition of the overlapping younger sediment.

BARREN TRAPS

In many areas barren (waterfilled) traps tend to be the rule rather than the exception. A number of possible explanations for this situation, most of which have been given before, are assembled and summarized at this point.

1. *No source material.* The absence of potential source material in the sedimentary section may be due to unfavorable climate, too rapid sedimentation, wrong depositional environment [166] (which includes a topographically high position on the sea floor), or the destruction of once-present source material during the dynamochemical stage.

2. *No generation of oil.* Inasmuch as we do not know the oil-producing processes, we can only guess at what may be responsible for lack of transformation of organic solid into liquid or gaseous hydrocarbons. Suggested possibilities in this regard include absence of the proper bacteria, absence of the necessary catalysts, inadequate time, and insufficient cover.

[164] H. D. Hedberg, L. C. Sass, and H. J. Funkhouser, "Oil Fields of Greater Oficina Area, Central Anzoategui, Venezuela," *Bull. Am. Assoc. Petrol. Geol.*, Vol. 31 (December, 1947), p. 2138.

[165] H. F. Davies, "Structural History and Its Relation to the Accumulation of Oil and Gas in the Rocky Mountain District," *Problems of Petroleum Geology* (Am. Assoc. Petrol. Geol., 1934), p. 690.

[166] Frank R. Clark, "Origin and Accumulation of Oil," *Problems of Petroleum Geology* (Am. Assoc. Petrol. Geol., 1934), pp. 334–335.

3. *Oil failed to reach trap.* This may have been due to inadequate permeability between source and trap, or it may be due to wrong timing (paragraph 6).

4. *The oil has escaped.* Regional tilting may have caused the oil to spill out of the trap, after which a reversal of the tilting reproduced the trap situation. Fissures and faults may have allowed the hydrocarbons to escape upward to the surface, where they became dissipated. Because no rock is absolutely impervious, a great enough span of geologic time might permit the more volatile hydrocarbons, at least, to disperse through the confining rocks without benefit of any fracture system.[167] Another and a very commonly cited method of oil-escape is flushing by circulating underground waters. Illing[168] states that as a general rule less oil is stored in the first 1000 feet of depth than in succeeding 1000-foot units, and he believes that the lesser accumulation at shallow depth has been due to the more active water circulation which is found there. He suggests that the oil and gas are dissipated long before the actual uncovering of the reservoir strata by erosion. For the case against oil migration or flushing by hydraulic action see Chapter 6.

The thesis of oil escape upward when a trap is tilted, or punctured by a fracture, is predicated upon the presence of water. The water-saturated zone extends only to the water table. Where the water table is high, as in humid belts, intersecting the surface in the topographically low spots, the oil will escape and join the surface runoff. Where the water table is deep, as in arid environments, the oil may remain perched at the water-table surface until evaporation of the more volatile constituents has reduced it to a tarry mass impregnating the rocks at that level. In arid regions of high elevation cut by deep valleys, the valley-floor elevation controls the water-table level except in confined aquifers. Under these conditions it is of no avail to look for oil in free (as opposed to confined) reservoirs in the anticlines above drainage level, for there is nothing to hold the oil up there. Furthermore, any oil once stored in these traps could have been drained out, along with the underlying water, by the downcutting of the canyons. Even the confined reservoirs would be drained of their fluids above creek level if a valley were cut through the impervious

[167] William B. Heroy, "Petroleum Geology," *Geol. Soc. Am. 50th Anniversary Vol.* (1941), pp. 512–548.

[168] Vincent C. Illing, "Role of Stratigraphy in Oil Discovery," *Bull. Am. Assoc. Petrol. Geol.,* Vol. 29 (July, 1945), p. 880.

cap rock into the underlying aquifer. Storm [169] describes a number of wells drilled on anticlines near the Colorado River in southeastern Utah where any oil that was trapped probably drained down the river in geologically recent time.

5. *Oil destroyed.* Hydrocarbons in rock can be destroyed in at least three ways: by relatively intense diastrophism; by weathering, and by the activity of hydrocarbon-consuming bacteria. For the last two methods of destruction to become operative, enough cover must be stripped so that the oil accumulation lies within the zone of oxidation. Heald [170] cites the Moorcroft field of Wyoming as an example of the exposure of an oil pool by erosion during the present cycle. No doubt many accumulations have been exposed and dissipated in the geologic past. It is equally probable that hydrocarbon deposits have been destroyed (or at least expelled) by diastrophism where the sedimentary rocks show any degree of metamorphism. However, with these exceptions, it is probably most difficult to destroy oil in the earth's crust. As the unstable crust teeters and twists, the oil in laterally persistent reservoirs moves around like the bubble in a carpenter's level; at times some of the oil may slip by the traps in its path and reach the surface, where it is lost. It should always be remembered that most of the movements of the earth's crust are infinitesimally slow; as a general (but not invariable) rule the oil can migrate with sufficient rapidity to remain in adjustment with the changing tectonic pattern.[171]

6. *Trap formed too late.* The timing of oil accumulation is of utmost importance. Obviously a trap is of no value if it does not come into existence until the hydrocarbons have ceased movement through the rocks. Van Tuyl and Parker [172] point out that in some areas the barren anticlines contain a greater thickness of the formations lying above the reservoir rocks than in adjacent productive anticlines. Presumably the anticlines overlain by thinner stratigraphic sections have been growing sporadically through a considerable span of geological time, whereas the anticlines containing normal sections have been formed by but one period of folding, and that relatively

[169] L. W. Storm, "Oil and Ground Water in High Rocky Mountain Structures," *Mines Mag.,* Vol. 39 (December, 1949), pp. 62–64.

[170] K. C. Heald, "Essentials for Oil Pools," *Elements of the Petroleum Industry* (Am. Inst. Min. Met. Engineers, 1940), p. 36.

[171] T. C. Hiestand, "Regional Investigations, Oklahoma and Kansas," *Bull. Am. Assoc. Petrol. Geol.,* Vol. 19 (July, 1935), pp. 948–970.

[172] F. M. Van Tuyl and Ben H. Parker, "The Time of Origin and Accumulation of Petroleum," *Quarterly Colo. School of Mines,* Vol. 36 (April, 1941), pp. 161–162.

recently. In the former case the oil is trapped early in an incipient phase of the upfold, and it stayed there during the subsequent periods of diastrophism which served to increase the relief of the anticline. Structures that did not have any closure in that much earlier period caught no oil. Often cited as an example of a trap formed too late to catch oil is the Kelsey dome, a prominent closed structure 18 miles northwest of the East Texas field and 15 miles east of the Van field.[173] The Kelsey dome has more closure in the surface rocks than the Van structure, but it has been tested by five dry holes drilled through the Woodbine formation which is the reservoir rock in both the Van and East Texas fields. There is no apparent difference between the dry Kelsey dome and the producing Van dome in regard to the nature of the associated organic rocks which presumably contained the oil source materials. A major difference does exist, however, in regard to the structural history of these two domes. The Van dome was a closed structure by the end of Woodbine time and has continued to be a closed structure to the present. The Kelsey dome, on the other hand, did not come into being until the Eocene. It is quite possible that the Van dome, by being in existence at an earlier date, trapped the oil going by, whereas the Kelsey dome arrived too late to partake of this accumulation.

[173] Alex W. McCoy and W. Ross Keyte, "Present Interpretations of the Structural Theory for Oil and Gas Migration and Accumulation," *Problems of Petroleum Geology* (Am. Assoc. Petrol. Geol., 1934), p. 302.

PART III

PRESENT AND FUTURE OIL SUPPLIES

In this, the concluding section, the distribution of oil and gas deposits by geographic, geologic, and political units is considered. Other subjects that are covered include the reserve situation and a forecast of where future discoveries can be anticipated. Last, Part III contains a discussion of how we can get the most out of the hydrocarbons we possess, and the potentialities in regard to synthetics and substitutes.

Chapter 9

DISTRIBUTION OF OIL AND GAS FIELDS—UNITED STATES

The introductory phase of this chapter includes a survey of the distribution of oil and gas fields from a tectonic standpoint. The geological occurrence of oil is followed by a geographic study in which the oil and gas fields are listed by continents, countries, and, within the United States, by states.

In the use of individual fields as examples, the writer has necessarily been limited to those for which descriptions have been published. Because of the natural tendency to "write up" the unique and ignore the commonplace, it is impossible to prevent some distortion in the surveys of the different areas that make up the bulk of this chapter.

TECTONIC CONTROLS ON THE OCCURRENCE OF OIL AND GAS

If a world map of oil and gas fields is superimposed upon geologic, tectonic, and relief maps, certain relationships immediately become apparent. As a general rule, the oil and gas fields shun the uplift areas and concentrate in the downwarped segments of the earth's crust. Some of the greatest concentrations of oil and gas fields occur along the continental margins. Most of the fields are to be found in belts that are topographically low. This environment is implied in the preceding statement regarding the occurrence of fields in coastal areas. But even in inland regions and up on plateaus of considerable elevation, the topographic position of the oil and gas fields tends to be low in comparison with the surrounding areas.

Most of the oil and gas fields of the world occur in structural sedimentary basins. This relationship is strikingly displayed in maps published by Weeks[1] showing the sedimentary basins and oil fields of each country. Sedimentary basins are downwarped areas; most of them were submergent through considerable periods of geologic time. Furthermore, these basins have been subject to intermittent sinkings, and the sediments deposited during such times of depression increase markedly in thickness between the edge and center of the basin. Special types of basins are *geosynclines,* which are elongate troughs of sedimentation, and *embayments.* Embayments are to be found along the continental margins, where the oceans in the geologic past have lapped up upon the continental borders to a greater extent than at the present. This overlap by marine waters has been accompanied by a downwarping of the inundated areas with a resultant seaward thickening of the sediment deposited, just as has happened in the more conventional basins.

In every example of basin downwarping, the coastal sinking has been accompanied and followed by diastrophism, which folded and faulted the sediments. Usually the diastrophism has been much more severe in the geosynclinal basins than in the other types.

There appear to be three controls on the general distribution of oil and gas fields within basin areas. The outer margin of the productive area is usually the zone where the cover above the lowest reservoir rocks becomes too thin to permit commercial accumulations beneath. The reservoirs themselves may crop out toward the rim, and beyond the sedimentaries in many basins is outcropping crystalline basement rock. In the geosynclines one margin of the producing area may be the approximate position of the 70 per cent isocarb; the increasing intensity of diastrophism in that direction produced a degree of metamorphism beyond the tolerance limit of the hydrocarbons. The third limitation on the distribution of oil fields within a basin is brought about by the increasing depth toward the center of the basin, which may make the search for, and exploitation of, oil deposits in this area uneconomic. However, with increased drilling depths, the area of these untested sections has diminished considerably, and in time they will disappear entirely. As a matter of fact, in many basins successively younger formations became oil-bearing basinward, and so even the central area may contain oil and gas deposits within reasonable depths.

[1] L. G. Weeks, "Highlights on 1947 Developments in Foreign Petroleum Fields," *Bull. Am. Assoc. Petrol. Geol.,* Vol. 32 (June, 1948), pp. 1093–1160; "Highlights on 1948 Developments in Foreign Petroleum Fields," *ibid.,* Vol. 33 (June, 1949), pp. 1029–1124.

The reasons for oil in downwarps are largely obvious.[2] Not only do such areas contain an adequate thickness of sedimentary rock for the occurrence and retention of large deposits of oil and gas but also the geological history has been such as virtually to insure that included within the thick stratigraphic section will be sediments rich in organic material (source rock) and rocks containing adequate porosity and permeability to function as reservoirs. Furthermore, as a general rule, such downwarped areas have been relatively quiet diastrophically so that the oil contained within has not been destroyed. The presence of traps to capture the oil on the flanks of sedimentary basins can be assumed. It is quite unlikely that sedimentary rock areas of any size exist which do not contain potential oil and gas traps. There have been enough movements of the earth's crust to insure the presence of both structural and varying-permeability traps. The relative importance of one type over another, and the variety of the traps present, are dependent upon the local diastrophic and sedimentation history.

Regional uplifts may also play a role in oil accumulation. Some of these, such as the La Salle anticline in the Illinois basin and the Nemaha granite ridge in the western interior basin, are local uplifts within much larger downwarps. Occasionally oil and gas deposits occur on the regional uplifts that lie between downwarps. These positive features are probably not actual areas of uplift but are structurally residual segments that stood still while the surrounding crust sank. Although erosion has stripped off most, if not all, of the sedimentary cover across many "uplift" areas, in such places as the Central Kansas uplift and the Cincinnati arch, enough of the sedimentary section has remained to permit accumulation of oil and gas.

TECTONIC CLASSIFICATIONS OF OIL AND GAS FIELD DISTRIBUTION. Ver Wiebe[3] proposed a tectonic classification for the oil fields of the United States in 1929. In this classification the United States is divided into several "petroliferous provinces," each of which is named after the dominating tectonic element. The petroliferous provinces within the United States, as named by Ver Wiebe, are the Appalachian geosyncline, Cincinnati arch, Eastern Interior coal basin, Michigan basin, Western Interior coal basin, Ouachita-

[2] Wallace E. Pratt, "Distribution of Petroleum in the Earth's Crust," *Bull. Am. Assoc. Petrol. Geol.,* Vol. 28 (October, 1944), pp. 1506–1509; H. de Cizancourt, "Location of Oil Fields in Tectonic Belts," *Science of Petroleum* (Oxford Univ. Press, 1938), Vol. 1, pp. 244–246.

[3] W. A. Ver Wiebe, "Tectonic Classification of Oil Fields in the United States," *Bull. Am. Assoc. Petrol. Geol.,* Vol. 13 (May, 1929), pp. 409–440; "Oil and Gas in the United States," *Science of Petroleum* (Oxford Univ. Press, 1938), Vol. 1, pp. 66–95.

Amarillo Mountain, Bend arch, Gulf embayment, West Texas, Rocky Mountain geosyncline, and Pacific geosyncline. Where desirable, the petroliferous provinces can be subdivided into "districts" and named after either a secondary tectonic feature or the geographic position.

Van der Gracht [4] classifies oil fields tectonically into two groups: (1) foredeeps of folded mountain belts, and (2) the mobile epicontinental shelf regions which he calls the forelands.

Pratt [5] emphasizes the great concentration of oil and gas that is known to occur in three intercontinental depressions in the earth's crust and calls attention to a fourth untested depression similar in tectonic setting to the other three. One of these intercontinental depressions is that lying within, and adjacent to, the Gulf of Mexico and the Caribbean Sea, between the continents of North and South America. Here are found the greatest oil deposits of the western hemisphere, including those in Colombia, Venezuela, Trinidad, and Mexico as well as the fields of the Gulf Coast of Louisiana and Texas. The second tectonically depressed area lies between, and upon contiguous corners of, Africa, Europe, and Asia, and includes the oil fields bordering the Red, Mediterranean, Caspian, and Black Seas, and the Persian Gulf where the Middle East oil deposits are being so actively explored today. The third of Pratt's intercontinental troughs includes "the environs of the shallow island-studded seas which lie between the continents of Asia and Australia in the Far East." Production has been obtained for a good many years from parts of this province including Borneo, Sumatra, Java, and New Guinea.

The unproved intercontinental depression described by Pratt is the border zone of the landlocked Arctic Sea, surrounding the North Pole and lying upon the northern extremities of the continents of North America, Europe, and Asia. This region is destined for much exploration in the future. Pratt's intercontinental depressed areas can be noted on the hemisphere maps, prepared by Weeks,[6] showing sedimentary basins (Fig. 220). Various smaller basins lying upon continental platforms, which are also important sources of oil and gas, can be noted on these maps. Many of the interior basins are, like the Arctic basin, still unexplored but are potential sources for hydrocarbons in the future.

[4] W. A. J. M. van Waterschoot van der Gracht, "The Geographical Distribution of Petroleum," *Science of Petroleum* (Oxford Univ. Press, 1938), Vol. 1, pp. 63–65.

[5] Wallace E. Pratt, "Distribution of Petroleum in the Earth's Crust," *Bull. Am. Assoc. Petrol. Geol.,* Vol. 28 (October, 1944), pp. 1506–1509.

[6] L. G. Weeks, "Highlights on 1947 Developments in Foreign Petroleum Fields," *Bull. Am. Assoc. Petrol. Geol.,* Vol. 32 (June, 1948).

The sedimentary basin map (Fig. 81) of North America shows, in addition to the petroliferous provinces named by Ver Wiebe for the United States, a great basin extending northwestward across the northern Great Plains, Alberta, and Northwest Territory to the Arctic. The southeastern end of this large trough is called the Williston Basin. Other northern latitude basins occur in the Paleozoic rock area bordering the southern end of Hudson Bay, in northwestern Alaska, in northern Alaska, and in the Canadian Arctic archipelago. At the present time, only the Alberta-Mackenzie trough is productive, although exploration is active in northern Alaska and some gas has been struck. Another potential petroliferous province is in northeastern North America in the maritime provinces of Canada. To the Gulf embayment province of Ver Wiebe should be added the South Atlantic coastal plain, which is a continuation of the same geologic conditions to the northeast. Sedimentary basins in North America south of the United States boundary include one covering a part of Lower California, the southward extension of the Gulf embayment province into Mexico, the Yucatan basin, and various minor basins in Central America, in Cuba, and on other islands of the Caribbean.

The oil-producing states of the United States will be covered following a general east-to-west order across the country. First to be considered will be the states lying within the Appalachian geosyncline petroliferous province.

General References. *Oil and Gas Journal,* Annual Review and Forecast number, Vol. 48 (Jan. 26, 1950); National Oil Scouts and Landmen's Association, "Oil and Gas Field Development in the United States," *Yearbook, 1949* (Review of 1948), Vol. 19 (1949); W. A. Ver Wiebe, *North American and Middle East Oil Fields* (Wichita, Kans., 1950); Ralph Arnold and William J. Kemmitzer, *Petroleum in the United States and Possessions* (Harper, 1931); U. S. Geological Survey, "Oil Field Development and Petroleum Geology, 1940–1944, Summarized by States," *Investigation of Petroleum Resources,* Hearings before a Special Committee Investigating Petroleum Resources, United States Senate, 79th Congress, First Session, Senate Resolution 36 (1945), pp. 506–531; U. S. Geological Survey, "Petroleum Geology Summarized by States," *Petroleum Investigation,* Hearings before a Subcommittee of the Committee on Interstate and Foreign Commerce, House of Representatives, 73rd Congress (Recess), House Resolution 441 (1934), pp. 910–1071; U. S. Geological Survey, *Geologic Map of the United States* and *Oil and Gas Map of the United*

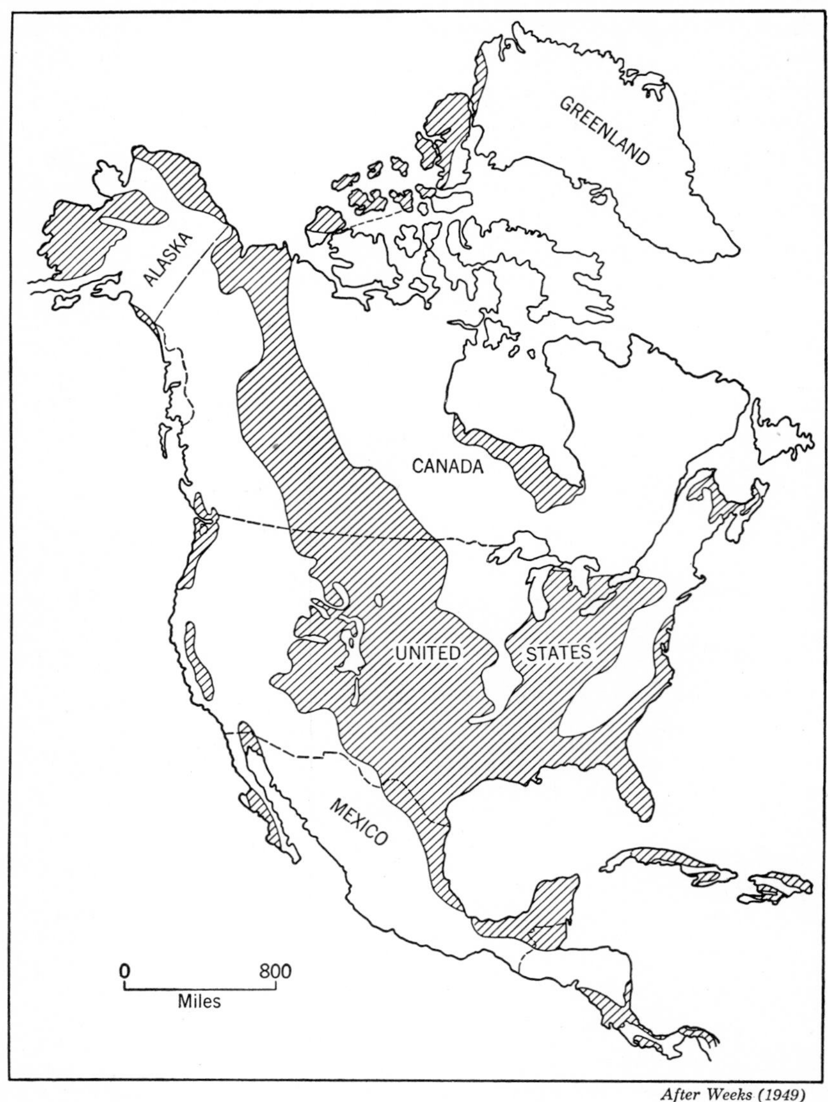

After Weeks (1949)

FIG. 81. North America. Sedimentary basins (shaded). *Courtesy American Association of Petroleum Geologists.*

States; Am. Assoc. Petrol. Geol., *Tectonic Map of the United States;* Max W. Ball, *This Fascinating Oil Business* (Bobbs-Merrill, Indianapolis, Ind., 1940).

New York [7]

(Figures 82–84)

The oil production of New York state is relatively insignificant, only amounting to 0.25 per cent of the country's total each year.

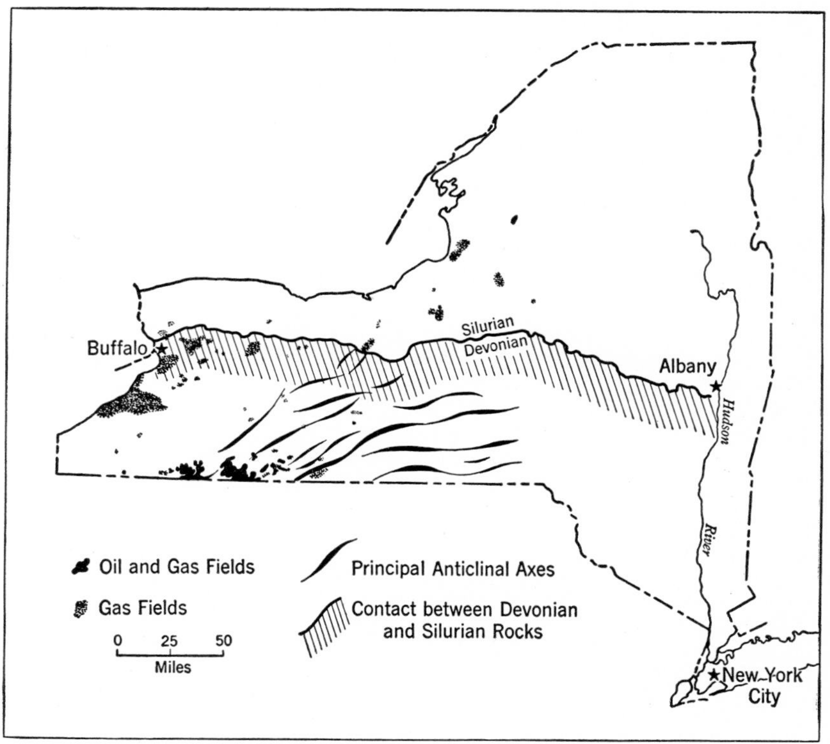

FIG. 82. Western New York. Principal anticlinal axes and oil and gas fields.

However, the fields are remarkably long-lived, and so New York has been a consistent producer of oil for many years. Furthermore, the

[7] John P. Herrick, *Empire Oil* (Dodd, Mead, New York, 1949); William Lynn Kreidler, "Oil and Gas Developments in New York during 1949," Am. Inst. Min. Met. Engineers, 1949 Production Statistics, *Jour. Petrol. Tech.*, Vol. 2 (June, 1950), pp. 29–30; E. R. McAuslan, "Developments in New York in 1949," *Bull. Am. Assoc. Petrol. Geol.*, Vol. 34 (June, 1950), pp. 1043–1047.

state has considerable gas production and the demand is so great that exploration continues to be active and has met with considerable success.

Even before Colonial times the oil springs of Allegany County were exploited by the Indians, and subsequently by the white settlers.

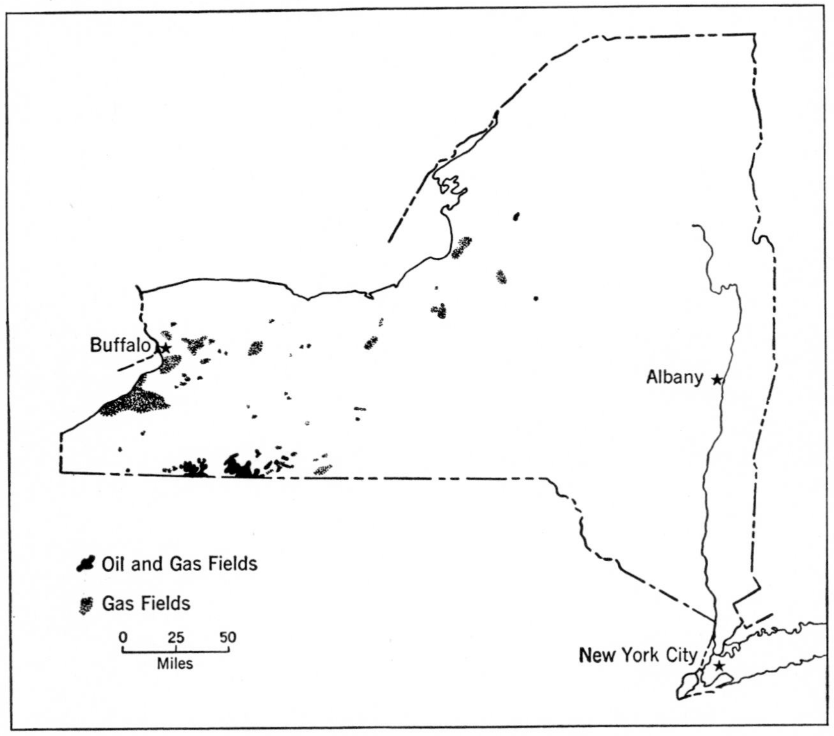

Fig. 83. New York oil and gas fields.

Shallow gas was struck near Fredonia in 1821 and piped into the local hotel. This is the first record of the transportation of natural gas in the United States. The first successful oil well was completed at Limestone, New York, in 1865. In 1872, drilling to the north extended the Bradford pool of Pennsylvania across the line into New York. Shortly afterwards oil production reached a peak in New York and then declined steadily until 1919, when secondary recovery by water flooding became legal and production climbed up to a second peak. Water flooding is still actively practiced in the state, and 1743 wells were drilled in 1948 for this purpose. About half of the wells were drilled to be oil producers; the other half were service (water input) wells. As a consequence of the practice of water drive the probable oil reserves of New York have been more than doubled.

The Appalachian geosyncline extends into western New York state. The axis of the geosyncline rises to the north, so that it can be said

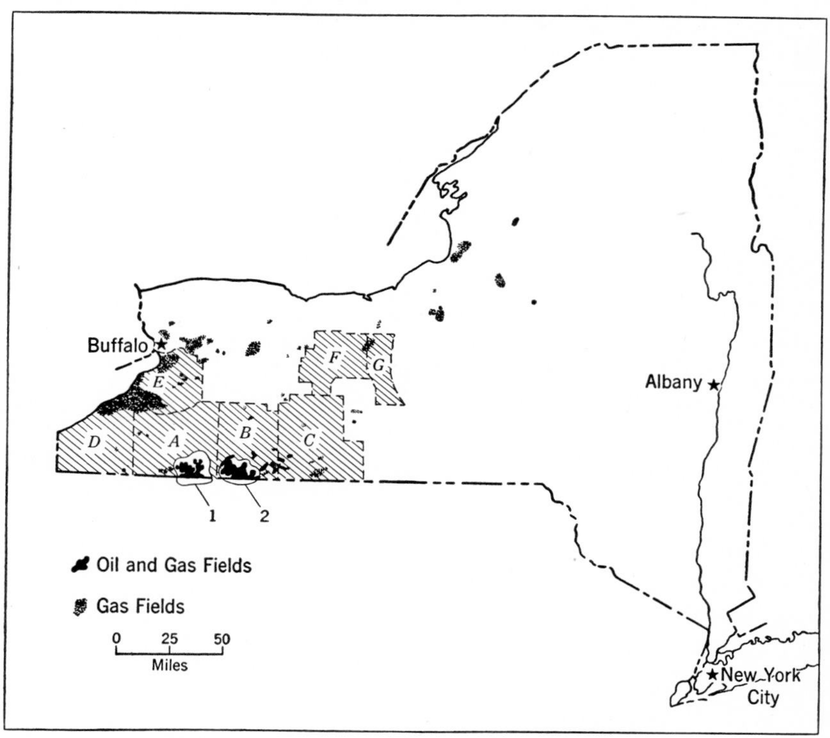

FIG. 84. New York index map. *A*, Cattaraugus County; *B*, Allegany County; *C*, Steuben County; *D*, Chautauqua County; *E*, Erie County; *F*, Ontario County; *G*, Seneca County; 1, Bradford oil field; 2, Richburg oil field.

that western New York contains the "prow" of this great structural trough. The regional dip in western New York is southward at a rate of between 30 and 50 feet per mile. The youngest Paleozoic formations are in western New York along the Pennsylvania line; pre-Cambrian rocks are exposed in northern New York. In southwestern New York are found the alternating anticlines and synclines with axes trending northeast for which western Pennsylvania is famous. The subsurface section in this area contains three important hydrocarbon reservoir rocks. The oil reservoirs are the Bradford and other sands of Upper Devonian age. Gas occurs in considerable volume in two older formations, the Oriskany sandstone, of Lower Devonian age, and the Medina sandstone, which is Silurian.

The oil fields of New York state are confined largely to Cattaraugus and Allegany counties, which lie just north of the Pennsylvania line in western New York. Most of the pools occur along the axis of the Bradford anticline, which crosses the line from Pennsylvania. Nodes

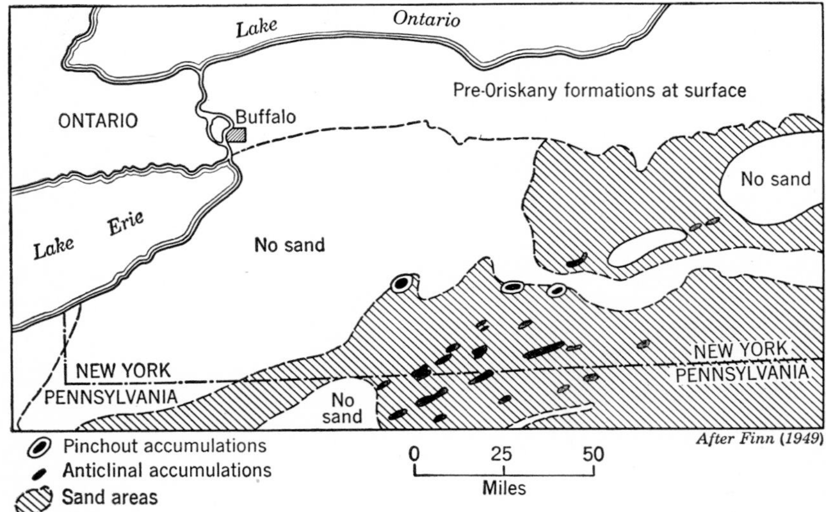

FIG. 85. Oriskany sandstone gas fields, New York, showing both anticlinal and "pinchout" accumulations. *Courtesy American Association of Petroleum Geologists.*

along the axis of this anticline are the Knapp Creek dome just across the line in Pennsylvania and the Richburg dome in Allegany County. The Bradford and the Richburg pools are the largest oil fields in New York state. The Bradford sands are lenticular, and so although the trapping is largely structural the distribution of oil on the folds is controlled to a considerable extent by the subsurface spread of the reservoir sands.

The gas fields of New York state occur in two groups. The larger is the group of gas fields south of Lake Ontario extending from Chautauqua and Erie counties at the east end of Lake Erie to the east end of Lake Ontario. The gas wells in this large district produce from the Medina sandstone in western New York, from Niagaran rocks in the field lying across the Ontario-Seneca County line, and from the Trenton southeast and east of Lake Ontario. The other gas district lies within and to the east of the oil-producing area in Allegany and Steuben counties. The reservoir rock is the Oriskany sandstone of Lower Devonian age. This district, which includes both northern Pennsylvania and southwestern New York, is relatively new, the first of the Oriskany discoveries having been made about 1930. In the following eighteen years 34 pools were discovered and developed in this area. In southern Allegany and Steuben counties the trapping has been structural, caused by doming and thrust faulting along prominent anticlinal axes. To the north, however, the Oriskany sand is discontinuous and three pools (Fig. 85) owe their accumulation to the up-dip wedgeout of this reservoir. Still farther to the northeast the sand reappears and several pools there have anticlinal trapping.[8]

Pennsylvania [9]

(Figures 86–88)

Although producing only about 0.66 per cent of the domestic oil production today, Pennsylvania has had a long and glorious history as a petroleum state and is even now producing over 11 million barrels of high-grade crude oil each year as well as considerable quantities of valuable natural gas. The occurrence of seeps in Pennsylvania, especially along Oil Creek, central Venango County, and the drilling of the discovery well for the United States in that vicinity in 1859 are described elsewhere in this volume. From 1859 to 1895 Pennsylvania led the states in petroleum production, but since that date it has been surpassed by the states to the westward. Exploration is still active in this area; of the approximately 3300 wells drilled in Pennsylvania in 1948 about one-fourth were wildcat or pool wells and the remainder were drilled in the water flooding program.

The oil and gas fields of Pennsylvania (Fig. 87) occupy a belt nearly 200 miles long and from 25 to 125 miles wide, crossing the western side of the state. The total number of named fields is in excess of 300, of which over half are gas fields. The greatest concentration of gas

[8] Fenton H. Finn, "Geology and Occurrence of Natural Gas in Oriskany Sandstone in Pennsylvania and New York," *Bull. Am. Assoc. Petrol. Geol.*, Vol. 33 (March, 1949), pp. 303–335.

[9] G. H. Ashley, "History of Development and Geologic Relationships of Appalachian Fields," *Bull. Am. Assoc. Petrol. Geol.*, Vol. 22 (April, 1938), pp. 416–430; Paul D. Torrey, "Origin, Migration and Accumulation of Petroleum and Natural Gas in Pennsylvania," *Problems of Petroleum Geology* (Am. Assoc. Petrol. Geol., 1934), pp. 447–484; Charles R. Fettke, "Developments in Pennsylvania in 1949," *Bull. Am. Assoc. Petrol. Geol.*, Vol. 34 (June, 1950), pp. 1048–1057.

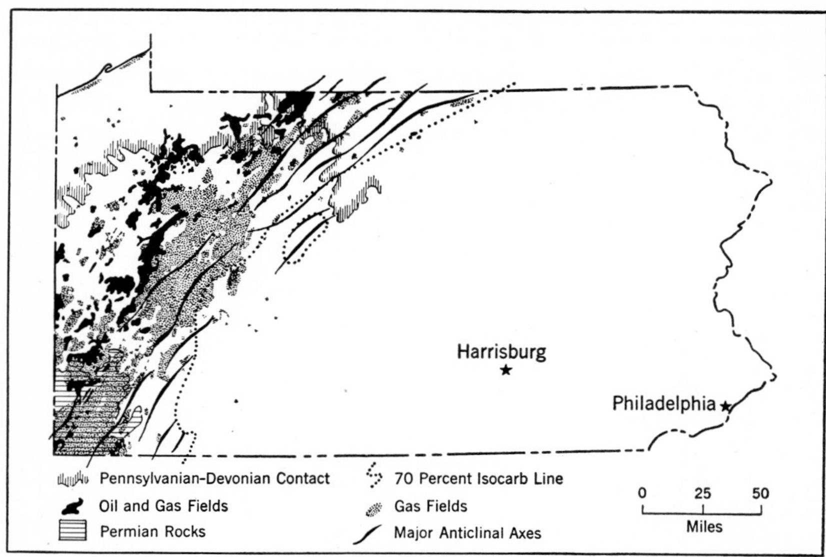

FIG. 86. Western Pennsylvania. Major structural features and oil and gas fields.

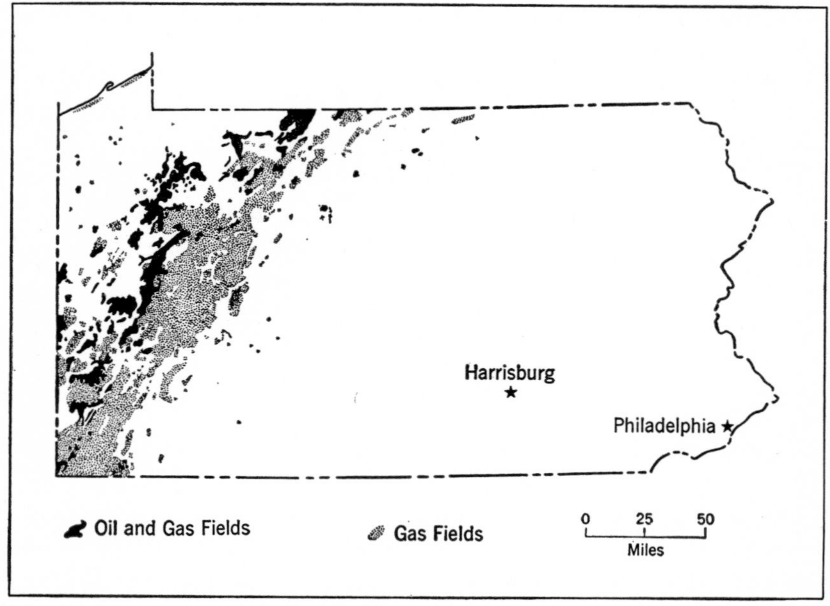

FIG. 87. Pennsylvania oil and gas fields.

fields is on the east side of the petroliferous zone, but many other gas fields are scattered across the zone to the westward. The eastern production limit is approximately the 70 per cent isocarb for gas and the 65 per cent isocarb for oil (Chapter 5).

The oil and gas deposits of Pennsylvania occur in the Appalachian geosyncline, which is a great spoon-shaped trough with a northeast-

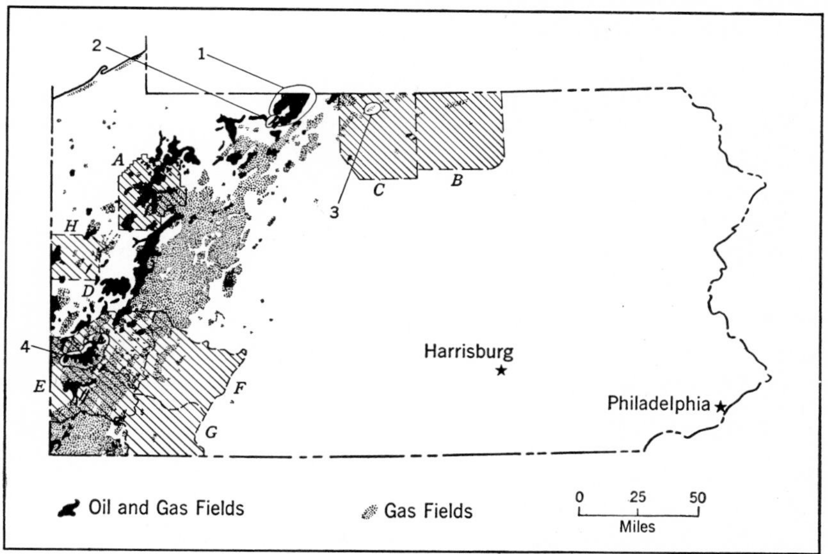

FIG. 88. Pennsylvania index map. *A,* Venango County; *B,* Tioga County; *C,* Potter County; *D,* Allegheny County; *E,* Washington County; *F,* Westmoreland County; *G,* Fayette County; *H,* Lawrence County; 1, Bradford oil field; 2, Music Mountain oil field; 3, Hebron gas field; 4, McDonald oil field.

southwest trend, plunging to the southwest from the prow in western New York state to the deepest point, close to the southwestern corner of Pennsylvania. Most of the east flank of this trough lies above the 70 per cent isocarb, owing to greater diastrophic activity in that direction. As a consequence the oil and gas fields lie along the axis and west flank of the Appalachian geosyncline. The trough is furrowed by a great series of parallel anticlines and synclines which are also parallel to the geosynclinal axis.

The principal reservoirs in Pennsylvania are sandstones and conglomerates. Most belong in either the Mississippian or Upper Devonian systems, although some oil has been obtained from Pennsylvanian rocks in the southwestern part of the state. An important gas reservoir is the Oriskany sandstone of Lower Devonian age. Altogether more than 70 distinct hydrocarbon reservoirs have been recognized and named in Pennsylvania.

Some oil and gas accumulations in this state are anticlinal, but in many the trapping is due to the lenticularity of the reservoir sand. The sand bodies tend to be elongate. Some appear to parallel old shorelines, but others run normal to the shorelines and probably represent stream channel fillings, especially in the distributaries of deltas. In most fields the lenticularity is due to the deposition of distinct sand bodies, but in a few a facies change from sand to shale has been responsible for the trapping. Accumulation in the Venango sand pools of northwestern Pennsylvania is illustrated in Fig. 70 in Chapter 8 as an example of accumulation in lensing sandstones.

Pennsylvania's most notable field, and one of the great oil fields of the United States, is the Bradford field,[10] which lies mostly in Pennsylvania but extends a short distance over the line into western New York. This field was discovered in 1871 and since then has produced more than half a billion barrels of oil. This field still accounts for the greater part of Pennsylvania's annual oil output, even after nearly 80 years of continuous production. In terms of current oil-field discoveries, the Bradford pool is shallow, with the reservoirs lying at depths ranging from 1000 to 1700 feet. This pool reached its peak in 1881 with a production of nearly 23 million barrels, which was 83 per cent of the country's entire output for that year. In 1890 the operators had discovered that water breaking through rusted casing in abandoned wells was reaching the oil sand and increasing the yield of adjacent oil wells. The Bradford production reached a low point in 1906, with only 2 million barrels. Subsequently the output slowly increased as the result of the operation of illegal water flooding. In 1921 water flooding was legalized by the state legislature, and by 1937 the production had risen to nearly 17 million barrels for a second peak in the production curve for this field. This great record can be explained by the geological situation. Unlike most Pennsylvania reservoir rocks, the Bradford sand is relatively widespread and up to 90 feet in thickness. The sand body carries across the large Bradford anticline, and accumulation is mainly anticlinal (Fig. 89).

One of the newer oil discoveries in Pennsylvania is the Music Mountain pool,[11] which was opened in 1937. Although this pool lies on the southwest flank of the Bradford anticline the accumulation is due

[10] Charles R. Fettke, "The Bradford Oil Field, Pennsylvania and New York," *Penn. Geol. Survey, Fourth Series, Bull.* M 21 (1938).

[11] Charles R. Fettke, "Music Mountain Oil Pool, McKean County, Pennsylvania," *Stratigraphic Type Oil Fields* (Am. Assoc. Petrol. Geol., 1941), pp. 492–506.

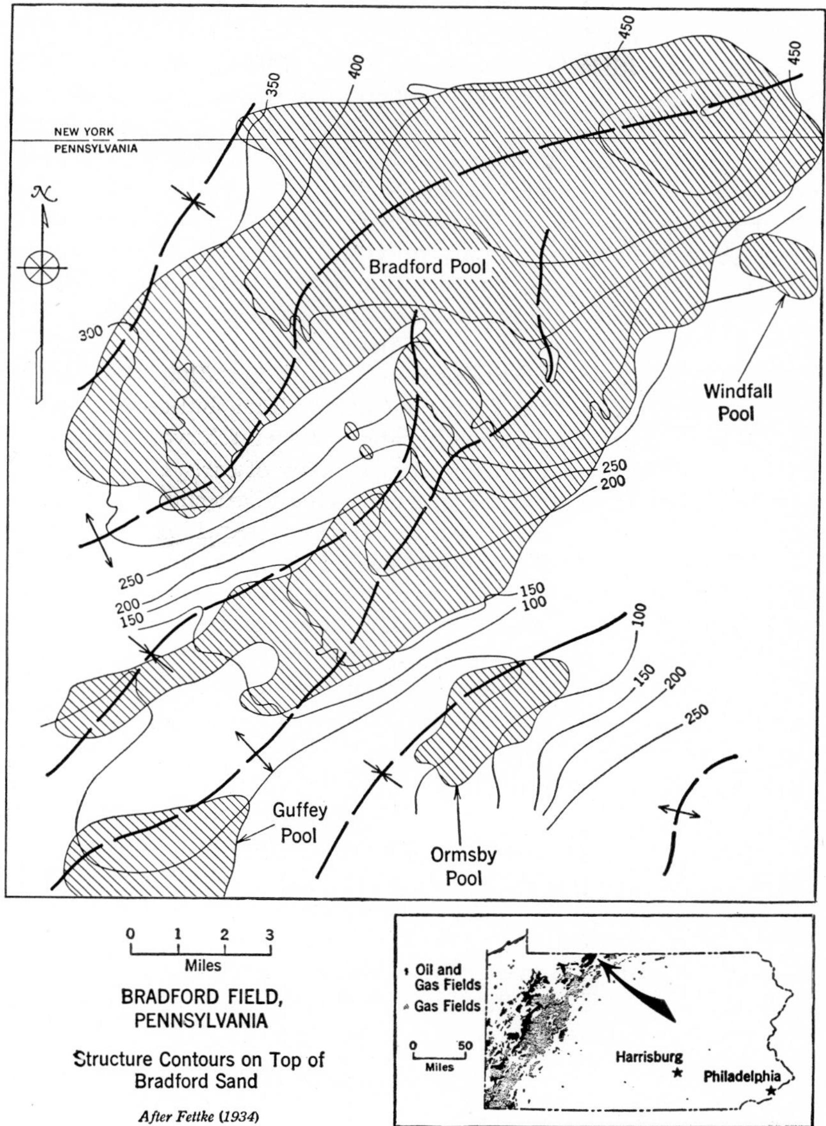

FIG. 89. Bradford field, Pennsylvania-New York. Relationship between structure and accumulation. *Courtesy Pennsylvania Geological Survey.*

entirely to varying permeability. The reservoir rock is an Upper Devonian sandstone which occurs in a shoestring lens, "probably the remains of an ancient offshore bar," about 4 miles long, 800 to 2000 feet wide, and with an average thickness of 35 feet.

Second only to Bradford in production is the McDonald field of Allegheny and Washington counties, which, with three adjacent fields, forms a producing area 15 miles long by 1 to 4 miles wide.[12] The field, discovered in 1891, contains two wells which had initial productions estimated to be close to 15,000 barrels per day. The principal reservoirs are the Conewango sands of Upper Devonian age, elongate lenticular bodies trending northeast-southwest, which were probably originally deposited as offshore bars and irregular sheetlike sands. Trapping is due primarily to the lenticularity of the sands.

The gas reservoirs of western Pennsylvania are divided into two classes, the shallow and the deep sand fields. The shallow sand fields produce from the Upper Devonian and younger reservoir rocks, and the deep sand fields produce from the Oriskany of early Devonian age, and to a slight extent from the overlying Onondaga chert. The deep sand production started in 1930 after discoveries in Tioga and Potter counties to the east of the Bradford field, and new gas finds are still being made in that area as well as to the north across the New York state line and to the southwest across western Pennsylvania. Typical of the Oriskany accumulations in Pennsylvania is the Hebron gas field,[13] which lies 35 miles southeast of Bradford. The Oriskany sandstone is laterally continuous in this area, and the trapping is anticlinal. The Hebron anticline extends across northern Pennsylvania and southwestern New York for 75 miles or more. The Hebron gas field occupies a local swelling on this anticline. It has a closure of 250 feet and a structural relief of 1500 feet. The structure is an elongate ellipse in plan; the field is 12 miles long at the top of the fold and 1½ miles wide across the anticlinal axis. In southwestern Pennsylvania in Westmoreland and Fayette counties are three gas fields in which the trapping is likewise anticlinal, but most of the accumulation has taken place not in the Oriskany sandstone but in the overlying deformed and fractured Onondaga chert.[14]

[12] A. I. Ingham, "Geology of McDonald and Adjacent Oil Fields, Allegheny and Washington Counties, Pennsylvania," (Abstract) Am. Assoc. Petrol. Geol., Vol. 32 (November, 1948), pp. 2153–2154.

[13] John R. Reeves, "Hebron Gas Field, Potter County, Pennsylvania," *Bull. Am. Assoc. Petrol. Geol.,* Vol. 20 (August, 1936), pp. 1019–1027.

[14] Fenton H. Finn, "Geology and Occurrence of Natural Gas in the Oriskany Sandstone in Pennsylvania and New York," *Bull. Am. Assoc. Petrol. Geol.,* Vol. 33 (March, 1949), pp. 303–335.

West Virginia [15]

(Figures 90–92)

West Virginia is an important gas-producing state, but its oil production amounts to only about 0.16 per cent of the country's annual

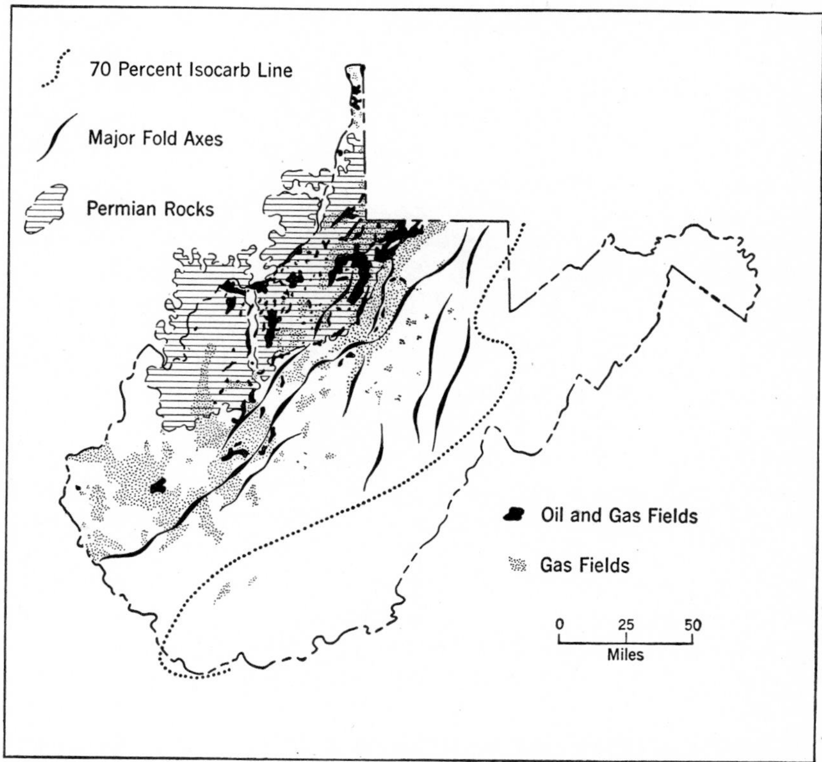

FIG. 90. West Virginia. Major structural features and oil and gas fields.

total, or half that of New York. This state is only slightly younger than Pennsylvania as a producer of petroleum. Both gas and oil were struck during the drilling of salt wells in West Virginia in the

[15] J. E. Billingsley, "Occurrences of Oil and Gas in West Virginia, Eastern Ohio, and Eastern Kentucky," *Problems of Petroleum Geology* (Am. Assoc. Petrol. Geol., 1934), pp. 485–514; James D. Sisler and R. C. Tucker, "Natural Gas in West Virginia," *Geology of Natural Gas* (Am. Assoc. Petrol. Geol., 1935), pp. 989–996; R. C. Tucker, "Developments in West Virginia in 1949," *Bull. Am. Assoc. Petrol. Geol.,* Vol. 34 (June, 1950), pp. 1063–1065.

latter part of the eighteenth century and the first half of the nineteenth century, and one enterprising salt producer began using gas to fire his furnaces in 1841. The first well drilled for the purpose of obtaining oil was started shortly after the completion of the Drake well and became a producer in early 1860 at a depth of 303 feet. In 1899 West

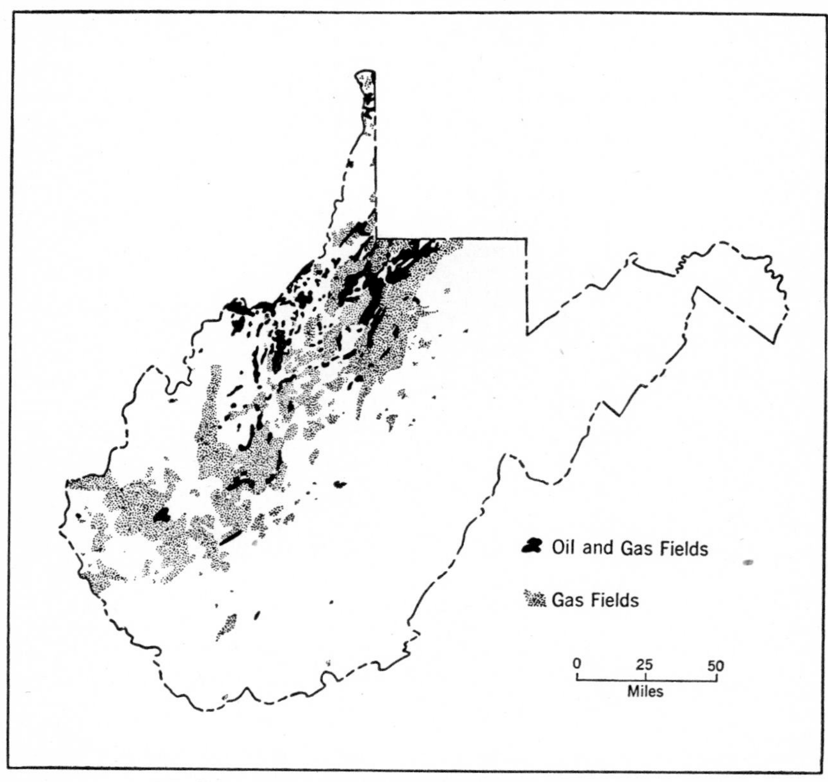

FIG. 91. West Virginia. Oil and gas fields.

Virginia surpassed Pennsylvania in oil output but did not remain ahead for long. During 1948 more wells were abandoned than were drilled. However, exploratory activity has not ceased; the large Sissonville gas field, producing from the Oriskany sand, was discovered in 1937, and a Berea sand oil pool was discovered in Jackson County in 1947.

The Appalachian geosyncline petroliferous province crosses from southwestern Pennsylvania into West Virginia and continues in a southwesterly direction, covering a path from 40 to 70 miles wide, across the western end of the state and into Kentucky. Along the northwest edge the oil and gas field belt overlaps the southeastern corner of Ohio. The deepest part of the Appalachian trough is in northern West Virginia, adjacent to the southwestern corner of Penn-

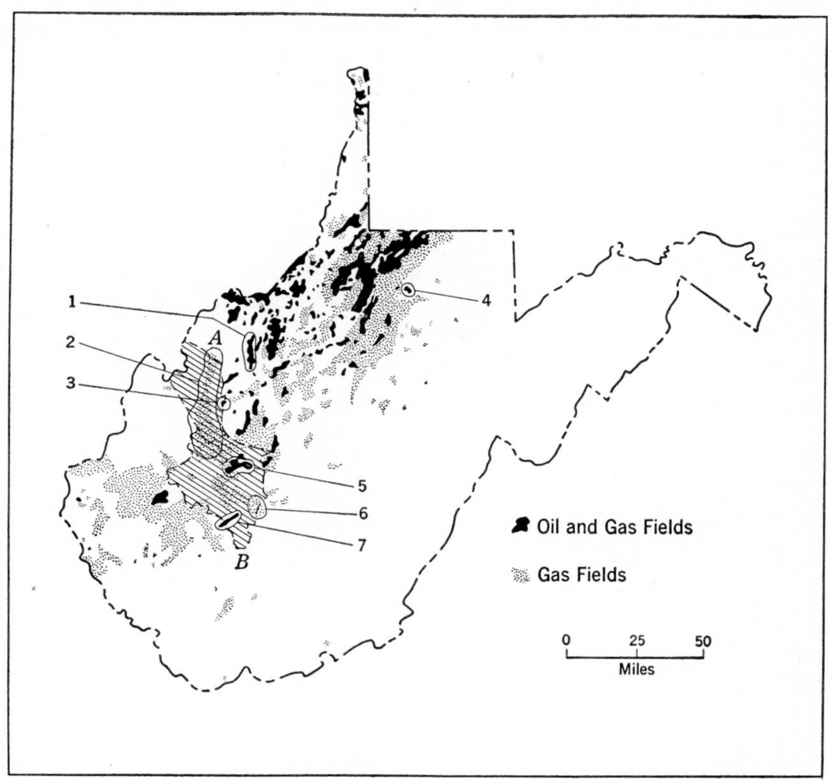

FIG. 92. West Virginia index map. *A,* Jackson County; *B,* Kanawha County; 1, Burning Springs oil field; 2, Sissonville gas field; 3, Gay-Spencer-Richardson oil field; 4, Shinnston oil field; 5, Blue Creek field; 6, Campbell's Creek-Boone County gas field; 7, Cabin Creek oil field.

sylvania. In this area occur Permian formations which are the youngest rocks to be found in the Appalachian province. The subsurface section contains reservoir rocks of Pennsylvanian, Mississippian, and Devonian age. The most important of these are sands in the Pennsylvanian Conemaugh and Pottsville sections, which are productive in the northwestern part of the state, the Greenbrier limestone, Big Injun, Weir, and Berea sandstones of Mississippian age, various discontinuous sands in the Catskill and Chemung of Upper Devonian age, and the Lower Devonian Oriskany sandstone.

The trapping of oil and gas in West Virginia has been due in some instances to the presence of pronounced anticlines and widespread porosity in the reservoir rocks, and in others to varying permeability caused by the lenticularity of the oil and gas sands. Anticlinal accumulation is best illustrated by the Burning Springs (Volcano) anticline (so named because of a gas seep), which occupies parts of four counties in northwestern West Virginia. This fold is 25 miles long and asymmetrical, with dips on the flanks ranging from 20° to 60°. Unlike most flexures in the Appalachian geosyncline this one does not parallel the geosynclinal axis but runs due north and south, cutting across the "grain" of the larger feature. Although much of the area covered by the Burning Springs anticline is unproductive owing to the tight nature of the sands, a large number of successful oil wells have been drilled close to the top of the anticline, most of them immediately to the west of the axis. The discovery well for West Virginia was drilled here, and in this general area the gravitational (originally referred to as the anticlinal) theory was first applied in the successful search for new oil and gas fields.

The Cabin Creek field,[16] 20 miles southeast of Charleston, illustrates the trapping of oil on a monocline due to the wedging-out of the reservoir sand in all directions. The reservoir rock, a Berea sandstone lens, is a typical shoestring, 12 miles long by ½ to 2 miles wide. It lies parallel to a nearby synclinal axis. No water is present; oil occupies the down-dip edge of the sand body, and gas the upper edge. Another Berea shoestring is the Spencer-Richardson-Bee Run-Yellow Creek oil and gas trend,[17] a discontinuous sand body extending for 60 miles in a northeast-southwest direction in northwest West Virginia. The Shinnston oil pool[18] to the northeast produces from a much less elongate lens of Upper Devonian sand. However, this sand is likewise water-free, and it occupies a monoclinal slope with gas concentrated along the up-dip edge. The so-called "synclinal pools" of West Virginia are illustrated (Fig. 50) and discussed in Chapter 8.

The largest concentration of gas fields in West Virginia is in Jackson and Kanawha counties, where wells scattered over 193,000 acres are

[16] Theron Wasson and Isabel B. Wasson, "Cabin Creek Field, West Virginia," *Bull. Am. Assoc. Petrol. Geol.*, Vol. 11 (July, 1927), pp. 705–719.

[17] E. T. Heck, "Gay-Spencer-Richardson Oil and Gas Trend, Jackson, Roane, and Calhoun Counties, West Virginia," *Stratigraphic Type Oil Fields* (Am. Assoc. Petrol. Geol., 1941), pp. 805–829.

[18] David B. Reger, "Shinnston Oil Pool, Harrison County, West Virginia," *ibid.*, pp. 830–846.

producing from the Oriskany sandstone.[19] The main pool, the Jackson County-Sissonville field, is 37 miles long and ranges in width from 2 to 15 miles. The eastern boundary of this field is the water line below the gas, and the western and southern boundaries are formed either by the sand pinching out or changing in facies to a rock of inadequate permeability. However, two of the smaller pools in this district, the Campbells Creek-Boone County and the Blue Creek, lie on the Warfield anticline, and structure is primarily responsible for accumulation.

Virginia [20]

(Figure 93)

Although the east flank of the Appalachian geosyncline occupies the western edge of Virginia, the Paleozoic sediments are highly folded and faulted and the carbon ratio is almost everywhere above what is usually considered the upper limit for hydrocarbons. Nonetheless, the state does have some gas, and one oil pool has been discovered.

The oldest hydrocarbon-producing area is the small Early Grove gas field [21] near Bristol along the Scott-Washington County line and about 4 miles north of the Tennessee line. Gas has been discovered in Buchanan County in the "pocket" between Kentucky and West Virginia,[22] and the discovery of gas in Rockingham County in northern Virginia has also been reported.[23]

The discovery, and so far only, oil field in Virginia is the Rose Hill field [24] in Lee County. This is the only oil field in the much-disturbed rocks of the Appalachian Valley of the eastern United States. Substantial oil seepages which have been known for many years led to the original drilling in the Rose Hill area. The discovery well was

[19] A. H. McClain, "Stratigraphic Accumulation in Jackson-Kanawha Counties Area of West Virginia," *Bull. Am. Assoc. Petrol. Geol.*, Vol. 33 (March, 1949), pp. 336–345.

[20] William M. McGill, "Explorations for Natural Gas and Petroleum in Virginia," *Trans. Am. Inst. Min. Met. Engineers* (separate, 1947?).

[21] Paul Averitt, "The Early Grove Gas Field, Scott and Washington Counties, Virginia," *Virginia Geol. Survey, Bull.* 56 (1941).

[22] Hollis G. Richards, "Developments in Atlantic Coastal States between New Jersey and North Carolina in 1948," *Bull. Am. Assoc. Petrol. Geol.*, Vol. 33 (June, 1949), p. 1011.

[23] Paul H. Price, "Discovery of Gas in Rockingham County, Virginia," *Bull. Am. Assoc. Petrol. Geol.*, Vol. 26 (February, 1942), p. 275.

[24] Ralph L. Miller, "Rose Hill Oil Field, Lee County, Virginia," *Structure of Typical American Oil Fields* (Am. Assoc. Petrol. Geol., 1948), Vol. 3, pp. 452–479; Philip Jenkins, "Current Drilling Evokes Interest in Virginia's Only Producing Oil Field," *Oil and Gas Jour.*, Vol. 47 (Aug. 19, 1948), pp. 72–74.

completed in 1942. The reservoir rock is Trenton (Ordovician) limestone, which lies at depths of 1000 to 1500 feet. The Trenton formation is not greatly disturbed but has been overthrust by younger Paleozoic rocks for a distance of several miles. The discovery and other early wells in the field were drilled in a fenster ("window") where erosion has cut through the overriding block and exposed the stationary block beneath. Accumulation appears to be in fractures in the brittle Trenton limestone and adjacent beds. By July, 1948,

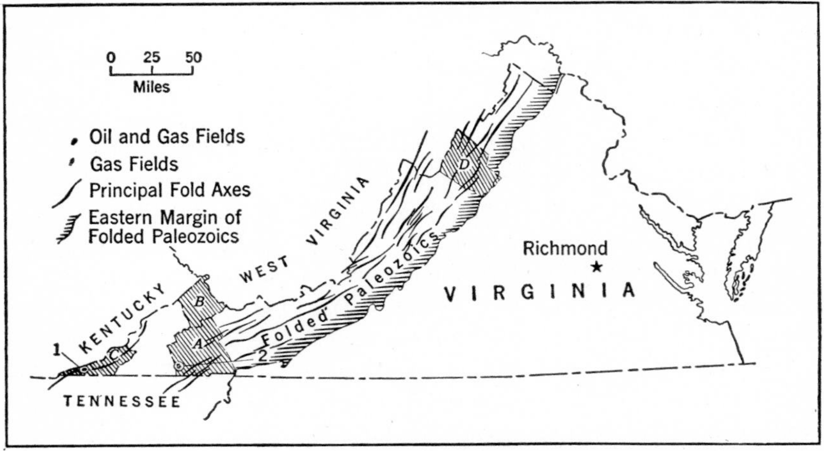

FIG. 93. Virginia index map. *A,* Washington County; *B,* Buchanan County; *C,* Lee County; *D,* Rockingham County; 1, Rose Hill oil field; 2, Early Grove gas field.

forty-four wells had been drilled, but only twenty-two were ever producers and eight of these had been abandoned. All the currently productive wells are in either the Four-Mile fenster in which the original discovery was made or in the Martins Creek fenster, 2 to 3 miles distant. Production during 1948 was about 200 barrels a day from the entire field.

Maryland

Maryland joined the list of hydrocarbon-producing states in 1949 when a successful gas well was drilled in Garrett County near the western edge of the "panhandle." The reservoir is a Devonian chert lying at a depth of 4450 feet.[25]

[25] Horace G. Richards. "Developments in Atlantic Coastal States Between New Jersey and North Carolina in 1949," *Bull. Am. Assoc. Petrol. Geol.,* Vol. 34 (June, 1950), p. 1224.

Kentucky[26]

(Figures 94–96)

Currently Kentucky is producing about 0.5 per cent of the annual domestic output. Oil was first discovered by design in this state in 1860 and natural gas in 1889; however, oil from a brine well in Cumberland County was bottled and sold for medicinal purposes as early as 1829. Oil seepages are quite common, especially in the southern

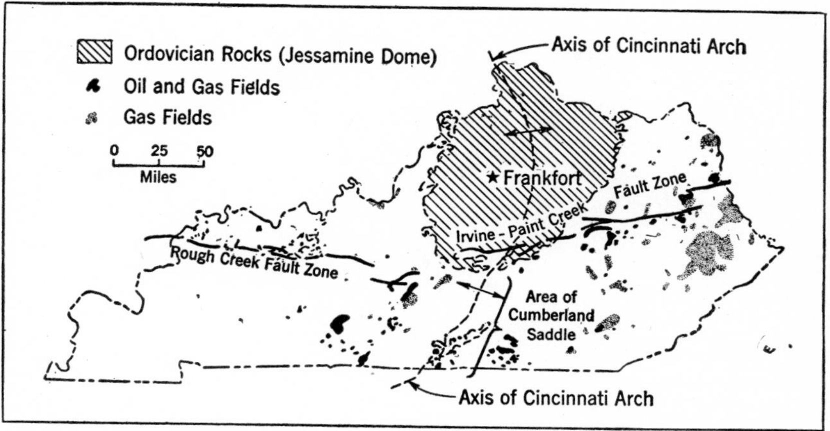

FIG. 94. Kentucky. Major structural features and oil and gas fields.

and eastern parts of the state. The first production peak was reached in 1921, after which the output declined until the Illinois basin development spread into western Kentucky and then the Kentucky production climbed again to a new and higher peak in 1946. Kentucky is divided geologically by the axis of the Cincinnati arch which crosses the state from north to south at its widest part. In northern Kentucky the axis of the arch rises over the large Jessamine dome, and at the south edge of the state the arch rises again toward the summit of the Nashville dome of central Tennessee. The intervening sag in south central Kentucky is known as the Cumberland saddle. To the east of the Cincinnati arch is the continuation of the Appalachian geosyncline, which enters northeastern Kentucky from southwestern West

[26] Daniel J. Jones, "Events Leading to Secondary Recovery in Kentucky," Reprint from *Bull. Appal. Geol. Soc.*, Vol. 1 (1949); E. Boyne Wood, "Oil and Gas Developments in Kentucky in 1949," *Bull. Am. Assoc. Petrol. Geol.*, Vol. 34 (June, 1950), pp. 1066–1072.

Virginia. This area is known as the eastern Kentucky coal basin. The stratigraphy is similar to that in the geosyncline to the northeast and the folds are the same characteristic elongate parallel anticlines and synclines. The eastern Kentucky coal basin is crossed from east to west by the Irvine-Paint Creek fault zone.

West of the Cincinnati arch is the western Kentucky coal basin, which is a continuation of the Eastern Interior coal basin of Illinois and Indiana. Western Kentucky contains the south rim of this regional

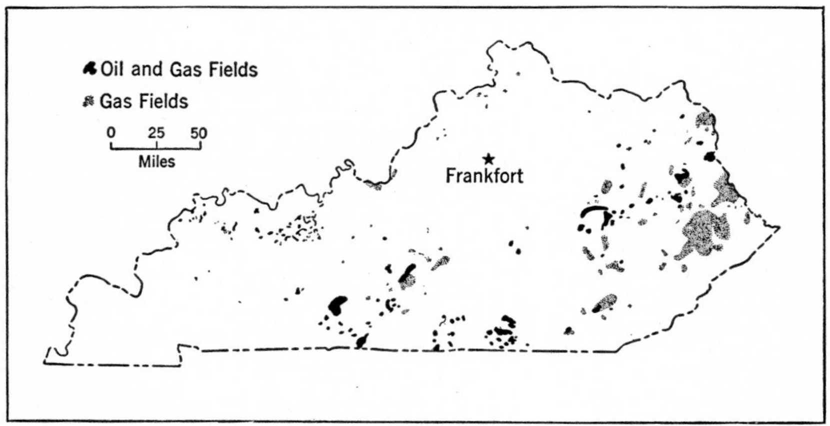

FIG. 95. Kentucky. Oil and gas fields.

basin. It is also crossed by an east-west fault zone known on this side of the arch as the Shawneetown-Rough Creek. The oldest exposed Paleozoic rocks in Kentucky crop out in the center of the Jessamine dome, and the youngest rocks occur in the centers of the two coal basins.

The oil and gas fields of Kentucky fall naturally into three districts, each one belonging to a different tectonic province. The fields of eastern Kentucky belong to the Appalachian province and are a continuation of similar accumulations occurring in West Virginia, Pennsylvania, and New York. The oil fields in the south central part of the state lie in two distinct groups, one on the west side of the Cincinnati arch axis, where it plunges down to make the Cumberland saddle, and the other on the east side. The western Kentucky fields belong geologically with those of the Illinois basin.

The oil and gas fields of eastern Kentucky produce from sandstone, limestone, and shale reservoir rocks ranging in age from lower Pennsylvanian to Ordovician. Important reservoirs are porous dolomites of Devonian and Silurian age; sandstones of Mississippian age contain oil in the extreme eastern part of this district, and gas has been discovered in fair quantity in the Ordovician St. Peter sandstone in the eastern part. As in other areas of the Appalachian geosyncline some accumulations are due to anticlinal structure and others to

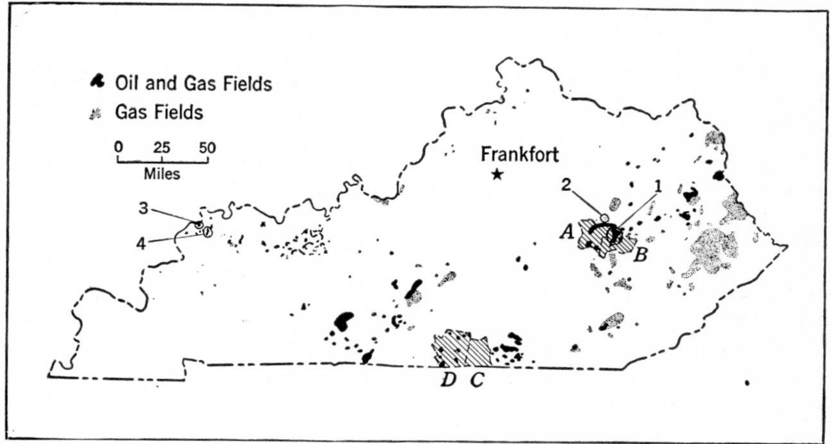

Fig. 96. Kentucky index map. *A,* Estill County; *B,* Lee County; *C,* Clinton County; *D,* Cumberland County; 1, Big Sinking oil field; 2, Furnace gas field; 3, Powell's Lake oil field; 4, Hitesville oil field.

varying permeability. One example of an eastern Kentucky oil field is the Big Sinking field [27] in Lee County. It lies about 5 miles south of the Irvine-Paint Creek fault zone, but apparently there is little relationship between the faulting and the occurrence of oil. The reservoir rock at Big Sinking is Niagaran (Silurian) dolomite, which has several zones of high porosity, owing to exposure at the surface in pre-Hamilton (Devonian) time. Trapping has been due to the tilting and truncation of the Niagaran dolomites with subsequent overlap and sealing by Devonian shale. According to Billingsley,[28] accumulation in the Irvine and Lee counties oil fields has been made possible by the sealing of sandstone and dolomitic reservoirs by up-dip wedg-

[27] Louise Barton Freeman, "Big Sinking Field, Lee County, Kentucky," *Stratigraphic Type Oil Fields* (Am. Assoc. Petrol. Geol., 1941), pp. 166–207.

[28] J. E Billingsley, "Occurrence of Oil and Gas in West Virginia, Eastern Ohio and Eastern Kentucky," *Problems of Petroleum Geology* (Am. Assoc. Petrol. Geol., 1934), p. 509.

ing. The eastern Kentucky gas fields occur both interspersed among the oil fields and in isolated accumulations to the east of the oil-bearing rocks. The gas is trapped in the structurally high areas where the reservoir rocks contain adequate porosity. The recently discovered Furnace field of Powell County has some large gas wells which produce from the St. Peter sandstone. This gas runs 42 per cent carbon dioxide.

The greater part of the production in south central Kentucky has come from the west side of the Cumberland saddle, but most of the current output is from the east side. The reservoirs range in age from Devonian to Ordovician, and carbonate rocks predominate. The most prolific reservoir is the so-called "Corniferous" limestone of Silurian age. Oil was recently discovered in the Knox dolomite of Cambro-Ordovician age by two wells drilled in Clinton County on the east side of the Cumberland saddle. These wells are small, but further exploration may uncover greater yields from this formation.

The western Kentucky accumulations are in Pennsylvanian sandstones and Mississippian sandstones and limestones just as they are to the northwest in southwestern Indiana and southeastern Illinois. The Powell's Lake field [29] in Union County, northwestern Kentucky, produces from two reservoirs, one a Pennsylvanian sandstone in which the trapping is due to the lenticularity of the rock, and the other a Mississippian limestone with anticlinal accumulation. Many of the wells which happen to be located above the lenticular Pennsylvanian sand and high enough on the Mississippian structure to be above water level are completed in both formations as producers. The Hitesville field, a McCloskey (Mississippian) limestone producer, which is also in Union County in western Kentucky, is described in some detail in Chapter 8 (Fig. 47) as an example of accumulation in the dome type of anticline.

Tennessee [30]

(Figure 97)

The production of oil in Tennessee is insignificant. This state was in the oil output column from 1860 to 1907, and it resumed production in 1916, but only in relatively minor amounts. A mild flurry was caused in 1948 by the discovery and development of two small

[29] W. I. Ingham, "Powell's Lake Oil Field, Kentucky," *Bull. Am. Assoc. Petrol. Geol.,* Vol. 32 (January, 1948), pp. 34–51.

[30] H. C. Milhous, "Oil and Gas Developments in Tennessee in 1949," *Bull. Am. Assoc. Petrol. Geol.,* Vol. 34 (June, 1950), pp. 1073–1077.

fields, one producing from the Ordovician Stones River formation and the other from the Cambro-Ordovician Knox dolomite. As a result more footage was drilled during 1948 than in any previous year.

The geology of Tennessee is dominated by the Nashville dome, a large node near the southern end of the exposed part of the Cincinnati arch. To the north the arch axis plunges downward to form the Cumberland saddle of southern Kentucky. On the east edge of the state is the Tennessee Valley, consisting of highly folded and faulted

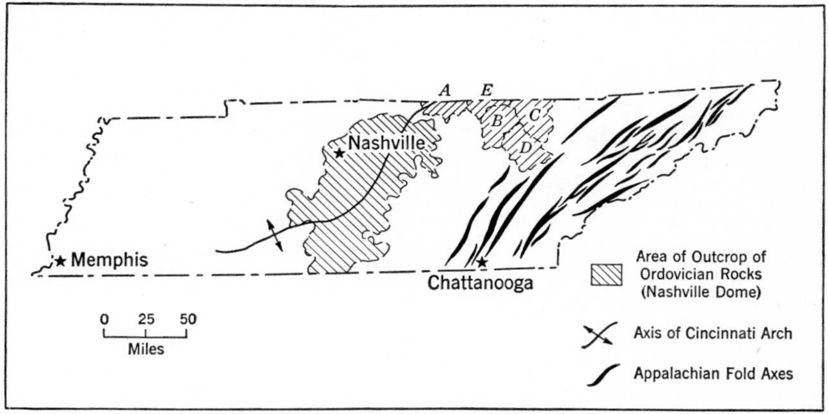

Fig. 97. Tennessee index map. *A,* Clay County; *B,* Fentress County; *C,* Scott County; *D,* Morgan County; *E,* Pickett County.

Ordovician and older rocks. The west side of the state is veneered by Cretaceous and Tertiary sediments of the Gulf embayment, an area that has been described as having some petroleum possibilities.[31]

The oil and gas fields of Tennessee are confined to four or five counties close to the Kentucky line on the east side of the Cumberland saddle. This area is a continuation of the eastern Cumberland saddle district of Kentucky. The older fields of northern Tennessee produce from Mississippian and Ordovician limestones. The Stones River discovery was in Clay County, and the Knox dolomite discovery in Pickett County. In Scott, Morgan, and Fentress counties on the eastern side of the district are some commercial gas fields. Accumulation in Tennessee appears to be due partly to varying permeability within the reservoir rocks but mainly to the presence of small folds.

[31] Carl A. Moritz, "Oil and Gas Possibilities of Southwestern Tennessee," *World Oil,* Vol. 128 (May, 1948), pp. 160–170.

Ohio[32]

(Figures 98–100)

The production in Ohio, which was at one time the foremost oil-producing state in the union, has dwindled both actually and relatively to such an extent that in recent years this state has produced

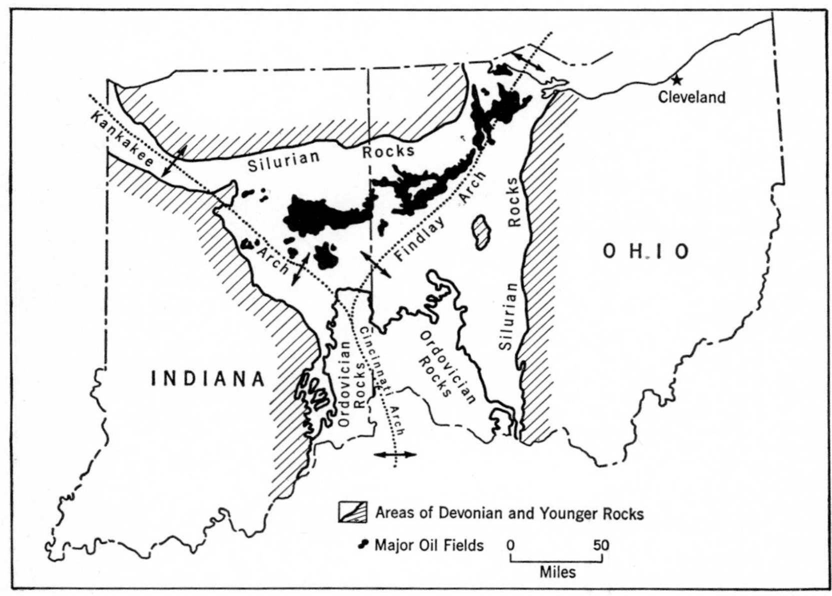

FIG. 98. Indiana and Ohio. Arch axes and oil fields producing from dolomitized Trenton limestone.

but 0.2 per cent of the country's total. Oil was at first produced commercially in 1860 in Washington County in the southeastern corner of the state. The discovery of gas in what soon became the great Lima-Indiana oil and gas field in northwestern Ohio took place in 1884. The Ohio part of this field reached maximum production in 1896, when the Trenton (Ordovician) reservoir rock yielded over 20 million barrels of oil. The third discovery in Ohio was that of the

[32] Orton C. Dunn, Jr., "Petroliferous Formations in Southeastern Ohio," *Oil and Gas Jour.*, Vol. 47 (Feb. 24, 1949), pp. 131–138; R. L. Alkire, "Oil and Gas Developments in Ohio during 1949," Am. Inst. Min. Met. Engineers, 1949 Production Statistics, *Jour. Petrol. Tech.*, Vol. 2 (June, 1950), pp. 59–64; R. L. Alkire and W. N. Tipka, "Developments in Ohio in 1949," *Bull. Am. Assoc. Petrol. Geol.*, Vol. 34 (June, 1950), pp. 1058–1062.

Clinton gas field, in 1887. In recent years the most active exploration has again been in eastern Ohio, where the Clinton sand has been the principal objective, with the Berea ranking second in importance. Some new oil and considerable new gas have resulted from this exploration activity.

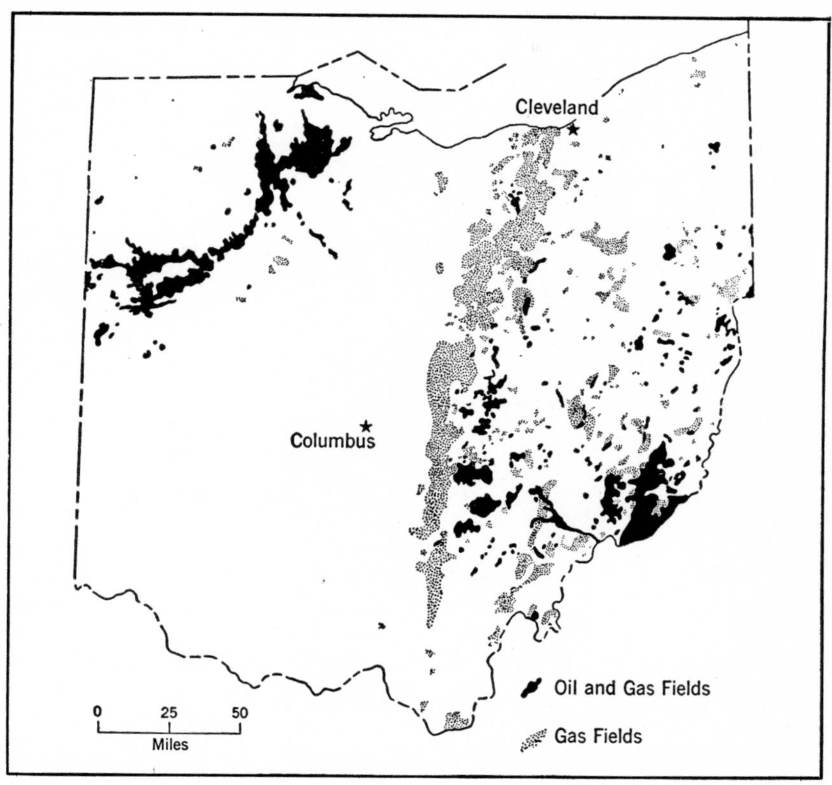

FIG. 99. Ohio. Oil and gas fields.

Structurally the greater part of Ohio lies on the west limb of the Appalachian geosyncline. The structurally deepest rocks are in the southeastern corner of the state which is closest to the axis of the Appalachian trough. From this area the strata rise to the north and especially to the west toward the axis of the Findlay arch, the right-hand fork of the Cincinnati arch, which crosses western Ohio from south to north. In northern Ohio the Findlay arch turns northeast and forms the backbone of the southwestern Ontario peninsula.

The oil fields of Ohio can be divided into two groups. In the eastern half of the state the accumulations are connected with the Appalachian geosyncline, and the fields belong geologically with those of Pennsylvania and West Virginia. However, there are obvious differences between the local structures on the west limb of the geosyncline and those in the axial zone. In the latter area the strata are folded into prominent parallel anticlines and synclines, whereas in eastern Ohio outside of Columbiana County anticlines are few and are mostly of the plunging type with a southeast trend. The accumulations of oil and gas in the western third of Ohio occur along the highest parts and down the west flank of the Findlay arch.

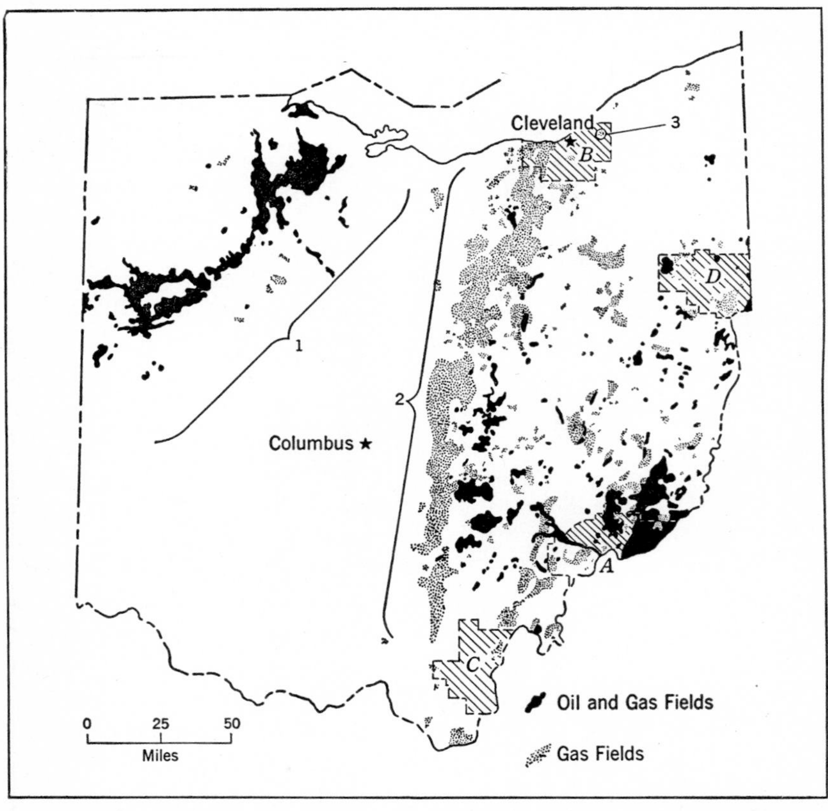

FIG. 100. Ohio index map. *A,* Washington County; *B,* Cuyahoga County; *C,* Gallia County; *D,* Columbiana County; 1, Lima-Indiana oil field; 2, Clinton gas field; 3, Mayfield gas field.

There is considerable difference between the reservoir rocks of eastern and western Ohio. In southeastern Ohio the same general series of Pennsylvanian and upper Mississippian sandstones which are productive in adjacent West Virginia are the reservoirs. The older and deeply buried formations rise toward the northwest and reach reasonable drilling depths in other parts of eastern Ohio, where some have been found to carry hydrocarbons. The most important of these older reservoirs are the Mississippian Berea sandstone, the Oriskany sandstone at the base of the Devonian, the Newburg "sand," which is in reality porous dolomite, lying within or immediately above the Niagaran group of Silurian age, and the "Clinton" sandstone, which is actually Medina (lower Silurian) in age. The western Ohio pools on the Findlay arch produce chiefly from the Trenton formation of Ordovician age.

Trapping in eastern Ohio is due largely to the up-dip wedging-out of reservoir sands on the flank of the eastward dipping monocline.[33] Most of the Oriskany gas fields, for example, which are confined by the distribution of the Oriskany to eastern and northeastern Ohio, occur along the west boundary of the sandstone where it wedges out up-dip.[34] In only two small gas fields so far discovered in this state in the Oriskany has accumulation been anticlinal.[35] The elongate Clinton gas field which extends from Lawrence County in southern Ohio northward to Lake Erie in Cuyahoga County owes its existence to the up-dip shaling of the Medina reservoir rock. The accumulation in the Clinton gas field was discussed in some detail in Chapter 8. In recent years a number of extensions and some new pools have been found in the Clinton sand to the east of the main north-south belt. Quite different is the accumulation in the Mayfield pool which produces gas from the Newburg porous dolomite of Niagaran (Silurian) age. This large gas field, which was discovered in 1938 and which lies only 16 miles to the east of the center of Cleveland, owes its existence to the presence of a broad structural dome.[36]

[33] E. V. O'Rourke, "Lensing Sands of Ohio," *Stratigraphic Type Oil Fields* (Am. Assoc. Petrol. Geol., 1941), pp. 382–385.

[34] Fenton H. Finn, "Geology and Occurrence of Natural Gas in Oriskany Sandstone in Pennsylvania and New York," *Bull. Am. Assoc. Petrol. Geol.,* Vol. 33 (March, 1949), Fig. 2, pp. 308–309.

[35] J. R. Lockett, "Oriskany Sand in Ohio," *Am. Assoc. Petrol. Geol.,* Vol. 32 (November, 1948), pp. 2154–2159.

[36] Howard E. Rothrock, "Mayfield Pool, Cuyahoga County, Ohio," *Bull. Am. Assoc. Petrol. Geol.,* Vol. 33 (October, 1949), pp. 1731–1746.

The Trenton production in the Lima-Indiana district is due entirely to irregularly distributed dolomitization porosity. The map (Fig.

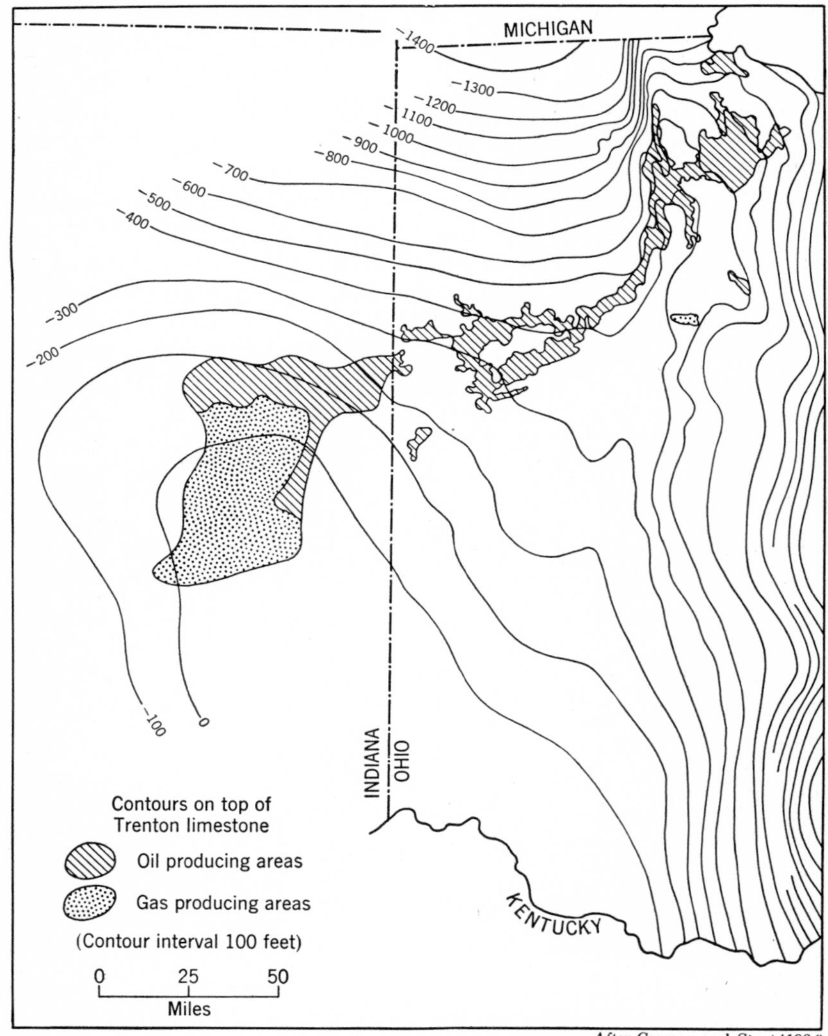

After Carman and Stout (1934)

Fig. 101. Lima-Indiana field.

101) of the Lima-Indiana oil and gas district shows that the hydrocarbons have accumulated along a broad belt extending from the top of the Kankakee arch in eastern Indiana northeastward into north-

western Ohio, crossing the axis of the Findlay arch and continuing some distance down the east flank.[37] The character of dolomitization porosity was discussed in Chapter 7 and its application to the trapping of oil in Chapter 8. Carman and Stout [38] have noted a very close correlation between magnesium content and oil production. No oil is found in the Trenton in this area unless the magnesium carbonate content is at least 20 per cent, and the best production occurs where the rock is a true dolomite. Most of the oil and gas in the Lima-Indiana district are found in the uppermost 20 to 30 feet of the dolomitized Trenton limestone. Northwestern Ohio has produced about three-fourths (75 per cent) of the total oil production of this district, and eastern Indiana the remainder.

Indiana [39]

(Figures 98, 102–103)

The recent annual production in Indiana has been in the neighborhood of 0.5 per cent of the country's total, placing this state in the same general category as Kentucky and Montana. Oil was discovered on the Indiana side of the Ohio-Indiana boundary in the Trenton dolomite in 1889, three years after the initial discovery of the Lima-Indiana district in northwestern Ohio. In the same year the first commercial well was completed in southwestern Indiana near Terre Haute. The state reached its production peak in 1905, after which the Trenton pools began to decline. The southwestern Indiana oil district, which heretofore had never produced any significant volume of oil, has been the scene of considerable activity since 1937, when the Illinois basin "boom" got under way. In the first decade of this new development 75 oil pools were discovered in southwestern Indiana, and new fields are still being discovered in this part of the state. As a result a second peak in production was reached in 1949, the greatest since the Trenton peak of 1905. It is interesting to note that there is still some successful probing of the Trenton reservoir in northeastern

[37] J. Ernest Carman and Wilber Stout, "Relationship of Accumulation of Oil to Structure and Porosity in the Lima-Indiana Field," *Problems of Petroleum Geology* (Am. Assoc. Petrol. Geol., 1934), Fig. 1, p. 522.

[38] J. Ernest Carman and Wilber Stout, *op. cit.*, p. 528.

[39] R. E. Esarey and B. E. Brooks, "Oil and Gas Developments in Indiana during 1949," Am. Inst. Min. Met. Engineers, 1949 Production Statistics, *Jour. Petrol. Tech.*, Vol. 2 (May, 1950), pp. 1–13; Alfred H. Bell and R. E. Esarey, "Developments in Illinois and Indiana in 1949," *Bull. Am. Assoc. Petrol. Geol.*, Vol. 34 (June, 1950), pp. 1078–1089.

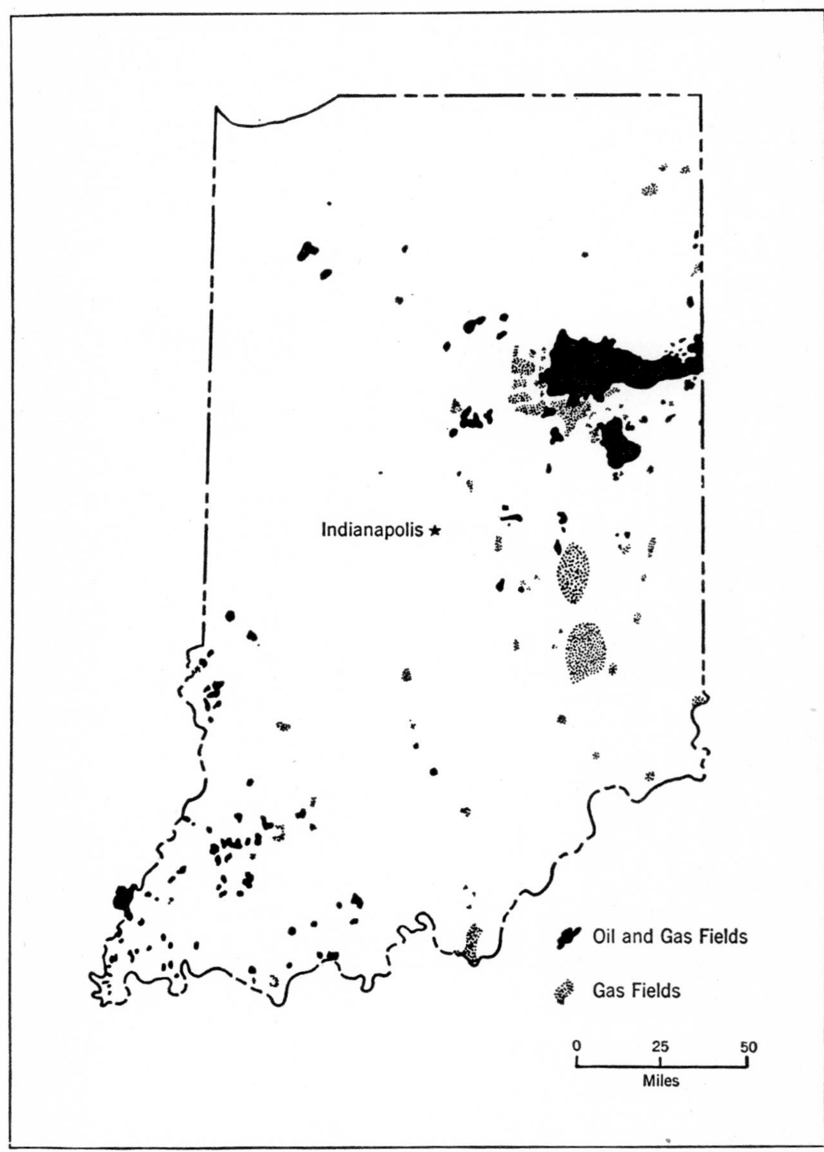

Fig. 102. Indiana. Oil and gas fields.

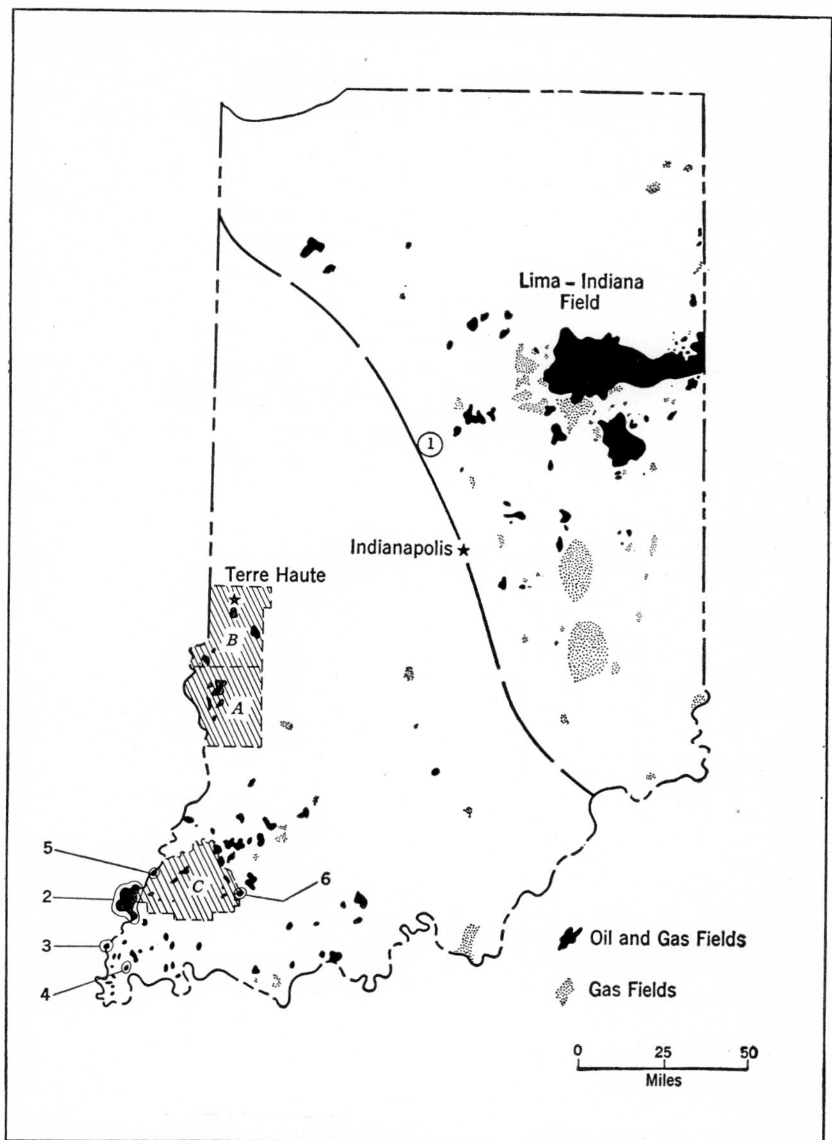

FIG. 103. Indiana index map. *A*, Sullivan County; *B*, Vigo County; *C*, Gibson County; 1, Lima-Indiana district; 2, Griffin oil field; 3, New Harmony oil field; 4, Mount Vernon oil field; 5, Rochester oil field; 6, Tri-County oil field.

Indiana. A few small producers are drilled each year in that area, but the annual production has been insignificant for many years.

The regional geology of Indiana is dominated by the Cincinnati arch and its northwest prong, the Kankakee arch. The strata dip to the southwest from the axis of the Kankakee arch into the Eastern Interior coal basin, which reaches its lowest point in southern Illinois not far west of the Indiana boundary. The basin is interrupted in eastern Illinois by the La Salle anticline, and the southwestern Indiana oil fields are largely concentrated in the "pocket" between Illinois and Kentucky where the axis of the anticline would cross the corner of Indiana if it continued this far south. However, at its southern end the La Salle anticline noses downward rapidly and for the most part has lost its identity by the time it reaches the Wabash River. The currently leading fields in southwestern Indiana are the Griffin and New Harmony, which belong to both Illinois and Indiana, here separated by the Wabash River, and the Mt. Vernon pool, entirely within Indiana.

The reservoir rock in northeastern Indiana is the Trenton dolomitized limestone. In southwestern Indiana a considerable number of reservoirs have been found, ranging in age from Pennsylvanian to Devonian, but those within the Mississippian system are of greatest importance. The Pennsylvanian reservoirs and most of those in the upper Mississippian are sandstones, whereas the older reservoirs are carbonate rocks. Included among the Mississippian limestone reservoirs that are productive in this area are the McCloskey "sands" which are prolific producers of oil in the Illinois basin. The most recent developments in Indiana have been the opening up of new Devonian fields in Sullivan and Vigo counties to the north of the "pocket" district.

The trapping of oil in the Trenton dolomitized limestone by varying permeability was described in the section on Ohio. In southwestern Indiana trapping in some pools is anticlinal, and in others accumulation has been brought about by the lenticularity of the sandstone reservoir rock. The new Devonian fields occupy anticlines, two of which were found by utilizing coal drill core data. The anticlinal structure is the result of "draping" of the Devonian reservoirs over Silurian reefs. The Rochester field of Gibson County, a relatively new discovery, is a stratigraphic trap accumulation. The reservoir rock is the Waltersburg sand of upper Mississippian age. The distribution of oil in the Tri-County and New Harmony fields was described in Chapter 8.

Illinois [40]

(Figures 104–106)

The state of Illinois accounted for approximately 3½ per cent of the United States production in 1949; this was also nearly 2 per cent of the world production for that year. Illinois has produced gas commercially since 1885 and oil since 1889. Between 1907 and 1914, Illinois ranked third among the oil-producing states, its annual output being exceeded only by that of California and Oklahoma. The first peak was reached in 1908 with a yield of nearly 4 million barrels. Subsequently, production declined until 1936, when new discoveries in the Illinois basin led to a spectacular increase and a second, much higher, peak in 1940. During that year, the production reached nearly 148 million barrels of oil, and Illinois was in fourth place among oil-producing states.

The tectonic map of Illinois shows a spoon-shaped basin with the deepest part of the bowl in the southeastern corner and with the long axis of the depression extending in a direction a little west of north and rising to the north. From the deepest point, the strata ascend gently toward the Ozark uplift on the west, the Wisconsin shield to the north, and the Findlay arch to the east. The eastward flank is interrupted northeast of the deepest part of the basin by the La Salle anticline, which generally parallels the basin axis both in direction and in plunge. Two much more local, but nonetheless prominent, anticlines, the Louden and the Salem, lie on the west flank of the basin. Extensive preglacial erosion planed off the surface in the Illinois area, exposing successively older rocks outward from the center of the basin, especially to the north toward the Wisconsin boundary. Subsequently, the great ice sheets deposited an average thickness of 100 feet of drift over practically the entire state of Illinois. As a consequence, the two most widely used and most successful prospecting methods for petroleum and natural gas are subsurface geology and the reflection seismograph.

The oil and gas fields of Illinois fall naturally into three geographic and geologic divisions: (1) the fields, oldest in time of discovery, which

[40] Alfred H. Bell, "Origin of the Oil and Gas Reservoirs of the Eastern Interior Coal Basin in Relation to the Accumulation of Oil and Gas," *Problems of Petroleum Geology* (Am. Assoc. Petrol. Geol., 1934), pp. 557–569; J. M. Weller and A. H. Bell, "Illinois Basin," *Bull. Am. Assoc. Petrol. Geol.,* Vol. 21 (June, 1937), pp. 771–788; Alfred H. Bell and R. E. Esarey, "Developments in Illinois and Indiana in 1949," *Bull. Am. Assoc. Petrol. Geol.,* Vol. 34 (June, 1950), pp. 1078–1089.

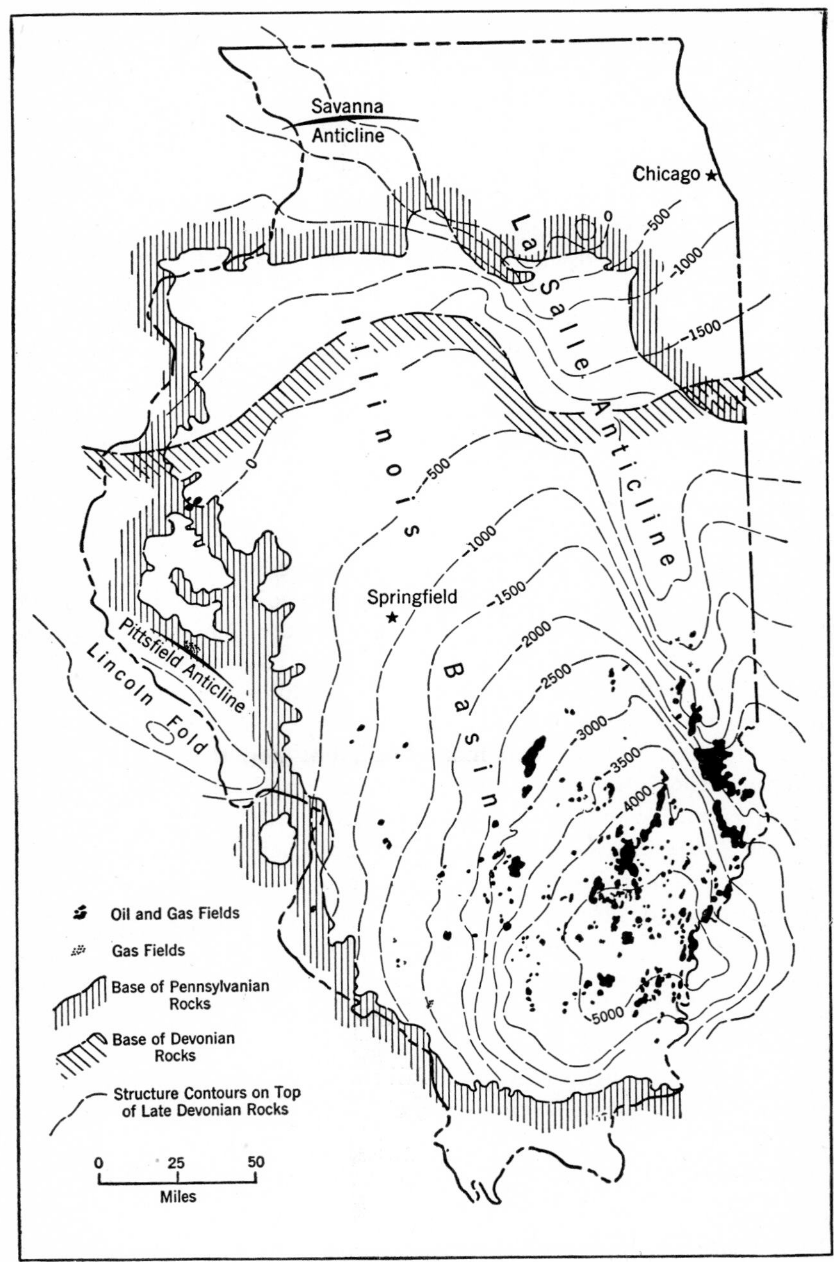

FIG. 104. Illinois. Major structural features and oil and gas fields.

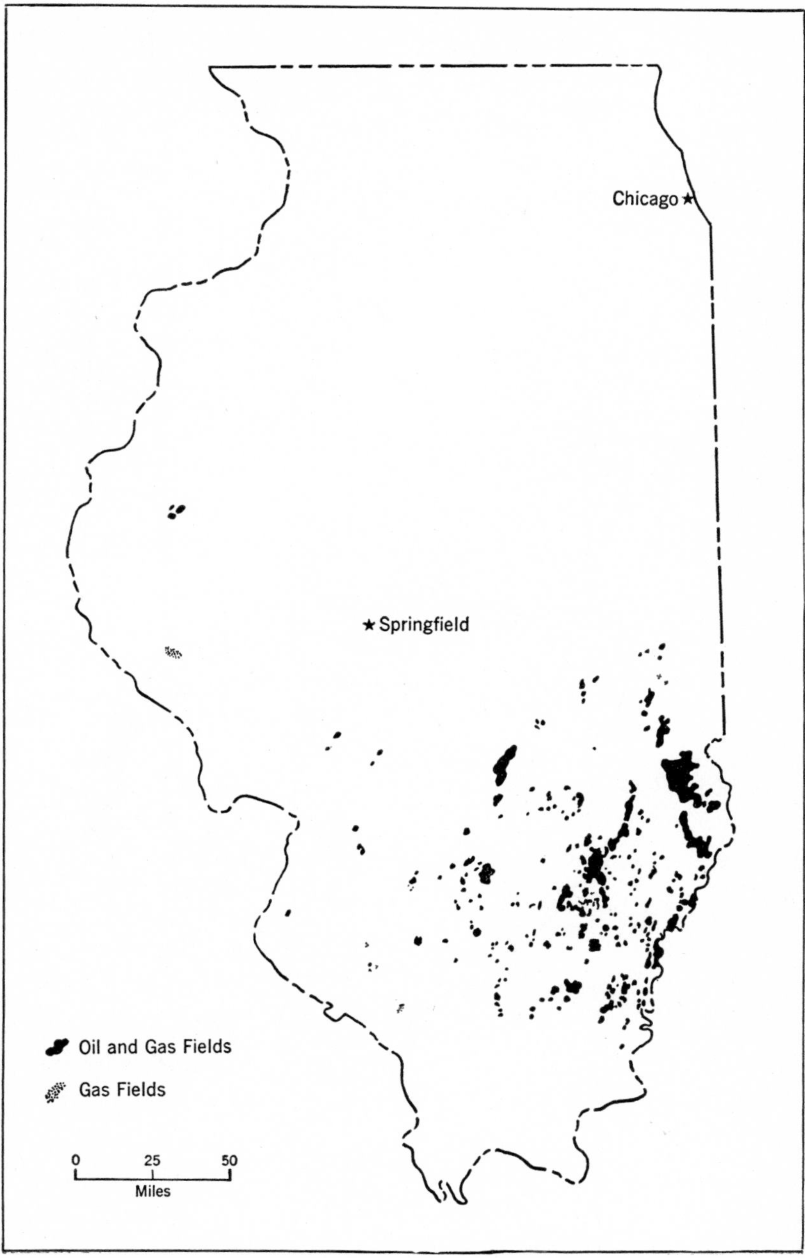

FIG. 105. Illinois. Oil and gas fields.

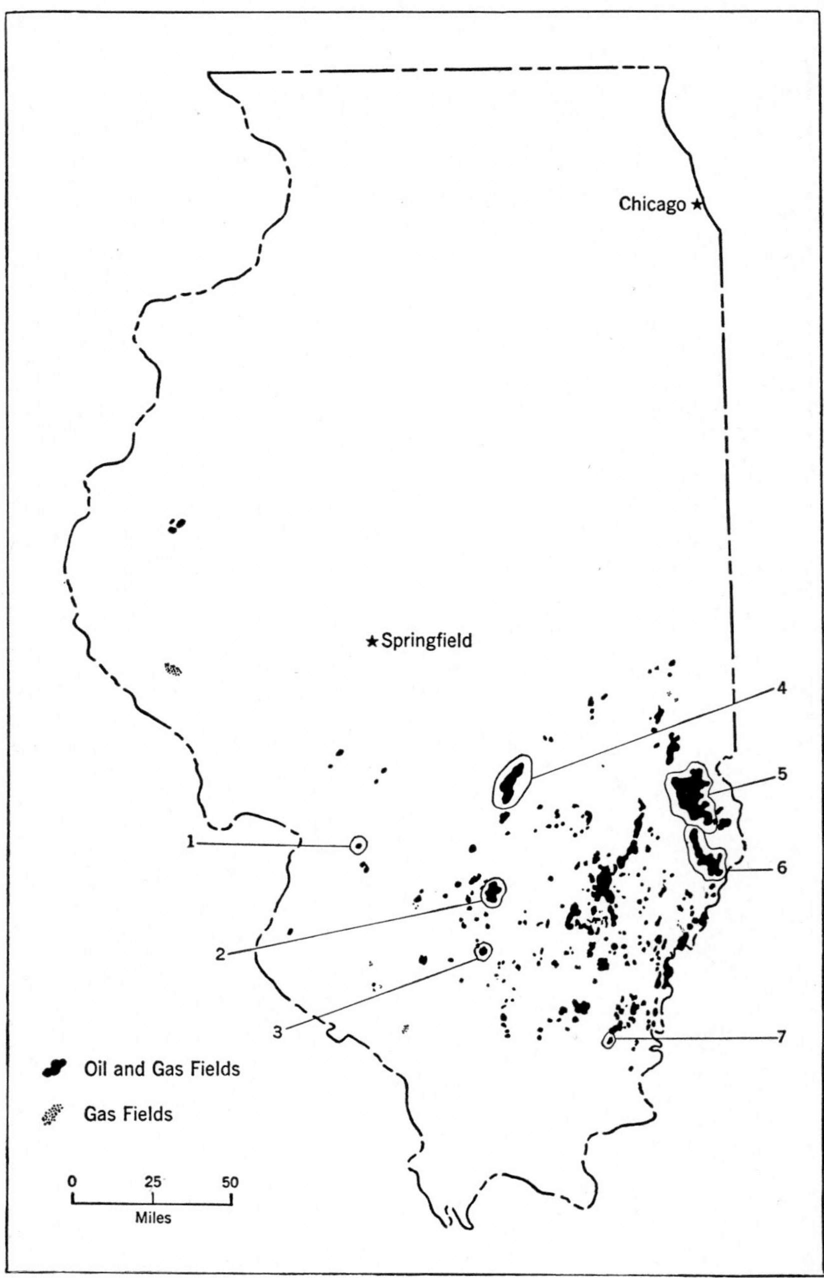

FIG. 106. Illinois index map. 1, Marine oil field; 2, Salem oil field; 3, Benton oil field; 4, Louden oil field; 5, Robinson oil field; 6, Bridgeport oil field; 7, Omaha oil field.

occupy the La Salle anticlinal belt toward its southern end; (2) the "basin" fields,[41] which lie in the deeper part of the Illinois basin immediately to the west of the La Salle anticline; and (3) the "western" Illinois fields which lie on the west flank of the basin. Older major fields are the Bridgeport and Robinson, which produce from Pennsylvanian reservoirs high on the La Salle anticline and which were discovered in 1906; examples of newer major fields are the Louden, discovered in 1937, and the Salem, discovered in 1938. Both these fields lie on the west flank and produce principally from Mississippian reservoirs.

Hake [42] in 1942 listed about 20 reservoir rocks that are productive in Illinois. Discoveries since that date have increased this number. The producing formations range in age from the lower Pennsylvanian down to the Ordovician, but in recent years both upper and lower Mississippian reservoir rocks have been outstanding in importance. Bell [43] estimated that in 1948 about 88 per cent of the total Illinois production came from Mississippian reservoirs, about 5.5 per cent from Pennsylvanian rocks, 3.7 per cent from the Devonian, 1.8 per cent from the Silurian, and 1.2 per cent from the Ordovician. The Ordovician reservoir is the Trenton,[44] which is the great reservoir in the Lima-Indiana district to the east where it lies much closer to the surface.

By far the greater part of the oil and gas so far discovered in Illinois has been trapped in anticlines. One of the most important oil accumulations in Illinois is that of the Salem field in Marion County.[45] The position of the Salem anticline is shown on the Illinois tectonic map (Fig. 104). To the north in Fayette County, but on the same trend, is the Louden field, with the oil occupying the Louden anticline.

The Salem field was discovered on July 1, 1938; six months later it ranked seventh in the United States on the basis of daily production, and two years later, after the rapid development of a prolific but short-lived Devonian reservoir beneath the original Mississippian producing zones, it ranked second.

41 Lynn K Lee, "Geology of Basin Fields in Southeastern Illinois," *Bull. Am. Assoc. Petrol. Geol.,* Vol. 23 (October, 1939), pp. 1493–1506.

42 B. F. Hake, "Geologic Distribution of Oil in The Illinois Basin," Am. Petrol. Inst., preprint Pittsburgh Meeting, 1942.

43 Alfred H. Bell, "Illinois Oil and Gas Field Development 1948," *Yearbook National Oil Scouts and Landmen's Association,* Vol. 19 (1949), p. 136.

44 George V. Cohee, "Trenton Production in Illinois," *Ill. Geol. Survey, Press Bull.* No. 39 (Sept. 13, 1941).

45 H. H. Arnold, Jr., "Salem Oil Field, Marion County, Illinois," *Bull. Am. Assoc. Petrol. Geol.,* Vol. 23 (September, 1939), pp. 1352–1373.

The field covers an area of about 14 square miles, and the anticline has closure at reservoir level of over 200 feet. Although permeability controls to some extent the distribution of oil in the reservoirs, the trapping is entirely anticlinal.

Three sandstones, the Benoist, Renault, and Aux Vases, of Chester (upper Mississippian) age, separated by only a few feet of shale and possessing a common oil-water contact, form the highest and most important group of reservoirs. The three formations are all interrupted by tight silty or shaly streaks, and only about half of their total thickness of 120 feet is effective reservoir rock. The next lower major reservoir is the McClosky oölitic limestone of lower Mississippian age, the most productive reservoir in Illinois but, in the Salem field, second in importance to the Chester sandstones. Lenses of porous oölitic limestone average about 15 feet thick in the Salem field. A sandy dolomite of Devonian age is productive beneath about 60 per cent of the total productive area in the Mississippian, and Trenton limestone produces beneath a quarter of the field from a depth of 4500 feet, the deepest production in Illinois.

The Benton field [46] occupies a considerably smaller anticline to the south in Franklin County. The reservoir rock at Benton is the Tar Springs sandstone of Chester (upper Mississippian) age. The trapping is anticlinal, but at the south end of the anticline there is abrupt gradation from sand to shale. Since the Benton field lies in an active coal-mining district, it was necessary to drill many of the wells through either operating or abandoned coal mines. For the operating mines, accurate maps were available, and the wells were located so as to pass through the centers of pillars at least 40 feet across instead of through mine openings. Where the mine had been abandoned and an accurate map showing the rooms and pillars was not available, considerable trouble occurred until a technique was developed for meeting this situation.

The Marine pool,[47] a limestone reef producer, was described and illustrated in the preceding chapter (Fig. 43) as an example of dome accumulation. Marine is typical of the three or four producing reefs so far discovered in Illinois,[48] and even in this field most of the oil has

[46] J. V. Howell, "Geology of Benton Field, Franklin County, Illinois," *Bull. Am. Assoc. Petrol. Geol.*, Vol. 32 (May, 1948), pp. 745–766.

[47] H. A. Lowenstam, "Marine Pool, Madison County, Illinois, Silurian Reef Producer," *Structure of Typical American Oil Fields* (Am. Assoc. Petrol. Geol., 1948), Vol. 3, pp. 153–188.

[48] H. A. Lowenstam, "Niagaran Reefs in Illinois and Their Relation to Oil Accumulation," *Ill. Geol. Survey, Rept. of Investigations* No. 145, 1950.

accumulated not in the reef itself but in the overlying detrital zone, which is anticlinal in structure because of the convex topographic surface of the reef. Another unusual field is the Omaha pool [49] in Gallatin County, near the southeast corner of Illinois. This extremely symmetrical dome contains igneous sills and dikes and is, in all probability, the result of upward pushing on the part of a laccolith or other type of subjacent intrusion. It also is illustrated in Chapter 8 (Fig. 30).

Michigan [50]

(Figures 107–109)

In recent years, Michigan has contributed about 1 per cent of the annual petroleum production in the United States. Oil was first discovered in this state at Port Huron in 1886, but it was not until 1926 that any substantial production was obtained, owing to the discovery the year before of oil at Saginaw. The Muskegon field was found in 1927, and Mt. Pleasant, the first of the important basin fields, was discovered in 1928. The most recent activity has been in the western side of the state, where several new pools have been discovered since 1946.

The regional structure of the southern peninsula of Michigan, which contains all the oil and gas fields so far discovered, is very simple. This area is an almost perfectly circular structural basin. The crystalline basement rocks, pre-Cambrian in age, crop out around the north rim of the basin in Wisconsin, the northern peninsula of Michigan, and Ontario. In the center of the basin, which is in the southern peninsula, the top of the pre-Cambrian rock lies at a probable depth of 14,000 feet. Erosion has not uncovered the basement rocks around the south rim of the Michigan basin, but formations as old as Ordovician are exposed there. The southern end of the Michigan basin lies inside the fork formed by the Kankakee and Findlay branches of the Cincinnati arch; the top of the arch forms the south rim.[51] The

[49] R. M. English and R. M. Grogan, "Omaha Pool and Mica-Peridotite Intrusives, Gallatin County, Illinois," *Structure of Typical American Oil Fields* (Am. Assoc. Petrol. Geol., 1948), Vol. 3, pp. 189–212.

[50] B. F. Hake, "Geologic Occurrence of Oil and Gas in Michigan," *Bull. Am. Assoc. Petrol. Geol.,* Vol. 22 (April, 1938), pp. 393–415; R. B. Newcombe, "Structure and Accumulation in the Michigan 'Basin' and Its Relation to the Cincinnati Arch," *Problems of Petroleum Geology* (Am. Assoc. Petrol. Geol., 1934), pp. 531–556; Richard H. Wolcott, "Developments in Michigan in 1949," *Bull. Am. Assoc. Petrol. Geol.,* Vol. 34 (June, 1950), pp. 1090–1096.

[51] George W. Pirtle, "Michigan Structural Basin and Its Relation to Surrounding Areas," *Bull. Am. Assoc. Petrol. Geol.,* Vol. 16 (February, 1932), pp. 145–152.

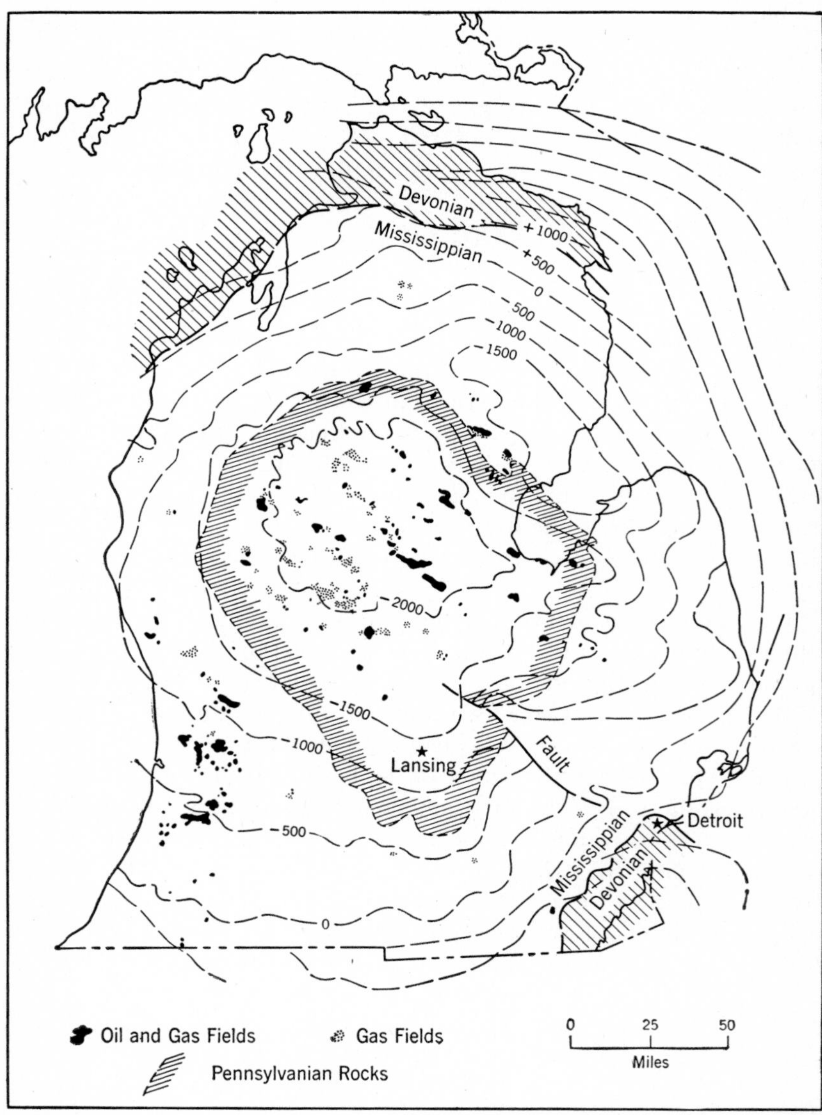

FIG. 107. Michigan. Structure contour map of Southern Peninsula. Also shown are Pennsylvanian rocks in center of basin and Mississippian-Devonian boundary toward rim. Contour datum is the top of the Dundee (Devonian) formation.

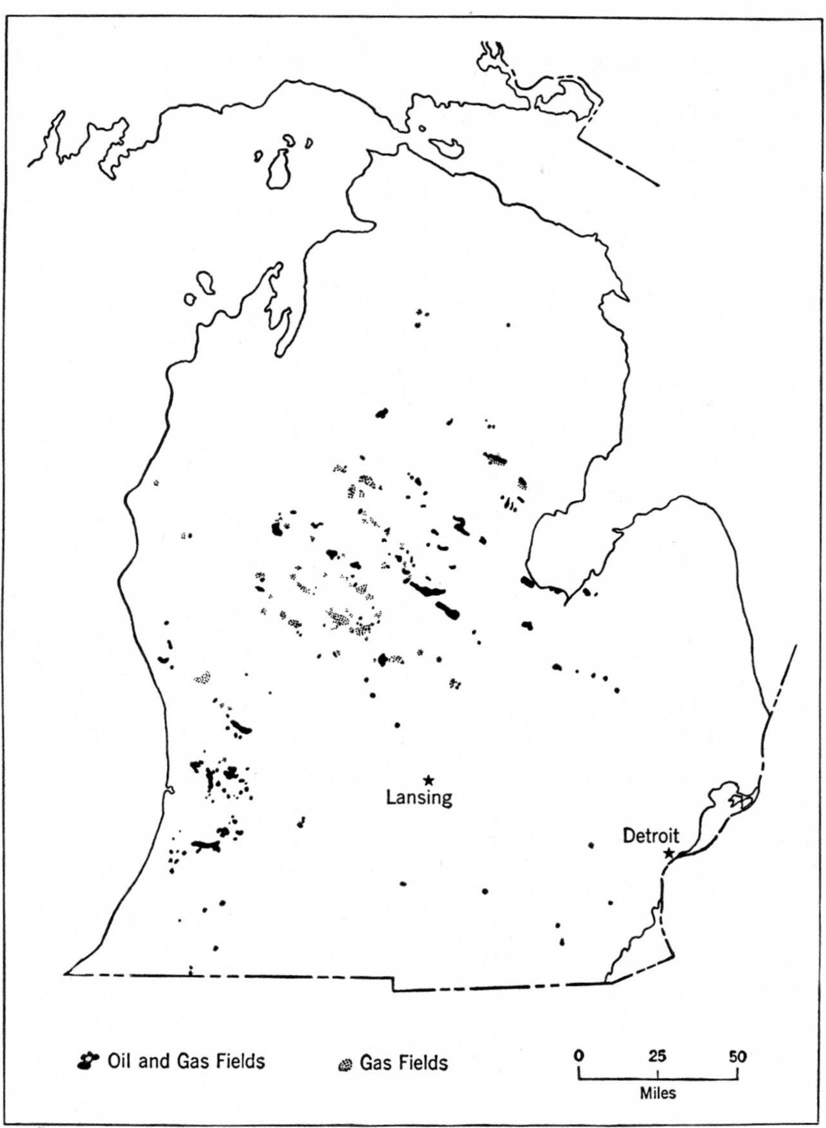

Fig. 108. Michigan. Oil and gas fields.

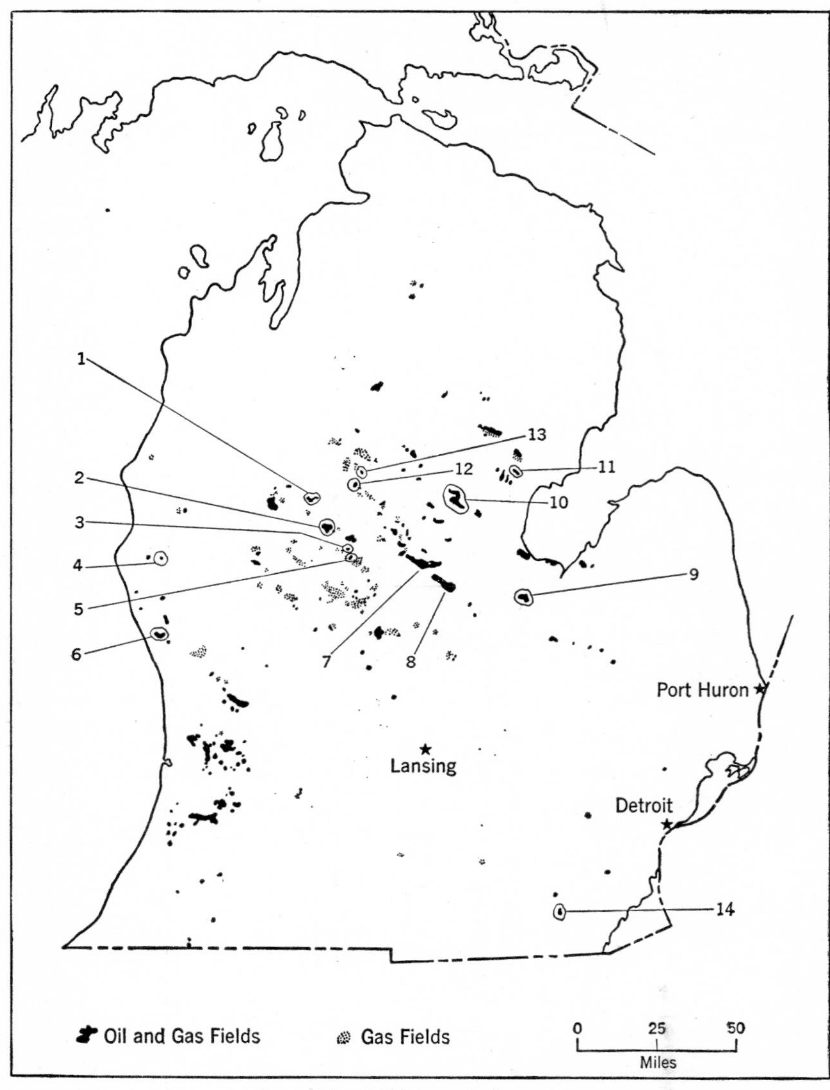

Fig. 109. Michigan index map.

1, Evart oil field.
2, Fork oil field.
3, Coldwater oil field.
4, Pentwater oil field.
5, Sherman oil field.
6, Muskegon oil field.
7, Mt. Pleasant oil field.
8, Porter oil field.
9, Saginaw oil field.
10, Buckeye oil field.
11, Deep River oil field.
12, Temple oil field.
13, Winterfield oil field.
14, Deerfield oil field.

southeastern flank of the Michigan basin contains the Howell anticline and fault; less prominent anticlines and terraces occur on the other flanks.

Toward the center of the Michigan basin the youngest bedrock formations are Pennsylvanian sediments which are covered by up to 800 feet of glacial drift. The areal geologic map shows a succession of older rocks in circular patterns surrounding the Pennsylvanian outcrop. The oldest rocks to reach the bedrock surface in the southern peninsula are Silurian, but in the northern peninsula the exposed Paleozoic section extends down to the pre-Cambrian. Within the basin several rock groups, notably the evaporite-containing Salina (Silurian) and Detroit River (Devonian), thicken greatly between outcrop zone and basin center. During these times, and to a somewhat lesser extent during several other sedimentation periods, the Michigan basin was sinking concurrently with the deposition of clastic, organic, and chemical sediment.

Ninety-nine per cent of the Michigan oil at present comes from carbonate rock reservoirs of Devonian age. The principal reservoir rock is the Dundee limestone; the overlying Traverse group is second and the underlying Detroit River group third. The greatest increase in recent years has been in Detroit River production. A small amount of oil has been produced from the Trenton dolomite in southeastern Michigan, and at least one field has produced commercially from the Berea sandstone of Mississippian age.

Gas is much more abundant than oil in sandstone reservoirs in Michigan. It has been found in the Berea and especially in the so-called "stray" sands of younger Mississippian age. A gas field is currently being developed along the Howell anticline in basal Salina (Silurian) dolomite.

The trapping of hydrocarbons in Michigan is mainly, but by no means exclusively, anticlinal. The central and southern parts of the Michigan basin are crossed by a series of parallel northwest-southeast anticlinal trends. Six or more of these have been mapped, and most of the Michigan basin oil so far discovered has accumulated in the structurally higher places along the anticlinal axes. In the northern part of the southern peninsula, the trends appear to change direction to northeast-southwest. As a general rule, the local anticlines are from 4 to 6 miles in length and from 1 to 1½ miles wide. They tend to be asymmetrical, with the deeper flank toward the basin, probably because of continued basin sagging after the anticline was formed.

The dips, even on the steeper side, rarely exceed 200 feet to the mile, and most of the closures fall between 50 and 100 feet.

The greater part of Michigan's current oil and gas production comes from three districts, of which the basin district is the largest. This district includes all the counties surrounding the central part of the basin. The western Michigan district lies to the west adjacent to the shores of Lake Michigan, and the southwestern Michigan district is south of the western Michigan district. Most of the oil in the southwestern Michigan district comes from Traverse rocks, whereas Dundee and Detroit River rocks are the principal reservoirs in the western Michigan and basin districts.

Because most of the outcrops in the southern peninsula of Michigan are around the periphery of the basin and not down the flanks where the reservoir rocks lie at adequate depth, it has not been possible to use surface methods of oil exploration. Furthermore, in many parts of the state the veneer of glacial drift is so thick that even the reflection seismograph and other geophysical instruments have not been successful prospecting tools. In a few areas, however, as in the Thumb and along the west shore of Saginaw Bay, the drift is thin enough so that some success has been possible with the reflection seismograph. With this exception, all the oil-finding in Michigan that has had the benefit of scientific guidance has been by means of subsurface geology. Where well data have not been adequate, the core drill has been used. The first discoveries in the basin area were made by means of the geologic data obtained during the drilling of brine wells. The more recent discoveries in western Michigan have been the result of an intensive core-drilling campaign.

Typical anticlinal accumulations in Michigan are the Muskegon,[52] Buckeye,[53] and Porter [54] oil fields. The Muskegon oil field was discovered in 1927 and was the first field of any appreciable size to be discovered in the state. The anticlinal trap is an irregular dome with some 60 to 70 feet of closure. The reservoir rocks are porous limestones of Devonian age. The Buckeye field consists of two oil pools occupying separate domes. Although the two domes are comparable in size and closure, the production of the north dome has been nearly four times as great as that of the south dome. This difference is

[52] R. B. Newcombe, "Geology of Muskegon Oil Field, Muskegon, Michigan," *Bull. Am. Assoc. Petrol. Geol.,* Vol. 16 (February, 1932), pp. 153–168.

[53] Carl C. Addison, "Buckeye Oil Field, Gladwin County, Michigan," *Bull. Am. Assoc. Petrol. Geol.,* Vol. 24 (November, 1940), pp. 1950–1982.

[54] Kenneth K. Landes, "Porter Oil Field, Midland County, Michigan," *Bull. Am. Assoc. Petrol. Geol.,* Vol. 28 (February, 1944), pp. 173–196.

attributed to changes in porosity and permeability over that short distance. The Porter field, the largest in cumulative production, was used to illustrate anticlinal trapping in Chapter 8 (Fig. 41).

A fairly recent discovery, the Pentwater field in Oceana County, on the Lake Michigan shore, produces from both the Traverse and the underlying Dundee. The Traverse pool is smaller, but the producing zone is thicker, with consequent anticipated higher per acre recovery. The Dundee production is from crystalline dolomite in the top 20 feet of the formation in a structure with only 15 feet of productive closure.[55]

Michigan is not without some unusual examples of trapping by varying permeability. Much of the natural gas in the state is produced from shoestring sands of Mississippian age.[56] Furthermore, the state contains several excellent examples of dolomitization porosity with oil accumulation confined to the dolomitized zones. Accumulation of this type at the Deep River field[57] was described in Chapter 8 (Fig. 73). Deep River was the leading Michigan field in annual production in 1949. The nearby and older Adams field exhibits exactly the same type of trapping. The Deerfield pool[58] near the southeastern corner of the state is the only Trenton producer and is actually an outlier of the Lima-Indiana district, in which the accumulation is due to local dolomitization. According to Addison,[59] the Sherman, Coldwater, Fork, Evart, Winterfield, and Temple fields are typical examples of the accumulation of oil in openings produced during dolomitization.

Nebraska

(Figure 110)

Although Nebraska is floored entirely with sedimentary rock, it has not had many oil or gas discoveries as yet and its contribution to the oil production of the United States has been negligible. The northward extension of the Nemaha uplift crosses southeastern Nebraska,

[55] Manley Osgood, Jr., "Developments in Michigan in 1948," *Bull. Am. Assoc. Petrol. Geol.,* Vol. 33 (June, 1949), pp. 877–882.

[56] Max W. Ball, T. J. Weaver, H. D. Crider, Douglas S. Ball, "Shoestring Gas Fields of Michigan," *Stratigraphic Type Oil Fields* (Am. Assoc. Petrol. Geol., 1941), pp. 237–266.

[57] Raymond S. Hunt, "Deep River Field, Michigan—Unique Example of Persistent Exploration," *Ind. Petrol. Assoc. Am. Monthly,* Vol. 19 (April, 1949), pp. 15 *et seq.*

[58] George D. Lindberg, "Deerfield Oil Field, Monroe County, Michigan," *Structure of Typical American Oil Fields* (Am. Assoc. Petrol. Geol., 1948), Vol. 3, pp. 305–318.

[59] Carl C. Addison, quoted in Kenneth K. Landes, "Porosity through Dolomitization," *Bull. Am. Petrol. Geol.,* Vol. 30 (March, 1946), p. 306.

and the northwestward extension of the Central Kansas uplift, which is known in western Nebraska as the Chadron arch, extends across that end of the state to the Black Hills uplift. The state contains parts of three basins, in two of which oil has been discovered. These are the northern extension of the Forest City basin of northeastern Kansas, which occupies the southeastern corner of Nebraska, and the western flank of the Denver basin, which lies west of the Cambridge

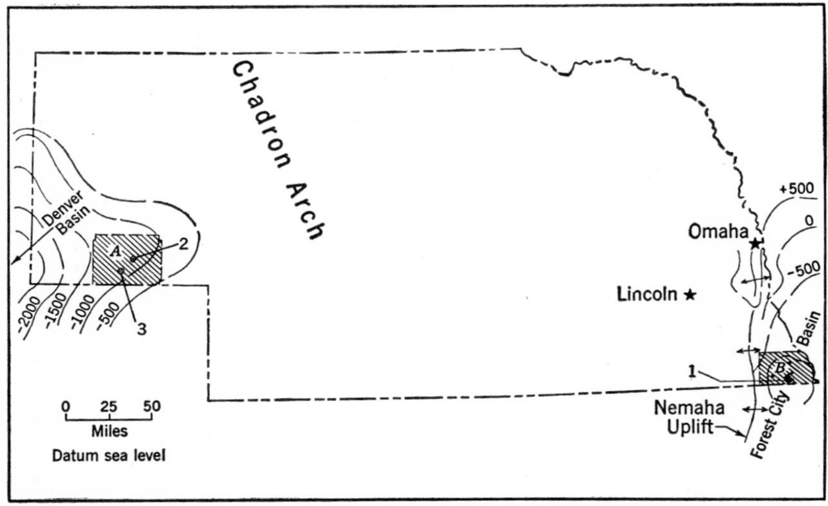

FIG. 110. Nebraska index map. *A*, Cheyenne County; *B*, Richardson County; 1, Falls City oil field; 2, Gurley oil field; 3, Huntsman gas field.

arch. Central and northern Nebraska are high on the rather indefinite south flank of the Williston basin of North and South Dakota.

The Falls City pool in Richardson County in southeastern Nebraska was discovered in 1939. Later three other pools were discovered in the same county. The principal reservoir rock is the Hunton limestone of Siluro-Devonian age. Trapping is anticlinal. Production declined fairly rapidly in each of the southeastern Nebraska fields soon after discovery.

The Nebraska corner of the Denver basin was the scene of an oil discovery during 1949. The pool, which has been named the Gurley, is in Cheyenne County. The discovery well had an initial production of 225 barrels per day from the First Dakota sandstone at a depth of 4400 feet. The third well drilled in this field found oil in the Third Dakota sandstone, 90 feet lower. Early in 1950 the Huntsman gas field, 8 miles to the southwest, was discovered. The Huntsman anticline is reported to have more than 100 feet of closure. An initial productive capacity of over 50 million cubic feet per day from the Third Dakota sand is indicated.[60]

A field as yet (June, 1950) unnamed has been discovered in Harlan County in south-central Nebraska.[61] The initial well was drilled one-half mile north of the Kansas line and 6 miles north of the nearest pre-existing oil field. This area is on the Central Kansas uplift.

Kansas [62]

(Figures 111–113)

During 1949, Kansas produced over 5½ per cent of the country's oil and about 3 per cent of the world's oil output. Exploration for oil and gas began in this state in 1860, and commercial production of natural gas has been continuous since 1886 and that of crude oil since 1889. Although Kansas was never in first rank among oil states, it did produce over 90 per cent of the Mid-Continent and Gulf Coast oil between 1889 and 1897. The first discoveries were made close to the eastern edge of the state, and for the first 33 years the production was largely from eastern Kansas. During that time, the great Eldorado and Augusta pools of Butler County and the prolific shoestring sand fields of Greenwood County were discovered and developed. In 1923, oil was found in the Fairport pool of Russell County in western Kansas, over 100 miles to the northwest of the nearest oil field. Subsequently, discoveries not only have filled in the greater part of the intervening space but also have spread to the southwest and west, so that today 69 out of 105 counties produce either oil or gas or both, and the list grows yearly.

Although most of the discoveries of recent years have been in western Kansas (as many as fourteen new fields in a single county in one year),

[60] William L. Herschman, "Drilling in Western Nebraska," *Oil and Gas Jour.*, Vol. 48 (May 4, 1950), pp. 146–148.

[61] Anon., "South-Central Nebraska Gets Oil," *Oil and Gas Jour.*, Vol. 49 (June 29, 1950), p. 113.

[62] W. A. Ver Wiebe, J. M. Jewett, and E. K. Nixon, "Oil and Gas Developments in Kansas During 1948," *Kans. Geol. Survey, Bull.* 78, 1949; J. M. Jewett, "Oil and Gas in Eastern Kansas," *Kans. Geol. Survey, Bull.* 77, 1949; J. M. Jewett and R. Kenneth Smith, "Oil-Bearing Rocks in Kansas," *Mines Mag.*, Vol. 39 (December, 1949), pp. 85 *et seq.*; J. H. Page, "Larger Gas Fields in Kansas," *Bull. Am. Assoc. Petrol. Geol.*, Vol. 24 (October, 1940), pp. 1779–1797; J. Robert Berg, "Developments in North Mid-Continent in 1949," *Bull. Am. Assoc. Petrol. Geol.*, Vol. 34 (June, 1950), pp. 1097–1105.

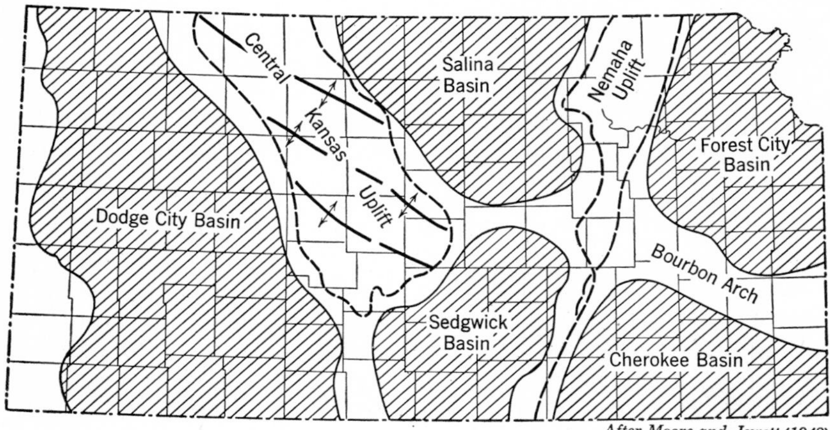

FIG. 111. Kansas. Early Pennsylvanian structural provinces. *Courtesy Mines Magazine.*

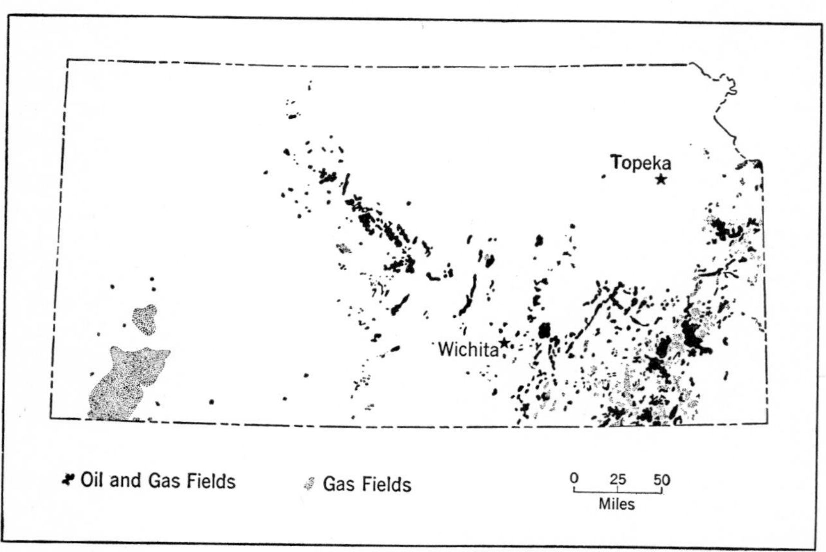

FIG. 112. Kansas. Oil and gas fields.

none of the newer discoveries has as yet surpassed in cumulative production the Eldorado field of eastern Kansas, and fields are still being found in that area. Considerable excitement was caused early in 1949 by the discovery of a new oil field in Wabaunsee County in northeastern Kansas.

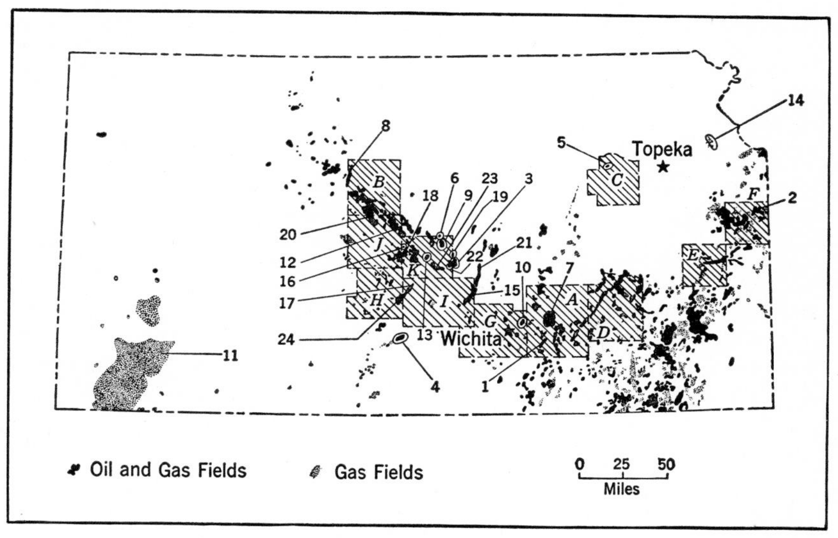

FIG. 113. Kansas index map.

A, Butler County.
B, Russell County.
C, Wabaunsee County.
D, Greenwood County.
E, Anderson County.
F, Miami County.
G, Sedgwick County.
H, Stafford County.
I, Reno County.
J, Barton County.
K, Rice County.

1, Augusta field.
2, Big Lake field.
3, Bornholdt field.
4, Cunningham field.
5, Davis Ranch field.
6, Edwards field.
7, Eldorado field.
8, Fairport field.
9, Geneseo field.
10, Greenwich field.
11, Hugoton gas field.
12, Kraft-Prusa field.
13, Lyons gas field.
14, McLouth gas field.
15, Nikkel field.
16, Orth field.
17, Peace Creek field.
18, Silica field.
19, Smyres field.
20, Trapp field.
21, Voshell field.
22, Welch field.
23, Wherry field.
24, Zenith field.

The bed rock is widely exposed in eastern Kansas, and most of the earlier finds of oil and gas in this area were the direct result of surface structure mapping. Modern and ancient floodplains, dune and loess deposits, and Tertiary rocks of continental origin mask the bed rock over much of the western two-thirds of the state, and so most of the discoveries there have been due to core-drill surveys, subsurface geology, and geophysical exploration. In recent years, most of the new finds have been credited to subsurface geology, although the core drill is still being used, and seismic and gravimetric surveys have also contributed to the list of discoveries. The new field in Wabaunsee County was found as a result of surface structure mapping, and in consequence the plane table and alidade once more have been restored as a prospecting method in this area.

Geographically, the Kansas oil fields are included in the northern Mid-Continent province; geologically, Kansas lies within the western Interior coal basin. This coal basin is bounded on the north by the Wisconsin shield, on the east by the Ozark uplift, and on the south by the Ouachita and Arbuckle-Amarillo uplifts, but the western boundary is rather indefinite. The Carboniferous coals do not extend very far west, but the structural basin continues westward until it merges with features belonging to the Rocky Mountain geosyncline.

Although the areal geologic map of Kansas shows the rock groups outcropping in bands which cross the state in a general north-south direction, with the oldest in the east and the youngest in the west, the truncation of westward-dipping strata in eastern Kansas and the general increase in topographic elevation across western Kansas make the three-dimensional picture of Kansas geology by no means simple.[63] The subsurface section contains some great unconformities, including especially the one that preceded the deposition of the Mississippian sediments. This unconformity can be observed by turning to the pre-Mississippian areal geologic map (Fig. 22). The most striking tectonic features in Kansas geology today are the Nemaha uplift and the Central Kansas uplift (Fig. 111). The Nemaha uplift crosses the state from north to south, and the axis plunges to the south. It was pushed up in post-Mississippian times, and extensive erosion in the early Pennsylvanian stripped off not only older Pennsylvanian sediments but also the Mississippian and Ordovician, so that along the axis in the northern higher parts of the uplift the later Pennsylvanian sediments rest directly upon pre-Cambrian crystalline rock. Farther down the flanks, or farther south, the same sediments overlie tilted and truncated Ordovician and Mississippian formations. Because the structure of the Nemaha uplift is reflected in the overlying sediments clear to the present surface, this great anticlinal ridge can be mapped by surface geologic methods.

The Central Kansas uplift is a much broader arch, but it has had a similar structural history. It also has a crystalline rock core and is

63 Raymond C. Moore and John M. Jewett, "Oil and Gas Fields of Kansas," *Mines Mag.*, Vol. 32 (October, 1942), pp. 481 *et seq.*

bordered by arched-up and beveled Ordovician and Mississippian sediments. It is crossed from northwest to southeast by three parallel anticlinal axes.

Five fairly distinct basins which contain a much more complete section of sedimentary rock surround the two uplifts. East of the Nemaha uplift, the Forest City basin occupies northeastern Kansas and extends over into northwestern Missouri, southeastern Nebraska, and southwestern Iowa. The Bourbon arch separates this basin from the Cherokee basin of southeastern Kansas and northeastern Oklahoma. Between the Nemaha uplift and the Central Kansas uplift are the Salina basin in the northern half of the state and the Sedgwick basin in the southern half. South and west of the Central Kansas uplift is the Hugoton embayment, formerly called the Dodge City basin, which is the northern extension of the Anadarko basin of western Oklahoma.

Although none of the Kansas sedimentary basins are deep in comparison with oil-producing basins in other states, the relatively thin sedimentary veneer which does occur in this state contains a large number of prolific oil and gas reservoir rocks.[64] These reservoirs range in age from pre-Cambrian to Cretaceous. The Cretaceous production consists of relatively insignificant amounts of gas found in the Pierre shale in northwestern Kansas. The great gas reservoirs of southwestern Kansas (Hugoton field) are carbonate rocks of Permian age. Throughout the earlier years, all the state's oil and gas came from rocks of Pennsylvanian age, but today only 22 per cent is derived from these rocks. There are many distinct reservoirs within the Pennsylvanian series of rocks. These include Pennsylvanian sandstones, especially lenticular sands in the Cherokee shale, which are the most prolific reservoirs in eastern Kansas, and younger Pennsylvanian limestones that produce large quantities of oil in some of the western Kansas fields. Mississippian rocks, which include the weathered "chat" (chert) at the top, the "Mississippi lime," and underlying sandstones, now produce about 10 per cent of the state's oil. The Siluro-Devonian Hunton and the Ordovician Viola and Simpson each produce about 5 per cent. The Hunton and Viola reservoirs are carbonate rocks, whereas the Simpson contains the St. Peter sandstone. Over half of the state's oil is currently coming from the Cambro-Ordovician Arbuckle dolomite, or "siliceous lime" formation. Some oil is also obtained from the basal Paleozoic sandstone, or conglomerate, which

[64] J. M. Jewett and R. Kenneth Smith, "Oil-Bearing Rocks in Kansas," *Mines Mag.*, Vol. 39 (December, 1949).

overlies the pre-Cambrian basement rock across the uplifts, and from cracks and crevices in the basement rock itself.

The Kansas oil and gas fields can be separated by districts based upon tectonic setting. The two uplift areas and the five basins described in a preceding paragraph all contain oil and gas fields.[65] In recent years, about two-thirds of the state's oil has come from the Central Kansas uplift district. Next in importance are the Sedgwick and Cherokee basins. The Nemaha uplift, at one time in first place, now produces only about 4 per cent of the state's oil. The Forest City, Dodge City, and Salina basins are as yet relatively minor sources of oil, but the Hugoton gas field in the Dodge City basin produces over 100 billion cubic feet of gas annually. The Sedgwick basin produces about 20 billion and the Central Kansas uplift about 12 billion cubic feet of gas in addition to their large oil yields.

Cherokee Basin. Most of the production in the Cherokee basin comes from Pennsylvanian reservoirs, although, in places, Mississippian and even Ordovician reservoirs are productive. The greater part of the oil and gas occurs in lenticular sandstones lying within the Cherokee shale. The shoestring sands of Greenwood County were described in Chapter 8 (Fig. 69) as an example of trapping in lenticular sandstone reservoirs.

Forest City Basin. The reservoirs in the Forest City basin in northeastern Kansas range from Pennsylvanian to Ordovician in age. This basin also contains a number of lenticular sand accumulations, some of them just as elongate as those of Greenwood County. They occur, however, in Pennsylvanian formations younger than the Cherokee. The shoestring sands of Anderson County have been described by Charles [66] and those in other northeastern Kansas counties by Rich.[67] Some of these pools were phenomenal in terms of percentage of investment return. The Big Lake pool of Miami County was exploited by wells drilled to an average depth of 400 feet, and each well had an initial production of about 400 barrels daily. The natural history of the trap in the McLouth gas field [68] is unusual. This field, discovered

[65] J. M. Jewett, "Review of Recent Oil and Gas Developments in Kansas," *Mines Mag.*, Vol. 37 (November, 1947), pp. 47 *et seq.*

[66] Homer H. Charles, "Oil and Gas Resources of Kansas; Anderson County," *Kans. Geol. Survey, Bull.* 6, Part 7 (1927).

[67] J. L. Rich, "Shoestring Sands of Eastern Kansas," *Bull. Am. Assoc. Petrol. Geol.*, Vol. 7 (March–April, 1923), pp. 103–113; "Further Observations on Shoestring Oil Pools of Eastern Kansas," *Bull. Am. Assoc. Petrol. Geol.*, Vol. 10 (June, 1926), pp. 568–580.

[68] Wallace Lee and Thomas G. Payne, "McLouth Gas and Oil Field, Jefferson and Leavenworth Counties, Kansas," *Kans. Geol. Survey, Bull.* 53, 1944.

in 1939, produces from a Pennsylvanian sandstone lying at the base of the Cherokee shale. Apparently the gas, with minor amounts of oil, was first trapped in an anticline, and then the oil beneath the gas dried out so that it made an effective seal between the underlying water and the overlying gas. Subsequently, regional tilting took place, but because of the locked-in nature of the hydrocarbons in the anticline, they have been unable to adjust to the new structural setting. The newest discovery in the Forest City basin, the Davis Ranch pool in Wabaunsee County,[69] is producing from the Viola (Ordovician) limestone in an anticlinal trap, the presence of which was discovered by surface structure mapping.

Nemaha Uplift. Along the axis of the Nemaha uplift most of the reservoirs are Ordovician, but off on the flanks, Mississippian rocks, as well as Ordovician, produce hydrocarbons. Nearly every pool in this district occupies a structural dome. Some are typical bald-headed structures, with trapping due to a combination of anticlinal folding plus overlap by impervious cap rock.

The Eldorado field [70] of Butler County, which flooded the domestic market in 1916, is the principal field of Kansas in terms of cumulative production, and in 1949 it was still producing enough oil to place it in seventh place in the state. This field directly overlies the "granite ridge" axis of the Nemaha uplift. The structure of the pre-Cambrian surface is reflected upward, producing a prominent upfold in the sedimentary rocks. The Eldorado anticline was first mapped by means of surface geology. The trapping at Eldorado is very similar to that in the Augusta field immediately to the south, which is illustrated and described in Chapter 8 (Fig. 39) as an example of anticlinal accumulation.

Sedgwick Basin. The Sedgwick basin, to the west of the Eldorado and Augusta fields and the Nemaha uplift, contains a number of important oil fields. Reservoirs range in age from Mississippian to Ordovician and include the Siluro-Devonian Hunton dolomite. Accumulation is largely anticlinal. The Voshell field [71] is a good example of anticlinal trapping. The structure is an elongate north-south anticline

[69] J. M. Jewett, "Oil Prospects in Eastern Kansas," *World Oil,* Vol. 130 (May, 1950), pp. 64–70.

[70] A. E. Fath, "Geology of the Eldorado Oil and Gas Field, Butler County, Kansas," *Kans. Geol. Survey, Bull.* 7 (1921); John R. Reeves, "Eldorado Oil Field, Butler County, Kansas," *Structure of Typical American Oil Fields* (Am. Assoc. Petrol. Geol., 1929), Vol. 2, pp. 160–167.

[71] T. C. Hiestand, "Voshell Field, McPherson County, Kansas," *Bull. Am. Assoc. Petrol. Geol.,* Vol. 17 (February, 1933), pp. 169–191.

with about 150 feet of closure. The fold appears to be as full of oil as its closure will permit. A fault along the west flank limits the production in that direction but has not been a cause of accumulation. The reservoir rocks are three limestones and sandstones ranging in age from Cambro-Ordovician to Mississippian.

The Voshell pool is but one of several accumulations along the trend of the Voshell anticline. The next pool to the south, the Nikkel,[72] illustrates a combination trap. The oil has moved up-dip to the west to the top of the Voshell anticline, but closure at the north end of the pool is obtained by the complete wedging-out of the Siluro-Devonian reservoir rock, the Hunton limestone. Anticlinal accumulation in the southeastern part of the Sedgwick basin is illustrated by the Greenwich pool [73] and by other pools along the same line of folding in Sedgwick County. On the northwest side of the Sedgwick basin, on the other hand, there is considerable trapping of the stratigraphic type where the lower Mississippian and Ordovician reservoirs, dipping off the Central Kansas uplift, have been truncated and overlapped. Examples are the Zenith pool [74] of Stafford County and the Peace Creek [75] field lying in Stafford and Reno counties. The Cunningham field [76] near the western edge of the Sedgwick basin is an anticlinal trap.

Salina Basin. The Salina basin district is still relatively insignificant as a producer of hydrocarbons. The reservoirs are similar to those in the Sedgwick basin, and accumulations are largely anticlinal.

Central Kansas Uplift. The prolific Central Kansas uplift district produces mostly from Ordovician reservoirs, but mid-Pennsylvanian formations are important carriers of oil in the northwestern part of the district. Accumulation is largely anticlinal, but around the periphery are many fields in which the oil has been trapped by wedgeout of the reservoir rock on the flanks of the uplift. In Chapter 8, one field used to illustrate accumulation of oil beneath unconformities was the Kraft-

[72] Arnold S. Bunte and Leo R. Fortier, "Nikkel Pool, McPherson and Harvey Counties, Kansas," *Stratigraphic Type Oil Fields* (Am. Assoc. Petrol. Geol., 1941), pp. 105–117.

[73] Arnold S. Bunte, "Subsurface Study of Greenwich Pool, Sedgwick County, Kansas," *Bull. Am. Assoc. Petrol. Geol.,* Vol. 29 (May, 1939), pp. 643–662.

[74] W. C. Imbt, "Zenith Pool, Stafford County, Kansas—An Example of Stratigraphic Trap Accumulation," *Stratigraphic Type Oil Fields* (Am. Assoc. Petrol. Geol., 1941), pp. 139–165.

[75] Joseph A. Kornfeld, "Peace Creek Field, A Stratigraphic Trap," *World Petroleum,* Vol. 14 (December, 1943), pp. 38–47.

[76] R. B. Rutledge and Howard S. Bryant, "Cunningham Field, Kingman and Pratt Counties, Kansas," *Bull. Am. Assoc. Petrol. Geol.,* Vol. 21 (April, 1937), pp. 500–524.

Prusa field (Fig. 78) of Barton County, which lies on the south limb of the uplift.

The Central Kansas district was discovered by the initial well of the Fairport pool, which was drilled in 1923. The Fairport anticline[77] (Fig. 7) is a very sharp elongate anticline with north-south trend which was recognized by surface mapping of the Cretaceous rocks. The structure is asymmetric, dipping much more steeply to the west than to the east, and increasing severalfold in magnitude with depth. Oil occurs in four porous zones in Pennsylvanian limestone. The discovery of Fairport led to many other discoveries in western Kansas on the Central Kansas uplift. Among the later fields is the Trapp in Russell and Barton counties which was found in 1936. Within a few years this field had become the leading producer in the state, and it still ranked first in 1949. The Trapp field is second only to El Dorado in cumulative production. The second field in Kansas in 1949 was the Kraft-Prusa, and the third was the Silica field in Barton and Rice counties which was discovered in 1931. These fields are also on the Central Kansas uplift. Near the southeast end of the uplift district some fields, including the Geneseo and Edwards oil fields and the Lyons gas field, are anticlinal accumulations, whereas other fields, lying still farther down the southeast flank of the uplift and including the Wherry, Welch, Bornholdt, and Smyres fields, owe their trapping to truncation and overlap of the pre-Pennsylvanian sediments flanking the uplift.[78]

The pool that really confounded and double-crossed the textbook writers is the Orth pool[79] of Rice County. The discovery well, drilled in 1932, produced at the rate of 1800 barrels daily from pre-Cambrian rock. Subsequently fourteen other oil wells were drilled into the pre-Cambrian and several gas wells were completed in the overlying Pennsylvanian sediments. The oil reservoir is the creviced top of the basement quartzite. The Orth pool is high on the Central Kansas uplift, and all the sedimentary veneer was stripped off by pre-Pennsylvanian erosion. The oil has probably migrated into the crevices in the pre-Cambrian rocks from topographically lower flanking sediments.

[77] Thomas H. Allan and M. M. Valerius, "Fairport Oil Field, Russell County, Kansas," *Structure of Typical American Oil Fields* (Am. Assoc. Petrol. Geol., 1929), Vol. 1, pp. 35–48.

[78] Stuart K. Clark, C. L. Arnett, and James S. Royds, "Geneseo Uplift, Rice, Ellsworth, and McPherson Counties, Kansas," *Structure of Typical American Oil Fields* (Am. Assoc. Petrol. Geol., 1948), Vol. 3, pp. 225–248; Harold E. McNeil, "Wherry Pool, Rice County, Kansas," *Stratigraphic Type Oil Fields* (Am. Assoc. Petrol. Geol., 1941), pp. 118–138.

[79] Walter A. Ver Wiebe, "Oil and Gas Resources of Western Kansas," *Kans. Geol. Survey, Min. Res. Circ.* 10 (1938), p. 108.

Hugoton Embayment. The major feature of the Dodge City basin is the Hugoton gas field which is described in Chapter 8 (Fig. 71) as an example of trapping by an up-dip facies change from pervious dolomite to impervious shaly carbonate rock. The dolomite is Permian in age.

Missouri

Although petroleum and natural gas have been produced intermittently in Missouri since 1899, the cumulative volume of both has been negligible.

Tectonically Missouri is dominated by the Ozark uplift, which has its highest point in the southeastern part of the state. The few and small oil and gas fields are concentrated on the northwest flank of the uplift near the Kansas line. Most of the oil wells have been in Cass and Jackson counties to the south of Kansas City. Gas also has been found in this area as well as in other small fields north of Kansas City. In 1942 the Tarkio pool was discovered in Atchison County in the northwest corner of the state. This is in the Forest City basin, which lies mainly in northeastern Kansas. Pennsylvanian sandstones and limestones are the reservoirs in all the fields so far discovered in Missouri. Trapping is mainly anticlinal, but the lenticularity of the Cherokee reservoir sands may also control accumulation.

Oklahoma [80]

(Figures 114–116)

About one-twelfth of the annual output of petroleum in the United States in recent years has come from Oklahoma. This state's share in the world's production amounted to 4.4 per cent in 1949. The discovery and development of oil fields in southern Kansas focused attention on the possibilities of Indian Territory (now northern Oklahoma) as early as 1884, but exploration was seriously impeded by the fact that most of the land belonged to various Indian tribes, and as a result the leasing was both involved and difficult. The first recorded crude-oil production in Oklahoma was in 1889, but the output was small until 1903, when a flowing well was struck near Bartlesville in Washington

[80] Alan G. Skelton and Martha B. Skelton, "A Bibliography of Oklahoma Oil and Gas Pools," *Okla. Geol. Survey, Bull.* 63 (1942); Robert H. Dott, "Discoveries Required to Maintain Status of Production in Oklahoma," *Oil Weekly* (Reprint), April 30, May 7, and May 14, 1934; J. F. Hardwick, "Developments in Oklahoma in 1949," *Bull. Am. Assoc. Petrol. Geol.*, Vol. 34 (June, 1950), pp. 1106–1122.

County in northeastern Oklahoma; after that the development of the state was rapid, and Oklahoma soon became a major producer.

Currently the greatest activity is in the Anadarko basin, which occupies the larger part of western Oklahoma. It has been reported that, in one group of eighteen deep wildcat wells drilled in this basin,

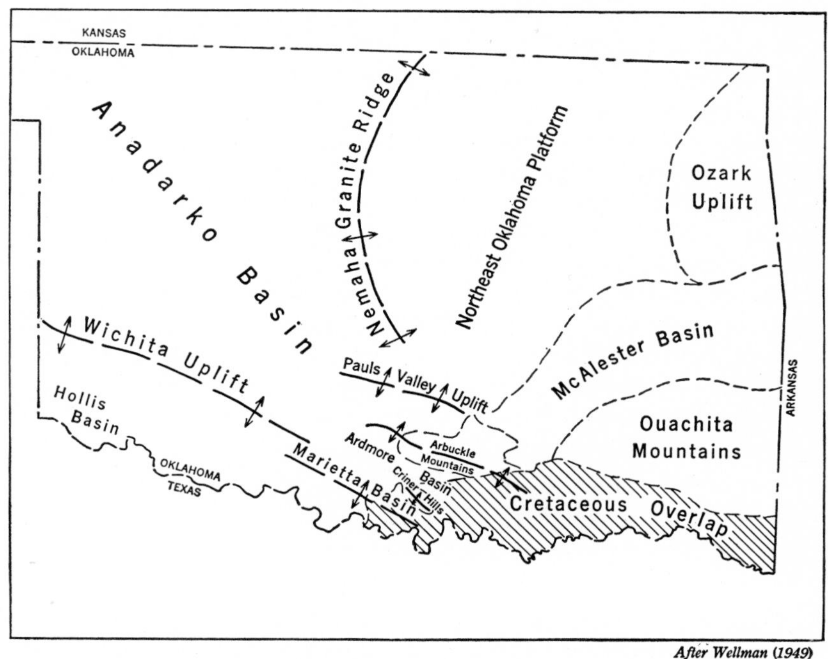

FIG. 114. Oklahoma (except panhandle). Major tectonic features. *Courtesy American Association of Petroleum Geologists.*

fifteen are opening up new oil fields.[81] Strikes are being made on the east, southeast, and south flanks of the Anadarko basin. Many new fields have been discovered in recent years in the southeast corner. This area is known as the southeastern embayment of the Anadarko basin, and it contains the "golden trend," a row of fields which crosses Garvin County from southeast to northwest and runs on into McClain and Grady counties. The producing formations are deep in the embayment, and one well is producing from a depth of 13,250 feet. The Ardmore basin, lying to the south of the southeast embayment,

[81] Anon., "Oklahoma: Fifty Years of Oil," *The Lamp,* Vol. 29 (November, 1947), p. 26.

has produced oil for many years and is also being successfully explored for deeper reservoirs.

Practically the entire evolution of prospecting techniques has taken place in Oklahoma. In the booming years from 1915 to 1920 the plane table and alidade were the tools of the geologist's trade, and during that relatively short space of time most of the bed-rock structures mappable by surface surveys were found. Subsequently and to some extent concurrently the core drill made its appearance, to be soon followed and in part superseded by geophysical instruments.

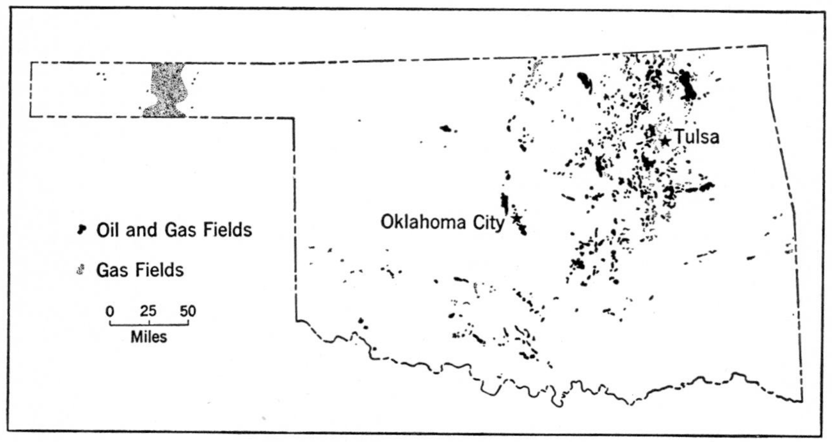

FIG. 115. Oklahoma. Oil and gas fields.

At present the seismograph is the most favored method of exploration in new territory, and the gravity meter is second in preference. Core drills are still employed in the western part of the state. New discoveries within the older districts have been largely due to subsurface geology.

Oklahoma contains examples of practically all types of tectonic features. It has major uplifts, basins of deposition, geosynclines that have been tightly folded and thrust-faulted, some profound unconformities, and convergence on a grand scale, and is even overlapped by sediments of the Gulf Coast embayment in the southeastern corner. Wellman [82] mapped fourteen distinct tectonic districts in Oklahoma (Fig. 114).

The major positive features in Oklahoma are the Ozark uplift to the northeast and the Ouachita-Arbuckle and Wichita uplifts in south-

[82] Dean C. Wellman, "Developments in Oklahoma in 1948," *Bull. Am. Assoc. Petrol. Geol.*, Vol. 33 (June, 1949), p. 894.

ern Oklahoma. The highest point on the Ozark uplift is in southern Missouri. Northeastern Oklahoma lies on the southwest flank of this

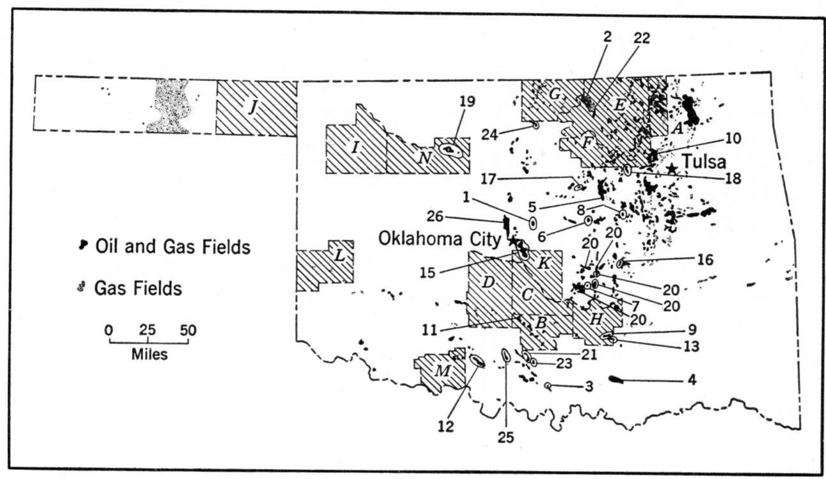

FIG. 116. Oklahoma index map.

A, Washington County.
B, Garvin County.
C, McClain County.
D, Grady County.
E, Osage County.
F, Pawnee County.
G, Kay County.
H, Pontotoc County.
I, Woodward County.
J, Beaver County.
K, Cleveland County.
L, Beckham County.
M, Cotton County.
N, Major County.

1, Arcadia-Coon Creek oil field.
2, Burbank oil field.
3, Crinerville oil field.
4, Cumberland oil field.
5, Cushing oil field.
6, Davenport oil field.
7, Dora oil field.
8, East Tuskogee oil field.
9, Fitts oil field.
10, Glenn oil field.
11, Golden Trend oil fields.
12, Healdton oil field.
13, Jesse oil field.
14, Morrison oil field.
15, Oklahoma City oil field.
16, Olympic oil field.
17, Ramsey oil field.
18, Red Fork oil field.
19, Ringwood oil field.
20, Greater Seminole oil field.
20*a*, Seminole City oil field.
20*b*, Earlsboro oil field.
20*c*, Bowlegs oil field.
20*d*, Little River oil field.
20*e*, Mission oil field.
20*f*, St. Louis oil field.
21, Sholem-Alechem oil field.
22, South Burbank oil field.
23, Tatums oil field.
24, Tonkawa oil field.
25, Velma oil field.
26, West Edmond oil field.

uplift. The Ouachita geosyncline and uplift crosses Arkansas and the eastern part of southern Oklahoma. It is succeeded to the west by the Arbuckle Mountain geosyncline and uplift, and the Wichita Mountains lie still farther to the west.

Major negative features in Oklahoma include especially the Anadarko basin which covers the greater part of western Oklahoma, the McAlester coal basin which lies immediately to the north of the Ouachita Mountains in east-central Oklahoma, and the Ardmore basin southwest of the Arbuckles. The Ardmore basin connects with the Anadarko basin to the northwest by a narrow passageway made possible by an offset between the Arbuckle and Wichita Mountain axes. The downwarp of the eastern part of southernmost Oklahoma permitted the invasion of Cretaceous seas during the early history of the Gulf embayment.

Two intermediate features are of utmost importance as oil-producing territory: the Northern Oklahoma platform and the Nemaha uplift. The former has been called the Hunton arch at its southern end north of the Arbuckle Mountains and the Chautauqua arch at its northern end. It is the structural divide between the McAlester basin on the east and the Anadarko basin on the west, and, at the same time, it is the saddle between the Arbuckle and the Ozark uplifts. The west side of the Northern Oklahoma platform is sharply delineated by the Nemaha Ridge. This uplift, which locally elevates the basement crystalline rocks some hundreds of feet above their normal levels, is a continuation of the feature of the same name in Kansas. Although buried to a greater depth than to the north, the Nemaha uplift in Oklahoma is very similar tectonically, including a series of faults along the crest with the dropped side to the east. The steep dips on the west side of the uplift lead directly into the Anadarko basin.

The geologic history of this part of the Mid-Continent has been marked by breaks in the depositional record accompanied by diastrophism, uplift, and erosion, which has resulted in several major unconformities. The greatest of these is the one beneath the Mississippian rocks; the pre-Chattanooga formations are truncated over a wide area (Fig. 22). The Ouachita geosyncline was an active trough of deposition in Pennsylvanian time, so that, while sediments of 2700 feet thick were being deposited in northern Oklahoma, 23,000 feet of rock were being laid down close to the axis of the Ouachita trough. The Pennsylvanian sediments also change in lithology from north to south; in northern Oklahoma they are mainly shales and limestones, and in the geosyncline they are shales and sandstones.

One major reason for the prolificacy of many of the Oklahoma oil pools is the large number of reservoirs that can be found in a single field. For example, the Cushing, Garber, East Seminole, and St.

Louis fields produce from at least six separate formations. Garber has produced from as many as fourteen different reservoirs. The age of the oil- and gas-producing rocks in Oklahoma range from Ordovician to Pennsylvanian. Most important are the "granite wash" at the base of the sedimentary section which is the reason for the active exploration today on the southwestern flank of the Anadarko basin, the Arbuckle, or "Siliceous Lime" of Cambro-Ordovician age, the Simpson formation (Ordovician) which contains the most productive oil reservoirs in the state, the Ordovician Viola limestone, the Siluro-Devonian Hunton limestone, various sandstones lying within the Cherokee shale of Pennsylvanian age which are prolific reservoirs in northeastern Oklahoma, and the Deese sandstones, also Pennsylvanian, which carry large quantities of oil in the southeastern part of the Anadarko basin.

As would be expected, the involved geological history of Oklahoma has presented this area with a considerable variety of accumulation traps. In the northern part of the Oklahoma platform, south of similar types of production in Kansas, the sandstone reservoirs lying within the Cherokee shale tend to be lenticular and even shoestring in form. Some of the great accumulations that focused attention on Oklahoma in the second decade of the present century are due to the up-dip wedgeout of thick Cherokee sandstones, or of the porosity within the sandstones. There are also anticlinal accumulations where these sandstones possess lateral continuity of porosity. The major unconformities are responsible for the trapping of oil in many fields, especially along the Nemaha uplift and to the south in the southeastern part in the Anadarko basin. Ordovician and Siluro-Devonian reservoir rocks wedge out beneath a cap of overlapping Pennsylvanian sediments in a part of this area, and in other places Pennsylvanian reservoirs abut against the flanks of hills composed of older rock.

The size and the unusual character of many of the varying-permeability-trap fields have given a very prominent place to this type of accumulation in Oklahoma. However, the simple, old-fashioned anticline has also produced much oil.[83] Most of the older fields of Oklahoma are of this type, and in some of the largest fields, including those composing the Seminole district, the greater part of the accumulation is anticlinal.

[83] Bess Mills-Bullard, "Oil and Gas in Oklahoma; Digest of Oklahoma Oil and Gas Fields," *Okla. Geol. Survey, Bull.* 40 Q (1928); C. W. Tomlinson, "Relation of Oil and Gas Accumulation to Geologic Structure in the Mid-Continent Region," *Problems of Petroleum Geology* (Am. Assoc. Petrol. Geol., 1934), pp. 571–579.

There is no universally accepted division of the oil and gas fields of Oklahoma by districts. In the regional survey that follows, the fields are grouped into districts based on geographic and tectonic position, plus the geologic age of the dominant reservoir rocks. The northeast Oklahoma platform is broken down into two districts, a northern and a southern. In the northern district the emphasis is on Cherokee sand reservoirs; in the southern, the greater part of the production comes from deeper and older reservoirs. The third district covers the axis and upper flanks of the Nemaha granite ridge. The fourth includes the north side of the Arbuckle Mountains, the southeastern embayment of the Anadarko basin, and the south side of the Paul's Valley uplift. The fifth district is the Ardmore basin, and the sixth is the Anadarko basin exclusive of the southeastern embayment but including the Oklahoma panhandle. A seventh district, the McAlester coal basin, produces gas only from folded Pennsylvanian sandstones in the Arkansas River Valley near the eastern edge of the state.[84] Still another district, recently opened up, is the Marietta basin south of the Wichita-Criner Hills uplift. Oil is being produced from shallow reservoirs in a number of recently discovered pools in Cotton County.[85]

Northeastern Oklahoma. This is the discovery district for Oklahoma. At the northern end of the northeastern Oklahoma platform most of the accumulation has been in lenticular sands of the Cherokee formation of Pennsylvanian age. Because of the westward dip of the strata the depths to these reservoirs becomes greater from east to west across the district. Fairly typical of the district is the Red Fork shoestring sand pool [86] which occupies parts of Pawnee, Creek, and Tulsa counties. This field was discovered in 1924. The reservoir rock is the Red Fork sandstone, which is the approximate equivalent of the Burbank, another Cherokee sand lying a short distance above the level of the Bartlesville sand. The Red Fork field is more than 10 miles long in a north-northwest direction and varies in width from one well location to half a mile. It differs from other shoestring sand bodies in that it does contain some water, and where the elongate

[84] Earl G. Colton, "Natural Gas in Arkansas Basin of Eastern Oklahoma," *Geology of Natural Gas* (Am. Assoc. Petrol. Geol., 1935), pp. 511–532.

[85] James D. Pate, "Cotton County, Poor Boys' Paradise," *World Oil,* Vol. 128 (October, 1948), pp. 122–126.

[86] Randall Wright, "Red Fork Shoestring Sand Pool, Pawnee, Creek, and Tulsa Counties, Northeastern Oklahoma," *Stratigraphic Type Oil Fields* (Am. Assoc. Petrol. Geol., 1941), pp. 473–491.

sand lens crosses a syncline it is filled with water. There is no water drive, however, and the water present appears to be completely sealed in along with the oil. As is true of the other shoestring sand accumulations the most logical conclusion is that the oil entered the porous and permeable sandstone during the compaction of the surrounding organic Cherokee shale. The reason for the water may be that insufficient oil was injected into the sand to displace completely all the water present.

Farther to the west in northernmost Oklahoma is Osage County with its many oil fields, including the famous Burbank.[87] The Burbank and South Burbank pools produce from the Burbank sand which lies at a depth of about 2800 feet and has an average thickness of 57 feet. This sand occurs in the lower part of the Cherokee shale formation of Pennsylvanian age. In these pools the sandstone reservoir rock, although lenticular in shape, is much larger than the oil accumulation and is filled with water down-dip below the oil. The regional dip is westward, and the oil has been impounded by the up-dip lensing out of the Burbank sand. In the main Burbank pool, above the level of the oil-water interface, there does not appear to be any relationship between the occurrence of oil and the local structure, but in the South Burbank pool a gas cap has accumulated in the structurally highest parts of the hydrocarbon-filled reservoir rock.

The great Glenn pool lies to the south of Burbank in eastern Creek County.[88] This field, discovered in 1906, was the first major oil pool in Oklahoma. The reservoir rock is the Bartlesville (Glenn) sandstone, which also lies within the Pennsylvanian Cherokee shale. The depth of the reservoir is about 1500 feet. Local structure is not important in controlling accumulation in this reservoir rock, but the regional structure and the lenticularity of the sand are of utmost importance. As in the Burbank pool, the regional dip is to the westward and the oil has been trapped by the up-dip lensing out of the sandstone. However, there is some production from the deeper

[87] N. W. Bass, H. B. Goodrich, and W. R. Dillard, "Subsurface Geology and Oil and Gas Resources of Osage County, Oklahoma," *U. S. Geol. Survey, Bull.* 900 (1942); J. Merville Sands, "Burbank Field, Osage County, Oklahoma," *Bull. Am. Assoc. Petrol. Geol.*, Vol. 11 (October, 1927), pp. 1045–1054; E. O. Markham and L. C. Lamar, "South Burbank Pool, Osage County, Oklahoma," *Bull. Am. Assoc. Petrol. Geol.*, Vol. 21 (May, 1937), pp. 560–579; H. T. Beckwith, "Oil and Gas in Oklahoma; Geology of Osage County," *Okla. Geol. Survey, Bull.* 40 T (1928).

[88] W. B. Wilson, "Geology of Glenn Pool of Oklahoma," *Structure of Typical American Oil Fields* (Am. Assoc. Petrol. Geol., 1929), Vol. 1, pp. 230–242.

Mounds ("Wilcox") sandstone of Ordovician age in which accumulation is entirely anticlinal.

The Cushing field [89] in western Creek County is the second field in Oklahoma in cumulative production. The structure is a pre-Pennsylvanian bald-headed anticline 20 miles in length overlapped by Pennsylvanian sediments. The Pennsylvanian formations are likewise anticlinal in structure, owing to recurrent movement. The reservoirs include seven Pennsylvanian sandstones and, beneath the unconformity, Ordovician sands and the Cambro-Ordovician Arbuckle dolomite. One Pennsylvanian "sand" is in reality an oölite. Below, in the Cherokee shale, is the Bartlesville sandstone, which was oil-bearing over the entire anticlinal crest, covering an area of 28 square miles. The Ordovician sands produced only from the tops of the domes superimposed upon the anticlinal axis, and the Arbuckle carried oil on one dome only where the overlying Ordovician sandstones had been removed during the pre-Pennsylvanian erosion interval. Much the greater part of the trapping at Cushing is anticlinal, but in the older reservoirs sealing of the truncated domes by overlap has been necessary.

A lens, the Prue, lying at the top of the Cherokee shale above the Bartlesville sandstone, has trapped and is producing oil in the Davenport field in Lincoln County,[90] in the western part of the district.

Central and Southern Oklahoma Platform. Trapping in lenticular sandstones is not confined to the northern end of the northeast Oklahoma platform. It is also found to the south, in the central and southern parts of the platform. Examples include the Dora and Olympic pools. The Dora pool [91] is in the so-called "Greater Seminole district" but is not a structural accumulation as are most of the others in this area. The producing sand, locally called the "Dora," is in the Thurman formation of Lower Pennsylvanian age. It occurs at depths ranging from 2750 to 3000 feet and has a maximum thickness of about 100 feet. The Dora is an irregular-shaped lens lying on a northwest dipping monocline. The reservoir sandstone is completely surrounded by shale, and it is believed that these shales are also the source rock for the oil trapped within the sand lens.

[89] T. E. Weirich, "Cushing Oil and Gas Field, Creek County, Oklahoma," *Structure of Typical American Oil Fields* (Am. Assoc. Petrol. Geol., 1929), Vol. 2, pp. 396–406.

[90] Stanley B. White, "Davenport Field, Lincoln County, Oklahoma," *Stratigraphic Type Oil Fields* (Am. Assoc. Petrol. Geol., 1941), pp. 386–407.

[91] W. I. Ingham, "Dora Oil Pool, Seminole County, Oklahoma," *Stratigraphic Type Oil Fields* (Am. Assoc. Petrol. Geol., 1941), pp. 408–435.

The Olympic pool [92] produces from a sand in the Senora formation of Pennsylvanian age which is slightly younger than the Thurman. Accumulation is very similar to that at Dora. The reservoir is a sand bar measuring about 6½ miles long with a maximum width of 1¼ miles. The sandstone interfingers with shale at its lateral margins.

Both "stratigraphic" and structural trapping are illustrated in the East Tuskegee pool,[93] which lies north of the Olympic pool. Oil in the Ordovician "Wilcox" sandstone is confined to two structural domes, but in the higher Misener sand (basal Mississippian) wells drilled at the apices of the domes have failed to find oil because of local lack of permeability in this reservoir. Misener production is confined to the flanks of the domes.

One of the greatest concentrations of oil in the country has been in the Greater Seminole district of Seminole and Pottawatamie counties.[94] Among the more important pools in the Greater Seminole district are the Seminole City, Searight, Earlsboro, Bowlegs, Little River, Mission, and St. Louis. The discovery and development of these pools in 1926 and the years immediately following led to serious overproduction in the Mid-Continent. At the height of production the Seminole district yielded 500,000 barrels of oil daily. The oil accumulation in this area is largely in Silurian, Devonian, and Ordovician reservoirs. The trapping is anticlinal, with the domes at the Ordovician level having closures of several hundreds of feet. However, the surface Pennsylvanian rocks show little or no closure, which explains why these fields were not discovered earlier.

To the northwest, east of the Nemaha uplift, are other accumulations of the structural type. One of these, the Arcadia-Coon Creek field in Oklahoma and Logan counties, is described and illustrated in Chapter 8 (Fig. 35) as an example of anticlinal trapping. Another example is the Ramsey oil pool,[95] which produces from a Simpson

[92] W. Reese Dillard, "Olympic Pool, Hughes and Okfuskee Counties, Oklahoma," *Stratigraphic Type Oil Fields* (Am. Assoc. Petrol. Geol., 1941), pp. 456–472; Allen W. Tillotson, "Olympic Pool, Hughes and Okfuskee Counties, Oklahoma," *Bull. Am. Assoc. Petrol. Geol.*, Vol. 22 (November, 1938), pp. 1579–1587.

[93] Joseph L. Borden and Ralph A. Brant, "East Tuskegee Pool, Creek County, Oklahoma," *Stratigraphic Type Oil Fields* (Am. Assoc. Petrol. Geol., 1941), pp. 436–455.

[94] A. I. Levorsen, "Greater Seminole District, Seminole and Pottawatamie Counties, Oklahoma," *Structure of Typical American Oil Fields* (Am. Assoc. Petrol. Geol., 1929), Vol. 2, pp. 315–361; H. L. Rau and K. A. Ackley, "Geology and Development of Keokuk Pool, Seminole and Pottawatamie Counties, Oklahoma," *Bull. Am. Assoc. Petrol. Geol.*, Vol. 23 (February, 1939), pp. 220–245.

[95] V. L. Frost, "Ramsey Oil Pool, Payne County, Oklahoma," *Bull. Am. Assoc. Petrol. Geol.*, Vol. 24 (November, 1940), pp. 1995–2005.

(Ordovician) sandstone folded into an almost circular dome faulted on the east flank. The dome has been truncated; about 130 feet of Mississippian limestone is absent across the top of the fold as the result of pre-Pennsylvanian erosion. The closure in the Simpson exceeds 200 feet, and wells have penetrated as much as 189 feet of oil-saturated sand. The fault on the east flank does not appear to have interfered with accumulation.

The Morrison [96] and other fields in Pawnee and Kay counties are additional examples of anticlinal trapping in this district.

Nemaha Uplift. The Nemaha uplift extends into Oklahoma from Kansas and occupies a relatively narrow belt southward from Kay across parts of Grant, Garfield, Noble, Logan, and Oklahoma counties. The two greatest fields in this district, Oklahoma City (Fig. 79) and West Edmond, were described in some detail in Chapter 8. These fields are outstanding examples of trapping by folding, truncation, and overlap. Oklahoma City is by far the largest field in Oklahoma in cumulative production, and it ranked second among individual fields in annual output in 1949. Another well-known field on the uplift is the Tonkawa.[97] This field is also a faulted and truncated anticline in the pre-Pennsylvanian which has been overlapped by Pennsylvanian sediments. The core of the pre-Pennsylvanian anticline is pre-Cambrian crystalline rock. The fold is reflected above the unconformity by the arched structure of the Pennsylvanian and Permian sediments. The Pennsylvanian section is about 3000 feet in thickness and contains a number of producing sandstones, of which two have yielded important quantities of gas and six have been commercial sources of oil. The trapping in these reservoirs is entirely anticlinal. The principal oil reservoirs at Tonkawa, however, are sandstones in the Simpson; trapping is due to a combination of structure and overlap seal. Some oil is also obtained from the crest of the buried anticline in the Arbuckle ("siliceous lime") formation of Cambro-Ordovician age.

North Arbuckle District. Diastrophism on the north flank of the Arbuckles has been intense, resulting in tight folding and overthrust faulting. In the northwest corner of the district the sediments of the Anadarko basin lap up on the flanks of Paul's Valley uplift. The

[96] Everett Carpenter, "The Morrison Field, Pawnee County, Oklahoma," *Bull. Am. Assoc. Petrol. Geol.,* Vol. 11 (October, 1927), pp. 1087–1096.

[97] Glenn C. Clark, "Wilcox Sand Production, Tonkawa Field, Oklahoma," *Bull. Am. Assoc. Petrol. Geol.,* Vol. 10 (September, 1926), pp. 885–891.

discovery of oil in the Fitts pool [98] in 1933 opened up this structurally complicated area for exploration. The Fitts pool is notable on account of its structural character as well as its unusual number of prolific reservoirs. Accumulation has taken place in a faulted anticline which lies within a graben on the north flank of the Arbuckle Mountain complex. Production is limited on the west and south by faults. The reservoir rocks lie within the Atoka (Pennsylvanian), Hunton (Siluro-Devonian), and the Viola, Bromide, and McLish (all Ordovician) formations. The Atoka reservoir is a thick sandstone, and it has produced great quantities of gas as well as oil. The Hunton contains two limestone reservoirs, one at the top and one at the bottom. The Viola limestone and various sandstones in the Bromide and in the upper McLish formations constitute a section nearly 800 feet thick which is classified as a single reservoir. The fifth or basal McLish sand is 200 feet thick and has an average productive thickness of 40 feet.

The nearby Jesse pool [99] is very similar structurally and stratigraphically to the Fitts pool. The trapping is due to the presence of a large anticline which is faulted on the south (Arbuckle Mountain) side. The faulting consists of a series of parallel step faults with the down side on the south flank of the anticline. Because of this fault zone, production is confined to the crest and north sides of the fold.

Southeast Anadarko Basin. Still newer discoveries have been made in the southeastern embayment of the Anadarko basin on the flanks of the Paul's Valley uplift. This very active zone lies in Garvin County some distance west of the Pontotoc County fields. Here are the "Golden Trend" [100] fields which produce mainly from the Deese sands as they abut against the older rocks flanking the Paul's Valley uplift. This type of trapping is illustrated in Chapter 8 (Fig. 80) as an example of sealing by offlap. The pools of the Golden Trend produced over 15 million barrels of oil in 1949, making this the greatest producing area in Oklahoma for that year.

Ardmore Basin. The Ardmore basin district lies to the south of the Arbuckle Mountains and extends northwest between the offset ends

[98] Don L. Hyatt, "Preliminary Report on the Fitts Pool, Pontotoc County, Oklahoma," *Bull. Am. Assoc. Petrol. Geol.*, Vol. 20 (July, 1936), pp. 951–974.

[99] W. Baxter Boyd, "Jesse Pool, Pontotoc and Coal Counties, Oklahoma," *Bull. Am. Assoc. Petrol. Geol.*, Vol. 22 (November, 1938), pp. 1560–1578.

[100] Robert M. Swesnik, "Golden Trend of South-Central Oklahoma," *Bull. Am. Assoc. Petrol. Geol.*, Vol. 34 (March, 1950), pp. 386–422; Robert R. Wheeler, "Golden Trend of Oklahoma-Current Problems," *Bull. Am. Assoc. Petrol. Geol.*, Vol. 34 (June, 1950), pp. 1287–1292.

of the Arbuckle and Wichita uplifts into the southeastern corner of the Anadarko basin immediately south of the Golden Trend group of oil pools. Like the north side of the Arbuckles this district is one of intense diastrophism, including faulting with displacements measured in the thousands of feet. At the east end of the district in Bryan and Marshall counties is the Cumberland oil field, which is illustrated and described in the preceding chapter (Fig. 36) as an example of anticlinal accumulation. Carter County, in the center of the district, contains older fields including Healdton, which illustrates anticlinal accumulation over a buried hill, Crinerville,[101] another anticline over a buried Ordovician hill, and the Tatums pool[102] in which, unlike the others, accumulation is due to the abrupt termination of the Pennsylvanian reservoir sands against an older hill upon which these sediments overlap.

Still farther to the westward, in the narrow belt between the Arbuckle and Wichita uplifts near the southeasternmost point of the Anadarko basin, is a zone of extremely complicated structure in which oil has been produced for many years. During and since World War II a deeper drilling program in this area has resulted in the discovery of some prolific reservoirs; some new fields have been found and some of the older fields have been regenerated. An example of a field restored to production is the Velma pool in Stephens County, which was originally developed in 1917 and which as the result of new deep discoveries became the most important individual field in Oklahoma for 1949 with a production of nearly 10 million barrels of oil. The Velma structure[103] appears at the surface as a prominent northwest-southeast anticlinal ridge formed by red Permian sandstone. The older production came from the deeper-arched Permian reservoirs, but the newer and more copious yield is being obtained from Pennsylvanian and older reservoirs which carry oil on the east flank of the surface anticline. A profound angular and erosional unconformity occurs beneath the veneer of Upper Pennsylvanian and Permian formations, and the older rocks are highly contorted and thrust-faulted.

The Sholem-Alechem[104] pool near by was discovered in 1923, but recent deeper developments are mainly responsible for its 6 million

[101] Sidney Powers, "Crinerville Oil Field, Carter County, Oklahoma," *Bull. Am. Assoc. Petrol. Geol.*, Vol. 11 (October, 1927), pp. 1067–1085.

[102] Glenn Grimes, "Tatums Pool, Carter County, Oklahoma," *Bull. Am. Assoc. Petrol. Geol.*, Vol. 19 (March, 1935), pp. 401–411.

[103] William W. Mallory, "Rocky Mountain Type Structure at Velma Pool, Stephens County, Oklahoma," *World Oil*, Vol. 129 (July 1, 1949), pp. 68–78.

[104] Harold R. Billingsley, "Sholem-Alechem Pool Presents Complex Geological Picture," *World Oil*, Vol. 130 (Feb. 1, 1950), pp. 61–66.

barrel yield in 1949, which placed it third in output for the year. This field is 9 miles long and as much as 2 miles wide. Its regeneration as an important source of oil was due to the discovery of oil in the deeper Springer (Pennsylvanian) sandstones. The Sholem-Alechem structure is a closely compressed anticline with a closure in the neighborhood of 1000 feet at the level of the deeper reservoirs. It is crossed by several faults, but they do not limit production. Accumulation is entirely anticlinal.

Anadarko Basin and Oklahoma Panhandle. This district is much larger in area than any of the others. The potential reservoir rocks sag down to great depths in western Oklahoma; a well in Woodward County at one time held the depth record for the United States. So far, successful exploration has been confined mainly to the eastern side and to the northwest flank where lies the Hugoton gas field of southwestern Kansas and Beaver County, Oklahoma. This field is described in the preceding section under Kansas. Several fields have been discovered recently north of Paul's Valley uplift in McClain and Cleveland counties. To the northwest in central Kingfisher County, approximately 20 miles west of the West Edmond field on the Nemaha uplift, a well has been drilled to a total depth of more than 9000 feet and is producing gas and distillate from both Simpson and Hunton reservoirs.[105] Still farther northwest, in eastern Major County, is the Ringwood field, discovered in 1947 but not actively developed until 1949. New discoveries have also been made in Beckham County, high on the southwest flank of the Anadarko basin. Gas and distillate have been found in an arkosic Pennsylvanian sandstone, "granite wash" from off the Wichita uplift to the south. The depth is over 9200 feet.[106]

Texas[107]

(Figures 117–118)

The state of Texas is not only the leading oil-producing state but also one of the great sources of world oil. During 1949 this state provided 42 per cent of the domestic oil production and 22 per cent of the world's output. The current Texas production approximately

[105] Dean C. Wellman, "Developments in Oklahoma in 1948," *Bull. Am. Assoc. Petrol. Geol.,* Vol. 33 (June, 1949), p. 902.

[106] Dean C. Wellman, *op. cit.,* pp. 895–901.

[107] Frank A. Herald (editor), "Occurrence of Oil and Gas in Texas (Progress Report)," *Texas Bur. Econ. Geol.* (February, 1949).

equals the combined output of Venezuela, the second country in world oil production, and Russia, the third country.

Although some oil had been produced earlier, the first real development of the petroleum industry in Texas took place in 1896 with the discovery of oil in the Corsicana fault trap pool in Navarro County in what is now referred to as the East Texas district. It was the discovery of the prolific Spindletop pool in 1901, however, which really focused attention upon the potentiality of Texas as an oil-producing state. The years immediately following were exciting ones in the Gulf Coast district, other large salt dome accumulations being found in rapid succession. The next major event in Texas petroleum history was the discovery of the Burkburnett and other large fields in northern Texas between 1911 and 1921. Concurrently, beginning in 1914, salt dome flank sands were found to carry oil in some of the Gulf Coast pools, and exploration took on new vigor in that area. East Texas, the scene of the initial Corsicana discovery, became an important source of oil beginning in 1922. In 1925 West Texas entered the production column in a big way, and a year later oil was discovered in the Panhandle district. The East Texas field itself, the greatest single accumulation yet to be found anywhere, was discovered in 1929. The Conroe field, which ushered in the era of deep supercap salt-dome discoveries in the Gulf Coast district, became productive in 1931.

From the geologic map alone it is possible to divide Texas into two parts, Mesozoic and Cenozoic Texas, and Paleozoic Texas. The former includes all southern and eastern Texas; the outcropping rocks are either Comanchean, Upper Cretaceous, or Tertiary formations which were deposited in the Gulf embayment and which outcrop in bands that roughly parallel the present Gulf Coast shoreline. The rocks increase in age inland. Paleozoic Texas extends over the rest of the state, covering northern and western Texas, including the Panhandle. Here the Paleozoic rocks lie at the surface except where mantled by a veneer of continental Tertiary or younger fluviatile or eolian sediments.

The most striking structural features of Texas are the Gulf embayment and two uplifts, the Llano and the Marathon. The embayment is probably the north flank of a great salt basin now largely covered by the Gulf of Mexico.[108] In any event the sea floor sank as the Cretaceous and Tertiary sediments were deposited, so that the stratigraphic section along the present shoreline, when completely explored,

[108] Clarence L. Moody, address at University of Michigan, March 9, 1950.

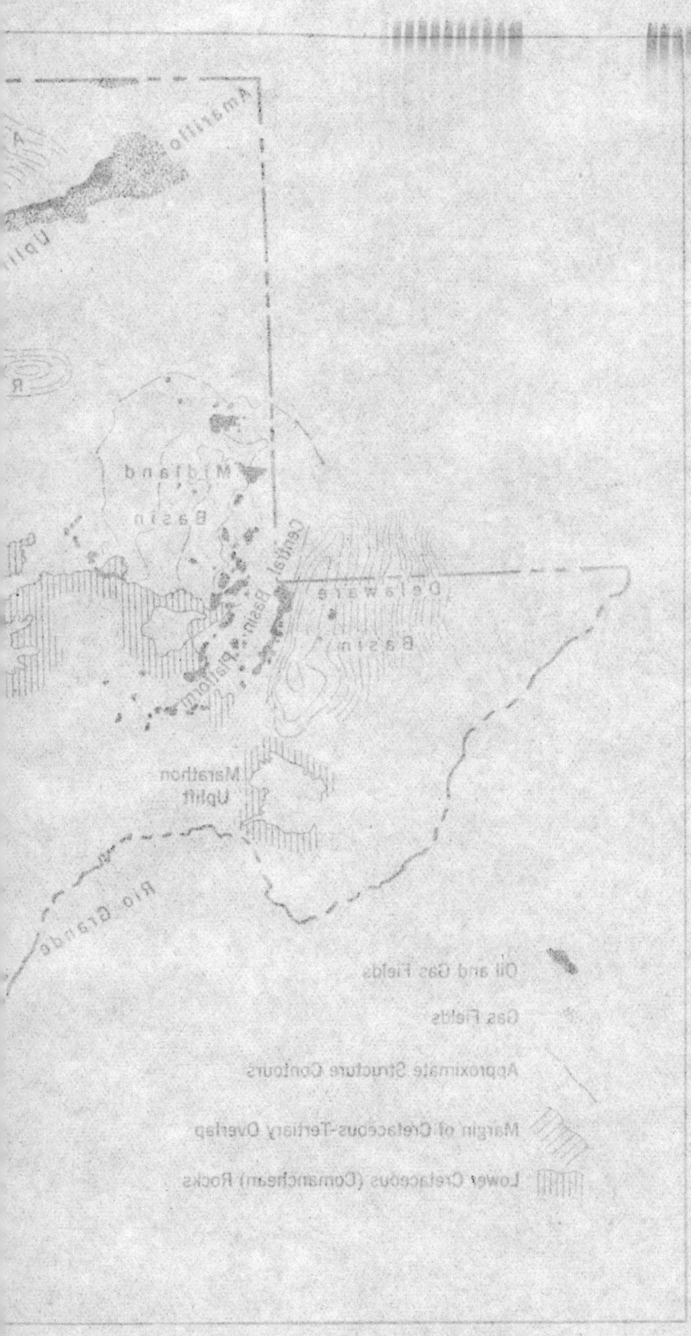

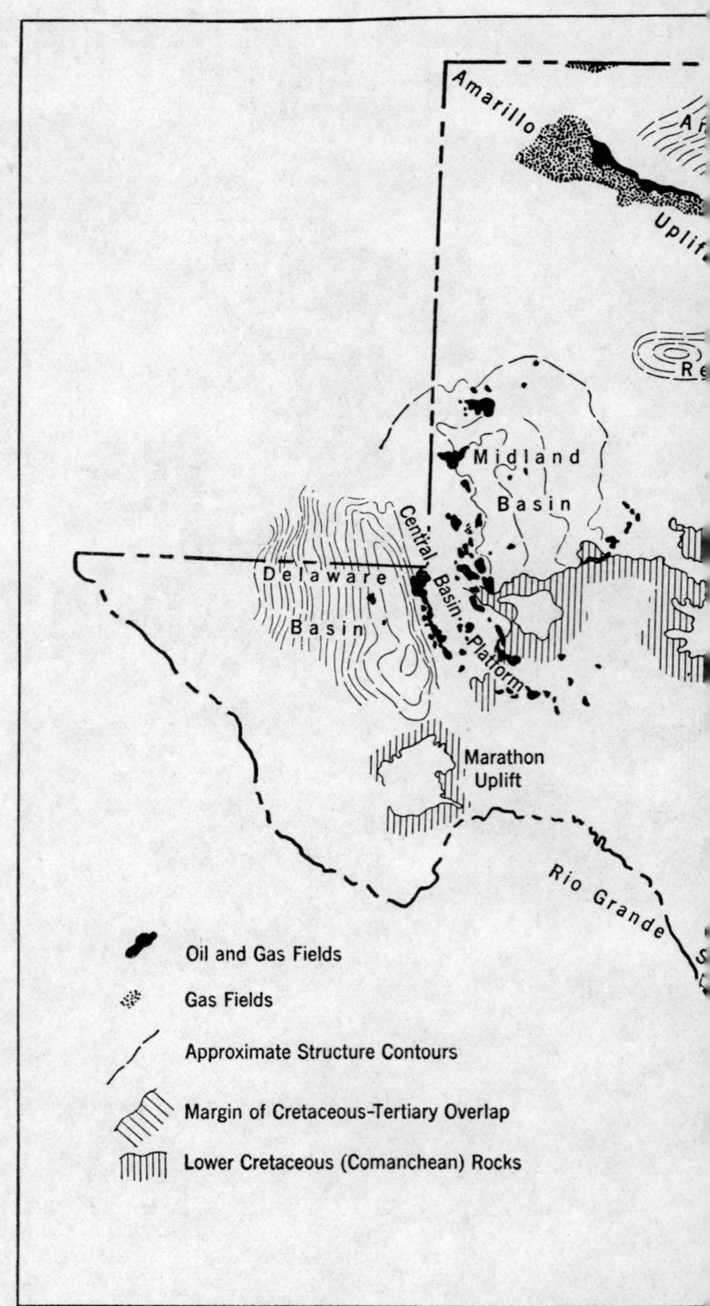
Amarillo
Uplift
Midland
Basin
Central Basin Platform
Delaware
Basin
Marathon
Uplift
Rio Grande
Oil and Gas Fields
Gas Fields
Approximate Structure Contours
Margin of Cretaceous-Tertiary Overlap
Lower Cretaceous (Comanchean) Rocks

Fig. 117. Texas. Gulf Coast

and major tectonic features.

probably will be found to measure somewhere between 45,000 and 75,000 feet in thickness. Inland from the embayment are the two uplifts named above, the Marathon in the southern part of western Texas and the Llano in the Central Mineral Region of central Texas, plus a third uplift, the Ouachita of southeastern Oklahoma and south-

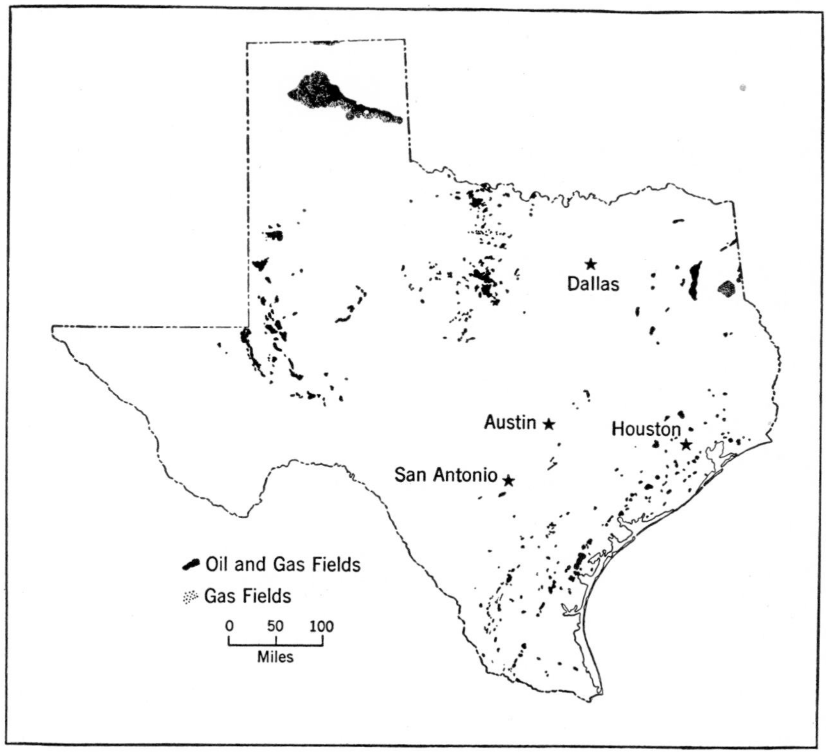

Fig. 118. Texas. Oil and gas fields.

western Arkansas. These uplifts are similar in that erosion has exposed very old rocks toward the center, and differences in resistance to erosion have caused the development of a fairly rugged topography. Within the embayment are lesser downwarps and upwarps and fractures. The southern part of the Texas Gulf embayment is furrowed by the Rio Grande syncline. East Texas has the Tyler basin, a near-circular downwarp which interrupts locally the normal Gulfward dip. From the bottom of the Tyler basin the strata rise gently but consistently eastward to the top of the Sabine uplift, a large dome with its highest point in northwestern Louisiana. Toward the inner edge of the embayment is a fault zone of great length. South of the Central Mineral Region this fault trend, referred to as the Balcones fault zone, is easterly. Farther east it curves around the Central Mineral Region, striking first northeast and then north. The Balcones zone appears to lose identity east of the Llano uplift, but another and similar fault zone known as the Luling-Mexia, which is offset slightly to the east, takes its place and continues northward until northwest of the Tyler basin, where it curves eastward through a 90° arc, proceeds east across northeastern Texas, and crosses the state line into southwestern Arkansas. On the north flank of the Tyler basin this fault zone is known as the Talco.

North of the Llano uplift is the Bend flexure or arch, which is in reality a northward-plunging spur of the uplift. This warping took place during the Pennsylvanian, and younger Pennsylvanian and Permian sediments were deposited unconformably across the arch so that it is not discernible on the areal geologic map. To the north is the east-west Red River uplift overlapping the Oklahoma line. This uplift is separated from the Wichita uplift still farther north by the Marietta basin of southwestern Oklahoma. On the northeast flank of the Bend arch is first the Fort Worth syncline or basin and then the Muenster uplift. Both have a northwest-southeast trend. The Muenster uplift appears to connect with the Wichita rather than with the adjacent Red River uplift.

West of the Llano region and north of the Marathan mountains is the great Permian basin of western Texas and southeastern New Mexico. This is in reality two major basins, the Midland to the northeast and the Delaware to the southwest, separated by the Central basin platform, a northwest-southeast trending residual feature which has resulted from the downwarping of the basins on either side.

The Panhandle of Texas is crossed from east to west by the Amarillo uplift which has a core of pre-Cambrian hills completely buried beneath much younger sediments. Northeast of the Amarillo uplift is the southwest flank of the Anadarko basin of western Oklahoma.

The stratigraphic section in Paleozoic Texas has Permian rocks at the top in most places. These are largely limestones, dolomites, shales, and evaporites (including salt and even potash), and they reach great thicknesses in the West Texas basins. The Pennsylvanian is especially well represented in the Bend arch area with as much as 6000 feet of limestones and clastics. Rocks of Mississippian, Devonian, and

Silurian age are present in various parts of this great area but are not very abundant. The Ordovician is widely present and of growing importance as a source of petroleum.

The stratigraphic section in the Gulf Coastal Plain has been thoroughly sampled and studied as far as explored by drilling, but there is without doubt an enormous thickness of rock yet to be penetrated by the drilling bit, especially close to and out beyond the present shoreline. The Quaternary is represented by Pleistocene sediments, and all the Tertiary epochs were times of abundant clastic deposition in this area. Upper and Lower Cretaceous sediments have not been reached by the drill in the coastal area but have been thoroughly explored in the interior of eastern Texas. The Upper Cretaceous rocks include both clastic and carbonate deposits. The Comanchean (Lower Cretaceous) section contains not only clastics and carbonates but also anhydrites. Beneath the Comanchean is a thick Jurassic section which has been explored by deep drilling in recent years. This section was somewhat unexpected, for the Jurassic deposits in the outcrop zone are relatively insignificant. Below the Smackover limestone of undoubted Jurassic age is a thick salt and red bed section which may be Jurassic or may be older (Permian?). Regardless of its geologic age this is probably the formation that supplied the salt for not only the interior but also the coastal salt domes.

The oil and gas reservoirs in Texas range in age from Pliocene to Ordovician. The Tertiary reservoirs are confined to the Gulf Coast belt. Among the well-known producing formations or zones are the Catahoula of the Miocene, the Frio and Vicksburg of the Oligocene, and the McElroy, Cockfield, Pettus, Yegua, and Wilcox of the Eocene. The outstanding Upper Cretaceous reservoir is the Woodbine sand, which carries the oil of East Texas and most of the fault pools. Permian carbonate rocks are the principal reservoirs in the Panhandle of Texas and in West Texas. The Strawn, Bend, and other Pennsylvanian formations carry the oil in North and West Central Texas. The Ordovician Ellenburger limestone is the deep reservoir of West Texas.

For many years geophysical prospecting has been used extensively in the Texas coastal plain. The seismograph was first used here as an exploration tool, and it is still the leading geophysical instrument. The gravity meter is also used, and the core drill too, but to a much less extent. Some surface work is done by means of pit digging to expose the bed rock. Outside of the coastal plain, subsurface geology is the most common discovery technique, but the seismograph, the gravity meter, and the core drill also are used.

In the discussion that follows, Texas has been divided into six districts (Fig. 119): East, Southeastern Gulf Coast, Southwest, North

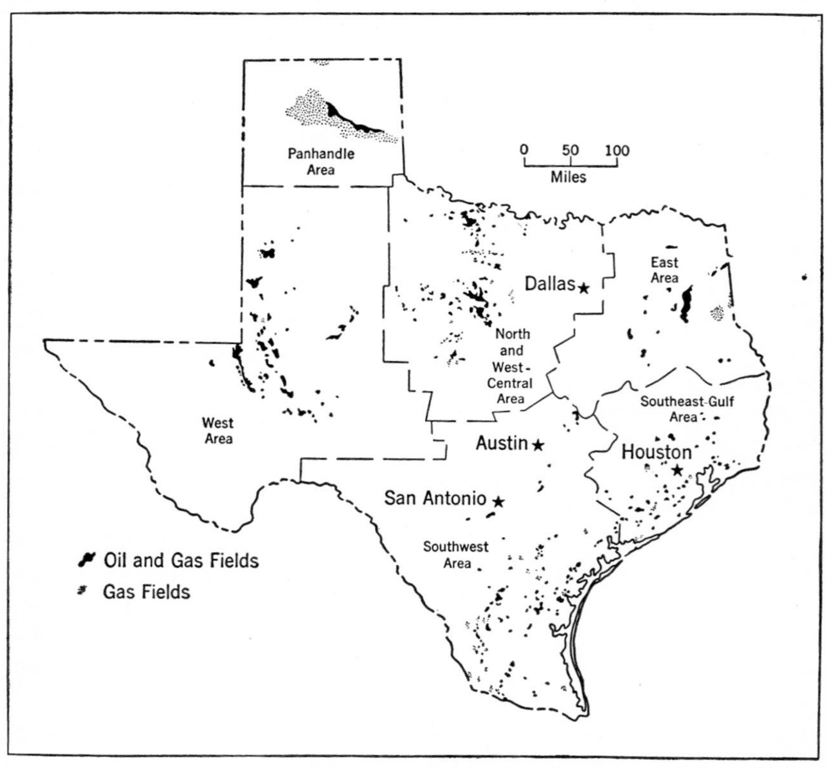

Fig. 119. Texas. District map.

and West Central, West, and Panhandle. The basis for the division is largely geologic but partly geographic for greater expediency. The divisions are those followed by the *Bulletin of the American Association of Petroleum Geologists* in its annual (June) review number devoted to exploration and development. This scheme is similar to, but not the exact equivalent of, various partitionings used by the Texas Railroad Commission (the state oil and gas regulatory body), the Oil Scouts, the *Oil and Gas Journal,* and the United States Bureau of Mines.

The East, Southeastern Gulf Coast, and Southwest districts all lie within the embayment. The other three districts are in Paleozoic Texas. The west flank of the Sabine uplift, the Tyler basin, and the Mexia-Talco fault zones are in the East Texas district. The Balcones fault zone and the Rio Grande syncline are in Southwest Texas. North and West Central Texas contain the Bend flexure and the Red River uplift. The Delaware basin, Central basin platform, and Midland basin are all parts of West Texas. The Amarillo uplift and one corner of the Anadarko basin lie in the Panhandle district.

These districts vary widely in importance in terms of oil production. In current production the West Texas district is at the top, followed by Southeastern Gulf, East, Southwest, North and West Central, and Panhandle, in the order named. The recent production of the Panhandle district has been about one-eighth that of its neighbor to the south, West Texas. In terms of overall (cumulative) production, East Texas is in first place, followed by Southeastern Gulf, West, North and West Central, Southwest, and Panhandle. The cumulative production of the Panhandle district is between one-fourth and one-fifth that of East Texas.

The greatest individual oil pool in Texas if not in the world is the East Texas field, which by Jan. 1, 1950, had produced over 2½ billion barrels of oil and will probably produce as much more before abandonment. The Yates pool of West Texas is second in cumulative production with about a third of a billion barrels. Almost as much oil has been produced from the various pools making up the Panhandle field. Conroe, in the Gulf Coast, and Hendrick, in West Texas, stand in fourth and fifth places respectively in cumulative production through 1949. During 1949 East Texas was still the leading field with an output of nearly 100 million barrels of oil. The other leading fields for the year were Slaughter-Leveland and Wasson in West Texas, and Hastings and Webster in the Southeastern Gulf Coast district.

East Texas (Fig. 120). The East Texas district is bounded on the north by Oklahoma, on the northeast by a corner of Arkansas, and on the east by Louisiana. To the south is the Southeastern Gulf Coast district, the two counties in the southwest corner of the district border on the Southwest Texas district, and directly west are the counties belonging in the West Central and North Texas district. The East Texas district includes forty-two counties, all of which except a few around the periphery produce oil or gas. Although the birthplace of the Texas oil industry was in Navarro County, where the first of the great fault line pools was discovered in 1896, after the remaining fault fields had been found additional discoveries were rather slow in com-

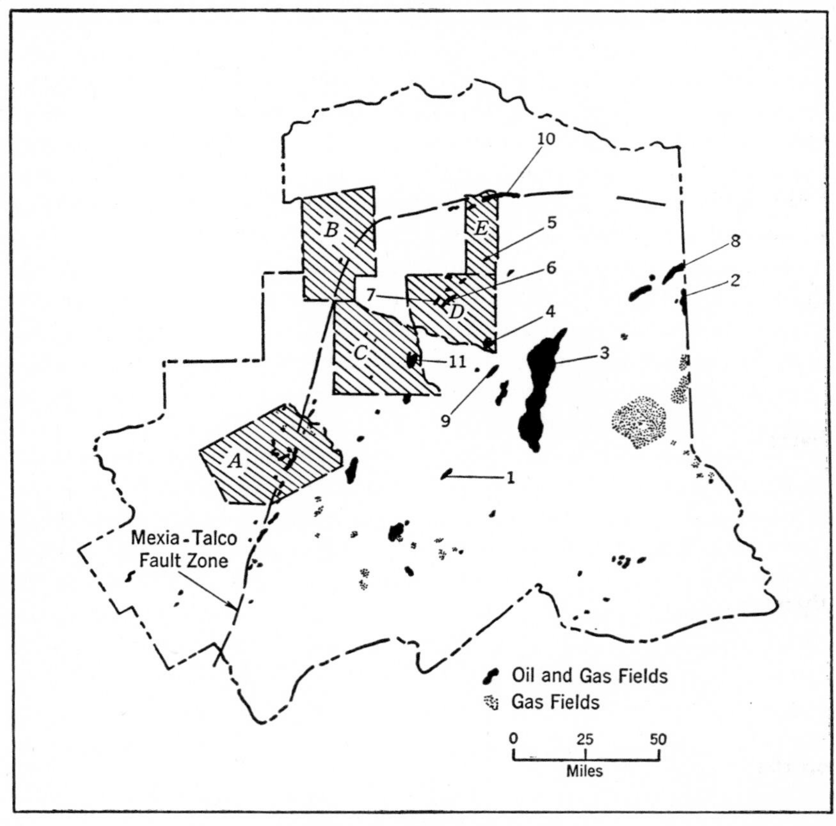

Fig. 120. East Texas index map.

A, Navarro County.
B, Hunt County.
C, Van Zandt County.
D, Wood County.
E, Franklin County.

1, Boggy Creek oil field.
2, Caddo oil field.
3, East Texas oil field.
4, Hawkins oil field.
5, Hope oil field.
6, Merigale oil field.
7, Quitman oil field.
8, Rodessa oil field.
9, Sand Flat oil field.
10, Talco oil field.
11, Van oil field.

ing, and it was not until the discovery of the East Texas field itself in 1930 that the district once more became prominent.

The East Texas district lies in the Coastal Plain or Gulf embayment province. Its most prominent tectonic features are the Sabine uplift which has its highest point in northwestern Louisiana, the

Tyler basin which occupies the middle of the district, and the Mexia-Talco fault zone which trends in a northerly direction along the west side of the district and then turns east in Hunt County and crosses the northern end of the district.

The most productive reservoir formation is the Woodbine sandstone of lowermost Gulfian (Upper Cretaceous) age. The younger Cretaceous Nacatoch and the older Comanchean Paluxy and Rodessa formations are other important reservoirs in the East Texas district.

Next to the phenomenal East Texas field the leading oil pool in cumulative production in the district is the Talco. However, the field which led all others in production for 1949, again excluding East Texas, was the Hawkins field. The traps and other details of the local geology of the East Texas, Talco, and Hawkins fields are described in Chapter 8. East Texas (Fig. 76) is used to illustrate wedge-outs due to truncation and overlap. Talco (Fig. 64) is an excellent example of fault trapping, and Hawkins (Fig. 61) shows domal accumulation, probably over a salt core.

On the east side of the East Texas district are two major fields which are partly in Texas and partly in northwestern Louisiana. One of these is the Caddo field, which is an anticlinal accumulation lying close to the top of the Sabine uplift. Only a relatively small part of the Caddo production has been obtained from the Texas side of the line. To the north is the elongate northeast-southwest Rodessa field, which has a greater acreage in Texas than in Louisiana but which has produced more oil on the Louisiana side of the line. Rodessa occupies the extreme northwest corner of Louisiana and extends a short distance into Arkansas as well as into Texas. Several major fields lie on the western and northern sides of the East Texas district, where the Mexia-Talco fault zone has furnished traps for oil accumulation. Among them, from south to north, are the South Groesbeck, North Groesbeck, Mexia, Wortham, Currie, North Currie, Richland, and Powell (Fig. 63) fields on the west side (Fig. 121) and the Talco on the north side. Two pools, both apparently small, have been discovered along this fault zone a few miles to the west of Talco.[109]

Many discoveries have been made, mostly since the East Texas strike, in the Tyler basin between the East Texas field and the Mexia-Talco fault zone. This basin also contains a number of salt domes; in several of these the salt has been penetrated by exploratory wells, and in one, the Grand Saline in Van Zandt County, the salt is exploited by

[109] Donald T. Gibson, "Developments in East Texas in 1949," *Bull. Am. Assoc. Petrol. Geol.*, Vol. 34 (June, 1950), p. 1173.

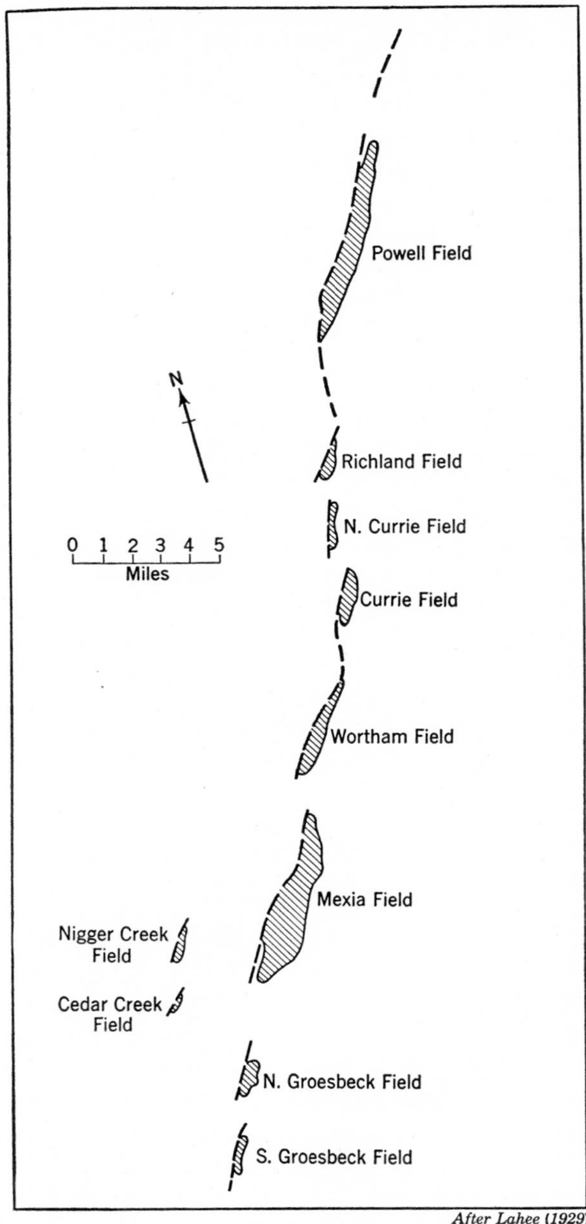

Fig. 121. Mexia fault zone fields, Texas. *Courtesy American Association of Petroleum Geologists.*

shaft mining. One interior salt dome was found to be productive of oil and gas. This is the Boggy Creek (Fig. 122),[110] which lies fairly close to the axis of the Tyler basin. The salt occurs at a depth of about 2500 feet and has a depressed area across the top. This saucer shape extends to the surface and results in exposures of youngest rock in the center of the structure instead of older rock as is the usual rule. Oil and gas are produced from the Woodbine formation on the southeast flank of the dome where it has been dragged up and truncated by the intrusion of the salt core.

Several other accumulations in the Tyler basin are in anticlines which appear to owe their existence to the presence of deep-seated salt cores. Gravity surveys across the Hawkins field report gravity minima at the center, which, with other criteria, indicate strongly the presence of salt at depth. The same is probably true of the Van field, in eastern Van Zandt County, which produces from a faulted anticline. The Quitman oil field [111] is also on a faulted anticline, but considerably more elongate than either the Van or Hawkins structures. The Quitman anticline trends northeastward across west central Wood County for a distance of about 7 miles and has closure in the neighborhood of 300 feet. A narrow graben occurs along the axis of the anticline. Quitman produces from two reservoirs, the relatively shallow "Harris" sand of Upper Cretaceous age, and the deeper and more prolific Paluxy sand of Comanchean age. The axial graben appears to be non-productive in the Harris zone but productive at the Paluxy level. Still another accumulation in the East Texas district in a faulted anticline is the Sand Flat field.[112] The New Hope field [113] in Franklin County on the north flank of the Tyler basin is, on the other hand, a simple, symmetrical anticline with no indications of faulting. The Merigale [114] field in Wood County, about 1½ miles southeast of the town of Quitman, is a fault accumulation. The reservoir rock is a sandstone belonging in the Upper Cretaceous. It carries oil only on the upthrown (southeast) side of the fault. The

[110] H. J. McLellan, E. A. Wendtlandt, and E. A. Murchison, "Boggy Creek Salt Dome, Anderson and Cherokee Counties, Texas," *Bull. Am. Assoc. Petrol. Geol.*, Vol. 16 (June, 1932), pp. 584–600.

[111] E. R. Scott, "Quitman Oil Field, Wood County, Texas," *Structure of Typical American Oil Fields* (Am. Assoc. Petrol. Geol., 1948), Vol. 3, pp. 419–431.

[112] L. D. Bartell, "Sand Flat Field, Smith County, Texas," *Bull. Am. Assoc. Petrol. Geol.*, Vol. 28 (November, 1944), pp. 1647–1648.

[113] R. A. Stehr, "New Hope Field, Franklin County, Texas," *Bull. Am. Assoc. Petrol. Geol.*, Vol. 29 (June, 1945), pp. 836–839.

[114] A. C. Wright, "Merigale Field, Wood County, Texas," *Bull. Am. Assoc. Petrol. Geol.*, Vol. 29 (December, 1945), pp. 1779–1780.

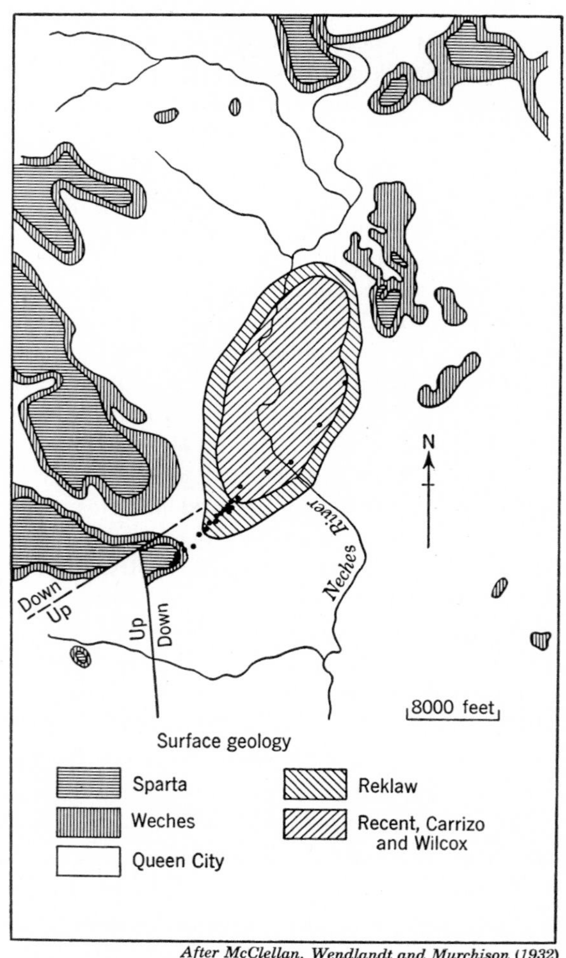

After McClellan, Wendlandt and Murchison (1932)

FIG. 122*A*. Boggy Creek field, Texas. Areal geologic map. *Courtesy American Association of Petroleum Geologists.*

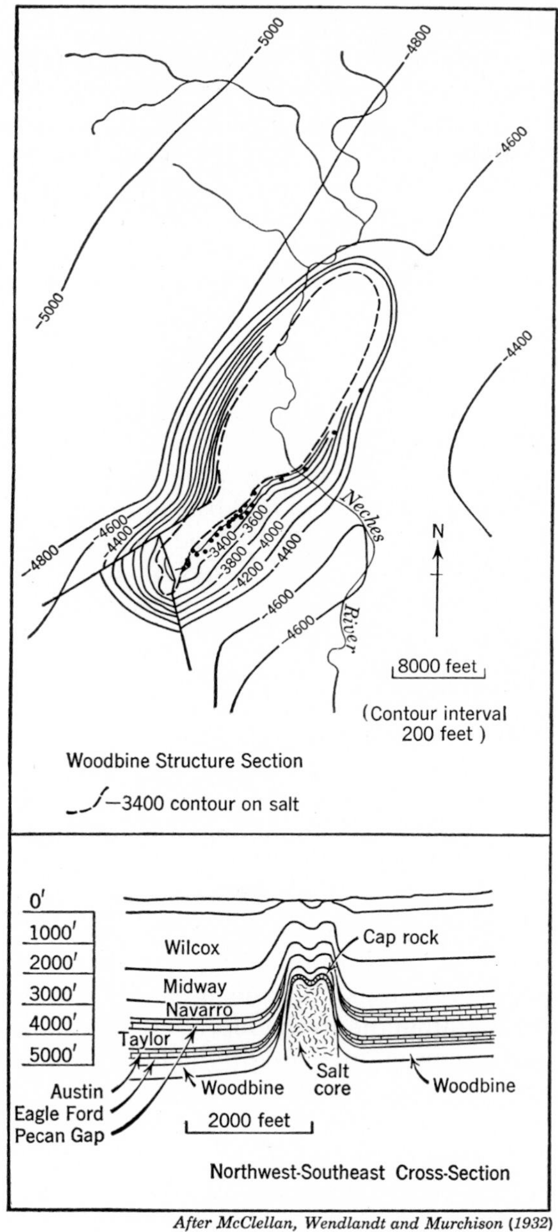

After McClellan, Wendlandt and Murchison (1932)

FIG. 122*B*. Subsurface structure contoured on Woodbine (Upper Cretaceous) sandstone. Lower: cross section, showing salt core. *Courtesy American Association of Petroleum Geologists.*

regional dip is southeasterly toward the axis of the East Texas geosyncline; oil moving up-dip through the reservoir rock became impounded in a plunging anticline by the impervious barrier which resulted from faulting. The Merigale fault is purely a local feature lying some distance basinward from the Mexia-Talco fault zone.

Southeastern Texas Gulf Coast (Fig. 123).[115] This district is also called "the Upper Gulf Coast of Texas," and the "Texas Salt Dome Province." It continues without geological break across southern Louisiana. The Southeastern Texas Gulf Coast district contains 26 counties and is bounded on the east by Louisiana, on the southeast by the Gulf of Mexico, on the southwest and west by the Southwestern Texas district, and on the north by the East Texas district.

The most productive part of the Southeastern Gulf district is the belt about three counties wide bordering the Gulf shoreline. Farther to the interior is a zone parallel to the coast in which very few discoveries have been made. Still farther inland at the northern edge of the district are a number of oil and gas pools which are more closely allied geologically with the Tyler basin accumulations of the East Texas district than with those of the Gulf Coast.

The Southeastern Gulf Coast district was discovered in 1901 when Captain Lucas drilled in the first of many 75,000-barrel-per-day wells in the Spindletop field. The reservoir was salt-dome cap rock, and several more prolific fields of this type were discovered during the next five years. In addition commercial sulfur deposits have been found in the cap rocks of Boling, Long Point, Bryan Mound, and Hoskins Mound. The second birth date in the history of the salt-dome district was the discovery in 1915 of flank production from the upturned and truncated deeper strata around the periphery of the salt core. Thereafter the so-called piercement domes were explored vigorously for flank reservoirs. The discovery of Goose Creek in 1917 initiated production from the arched supercap strata above an assumed salt core at an unknown depth beneath. However, it was not until the development of the large Conroe field in 1931 that the search for this type of accumulation became intensive. Subsequently many fields

[115] James L. Ballard, "Developments in Upper Gulf Coast of Texas in 1949," *Bull. Am. Assoc. Petrol. Geol.*, Vol. 34 (June, 1950), pp. 1179–1190; Frank J. Gardner, *Texas Gulf Coast Oil* (Rinehart Oil News Co., Dallas, 1948); Cecil W. Smith, "Gulf Coast Oil Fields," *World Oil* (Gulf Coast Issue), Vol. 130 (June, 1950), pp. 60–92; Paul B. Leavenworth and Sidney A. Parkans, Jr., "Oil and Gas Developments in the Upper Gulf Coast During 1949," Am. Inst. Min. Met. Engineers, 1949 Production Statistics, *Jour. Petrol. Tech.*, Vol. 2 (June, 1950), pp. 14–28.

of the deep-seated salt-core type have been found both in the Southeastern Texas and the Southern Louisiana Gulf Coast districts.

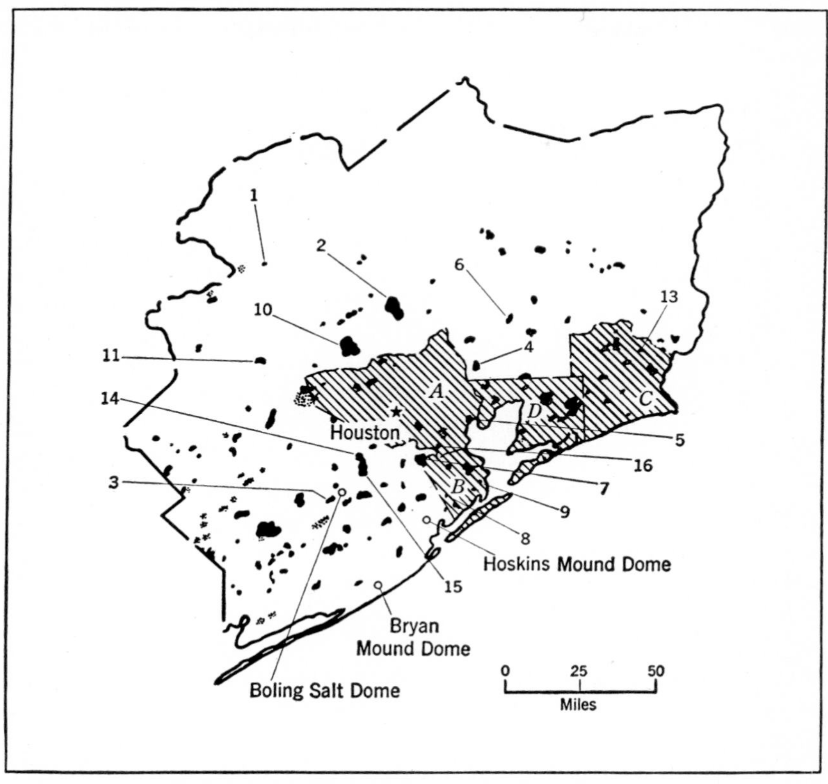

Fig. 123. Southeastern Texas Gulf Coast index map.

A, Harris County.
B, Galveston County.
C, Jefferson County.
D, Chambers County.

1, Clay Creek oil field.
2, Conroe oil field.
3, Damon Mound oil field.
4, Esperson oil field.
5, Goose Creek oil field.
6, Hardin oil field.
7, Hastings oil field.
8, High Island oil field.
9. Hitchcock oil field.
10, Katy oil field.
11, Raccoon Bend oil field.
12, South Cotton Lake oil field.
13, Spindletop oil field.
14, Sugarland oil field.
15, Thompson oil field.
16, Webster oil field.

A second type of trap in the Gulf Coast district is the Gulf Coast faulted anticline illustrated in Chapter 8 by the West Tepetate field of Louisiana (Fig. 62). The faulting is parallel to the shoreline, and the downblock is on the Gulf side. The normal Gulfward dip is reversed immediately south of the fault so that some closure is present without the intervention of the fault plane. Hydrocarbons moving up the regional dip are caught in these anticlines parallel to the strike of the sedimentary strata.

The Gulf Coast reservoir strata range in age from Miocene to Eocene. Among the more important producing zones are the Discorbis, Heterostegina, and Marginulina of the Upper Oligocene, the Frio of the Lower Oligocene, the Yegua-Cockfield of the Middle Eocene, and sandstones of the Lower Eocene Wilcox formation.

The leading Southeastern Texas Gulf Coast fields in 1949 were, in descending order, the Hastings, Webster, Thompson, and Conroe. The Conroe is much the largest in cumulative production. Both the Texas and Louisiana Gulf Coast districts have been the scene of the discovery of many deep, high-pressure, gas-distillate fields. These fields are notable for the large gas cap which contains, in addition to the usual gaseous compounds, hydrocarbons that are liquid at lesser pressures. These liquefy between the reservoir and the surface, and after reaching the surface. The practice of returning the non-liquefiable gas to the reservoir in order to maintain reservoir pressure was described in Chapter 3.

Four fields in the Southeastern Texas Gulf Coast are cited in Chapter 8 to illustrate various types of trapping. Spindletop (Fig. 57) shows both cap and flank accumulation, Damon Mound (Fig. 59) also illustrates flank production, and High Island (Fig. 58) shows accumulation beneath an overhanging salt dome. The Conroe (Fig. 60) field is illustrated in Chapter 8 as an example of supercap accumulation. The first of the supercap fields to be discovered, Goose Creek,[116] is in Harris County about 25 miles southeast of Houston. This field was discovered by a well drilled in 1908 after a party of oil men, including a geologist, had noticed gas seeps in that area while on a fishing trip. The discovery well was completed at a depth of 1600 feet for an initial production of 800 barrels. Further exploration was discouraging until 1916, when a 10,000-barrel well was brought in, and subsequently some wells were rated as high as 35,000 barrels per day. Although production has been obtained from a number of sandstone reservoirs lying at various depths, no well has as yet penetrated the assumed salt core. A notable feature at Goose Creek has been the marked subsidence of the surface overlying the center of the field. The land

[116] H. E. Minor, "Goose Creek Oil Field, Harris County, Texas," *Bull. Am. Assoc. Petrol. Geol.*, Vol. 9 (March–April, 1925), pp. 286–297.

there originally stood ½ foot to 2 feet above high tide, but after a couple of years of active exploitation the surface had subsided until at high tide 2 to 3 feet of water inundated the central part of the oil field. This subsidence is thought to be due to the pumping of sand and water (which causes dehydration of the clays) along with oil from the reservoir.[117]

The Raccoon Bend oil field [118] is another supercap accumulation. Oil was discovered here in 1928, and this structure likewise was thought to have a salt core, an assumption that was verified in 1946 when a well drilled to a depth of 11,447 feet entered salt.[119] The Sugarland oil field [120] is another supercap field in which the drill has penetrated the salt core. The Clay Creek salt dome [121] is notable for its central depression with oil and gas produced from around the rim of this cuplike structure. The Esperson dome [122] is unusual in that the salt core was thrust upward at an angle so that the crest of the anticline in the overlying oil-bearing strata shifts southward with depth.

The Katy field [123] covers about 30,000 acres and is one of the major gas-condensate accumulations so far discovered in the United States. The trap is a broad, unfaulted dome. Gas condensate and oil are produced from six or more sandstone reservoirs lying in the Yegua (Eocene) formation between depths of 6250 and 7450 feet.

The Gulf Coast district also contains some varying-permeability traps. A part of the production in the Hardin field is obtained from a sand lens or bar which is a completely enclosed and sealed reservoir.[124] The Hitchcock field, in Galveston County, owes its trapping

117 W. E. Pratt and D. W. Johnson, "Local Subsidence of the Goose Creek Oil Field," *Jour. Geol.*, Vol. 34 (October–November, 1926), pp. 577–590; L. C. Snider, "A Suggested Explanation for the Surface Subsidence in the Goose Creek Oil and Gas Field of Texas," *Bull. Am. Assoc. Petrol. Geol.*, Vol. 11 (July, 1927), pp. 729–745.

118 L. P. Teas and Charis R. Miller, "Raccoon Bend Oil Field, Austin County, Texas," *Gulf Coast Oil Fields* (Am. Assoc. Petrol. Geol., 1936), pp. 676–708.

119 H. J. McLellan, "Raccoon Bend Salt Dome, Austin County, Texas," *Bull. Am. Assoc. Petrol. Geol.*, Vol. 30 (August, 1946), pp. 1306–1307.

120 W. B. McCarter and P. H. O'Bannon, "Sugarland Oil Field, Fort Bend County, Texas," *Gulf Coast Oil Fields* (Am. Assoc. Petrol. Geol., 1936), pp. 709–733.

121 William Boyd Ferguson and Joseph W. Minton, "Clay Creek Salt Dome, Washington County, Texas," *op. cit.*, pp. 757–779.

122 W. L. Goldston, Jr., and George D. Stevens, "Esperson Dome, Liberty County, Texas," *op. cit.*, pp. 857–879.

123 A. P. Allison, *et al.*, "Geology of Katy Field, Waller, Harris, and Fort Bend Counties, Texas," *Bull. Am. Assoc. Petrol. Geol.*, Vol. 30 (February, 1946), pp. 157–180.

124 S. Russell Casey, Jr., and Ralph B. Cantrell, "Davis Sand Lens, Hardin Field, Liberty County, Texas," *Stratigraphic Type Oil Fields* (Am. Assoc. Petrol. Geol., 1941), pp. 564–599.

to domal structure on three sides and complete wedging-out of the reservoir sand on the fourth side.[125]

It is in the Gulf Coast districts of Louisiana and Texas that the reflection seismograph has had its greatest success. Most of the discoveries in recent years in this area have been due to a combination of seismograph surveying and subsurface geology. Gravity methods, using first the torsion balance and later the gravity meter, have also been successful. The discovery of the South Cotton Lake field in 1937 followed an integrated approach, using the torsion balance, the reflection seismograph, and subsurface geology.[126]

Although many of the fields along the Texas Gulf are practically at the water's edge, and there can be no doubt that oil-filled traps also lie beneath the open waters of the Gulf of Mexico, offshore exploration on the Texas side of the Texas-Louisiana boundary have so far been disappointing. By mid-1949 fourteen wells had been drilled and abandoned. One of these, in offshore Jefferson County, struck oil, and the discovery was named the Sabine Pass field. But two offsets were dry, and the discovery well itself was abandoned after producing 11,500 barrels of oil. Leases have been purchased to date for 33 areas off the Texas coast which can be assumed to cover potential oil-bearing structures.[127] Most of these are still untested.

Southwest Texas (Fig. 124). The Southwestern Texas district,[128] sometimes referred to as "South Texas," contains 61 counties. It is bordered on the southeast by the Gulf of Mexico, on the south and southwest by the Republic of Mexico, on the northwest by the West Texas district, on the north by the North and West Central Texas district, and on the northeast and east by a corner of the East Texas district and the Southeastern Texas Gulf district.

The Thrall field, a serpentine producer in Williamson County, was discovered in 1915. The Luling field, a fault accumulation also in the interior, was opened up in 1922. The first discoveries in the coastal part of the Southwestern Texas district were made in Refugio County in 1929. This county is still a leading oil-producing area.

[125] Michel T. Halbouty and Benjamin T. Simmons, "Hitchcock Field, Galveston County, Texas, Showing Stratigraphic Accumulation and Structure," *op. cit.,* pp. 641–660.

[126] Joseph M. Wilson, "South Cotton Lake Field, Chambers County, Texas," *Bull. Am. Assoc. Petrol. Geol.,* Vol. 25 (October, 1941), pp. 1898–1920.

[127] J. Ben Carsey, "Geology of Gulf Coastal Area and Continental Shelf," *Bull. Am. Assoc. Petrol. Geol.,* Vol. 34 (March, 1950), p. 385.

[128] Cecil W. Smith, "Gulf Coast Oil Fields," *World Oil,* Vol. 130 (June, 1950), pp. 60–92.

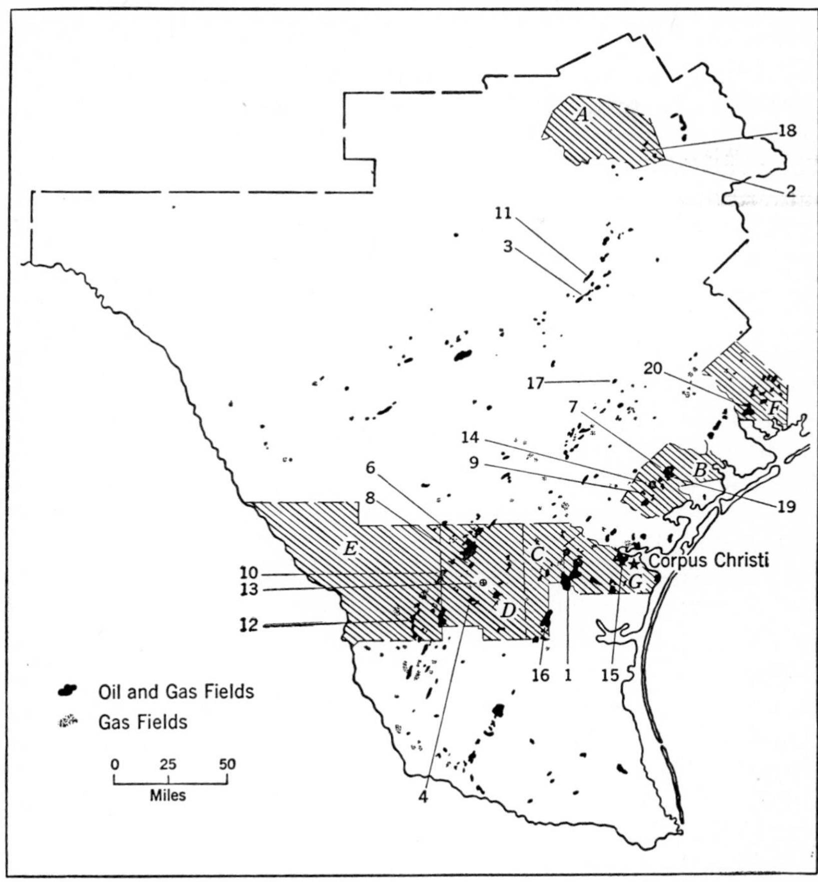

Fig. 124. Southwest Texas index map.

A, Williamson County.
B, Refugio County.
C, Jim Wells County.
D, Duval County.
E, Webb County.
F, Jackson County.
G, Nueces County.

1, Agua Dulce-Stratton oil field.
2, Chapman oil field.
3, Darst Creek oil field.
4, Driscoll oil field.
5, Edna oil field.
6, Government Wells oil field.
7, Greta oil field.
8, Hoffman oil field.
9, La Rosa oil field.
10, Lopez oil field.
11, Luling oil field.
12, O'Hern oil field.
13, Palangana sulfur dome.
14, Refugio oil field.
15, Saxet oil field.
16, Seeligson oil field.
17, Slick-Wilcox oil field.
18, Thrall oil field.
19, Tom O'Connor oil field.
20, West Ranch oil field.

Most of the oil fields of the Southwest district occur in the eastern part in a zone extending inland from the Gulf of Mexico to a depth of five or six counties. The oil fields within this zone tend to lie in trends parallel to the shoreline. Scrafford[129] subdivides the Southwest Texas district by the geologic age of the producing formations. These subdivisions, named in order from the interior of the district outward toward the coast line, are: (1) pre-Cretaceous, (2) Cretaceous, (3) lower Eocene, (4) upper Eocene, (5) lower Oligocene, (6) upper Oligocene and lower Miocene.

The northwestern side of the Southwest Texas district is dominated by the Llano uplift, which exposes the pre-Cambrian crystalline rocks in the core of the Central Mineral Region, and the plateau formed by the Edwards (Comanchean) limestone to the southwest.

A prominent tectonic feature in this area is the Balcones fault zone, which lies along the periphery of the Edwards plateau curving around the Llano uplift, southeast and east of the Central Mineral Region. It connects to the north, by a slight offset, with the Mexia-Talco fault zone. Production in this zone is from Cretaceous rock, especially the Lower Cretaceous Edwards limestone, and fault trapping is the dominant mode of accumulation. Southeast of this belt of older rocks is the Coastal plain, floored by Upper Cretaceous and Tertiary sediments dipping and thickening Gulfwards. The south end of the district contains the Rio Grande syncline, a southeastward-plunging structural trough, which causes the strike of the embayment sediments to curve to the west in the southern part of the district.

The reservoirs in the Coastal zone of Southwest Texas are similar in range and characteristics to those in the Southeastern Gulf district. They are sands lying within the lower Miocene, Oligocene, and Eocene. Of utmost importance are the Oligocene Frio and the Eocene Wilcox formations. In the interior zone the Southwestern district produces from Upper Cretaceous and Comanchean sandstones, limestones, and even serpentines.

The leading fields in Southwest Texas in 1949 were the Tom O'Connor, the Seeligson, and the Agua Dulce-Stratton. These fields lie in a Frio (lower Oligocene) trend which runs parallel to the Gulf shoreline, northeast from southern Jim Wells County to Refugio County. Extending inland from the coast in the southern part of the district is an isolated group of salt domes (Fig. 54) in which the salt

[129] Bruce Scrafford, "Developments in South Texas in 1949," *Bull. Am. Assoc. Petrol. Geol.*, Vol. 34 (June, 1950), pp. 1158–1169.

cores have been penetrated by the drill. One of these salt domes, Palangana, contains cap-rock sulfur. It is quite possible that the no-salt-dome area between the southwestern group and the salt domes of the Southeastern Texas Gulf Coast district is merely a belt in which the tops of the salt cores lie at such depths that they have not yet been struck in drilling. Many of the producing anticlines and domes in the Tertiary producing belt of Southwest Texas have all the ear-marks of salt-cored structures, and eventually salt cores may be discovered across this "barren" territory.

Two of the Balcones fault zone pools that have been described are the Luling[130] and the Darst Creek[131] which lies a few miles to the south of Luling. The impounding of oil is almost exactly the same in these two fields, although they occupy separate faults. The oil occurs in the top of the Edwards (Comanchean) limestone in a plunging anticline on the upfaulted block. The reservoir limestone has been dropped down on the west side of the fault, bringing the younger and relatively impervious Taylor marl against the broken edge of the eastward-dipping Edwards revervoir rock.

At the north side of the Southwest Texas district, especially in Williamson County, are accumulations of oil in porous serpentine reservoirs. One of these, the Chapman field, is illustrated and described in Chapter 8 (Fig. 74).

The Eocene belt is the farthest inland of the Tertiary zones. Duval County contains an unusual concentration of Eocene fields. Many of the accumulations in this trend are dependent upon variations in the permeability of the reservoir rock.[132] The Lopez oil field[133] and the O'Hern field,[134] both of which lie along the boundary between Duval and Webb counties, have been cited as illustrations of stratigraphic traps. The Driscoll pool,[135] which lies entirely within Duval County, owes its existence to the up-dip wedging out of the reservoir sand.

130 Ernest W. Brucks, "Luling Oil Fields, Caldwell and Guadalupe Counties, Texas," *Structure of Typical American Oil Fields* (Am. Assoc. Petrol. Geol., 1929), Vol. 1, pp. 256–281.

131 H. D. McCallum, "Darst Creek Oil Field, Guadalupe County, Texas," *Bull. Am. Assoc. Petrol. Geol.,* Vol. 17 (January, 1933), pp. 16–37.

132 James C. Freeman, "Strandline Accumulation of Petroleum, Jim Hogg County, Texas," *Bull. Am. Assoc. Petrol. Geol.,* Vol. 33 (July, 1949), pp. 1260–1270.

133 J. Boyd Best, "Lopez Oil Field, Webb and Duval Counties, Texas," *Stratigraphic Type Oil Fields* (Am. Assoc. Petrol. Geol., 1941), pp. 680–697.

134 G. G. Barnett, "O'Hern Field, Duval and Webb Counties, Texas," *op. cit.,* pp. 722–749.

135 I. R. Sheldon, "Driscoll Pool, Duval County, Texas," *Gulf Coast Oil Fields* (Am. Assoc. Petrol. Geol., 1936), pp. 620–630.

Accumulation in the nearby Government Wells oil field,[136] which is one of the larger fields of the Southwest Texas district, is due to a combination of tilting, folding, faulting, and sandstone lenticularity. The trap is closed by regional dip in one direction, by faulting in a second, by folding in a third, and by loss of permeability in a fourth. The Hoffman field,[137] yet another Duval County field, differs from most of its neighbors in being a structural accumulation. The trap at the Hoffman field is a broad, low anticline with only about 40 feet of closure in the upper Eocene sandstone reservoirs. To the northeast on the same trend is the Slick-Wilcox field,[138] which illustrates accumulation in a faulted dome. The fault cuts across the south side of the dome, fairly high on the flank. Accumulation is to the north on the upside of the fault.

The Oligocene trend, which lies about one county inland from the Gulf shore, is the leading source of oil in the Southwest Texas district at the present time. The same two distinct types of structure that are responsible for accumulation in the Southeastern Texas Gulf district occur in the Oligocene zone of Southwest Texas. Some fields, such as the Refugio [139] and the Greta [140] of Refugio County and the West Ranch [141] and the Edna [142] in Jackson County, produce from broad, fairly flat domes which may or may not be faulted and which are highly suggestive of deep underlying salt cores. The Edna field is a gas field, and the structure was discovered by surface geologic mapping. The center of the dome is marked at the outcrop by a wooded sand inlier about 6000 feet in diameter. The Refugio field is one of the major fields in the district, and it shows indication of several periods of folding. After each period of folding or tilting, the hydrocarbons appear to have adjusted to the new structural environment by migration.

[136] John Trenchard and J. Barney Whisenant, "Government Wells Oil Field, Duval County, Texas," *op. cit.*, pp. 631–647.

[137] Harvey Whitaker, "Hoffman Field, Duval County, Texas," *Bull. Am. Assoc. Petrol. Geol.*, Vol. 24 (December, 1940), pp. 2126–2142.

[138] Louie Sebring, Jr., "Slick-Wilcox Field, Dewitt and Goliad Counties, Texas," *Bull. Am. Assoc. Petrol. Geol.*, Vol. 32 (February, 1948), pp. 228–251.

[139] Phillip F. Martyn, "Refugio Oil and Gas Field, Refugio County, Texas," *Bull. Am. Assoc. Petrol. Geol.*, Vol. 22 (September, 1938), pp. 1184–1216.

[140] R. A. Stamey, J. C. Montgomery, and H. D. Easton, Jr., "Greta Oil Field, Refugio County, Texas," *Gulf Coast Oil Fields* (Am. Assoc. Petrol. Geol., 1936), pp. 648–663.

[141] A. J. Bauernschmitt, Jr., "West Ranch Oil Field, Jackson County, Texas," *Bull. Am. Assoc. Petrol. Geol.*, Vol. 28 (February, 1944), pp. 197–216.

[142] M. M. Kornfeld and C. R. Steinberger, "Edna Gas Field, Jackson County, Texas," *Bull. Am. Assoc. Petrol. Geol.*, Vol. 25 (January, 1941), pp. 104–119.

The La Rosa field,[143] also in Refugio County, is an excellent example of the second ("Tepetate") type of trap in the Gulf Coast zone,

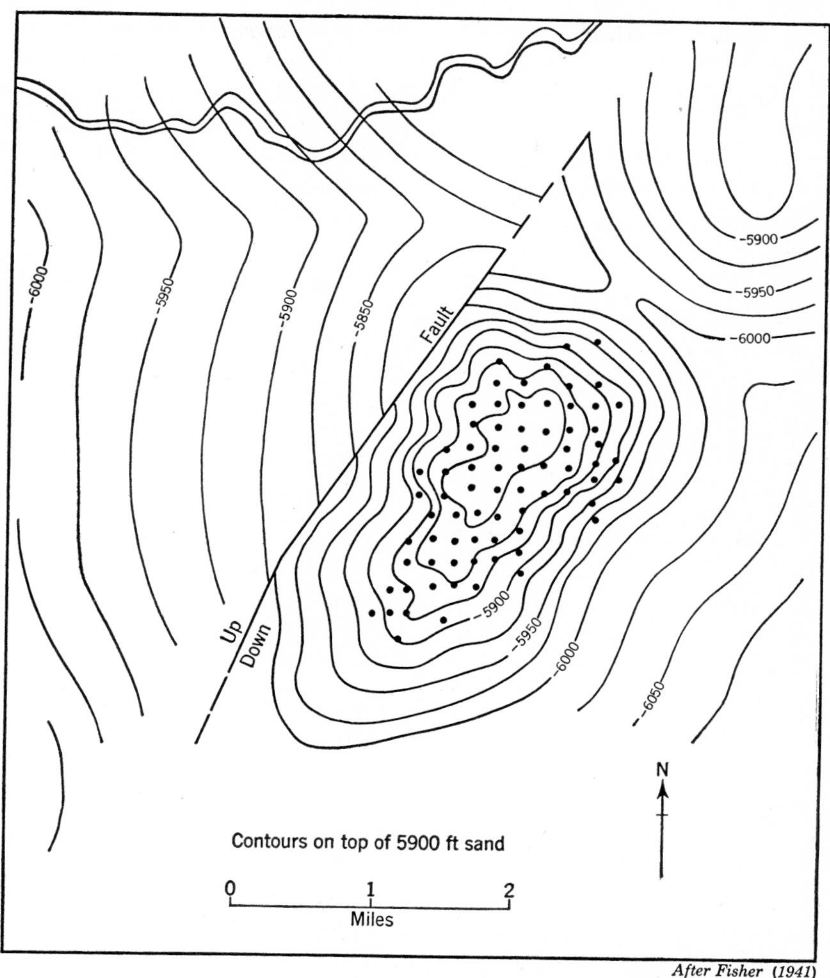

Fig. 125. La Rosa Field, Texas. Accumulation in dome in down-faulted block. *Courtesy American Association of Petroleum Geologists.*

anticlinal accumulation in the downfaulted block (Fig. 62). The anticline lies immediately to the south of the fault which parallels the Gulf shoreline. The distribution of the oil across the La Rosa anti-

[143] Barney Fisher, "La Rosa Field, Refugio County, Texas," *Bull. Am. Assoc. Petrol. Geol.,* Vol. 25 (February, 1941), pp. 300–317.

cline is limited on the north by the position of the fault plane (Fig. 125).

Most of the production in the Oligocene belt comes from sandstones in the Frio formation. As many as thirty-nine separate reservoirs have been found in this belt, and a single field may contain nine or more. Common practice is to complete some of the wells in two different reservoirs.

The Saxet field [144] produces from both the Frio, of lower Oligocene age, and younger Oligocene and Miocene sands. It is in Nueces County near Corpus Christi, to the east of the main Frio belt. Saxet is one of the major fields of the Southwest Texas district. Accumulation is in a large dome which is crossed, high on the northwest flank, by a major fault. The downfaulted side is on the southeast toward the Gulf, but production is found across the fault plane on the north side. Several minor compensating faults are also present. It is believed that the major fault supplied a channelway for migrating gas which filled the shallower sands with gas under such high pressure that a score or more of "blowouts" took place during the development of the field.

North and West Central Texas (Fig. 126).[145] North and West Central Texas are here considered as one district. To the north are the Red River and the state of Oklahoma. The East Texas district lies to the east, Southwest Texas district to the south, and West Texas to the west. The oil and gas fields in North and West Central Texas are mainly concentrated along the Bend Arch which trends north across the central part of the district.

North Texas first produced commercially in 1904, when the Petrolia field in Clay County was discovered. However, the district did not become an important source of world oil until 1911, after the discovery of the Burkburnett-Electra fields in Wichita County. These fields and others were developed rapidly during the ensuing decade under true "boomtown" conditions. Subsequently the district declined until the discovery of a deep Pennsylvanian reservoir in the older KMA field in 1938 and two years later a still deeper Ellenburger (Ordovician) reservoir which led to greatly renewed activity not only in the KMA pool but throughout the district.

144 J. C. Poole, "Saxet Oil and Gas Field, Nueces County, Texas," *Bull. Am. Assoc. Petrol. Geol.,* Vol. 24 (October, 1940), pp. 1805–1835.

145 J. B. Moorhead and William Otis Ham, Jr., "Developments in North and West-Central Texas in 1949," *Bull. Am. Assoc. Petrol. Geol.,* Vol. 34 (June, 1950), pp. 1150–1157.

The Central Mineral Region, or Llano uplift, is at the southern end of the district, and the Bend flexure extends northward from

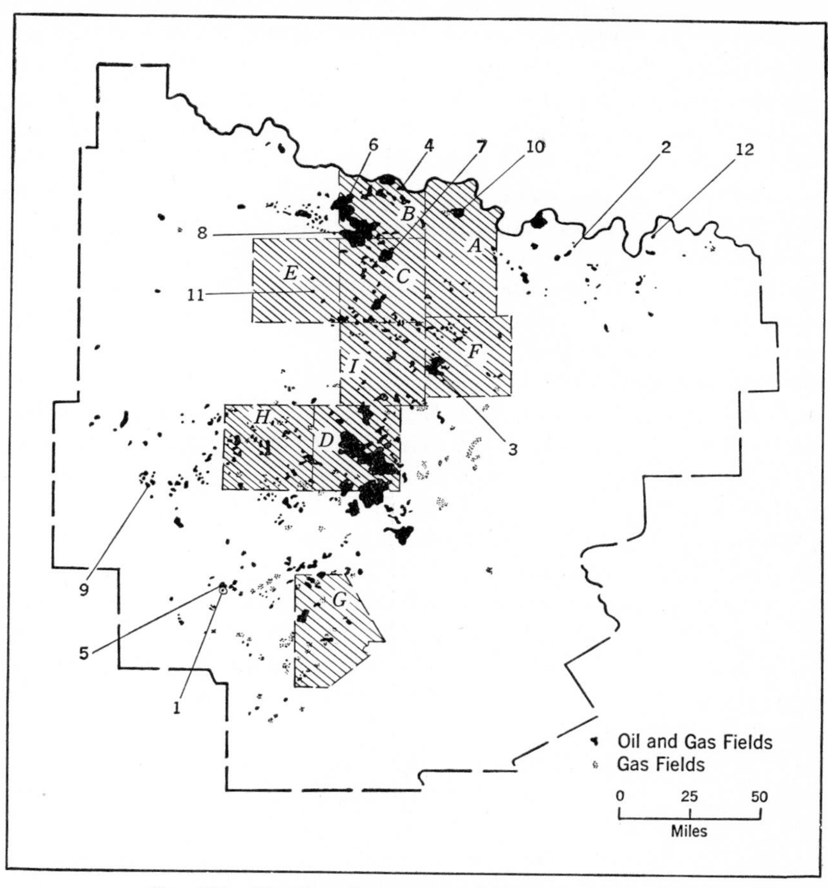

FIG. 126. North and west central Texas index map.

A, Clay County.
B, Wichita County.
C, Archer County.
D, Stephens County.
E, Baylor County.
F, Jack County.
G, Brown County.
H, Jackford County.
I, Young County.

1, Blake oil field.
2, Bowers oil field.
3, Bryson oil field.
4, Burkburnett oil field.
5, Cross Cut oil field.
6, Electra oil field.
7, Hull-Silk oil field.
8, K M A oil field.
9, Noodle Creek oil field.
10, Petrolia oil field.
11, Seymour oil field.
12, Walnut Bend oil field.

there to Archer County. Along the northern edge of the district are the Red River and Muenster uplifts, with the Fort Worth syncline parallel to, and southwest of, the latter feature. Most of the oil that has been produced in this district has come from anticlines or other types of traps lying upon either the Bend flexure or the Red River uplift. The leading fields in cumulative production through 1949 are the Burkburnett, Electra, and KMA. The KMA was first in annual output during 1949.

Most of the oil in the North and West Central district comes from sandstone and limestone reservoirs of Pennsylvanian age. These "sands" range in age from Cisco (Upper Pennsylvanian) to Bend (Lower Pennsylvanian). One field may contain six, eight, or even more reservoirs. The Ordovician Ellenburger limestone began producing in the KMA field in 1940.

Accumulation in this district has been controlled largely by structure, but in many instances variations in porosity have controlled distribution of oil within the closed area. Trapping in some fields has been due to either the wedging-out or the up-dip shaling of the sandstone reservoir. Several of the larger fields, including the KMA and Hull-Silk, lie on the South Electra fold which cuts across parts of Wichita, Archer, and Clay Counties.[146] Thompson [147] has noted that, although all the oil in the Hull-Silk pool lies within the anticlinal closure, variable porosity within the different reservoirs controls the distribution across the top of the structure. The Petrolia dome is a marked structural feature overlying a granite knob along the axis of the Red River uplift.[148] Accumulation in Stephens County to the south, high on the Bend Arch, is likewise anticlinal.[149] The principal reservoir in this area is limestone belonging in the Bend series of Lower Pennsylvanian age.

Accumulation in the Walnut Bend pool [150] occupies an elongate anticline, but in only two of the five reservoirs is the permeability adequate for complete occupancy of the upfold; in the other three the oil has been trapped on the anticlinal flanks, owing to gradation from sandstone into shale. In the Bowers field [151] oil is obtained from

146 J. J. Maucini, "Developments in North-Central and West-Central Texas, 1938," *Bull. Am. Assoc. Petrol. Geol.,* Vol. 23 (June, 1939), p. 845.

147 Edwin I. Thompson, "Hull-Silk Oil Field, Archer County, Texas," *Stratigraphic Type Oil Fields* (Am. Assoc. Petrol. Geol., 1941), pp. 661–679.

148 Frank E. Kendrick and H. C. McLaughlin, "Relation of Petroleum Accumulation to Structure, Petrolia Field, Clay County, Texas," *Structure of Typical American Oil Fields* (Am. Assoc. Petrol. Geol., 1929), Vol. 2, pp. 542–555.

149 W. K. Esgen, "Relation of Accumulation of Petroleum to Structure in Stephens County, Texas," *ibid.,* pp. 470–479.

150 William J. Hilseweck, "Walnut Bend Pool, Cook County, Texas," *Stratigraphic Type Oil Fields* (Am. Assoc. Petrol. Geol., 1941), pp. 776–805.

151 A. B. Brown, "Bowers Field, Montague County, Texas," *Bull. Am. Assoc. Petrol. Geol.,* Vol. 27 (January, 1943), pp. 20–37.

eight separate reservoirs of Pennsylvanian age. The structure is an anticline, but in six out of the eight producing zones variable porosity determines the distribution of oil.

The North and West Central district contains at least one productive reef, the Seymour pool in Baylor County.[152] Unlike most other pools in North Texas, production at Seymour is limited to a single reservoir rock, the reef limestone belonging in the Canyon group of Pennsylvanian age. The pay section is a fossiliferous limestone from 2 to 12 feet in thickness. It follows the dome shape of the top of the reef; although not in an anticlinal fold the accumulation can be considered to be due to the pseudo-anticlinal structure. In the Bryson [153] oil field in Jack County the oil has been impounded by the up-dip shaling of a 250-foot sandstone reservoir series. At the Noodle Creek pool [154] oil has accumulated on the flank of an anticlinal ridge owing to the up-dip wedgeout of porosity in the reservoir limestone. In at least two fields in Brown County, the Cross Cut and Blake,[155] oil and gas occur in lenticular sands, but they invariably occupy the structurally highest parts of the reservoirs.

West Texas (Fig. 127). The West Texas district is bounded on the north by the Panhandle district, on the northeast by the North and West Central district, on the southeast by the Southwest Texas district, on the south by the Rio Grande River and the Republic of Mexico, and on the northwest by the state of New Mexico. Geologically, however, the six counties in southeastern New Mexico are a part of the West Texas or Permian basin province. The West Texas district covers forty-one Texas counties, but the number of oil-producing counties is considerably less. The oil and gas fields are largely confined to a belt about four counties wide extending north and south from the southeastern corner of New Mexico.

Although West Texas has been producing oil since 1913, it was not until the discovery of the Big Lake pool in Reagan County in 1923 that this district began its meteoric rise as an oil-producing area which has made it today not only the leading Texas district but also one of the great sources of world oil.

[152] James K. Murphy, Paul E. M. Purcell, and H. E. Barton, "Seymour Pool, Baylor County, Texas," *Stratigraphic Type Oil Fields* (Am. Assoc. Petrol. Geol., 1941), pp. 760–775.

[153] T. C. Hiestand, "Bryson Oil Field, Jack County, Texas," *op. cit.*, pp. 539–547.

[154] H. W. Imholz, "Noodle Creek Pool, Jones County, Texas," *op. cit.*, pp. 698–721.

[155] Edgar D. Klinger, "Cross Cut-Blake District, Brown County, Texas," *op. cit.*, pp. 548–563.

The most obvious tectonic feature in West Texas [156] is the Marathon uplift in the Big Bend of the Rio Grande River which brings lowermost Paleozoic rocks to the surface. To the north, and extending into southeastern New Mexico a short distance west of the southeast corner, is the Delaware basin. This basin is bordered on the east by the Central basin platform on which most of the oil fields of the district are concentrated. To the northwest of the Central basin platform, extending in an east-west direction across southeastern New Mexico, is the Northwestern shelf area. Due north of the Central basin platform is the northeasterly extension of the Northwestern shelf area, which is known as the North basin platform. East of both the Central basin platform and the North basin platform is the great Midland basin, which is succeeded still farther east by the Eastern basin platform. Crossing the northern end of the West Texas district is the Matador uplift. Second only to the Central basin platform in its concentration of oil fields is the Northwestern shelf-North basin platform. The Eastern platform stands third in importance. In the two basins, the Midland and the Delaware, oil fields are much less abundant.

The reservoir rocks in the West Texas district are sandstones and especially limestones ranging in age from Upper Permian to Cambro-Ordovician. The major reservoirs underlie the Upper Castile formation which contains the great salt and potash deposits of the Texas-New Mexico area. Both the Guadalupe and the Leonard of the Permian contain important reservoirs, including the Capitan reef limestone. Oil has been found in quantity also in the Wolfcamp rocks of Lower Permian age. Most of the earlier production of the district came from Permian formations, and these reservoirs are still important sources of oil.

All the enormous reserves discovered in Scurry County in 1949–1950 occur in Pennsylvanian reefs provisionally assigned to the Canyon group of Middle Pennsylvanian age. The underlying Strawn, of Lower Pennsylvanian age, which is so important as a source of oil in the North and West Central Texas district, is oil-bearing in some West Texas fields. Oil has been found in both Devonian and Silurian rocks. Many fields produce from Simpson and other Ordovician for-

[156] John E. Galley and G. S. Corey, "Developments in West Texas and Southeast New Mexico in 1949," *Bull. Am. Assoc. Petrol. Geol.,* Vol. 34 (June, 1950), pp. 1129–1143; Philip B. King, "Permian of West Texas and Southeastern New Mexico," *Bull. Am. Assoc. Petrol. Geol.,* Vol. 26 (April, 1942), pp. 535–763; Robert E. King *et al.,* "Résumé of Geology of the South Permian Basin, Texas and New Mexico," *Bull. Geol. Soc. Am.,* Vol. 53 (April 1, 1942), pp. 539–560.

mations, and the Ellenburger limestone of Cambro-Ordovician age is an outstanding reservoir.

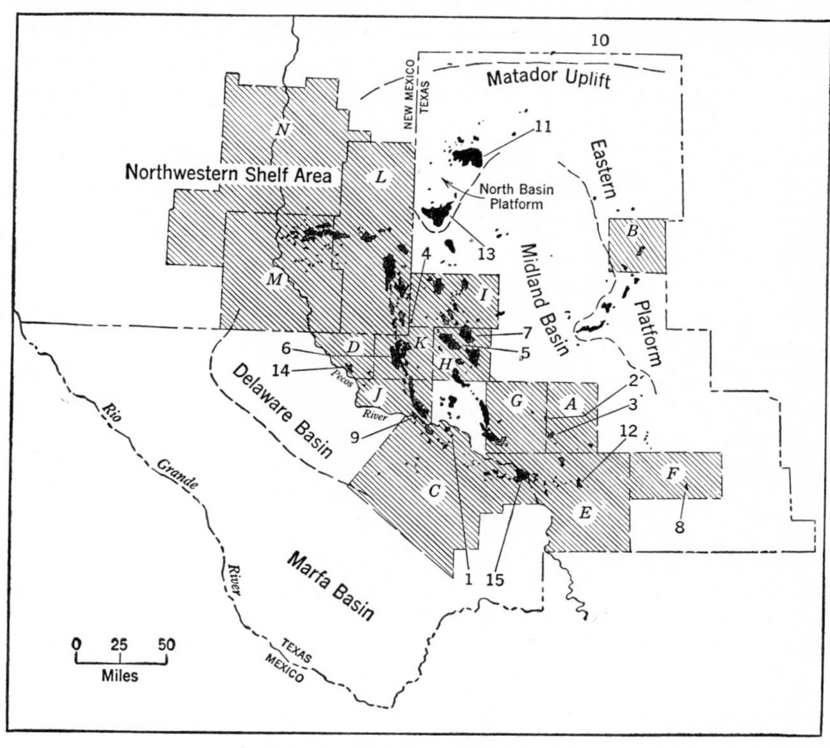

FIG. 127. West Texas index map.

A, Reagan County.
B, Scurry County.
C, Pecos County.
D, Loving County.
E, Crockett County
F, Schleicher County.
G, Upton County.
H, Ector County.
I, Andrews County.
J, Ward County.
K, Winkler County.
L, Lea County, New Mexico.
M, Eddy County, New Mexico.
N, Chaves County, New Mexico.

1, Apco oil field.
2, Benedum oil field.
3, Big Lake oil field.
4, Dollarhide oil field.
5, Goldsmith oil field.
6, Hendrick oil field.
7, North Cowden oil field.
8, Page oil field.
9, Payton oil field.
10, Petersburg oil field.
11, Slaughter-Leveland oil field.
12, Todd oil field.
13, Wasson oil field.
14, Wheat oil field.
15, Yates oil field.

The leading fields in total production in the West Texas district are the Yates at the extreme southeastern end of the Central basin uplift, the Hendrick on the west side of the Central basin platform immediately south of the southeastern corner of New Mexico, and the Wasson at the southwest end of the North basin platform. In 1949 the Slaughter-Leveland field toward the north end of the North basin platform was in first place in annual production, followed by the Wasson and the Yates. The greatest activity, however, in 1949–1950 was in Scurry County (Fig. 128), toward the north end of the Eastern platform, where a Pennsylvanian reef has been found to be productive over a probable length, in a northeast-southwest direction, of 20 miles,

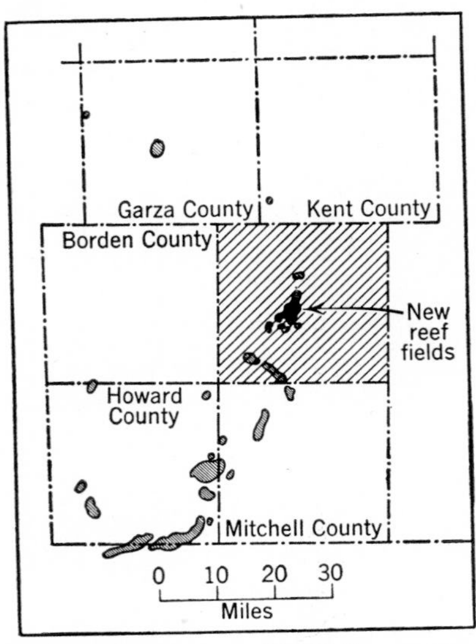

Fig. 128. New reef fields of Scurry County, Texas (Scurry County shown by diagonal lines). *Courtesy Oil and Gas Journal.*

and a width of 6 miles at the broadest point. Furthermore, the actual production limit to the southwest and northeast had not in February, 1950, been definitely fixed by dry holes.[157] The top of the reef is very uneven topographically, resulting in wide variations in reservoir thickness. Although some wells are reported to have penetrated as much as 700 feet of reef rock, the thickness of the oil-bearing sections above the oil-water interface ranges at the present state of development from about 100 to 400 feet. Estimates of the total reserve available in the Scurry County reefs range as high as 1 billion barrels.

Three of the West Texas fields were used in Chapter 8 to illustrate various types of trapping. These are the Big Lake (Fig. 45) of Reagan

[157] D. H. Stormont, "Scurry County's New Reef Fields," *Oil and Gas Jour.*, Vol. 48 (February 2, 1950), pp. 46 *et seq.;* "Scurry County Limestone Reef Development," *ibid.*, Vol. 48 (July 7, 1949), pp. 54 *et seq.*

County in the Midland basin, an unusually symmetrical dome, the Apco (Fig. 77) field of Pecos County near the southern end of the Central basin platform, which produces from an overlapped dolomite wedge, and the Wheat (Fig. 49) pool of Loving County in the Delaware basin which illustrates possible terrace trapping. The mode of accumulation in a few other fields scattered across the West Texas district is described briefly in the following paragraphs.

The Page field [158] is in the southeastern part of the district where the Eastern platform merges with the Edwards plateau. The reservoir rock is a porous limestone lying within the Strawn (Pennsylvanian). The production, mostly gas, comes from a structurally high area which may be a reef. The Todd field [159] in Crockett County in the Midland basin to the west of Schleicher County produces in part from a crinoidal reef limestone within the Strawn. The upper surface of the crinoidal limestone is domelike, but production is limited on the east side by the disappearance of the limestone in that direction. This reef is merely a protuberance on the west flank of a large dome in the Ordovician Ellenburger limestone. The Ellenburger is productive clear across the dome.

The Benedum field [160] lies along the Upton-Reagan County line in the southern part of the Midland basin. It produces from Pennsylvanian, Silurian, and Cambro-Ordovician (Ellenburger) reservoirs. The trap is a pronounced dome faulted on the east flank.

On the Central basin platform most of the accumulation is due to the presence of local anticlines. Examples are the Goldsmith [161] and North Cowden fields,[162] both in Ector County on the east side of the platform about midway between the north and south ends. These anticlines are from 7 to 10 miles long and up to 4 miles wide.

The Payton pool [163] lies along the Pecos River on the west side of the Central basin platform and produces oil from a 240-foot-thick zone of Yates (Permian) sandstone. The trap is an elongate anticline

[158] Roscoe Simpson, "Page Field, Schleicher County, Texas," *Bull. Am. Assoc. Petrol. Geol.,* Vol. 25 (April, 1941), pp. 630–636.

[159] Robert F. Imbt and S. V. McCollum, "Todd Deep Field, Crockett County, Texas," *Bull. Am. Assoc. Petrol. Geol.,* Vol. 34 (February, 1950), pp. 239–262.

[160] Charles J. Deegan, "Benedum Field Is Established as Three-Pay Major Reserve," *Oil and Gas Jour.,* Vol. 48 (May 19, 1949), pp. 183 *et seq.*

[161] Addison Young, Max David, and E. A. Wahlstrom, "Goldsmith Field, Ector County, Texas," *Bull. Am. Assoc. Petrol. Geol.,* Vol. 23 (October, 1939), pp. 1525–1552.

[162] Sam C. Giesey and Frank F. Fulk, "North Cowden Field, Ector County, Texas," *Bull. Am. Assoc. Petrol. Geol.,* Vol. 52 (April, 1941), pp. 593–629.

[163] Richard E. Gile, "Payton Pool, Pecos and Ward Counties, Texas," *Bull. Am. Assoc. Petrol. Geol.,* Vol. 26 (October, 1942), pp. 1632–1646.

with a northwest-southeast trend, but production is limited on the east flank of the anticline by gradation from sand into sandy shale and anhydritic sand. Farther to the north on the west side of the platform, near the southwestern corner of Andrews County, is the Dollarhide field,[164] famous for the storage of oil in large caverns in the Fusselman limestone of Silurian age. The trapping is anticlinal not only in the Fusselman but also in the higher Devonian and deeper Ellenburger reservoirs.

Along the northwestern side of the Central basin platform, extending north from the Pecos River across Ward and Winkler counties, Texas, and into Lea County, southeastern New Mexico, is the so-called "sand belt." [165] As in the Payton field the reservoir rock is Pennsylvanian sandstone and the trapping is due to a combination of anticlinal structure plus a facies change from permeability to impermeability to the east.

The Wasson field,[166] a major field in west Texas, lies at the south end of the North basin platform. Accumulation appears to be in a reef in Permian rock. The reservoir is a porous dolomite several hundred feet below the top of the San Andres formation. The Petersburg pool [167] is at the north edge of the district on the Matador uplift. This pool produces from a porous limestone, perhaps a reef, which has anticlinal closure.

A recent survey of the types of traps in 445 fields in west Texas and southeastern New Mexico showed that 139 are anticlines, 35 are reefs, 3 are faults, and the remaining 268 of the varying-permeability type. However, 8 major fields with anticlinal traps have produced 44 per cent of the oil.[168]

Texas Panhandle.[169] The Panhandle district includes the northernmost twenty-five counties in northwesternmost Texas. It is bounded

[164] D. H. Stormont, "Huge Caverns Encountered in Dollarhide Field," *Oil and Gas Jour.*, Vol. 47 (April 7, 1949), pp. 66 *et seq.*

[165] R. L. Denham and W. E. Dougherty, "'Sand Belt' Area of Ward and Winkler Counties, Texas, and Lea County, New Mexico," *Stratigraphic Type Oil Fields* (Am. Assoc. Petrol. Geol., 1941), pp. 750–759.

[166] W. T. Schneider, "Geology of Wasson Field, Yoakum and Gaines Counties, Texas," *Bull. Am. Assoc. Petrol. Geol.*, Vol. 27 (April, 1943), pp. 479–523.

[167] R. W. Mallory, "Petersburg Oil Pool, Hale County, Texas," *Bull. Am. Assoc. Petrol. Geol.*, Vol. 32 (May, 1948), pp. 780–789.

[168] J. H. Bartley and R. T. Cox, "Types of Oil and Gas Traps in West Texas and Southeastern New Mexico," *Am. Assoc. Petrol. Geol., Program Annual Meeting* (1950), p. 18.

[169] Paul H. Horn, "Developments in Texas Panhandle in 1949," *Bull. Am. Assoc. Petrol. Geol.*, Vol. 34 (June, 1950), pp. 1123–1128; Henry Rogatz, "Geology of Texas Panhandle Oil and Gas Field," *Bull. Am. Assoc. Petrol. Geol.*, Vol. 23

on the north and east by Oklahoma, at the southeast corner by the North Texas district, on the south by the West Texas district, and on the west by New Mexico. The distribution of oil and gas fields is shown in Fig. 129. Gas is produced in a broad belt which crosses four counties in a direction slightly north of west and then swings north, crossing into the panhandle of Oklahoma and connecting with the

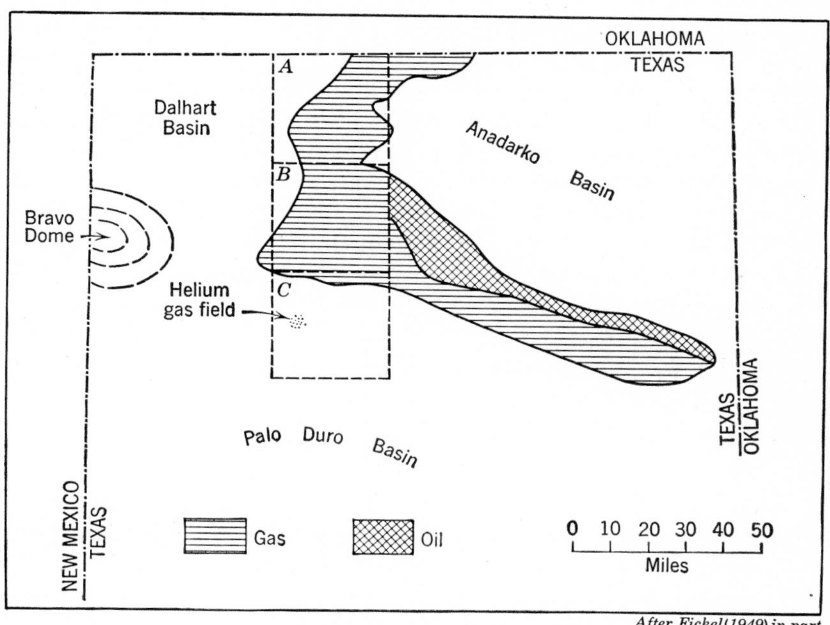

FIG. 129. Panhandle district, Texas, index map. *A*, Sherman County; *B*, Moore County; *C*, Potter County. *Courtesy American Association of Petroleum Geologists.*

Hugoton gas field of southwestern Kansas. Actually that part of the gas field lying north of the Moore-Sherman County line in the Texas Panhandle is known as the South Hugoton field, and the term Panhandle oil and gas field is confined to the east-west trend which overlies the buried Amarillo Mountains. This field is approximately 130 miles long and has an average width of 20 miles. The gas area exceeds 1½ million acres, but the oil is confined to the north side of the gas-producing belt. Although the oil-producing trend extends over a distance

(July, 1939), pp. 983–1053; E. G. Dahlgren, "The Panhandle Field: The World's Largest Natural Gas Reserve," *Gas,* Vol. 22 (July, 1946), pp. 44–51; Victor Cotner and H. E. Crum, "Geology and Occurrence of Natural Gas in Amarillo District, Texas," *Geology of Natural Gas* (Am. Assoc. Petrol. Geol., 1935), pp. 385–415.

of 90 miles the actual acreage that has been proved productive is only about 83,000.

The discovery gas well for the Panhandle district was completed in 1918, and the first oil well in 1921. These discoveries were the direct result of geological observation. Because of remoteness from market, development was slow at first, and it was not until 1926 that the Panhandle district first became a large producer of oil. The building of gas pipe lines to eastern markets was followed by rapid development of the gas field, which proved to have the greatest volume of reserve gas of any field so far discovered anywhere in the world. During the active exploratory phase helium-bearing natural gas was found occupying a separate dome in Potter County. The entire output from this field is piped to a United States Bureau of Mines helium extraction plant near Amarillo.

The major tectonic feature in the Panhandle district is the Amarillo uplift, which extends into Texas from western Oklahoma and which is obscured by a mantle of continental Tertiary sediments except where the deeper stream valleys have penetrated through to the underlying bed rock. The core of the uplift is pre-Cambrian crystalline rock, the completely buried "Amarillo Mountains." To the northeast is the western end of the Anadarko basin, and in the northwest corner is the Dalhart basin. South of the uplift and extending to the Matador uplift, which crosses the northern end of the West Texas district, is the Palo Duro basin. The Bravo dome separates the Dalhart basin from the northwestern part of the Palo Duro basin.

The lowest reservoir rock is arkose or "granite wash," which is the result of simultaneous erosion of the granitic core of the Amarillo Mountains and deposition on the nearby sea floor during Pennsylvanian time. Higher Pennsylvanian limestone is also productive in part of the district. The most widespread reservoirs are the so-called "white" and "brown" dolomites of Permian age. The greater part of the gas occurs in these higher dolomites, and it is in this series of reservoir rock that the gas accumulation is continuous from the Texas Panhandle across the Oklahoma panhandle and into southwestern Kansas.

Although the map (Fig. 129) shows the oil-producing area to be a continuous one, in reality it is a belt on the north flank of the buried Amarillo Mountains along which are many separate and distinct oil accumulations. The largest in cumulative production of these individual pools is the Borger, but the West Pampa field was the largest producer of oil in 1949. Although some of the accumulations are due to the lenticularity of the granite wash reservoir rock, most oil trapping has been anticlinal, each pool occupying a dome or other type of upfold.

The gas field, on the other hand, is a virtually continuous producing area from one end to the other and from one side to the other. Most of the gas has accumulated in the higher Permian dolomites which are arched into a great anticline across the Amarillo uplift. Gas occurs south of the Amarillo axis as well as north. In the South Hugoton gas field, as in the Hugoton area, the trapping is due to a lessening of the permeability on the west flank of the Anadarko basin due to the increased content of silt and clay in the reservoir dolomite. Accumulation in the helium gas field in Potter County is in a small but unusually symmetrical dome.

The limiting of the oil accumulation so far discovered to the north side of the Amarillo uplift implies that the source material must lie to the northeast, down the flanks of the Anadarko basin. So far, however, attempts to find accumulations on this flank north and east of the Amarillo uplift have not been successful. There have been a number of other unsuccessful attempts to find commercial accumulations of hydrocarbons on the south side of the Panhandle district in the Palo Duro basin.

Louisiana [170]

(Figures 130–132)

The state of Louisiana was credited in 1949 with over 10½ per cent of the domestic oil production. Its share in the world's output during the same period was over 5½ per cent, which was slightly more than that of Saudi Arabia and a little less than that of Iran.

It is customary to consider Louisiana as two oil-producing districts, north Louisiana and the Louisiana Gulf Coast. The dividing line is shown on the accompanying map (Fig. 132). Geologically, the north Louisiana district is a part of a greater district that includes southern Arkansas and northeastern Texas. Similarly, the Louisiana Gulf Coast district is an arbitrary segment of a tectonic division including the Texas Gulf Coast and the shoreline zones of the states to the east.

[170] Leo W. Hough and Arnold C. Chauviere, "Oil and Gas Developments in Louisiana during 1949," Am. Inst. Min. Met. Engineers, *Jour. Petrol. Tech.*, Vol. 2 (June, 1950), pp. 31–58; S. L. Digby *et al.*, "Oil and Gas Developments in Louisiana during 1948–1949," La. Dept. Conservation, *Nineteenth Biennial Reports*, 1948–1949, pp. 26–96, 1950.

The cumulative oil production for south Louisiana is nearly double that of north Louisiana, and the 1949 yield was nearly three times greater. However, north Louisiana contains several major gas fields that give it prominence among gas-producing areas. The cumulative

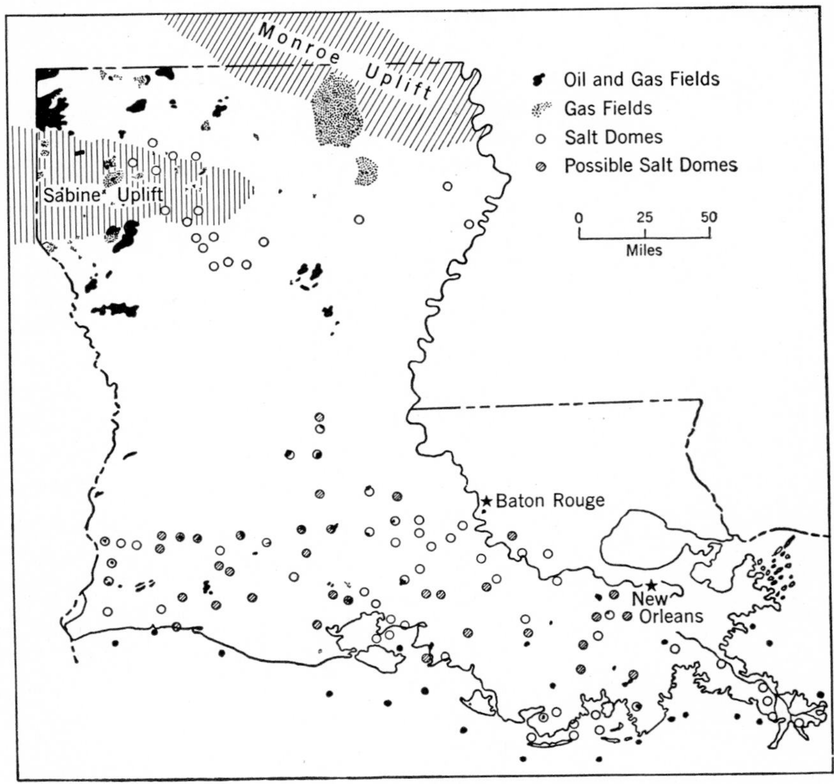

FIG. 130. Louisiana. Major uplifts, salt domes, and fields.

production in south Arkansas is not far behind that of north Louisiana, but the Arkansas production for 1949 was only three-fifths that of north Louisiana.

Louisiana had no important production in either oil or gas until the discovery of the Jennings salt dome field in 1902. This exploration was a direct result of the discovery of Spindletop across the line in Texas in 1901. No important finds were made in north Louisiana until 1905, when gas was discovered in the Caddo field, in which oil was found the following year.

Many new discoveries have been made in northern Louisiana since 1905, including Rodessa in 1930, but the Gulf Coast discoveries have perhaps been the more spectacular. In 1938 the first oil field (Creole) was found in the open waters of the Gulf of Mexico. In 1948, seven new fields were found in the open Gulf in that one year alone.

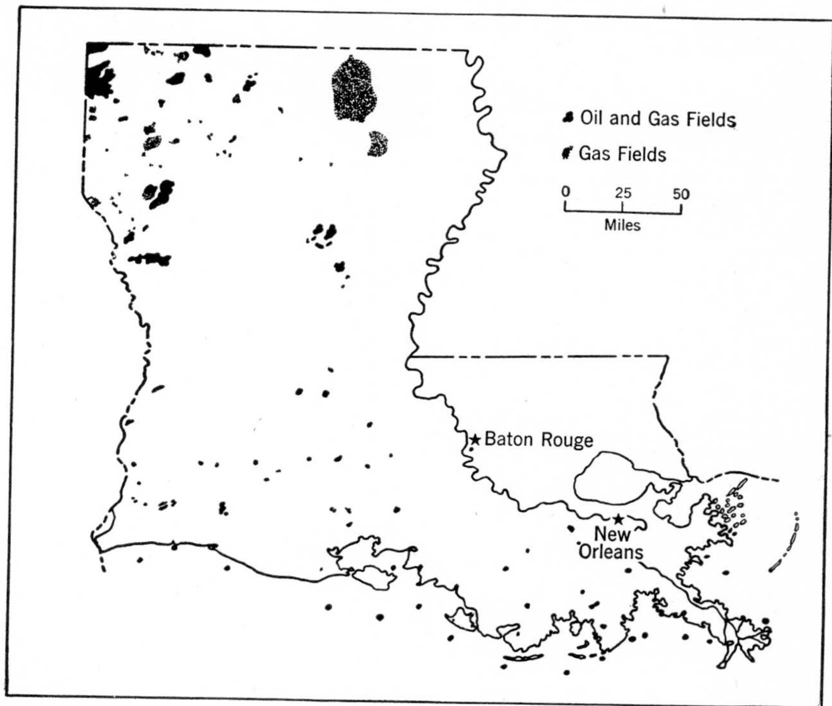

Fig. 131. Louisiana. Oil and gas fields.

Exploration around salt domes discovered years before has resulted in finding several new reservoirs in recent years. In 1943 prolific production was obtained in sandstones of Frio (Oligocene) age on the north flank of the Vinton salt dome, which was discovered in 1910. In the same year an exploratory well was drilled 3000 feet through cap rock and salt at the Vermilion Bay dome before the overhang was broken through and oil was discovered trapped below at a depth of 9500 to 10,900 feet. Another discovery of 1943 was the first well in the Miocene trend east of the Mississippi River.

The Gulf Coast of Louisiana and Texas, especially Louisiana, is notable for the volume of hydrocarbons produced from considerable

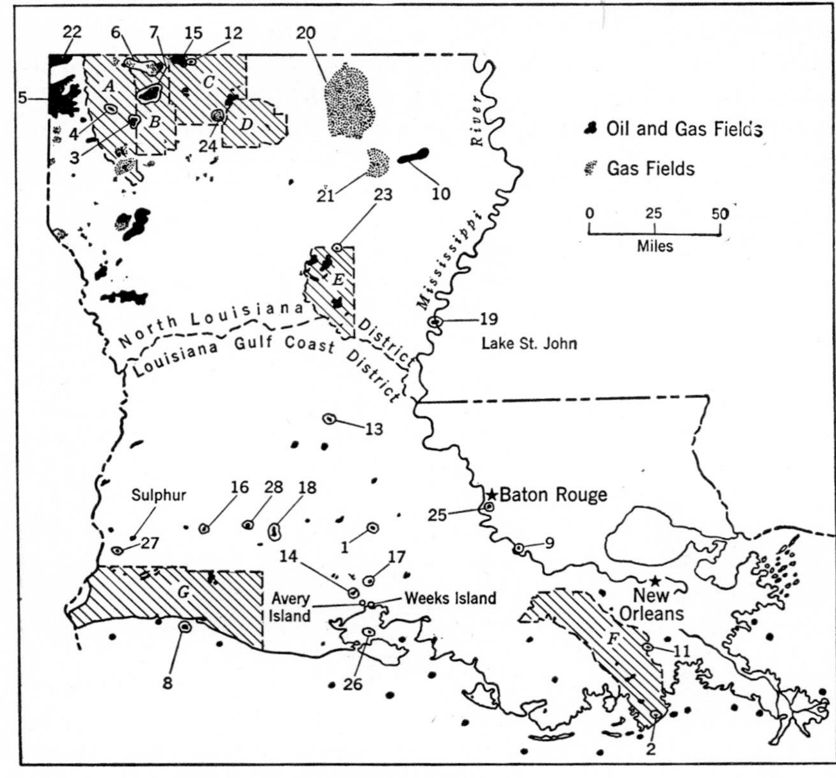

FIG. 132. Louisiana index map.

A, Bossier Parish.
B, Webster Parish.
C, Claiborne Parish.
D, Lincoln Parish.
E, LaSalle Parish.
F, LaFourche Parish.
G, Cameron Parish.

1, Anse la Butte oil field.
2, Bay Marchand oil field.
3, Bellevue oil field.
4, Benton oil field.
5, Caddo oil field.
6, Carterville-Sarepto-Shonzaloo oil field.
7, Cotton Valley oil field.
8, Creole oil field.
9, Darrow oil field.
10, Delhi-Big Creek oil field.
11, Delta Farms oil field.
12, East Haynesville oil field.
13, Eola oil field.
14, Erath oil field.
15, Haynesville oil field.
16, Iowa oil field.
17, Jefferson Island oil field.
18, Jennings oil field.
19, Lake St. John field.
20, Monroe gas field.
21, Richland gas field.
22, Rodessa oil field.
23, Standard oil field.
24, Sugar Creek oil field.
25, University oil field.
26, Vermilion Bay oil field.
27, Vinton oil field.
28, West Tepetate oil field.

depths, although at the moment this region holds neither the record for the deepest production nor that for the deepest exploratory test drilled. Nevertheless, south Louisiana produces more hydrocarbons from depths below 12,000 feet than any other district in the world. A considerable percentage of the fields producing from these depths are the so-called "gas-condensate" type. For example, of the fields discovered on the Gulf Coast in 1948, thirteen were oil fields, eleven condensate fields, and four gas fields.[171] Three of these oil fields, and two each of the condensate and gas fields, were found in the Gulf of Mexico. The discoveries during the same period in northern Louisiana consisted of three oil fields, one distillate field, and four gas fields.[172]

The seismograph is the principal exploring implement used in both north Louisiana and in the Gulf Coast district, including the open waters of the Gulf. The gravity meter and the core drill are also used to some extent in northern Louisiana, and subsurface geology is employed in both areas.

All Louisiana lies within the Gulf embayment province. No rocks older than Tertiary are exposed, except around some of the interior salt domes, where Cretaceous rocks have been pushed to the surface. Cretaceous, Comanchean, and Jurassic sediments are reached by the drill in northern Louisiana. The Gulfward-dipping embayment sediments are interrupted by a major tectonic feature in northwestern Louisiana, the Sabine uplift. This uplift is a dominating influence on accumulation not only in northwestern Louisiana but also in southern Arkansas and northeastern Texas. To the east of the Sabine uplift is a synclinal, or graben, zone, and then the strata rise once more to cross the Monroe uplift of northeastern Louisiana. The Monroe uplift is decidedly subordinate in relief and area to the Sabine.

As in the southeast Gulf Coast district of Texas, the Miocene sediments thicken greatly southward so that it is possible to drill wells to depths exceeding 13,000 feet in the coastal area without getting below rocks deposited during this time interval. The coastal belt contains many salt-cored structures, and most of the oil fields there are due to accumulation either in traps produced by salt piercement or in faulted domes that are known or assumed to overlie salt cores. A second kind of Gulf Coast trap is the "Tepetate type" structure,

[171] William McBee, Jr., and Paul J. Orchard, "Developments in Louisiana Gulf Coast in 1948," *Bull. Am. Assoc. Petrol. Geol.*, Vol. 33 (June, 1949), pp. 979–989.

[172] John R. Williams, "Developments in Arkansas and North Louisiana in 1948," *Bull. Am. Assoc. Petrol. Geol.*, Vol. 33 (June, 1949), pp. 990–1001.

in which accumulation takes place in an anticline on, but close to the edge of, a downfaulted block. This is illustrated in Chapter 8 (Fig. 62), with the West Tepetate field of Louisiana used for an example.

Some of the salt cores approach so near the surface, especially in the Five Islands area of the Mississippi delta, that they have been the scene of salt mining for many years. Salt production started in 1867 on Avery Island, in 1902 on Weeks Island,[173] and in 1922 on Jefferson Island. Cap rock sulfur is obtained by the Frasch process at the Lake Washington salt dome in Plaquemines Parish and was formerly exploited at Sulphur in Calcasieu Parish in southwestern Louisiana, but this deposit was exhausted in 1924. Sulfur has also been mined at the Jefferson Island [174] salt dome, but the supply is now depleted.

The tectonically negative area between the Sabine and Monroe uplifts is an interior salt-dome district containing seventeen known salt cores. Neither oil nor gas has as yet been found associated with the shallow northern Louisiana salt intrusions. Some of them lie close enough to the surface so that solution effects are visible in the topography, and in two places, at the Winnfield dome and at Pine Prairie, the cap rock is exposed, making possible "hard rock" quarries. The limestone at these two localities is now depleted.

The outcropping rocks of northern Louisiana are of the same general age as the reservoir rocks of the Gulf Coast. The Gulf Coast rocks range in age from Miocene to Eocene and include especially the *Discorbis, Heterostegina, Marginulina,* Frio, and Vicksburg sands of the Oligocene, various reservoirs of the Jackson and Claiborne groups of the Eocene, and the still older Eocene Wilcox formation.

The youngest important reservoir rock in the northern Louisiana district is the Wilcox formation of lower Eocene age. Considerable oil is also obtained from Upper Cretaceous sediments, from the Paluxy and older Comanchean formations, and from the Cotton Valley and Smackover limestones of Jurassic age.

Northern Louisiana.[175] The oil fields in Northern Louisiana that have led in total production since discovery are the Caddo, Haynes-

[173] G. D. Harris, "Rock Salt," *La. Geol. Survey, Bull.* 7 (1908).

[174] Lawrence O'Donnell, "Jefferson Island Salt Dome, Iberia Parish, Louisiana," *Gulf Coast Salt Domes* (Am. Assoc. Petrol. Geol., 1936), pp. 983–1025.

[175] Shreveport Geol. Soc., *1945 Reference Report on Certain Oil and Gas Fields of North Louisiana, South Arkansas, Mississippi, and Alabama,* Vol. 1 (1946), Vol. 2 (1947), Shreveport; Milton W. Corbin, "Developments in Arkansas and North Louisiana in 1949," *Bull. Am. Assoc. Petrol. Geol.,* Vol. 34 (June, 1950), pp. 1199–1211.

ville, and Rodessa. The Rodessa field is second only to Caddo in cumulative production, but since it overlaps into Texas and Arkansas, it must share its production statistically with those states. In terms of oil production during 1949, the Delhi-Big Creek field was in first place and the Lake St. John field in second place. Louisiana is second among the natural gas-producing states largely because of the great Monroe gas field in the northeastern part of the state.

Several different types of trapping occur in northern Louisiana. Numerically, at least, anticlinal accumulation appears to dominate, but in some of the larger pools trapping has been due either to faults or to variable permeability. The Caddo field, the largest in total production, is a bald-headed structure with most of the gas and some of the oil coming from Upper Cretaceous reservoirs arched over the buried truncated anticline and with most of the oil coming from three of the truncated Comanchean formations on the flanks of the anticline beneath the unconformity.[176] Caddo lies close to the top of the Sabine uplift in northwestern Louisiana. It overlaps slightly into east Texas.

The Rodessa field is on the northwest flank of the Sabine uplift in the very northwesternmost corner of Louisiana.[177] The field is unusually elongate, with a northeast-southwest trend that carries it into Arkansas in one direction and Texas in the other. The total length is 33 miles, and the maximum width 4½ miles. Trapping is due to the presence of a major fault which has a displacement of about 500 feet at the reservoir level. The southeast side of the fault, the up-dip side in terms of the Sabine uplift, is the down side; accumulation is in the uplifted block immediately to the northwest of the fault. Oil moving up-dip from structurally lower parts of northeastern Texas became impounded by the presence of impervious rock across the fault plane. Many minor faults occur in the upfaulted block parallel to the major fault. Oil and gas are produced from several Comanchean reservoirs, of which the principal one is the Rodessa sand of the Trinity Group. Rodessa was discovered in 1930 and was explored and exploited both vigorously and wastefully until the Louisiana legislature passed conservation laws, which became effective on Jan. 1, 1937. In the immediately preceding month, an estimated 700 million

[176] Corbin D. Fletcher, "Structure of Caddo Field, Caddo Parish, Louisiana," *Structure of Typical American Oil Fields* (Am. Assoc. Petrol. Geol., 1929), Vol. 2, pp. 183–195.

[177] C. C. Clark, "Rodessa Field, Caddo Parish, Louisiana, Cass and Marion Counties, Texas, Miller County, Arkansas," *Shreveport Geol. Soc. Guide Book, 14th Annual Field Trip* (1939), pp. 59–63.

cubic feet of gas per day was burned in the field because there was no market for gas at the time and the operators were solely interested in the accompanying oil.[178]

The Benton field [179] in Bossier Parish, but a few miles southeast of the Rodessa field, is a gas and distillate field producing from the Cotton Valley formation of Jurassic age at depths below 8000 feet. Accumulation is in an elliptical dome. The Bellevue oil field [180] in the same parish also illustrates anticlinal trapping. The principal reservoir rock is the Nacatoch sand, which lies high in the Upper Cretaceous and which occurs at Bellevue at the extremely shallow depth of 300 to 400 feet. The structure at the Nacatoch level is a faulted dome with fairly flat top, the presence of which had been suspected after surface geological observation but which was first mapped in detail by a core-drill survey. It has been suggested that the flowage of salt at depths below those so far tested (6147 feet) created the Bellevue dome by forcing the overlying formations up as much as 2000 feet above their normal elevations. An average yield of 11,000 barrels per acre from depths under 400 feet makes the Bellevue field a phenomenal one in terms of investment return. The Carterville-Sarepta and Shongaloo fields [181] also illustrate anticlinal accumulation but with distribution of the oil governed to a considerable extent by the degree of permeability of the reservoir sandstones. These fields lie south of the Arkansas line in Bossier and Webster parishes. Their structure is also credited to salt flowage at depth. The Cotton Valley field,[182] which lies wholly in Webster Parish, is one of the larger oil fields of northern Louisiana. The most important reservoirs are the Bodcaw and Davis sands within the Cotton Valley formation of Jurassic age. The Bodcaw reservoir lies at an average depth of 8100 feet, and accumulation is due to the presence of an arcuate elliptical anticline with 600 feet of productive closure at the Bodcaw level. The Davis sand occurs approximately 260 feet below the Bodcaw and has a productive closure of about 750 feet. Other fields illustrating anticlinal accumulation in northwestern north

[178] *Thirteenth Biennial Report, Department of Conservation, State of Louisiana, 1936–1937* (1938), p. 338.

[179] Shreveport Geol. Soc., *1945 Reference Report,* Vol. 2 (1947), pp. 394–396.

[180] A. F. Crider, "Geology of Bellevue Oil Field, Bossier Parish, Louisiana," *Bull. Am. Assoc. Petrol. Geol.,* Vol. 22 (December, 1938), pp. 1658–1681.

[181] G D. Thomas, "Carterville-Sarepta and Shongaloo Fields, Bossier and Webster Parishes, Louisiana," *Bull. Am. Assoc. Petrol. Geol.,* Vol. 22 (November, 1938), pp. 1473–1503.

[182] Shreveport Geol. Soc., *1945 Reference Report,* Vol. 2 (1947), pp. 412–419.

Louisiana are East Haynesville [183] and Sugar Creek,[184] both in Claiborne Parish.

The large Monroe gas field [185] (Fig. 133) and the somewhat smaller Richland [186] field to the southeast are both examples of truncation with sealing by overlap. The Lower and Upper Cretaceous sedimentary section, which contains the gas reservoirs, was tilted westward, beveled by erosion, and then buried beneath unconformable Tertiary sediments that trapped the gas in the truncated permeable strata beneath. Later both areas were arched upward, and so the structure of the Tertiary rocks shows two large domes.

Eastern north Louisiana contains the Delhi-West Delhi-Big Creek oil field,[187] which is currently the most productive field in the district. The trapping in this field is due to varying permeability brought about by truncation and overlap. The regional dip is to the southeast off the Monroe uplift. The principal reservoirs are the Tuscaloosa (Upper Cretaceous) and Paluxy (Lower Cretaceous). The Tuscaloosa sand is spread over the underlying unconformable Lower Cretaceous surface, including the beveled edges of the Paluxy. Because of this contact, the Paluxy and Tuscaloosa constitute a single reservoir. The Tuscaloosa and younger Cretaceous formations are in turn beveled and overlapped by the Monroe gas rock, supplying the seal that keeps the hydrocarbons within the underlying reservoir rock.

The second field in current production, the Lake St. John, lies near the southeastern corner of the north Louisiana district. This field contains seven distinct reservoirs, ranging in age from middle Eocene to Lower Comanchean. The hydrocarbons obtained range from nearly dry gas through distillate to crude oil.[188] The trap is a faulted dome; geophysical surveys have shown the presence of a gravity minimum at the center of the dome, which suggests the presence of a deep-seated salt core.

[183] Shreveport Geol. Soc., *op. cit.,* pp. 434–436.

[184] C. C. Clark, "Sugar Creek Field, Claiborne Parish, Louisiana," *Bull. Am. Assoc. Petrol. Geol.,* Vol. 22 (November, 1938), pp. 1504–1518.

[185] Preston Fergus, "Monroe Gas Field, Louisiana," *Geology of Natural Gas* (Am. Assoc. Petrol. Geol., 1935), pp. 741–772.

[186] Dugald Gordon, "Richland Gas Field, Richland Parish, Louisiana," *ibid.,* pp. 773–786.

[187] Shreveport Geol. Soc., *1945 Reference Report,* Vol. 2 (1947), pp. 397–401; pp. 420–427; P. A. Bloomer, Jr., "Subsurface Study of the Delhi Area, Franklin and Richland Parishes, Louisiana," *La. Geol. Survey, Geol. Pamphlet* 4 (1946).

[188] Shreveport Geol. Soc., *op. cit.,* pp. 445–452.

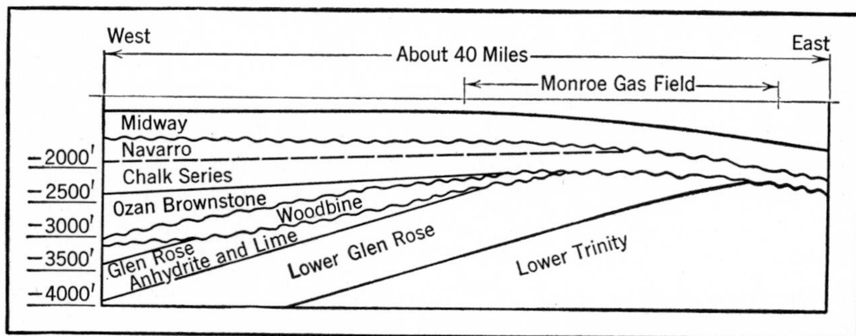

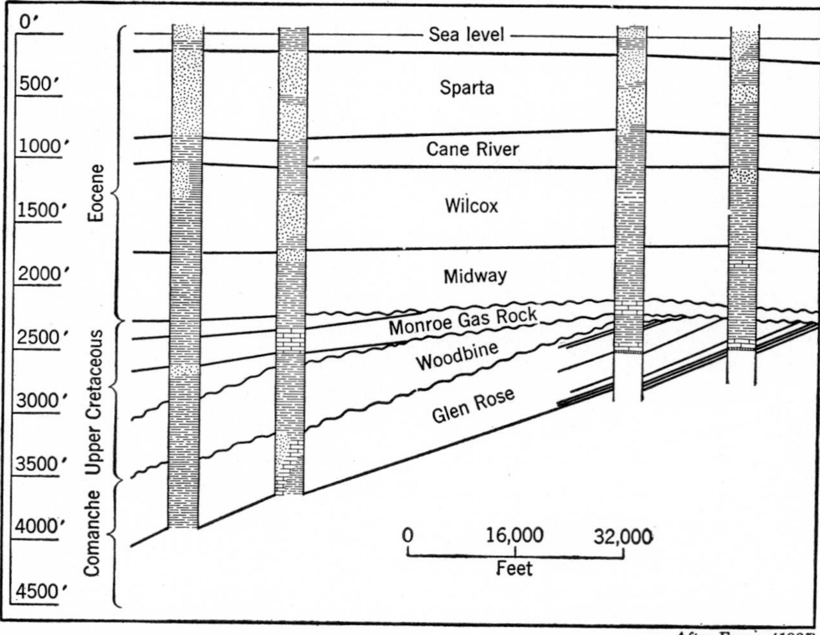

After Fergus (1935)

Fig. 133. Monroe gas field, Louisiana. Upper: regional cross section through north-central part of field. Lower: close-up showing reservoir rock. *Courtesy American Association of Petroleum Geologists.*

In the southern part of the district, in La Salle Parish, is another concentration of oil fields. In at least one of these, the Standard,[189] the trapping is anticlinal.

Louisiana Gulf Coast.[190] The leading fields in the Louisiana Gulf Coast district in cumulative production are the Jennings and the Iowa; the leading fields during 1949 were Delta Farms and Erath. As the salt-dome fields of the Gulf Coast were discussed in Chapter 8, they will not be considered in any great detail here. The discovery well of the Jennings field [191] was drilled only eight months after the completion of the Lucas discovery at Spindletop. It was located where it was because of gas seepages on a topographic mound. From 1901 until 1929 the production at Jennings was obtained exclusively from arched Miocene sediments overlying the cap rock. These are shallow reservoirs lying within 2000 feet of the surface. In 1929 the first Oligocene flank production was discovered at a depth of more than 7500 feet. However, extensive exploitation of the dragged-up complexly faulted, flank sands did not begin until 1936. It is estimated that eventually as much oil will be obtained from the flanks as from the supercap reservoirs.

The hiatus between the discovery of shallow supercap reservoirs and of flank reservoirs was even greater at Anse la Butte dome.[192] This salt-cored structure was discovered in 1901, but it was not until 1940 that flank production was found. At Anse la Butte the salt rises to within 160 feet of the surface. The reservoirs range in age from Pleistocene to Miocene and in depth from a few hundred feet to more than 9000 feet.

The first salt dome found to be oil-bearing east of the Mississippi River was the Darrow dome,[193] which lies on the left bank of the Mississippi River, between Baton Rouge and New Orleans. The Darrow dome produces from both supercap and flank sands. They are thought to belong to the same Miocene formation, although they are spread apart several thousand feet by the intrusion of the salt core.

[189] Shreveport Geol. Soc., *op. cit.*, pp. 464–466.

[190] Cecil W. Smith, "Gulf Coast Oil Fields," *World Oil* (Gulf Coast Issue), Vol. 130 (June, 1950), pp. 92–120; George N. May, "Developments in Louisiana Gulf Coast in 1949," *Bull. Am. Assoc. Petrol. Geol.*, Vol. 34 (June, 1950), pp. 1191–1198.

[191] C. B. Roach, "Subsurface Study, Jennings Field, Acadia Parish, Louisiana," *Bull. Am. Assoc. Petrol. Geol.*, Vol. 27 (August, 1943), pp. 1102–1122.

[192] Fred W. Bates and Jay B. Wharton, Jr., "Anse la Butte Dome, St. Martin Parish, Louisiana," *Bull. Am. Assoc. Petrol. Geol.*, Vol. 27 (August, 1943), pp. 1123–1156.

[193] Carroll E. Cook, "Darrow Salt Dome, Ascension Parish, Louisiana," *Bull. Am. Assoc. Petrol. Geol.*, Vol. 22 (October, 1938), pp. 1412–1422.

Much the greater part of the production has come from truncated reservoirs at depths averaging 5700 feet on the eastern and southwestern flanks and 7000 feet on the southeastern flank. The reservoir sandstones have been dragged up so that they lodge against the salt mass at relatively high angles. As a result, the width of the producing zone is extremely narrow, which makes it difficult to find from the surface.

The discovery field in the open waters of the Gulf of Mexico, the Creole,[194] lies off Cameron Parish in southwestern Louisiana. This field occupies but a small part of a large domed area that was outlined by a seismograph survey. Oil occurs in three sands of Middle and Lower Miocene age, ranging in depths from 5100 to 6600 feet. Trapping is brought about by faulting, which seals the producing sands against shale bodies. A drawing of a model of this field is reproduced in Chapter 8 (Fig. 66).

During the first half of 1949, a well drilled 4 miles off the coast at La Fourche Parish struck salt at a depth of 2131 feet.[195] A second well struck oil on the flanks of this submarine salt dome. Subsequently, six more producing wells have been drilled in this, the Bay Marchand, field. Four sands that produce have been found, ranging in depth from 2900 to 5100 feet.

In addition to Creole and Bay Marchand, ten other fields had been discovered in the open waters of the Gulf of Mexico off Louisiana by mid-1949. Carsey has estimated that at least 87 potential oil-bearing structures have already been discovered in Louisiana waters at a depth shallow enough to warrant leasing.[196] He also notes that at least ten fields on the mainland are in reality situated upon recently constructed natural levees of the Mississippi delta in what was open water of the Gulf not very long ago, so there is nothing new about continental shelf production.

Faulting also played a prominent role in the accumulation of oil in the Eola field in the northern part of the south Louisiana district.[197] The main production comes from sands in the Lower Eocene at an average depth of 8500 feet. Accumulation is made possible by the

[194] Theron Wasson, "Creole Field, Gulf of Mexico, Coast of Louisiana," *Structure of Typical American Oil Fields* (Am. Assoc. Petrol. Geol., 1948), Vol. 3, pp. 281–298.

[195] J. E. Kastrop, "The California Company's Bay Marchand Field," *World Oil,* Vol. 129 (August, 1949), p. 76.

[196] J. Ben Carsey, "Geology of Gulf Coastal Area and Continental Shelf," *Bull. Am. Assoc. Petrol. Geol.,* Vol. 34 (March, 1950), pp. 361–385.

[197] Fred W. Bates, "Geology of Eola Oil Field, Avoyelles Parish, Louisiana," *Bull. Am. Assoc. Petrol. Geol.,* Vol. 25 (July, 1941), pp. 1363–1395.

presence of a prominent plunging anticline, which appears to be a structural offshoot from the Cheneyville salt dome, with a complex system of normal faults truncating the plunging anticline and thus supplying closure.

Combination trapping is shown in the University oil field, which lies east of the Mississippi in East Baton Rouge Parish.[198] Oil and gas are obtained from four Miocene sandstones ranging in depth from 4300 to 7100 feet. Three of the producing sandstones, including the main oil-producing ("6400 foot") sand, show structural trapping in a relatively steep-sided dome with a gently rounded top. The "4300 foot" gas sand, however, pinches out to the northwest so that approximately only the southeast half of the dome is productive at this level. In common with other domes in the Louisiana Gulf district, the University structure has probably been the result of the intrusion of a deep-seated salt core.

Arkansas [199]

(Figures 134–136)

In 1949 Arkansas contributed a little more than 1½ per cent of the nation's total oil production. Although the northwestern part of this state began producing natural gas in about 1899, it was not until 1921, when the El Dorado pool in the southern part of the state was discovered, that Arkansas entered the oil-producing column. A year later the prolific Smackover pool, in which some wells were credited with initial productions of as much as 70,000 barrels a day, was found. This flood of oil pushed Arkansas into fourth place among oil-producing states in 1925, but additional discoveries were slow in coming and subsequently production declined to far below the peak year. A campaign to explore the deeper reservoirs in southern Arkansas got under way in 1937, and a number of new pools, and deeper reservoirs in older fields, resulted. During 1949 seven new fields were discovered, as well as four new oil reservoir zones in old fields. The reflection seismo-

[198] Michel Halbouty, "Stratigraphic Reservoirs in University Oil Field, East Baton Rouge Parish, Louisiana," *Stratigraphic Type Oil Fields* (Am. Assoc. Petrol. Geol., 1941), pp. 208–236.

[199] D. K. MacKay and L. F. Danforth, "Oil and Gas Developments in Arkansas in 1948," Am. Inst. Min. Met. Engineers, *Statistics of Oil and Gas Development and Production* (1949); Shreveport Geol. Soc., *1945 Reference Report on Certain Oil and Gas Fields of North Louisiana, South Arkansas, Mississippi, and Alabama,* Vols. 1 (1946) and 2 (1947); George H. Fancher and D. K. MacKay, "Secondary Recovery of Petroleum in Arkansas—A Survey," Arkansas Oil and Gas Commission (El Dorado, 1946).

graph has been extensively employed in southern Arkansas as a prospecting tool. However, the gravity meter, magnetometer, and core drill are also used in this area.[200]

Geologically, Arkansas can be divided into almost equal halves by a diagonal line extending from northeast to southwest across the state.

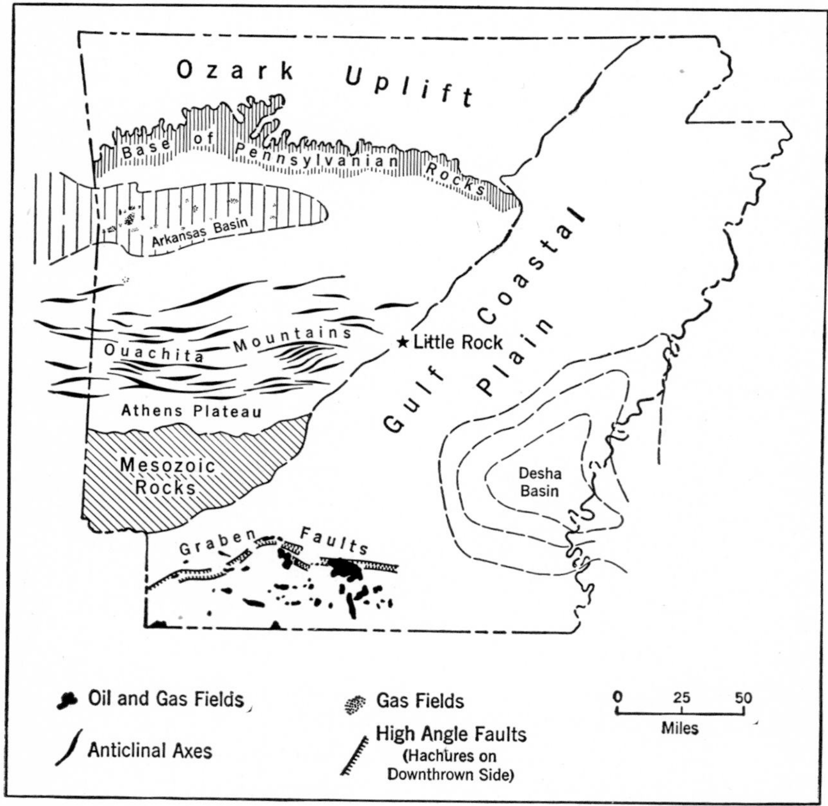

FIG. 134. Arkansas. Major tectonic features and oil and gas fields.

The northwest segment is underlain by Paleozoic rocks, whereas the southeast half belongs in the Gulf Coastal Plain province where the rock formations at the surface were deposited during the great Mesozoic and Cenozoic overlaps of the Gulf embayment. Cenozoic (Quaternary and Tertiary) rocks lie at the surface over all the Arkansas Coastal

[200] Milton W. Corbin, "Developments in Arkansas and North Louisiana in 1949," *Bull. Am. Assoc. Petrol. Geol.*, Vol. 34 (June, 1950), pp. 1199–1211.

Plain belt except for a small area of Upper and Lower Cretaceous outcrops in the southwestern part of the state.

Northwestern Arkansas belongs geologically with Oklahoma to the west and Missouri to the north. Across northern Arkansas, west of the

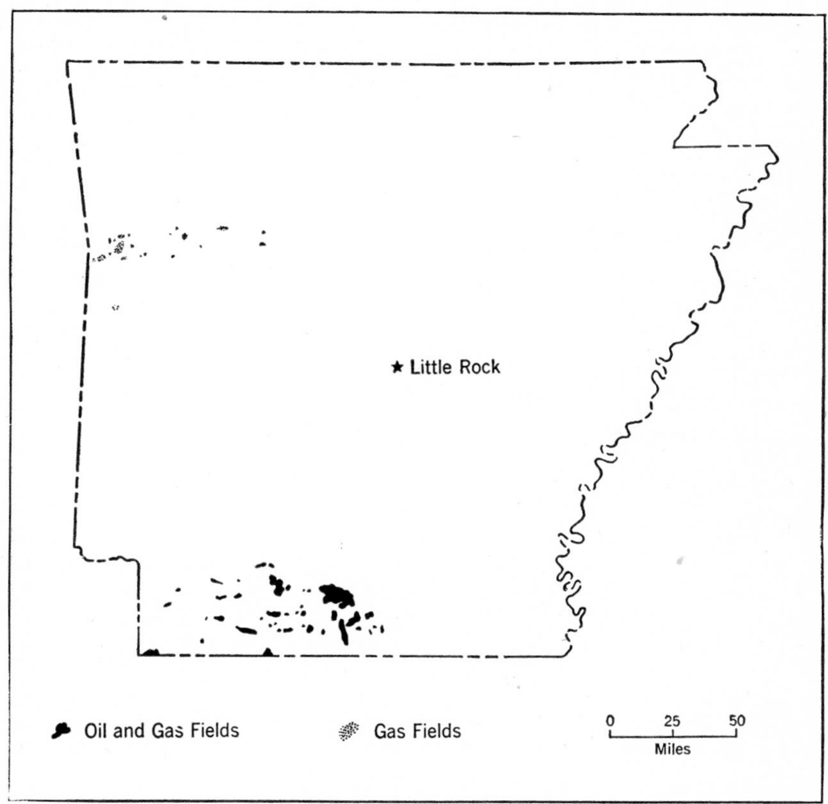

Fig. 135. Arkansas. Oil and gas fields.

Gulf embayment, the regional structure is controlled by the Ozark uplift of southern Missouri. To the south, in western Arkansas, is the east-west synclinal Arkansas Valley district of Paleozoic sediments containing some commercial accumulations of gas along faulted anticlines. At the southern end of the Paleozoic belt is the Ouachita Mountain anticlinorium, noted for the intense deformation of the local rocks.

The Coastal Plain half of Arkansas lies within the widespread Gulf embayment province of Texas, Louisiana, and states to the eastward. Tectonically, southern Arkansas belongs with Louisiana. It occupies the northeast flank of the Sabine uplift, the highest point of which is in northwestern Louisiana. The regional dip in the Upper Cretaceous beds is southeastward, then eastward into the Desha basin of south-

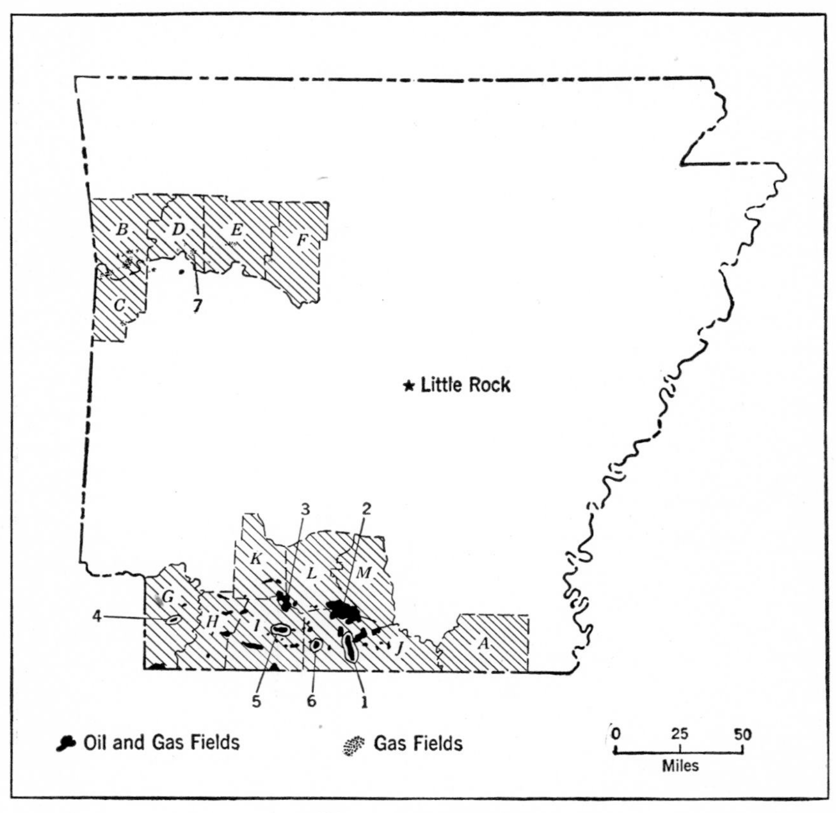

FIG. 136. Arkansas index map.

A, Ashley County.
B, Crawford County.
C, Sebastian County.
D, Franklin County.
E, Johnson County.
F, Pope County.
G, Miller County.
H, Lafayette County.
I, Columbia County.
J, Union County.
K, Nevada County.
L, Ouachita County.
M, Calhoun County.
1, Eldorado oil field.
2, Smackover oil field.
3, Stephens oil field.
4, Fouke oil field.
5, Magnolia oil field.
6, Schuler oil field.
7, White Oak gas field.

eastern Arkansas. The dip in the Lower Cretaceous and Jurassic formations, however, is southwest and south. A belt of long, narrow graben faults runs from west to east across southwestern Arkansas and appears to line up with the northeastern end of the Mexia-Talco fault zone of east Texas.

The reservoir rocks of southern Arkansas all lie within the Gulf embayment sediments, at least as so far developed. These range in age from the Nacatoch sandstone of Gulf (Upper Cretaceous) age down to the Jurassic Smackover limestone. Between the Nacatoch sandstone and the Smackover limestone are numerous other reservoirs belonging in the Gulf series (Upper Cretaceous), Comanchean series (Lower Cretaceous), and the Cotton Valley beds (upper Jurassic).

The principal reservoir rocks in the Arkansas River district in the Paleozoic belt are sandstones lying within the Atoka formation of the lower Pennsylvanian.

The hydrocarbon deposits of Arkansas also fall into two very distinct districts. One is the Paleozoic area in northwestern Arkansas, where only dry gas has been found to date. The gas-producing area lies in the eastern part of the McAlester coal basin of eastern Oklahoma. The other district is the southern part of the state, far enough south of the edge of the Gulf embayment so that a thick series of Mesozoic and Cenozoic sediments is present. Here are found the oil fields, which are scattered over parts of eight counties and which constitute the northern edge of an oil-producing district encompassing southern Arkansas and northern Louisiana.

Northwestern Arkansas Gas District. The gas fields are most numerous in the vicinity of Fort Smith on the Arkansas River, a short distance east of the Oklahoma line. Crawford County has the most pools, but some gas has been found to the south, in Sebastian County, and the district extends eastward down the Arkansas River valley across Franklin and Johnson counties and into western Pope County. The largest current production is from the White Oak field, discovered in 1943, in Franklin County. The trapping of the gas is anticlinal, but erratic permeability of the sandstone reservoirs and faults causes some irregularities in distribution. The gas is exceptionally dry. It breaks all the rules by being present in rocks in which the carbon ratios range from 82 to 87.[201]

Southern Arkansas Oil District. Most of the oil fields of Arkansas lie in the southern tier of counties extending from Miller on the Texas line across Lafayette, Columbia, and Union counties and into Ashley County. The district extends far enough north to include southern Nevada, Ouachita, and Calhoun counties in the second tier north of the Louisiana border. Structural traps are by far the most common type in the fields so far discovered in southern Arkansas. Out of twenty-

201 Carey Croneis, "Natural Gas in Interior Highlands of Arkansas," *Geology of Natural Gas* (Am. Assoc. Petrol. Geol., 1935), pp. 533–574.

five fields studied and described by the Shreveport Geological Society,[202] eighteen show anticlinal accumulation and the remaining seven are fault traps. The longer axes of most of the anticlines trend east and west, parallel to the regional strike. The fault accumulations are also remarkably alike. The fault lines tend to follow an easterly direction; the down side is to the north; and accumulation is immediately south of the fault in the up block. The oil moving up the regional dip from the south has been blocked by impervious material across the fault plane.

The discovery field for Arkansas, the El Dorado, is a stratigraphic trap on a structural terrace. The second field discovered, the Smackover, stands at the top in cumulative production and was in second place in annual production in 1949. It produces from a number of sands in the Upper Cretaceous, the uppermost of which is the Nacatoch, which lies at an average depth of 2000 feet. The oil-bearing sands occur as lenses in a section 200 feet thick. In 1939 Smackover had a second "boom" following the discovery of oil in the much deeper Jurassic limestone that became known as "Smackover lime." This limestone was subsequently found to be present and productive in other pools in southern Arkansas and northern Louisiana. The major structural features at Smackover are the Norphlet dome on the east, separated by a syncline from the Lovann terrace on the west, and a downthrown block to the north. The trapping in the Upper Cretaceous sands at the east end of the field is due to the closure on the dome, but at the western edge trapping appears to be due to the shaling out of the Meakin reservoir sand. Even in the structurally closed part of the field, the distribution of producing wells is controlled to a considerable extent by the porosity and permeability of the reservoirs.

The nearby Stephens oil field [203] was discovered at about the same time as the Smackover field. However, Stephens is a typical Arkansas fault field. A strike fault has severed the Upper and Lower Cretaceous reservoir rocks, trapping the oil that has ascended up-dip from the south in the upthrown block. A little more complicated is the accumulation in the Fouke field of Miller County.[204] This field lies in the previously mentioned graben zone near the southwestern corner

[202] *Op. cit.*

[203] W. C. Spooner, "Stephens Oil Field, Columbia and Ouachita Counties, Arkansas," *Structure of Typical American Oil Fields* (Am. Assoc. Petrol. Geol., 1929), Vol. 2, pp. 1–17.

[204] C. B. Schwartz, "Fouke Oil and Gas Field, Miller County, Arkansas," *Structure of Typical American Oil Fields* (Am. Assoc. Petrol. Geol., 1948), Vol. 3, pp. 5–23.

of Arkansas. Oil moving up-dip to the north has been impounded by a fault, but curiously enough there is some north dip on the north (down) side of the fault, and a negligible amount of oil accumulated on that side. The principal reservoirs are the Paluxy (Lower Cretaceous) sandstones. In 1947 gas and condensate were struck in the deeper Kilpatrick limestone of the Rodessa formation, which is also Comanchean in age, but the Kilpatrick reservoir is unimportant, as yet at least.

A typical recent discovery in southern Arkansas is the Schuler field in Union County, about 18 miles southwest of El Dorado, Arkansas.[205] The principal reservoir is the Jones sand at the base of the Cotton Valley formation (Jurassic), which produces at depths between 7500 and 7650 feet. The discovery well, which was drilled in 1937, struck a heavy flow of oil in the Jones sand. Trapping is anticlinal, but lenticularity of the sand is also a factor. The subsurface contours show the presence of two domes on the Schuler anticline; oil fills not only both domes but the intervening saddle area as well. Repressuring of the Jones sand reservoir by both gas and water has proved highly successful.

The field leading in oil production in southern Arkansas in 1949 was the Magnolia,[206] which was discovered in 1938 by a well located after surface geology and seismograph work had indicated the presence of a large anticline. The field lies a short distance east of Magnolia, the county seat of Columbia County. It is 6 miles long and 1½ miles wide. The long axis trends almost due east. The trap is an elliptical, fairly symmetrical anticline with nearly 300 feet of closure above the oil-water interface. The principal reservoir is the Reynolds oölite member of the Jurassic Smackover formation, topped about 7350 feet beneath the surface.

Mississippi [207]

(Figures 137–139)

In 1949 the state of Mississippi was credited with a little more than 2 per cent of the domestic petroleum output and a little over 1 per

[205] Warren B. Weeks and Clyde W. Alexander, "Schuler Field, Union County, Arkansas," *Bull. Am. Assoc. Petrol. Geol.*, Vol. 26 (September, 1942), pp. 1467–1516.

[206] Shreveport Geol. Soc., *1945 Reference Report on Certain Oil and Gas Fields of North Louisiana, South Arkansas, Mississippi, and Alabama*, Vol. 1, pp. 37–41.

[207] Shreveport Geol. Soc., *1945 Reference Report on Certain Oil and Gas Fields of North Louisiana, South Arkansas, Mississippi, and Alabama* (1946, 1947), two vols.; William Clifford Morse, "Mississippi Oil Resources," *World Petroleum*, Vol. 16

cent of the world production. The first commercial discovery of hydrocarbons in this state occurred in 1926, when the small Amory gas field in Monroe County in northeastern Mississippi was found. The much larger Jackson gas field was discovered in 1930, and the first oil field, the Tinsley, became productive late in 1939. This discovery brought about an extensive exploration program that reached a peak in 1940, when sixty-eight geophysical parties were in the field at one time. The subsequent wildcatting was at first highly disappointing, but by 1943 exploration began to pay dividends, and discoveries are still continuing. There are now over thirty oil fields, gas fields, and gas-condensate fields.

The oldest extensive surface formations in Mississippi are Cretaceous sediments in the northeastern part of the state. Successively younger Tertiary formations crop out to the south and west, and Quaternary deposits overlie the Tertiary in the Mississippi Valley and along the Gulf Coast shore zone.

In the very northeastern corner of the state, Paleozoic formations of Mississippian age crop out beneath the feather edge of embayment deposits. Throughout a considerable area in northern Mississippi, the Paleozoic formations lie within less than 6000 feet of the surface. This is the western end of a Paleozoic basin to which the name "Black Warrior" [208] has been applied. Its extent and significance will be discussed in the section on Alabama. Within the embayment deposits, the most prominent tectonic feature is the Jackson dome of southwest central Mississippi, which covers many square miles and has a closure of more than 1500 feet. To the south the strata dip Gulfward, but to the north the dip is largely westward toward the bottom of the Desha basin, the lowest point in the Mississippi embayment, in eastern Arkansas.

A third belt of interior salt domes crosses Mississippi in a southeasterly direction from northeastern Louisiana across the Alabama line. So far as is known at present, the coastal domes of Louisiana do not extend east of East Baton Rouge Parish, but the southeasterly trend of the interior domes brings them fairly near the coast north of Mobile in southwestern Alabama. For the past several years, new salt domes have been discovered each year in Mississippi. Depths to the top of the salt range from less than 1000 feet to more than 13,000 feet. In

(February, 1945), pp. 53–54; F. T. Holden, "Developments in Southeastern States in 1949," *Bull. Am. Assoc. Petrol. Geol.*, Vol. 34 (June, 1950), pp. 1215–1223.

[208] F. F. Mellen, "Black Warrior Basin, Alabama and Mississippi," *Bull. Am. Assoc. Petrol. Geol.*, Vol. 31 (October, 1947), pp. 1801–1816.

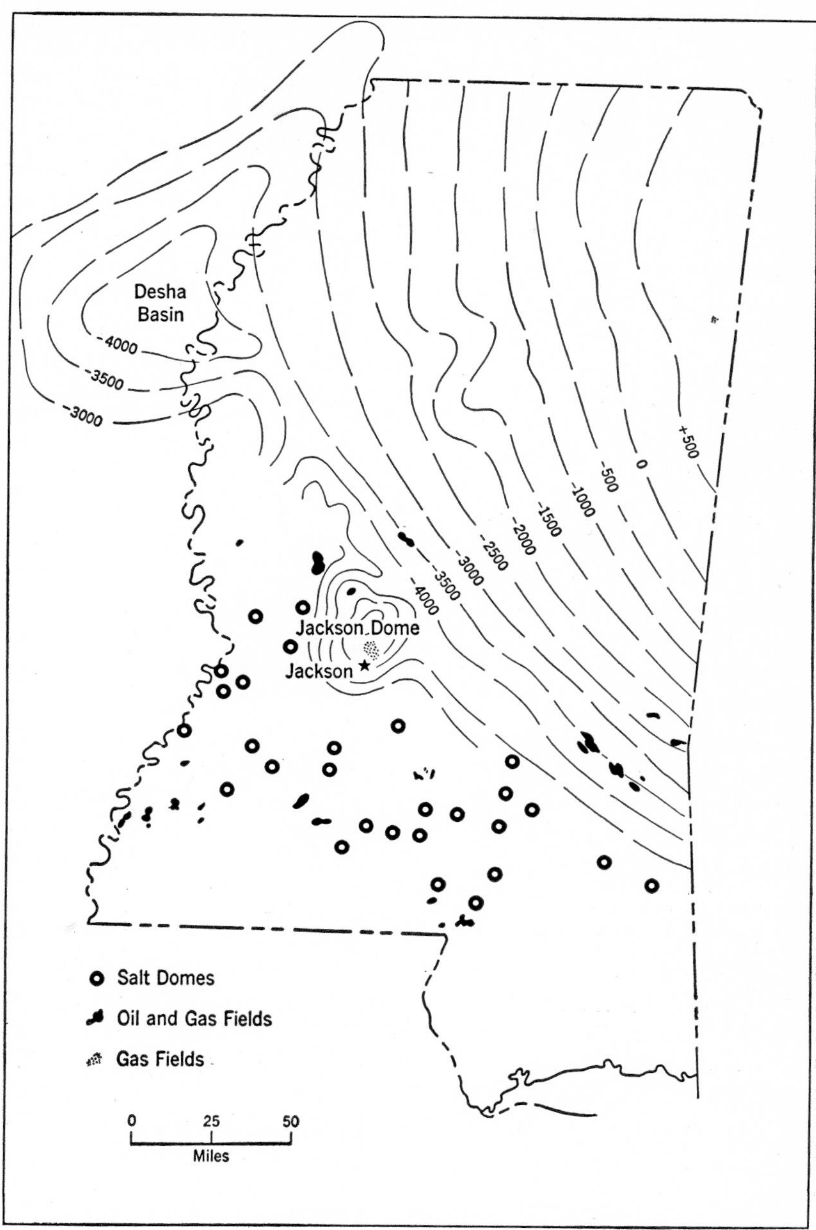

FIG. 137. Mississippi. Major structural features, salt domes, and oil and gas fields.

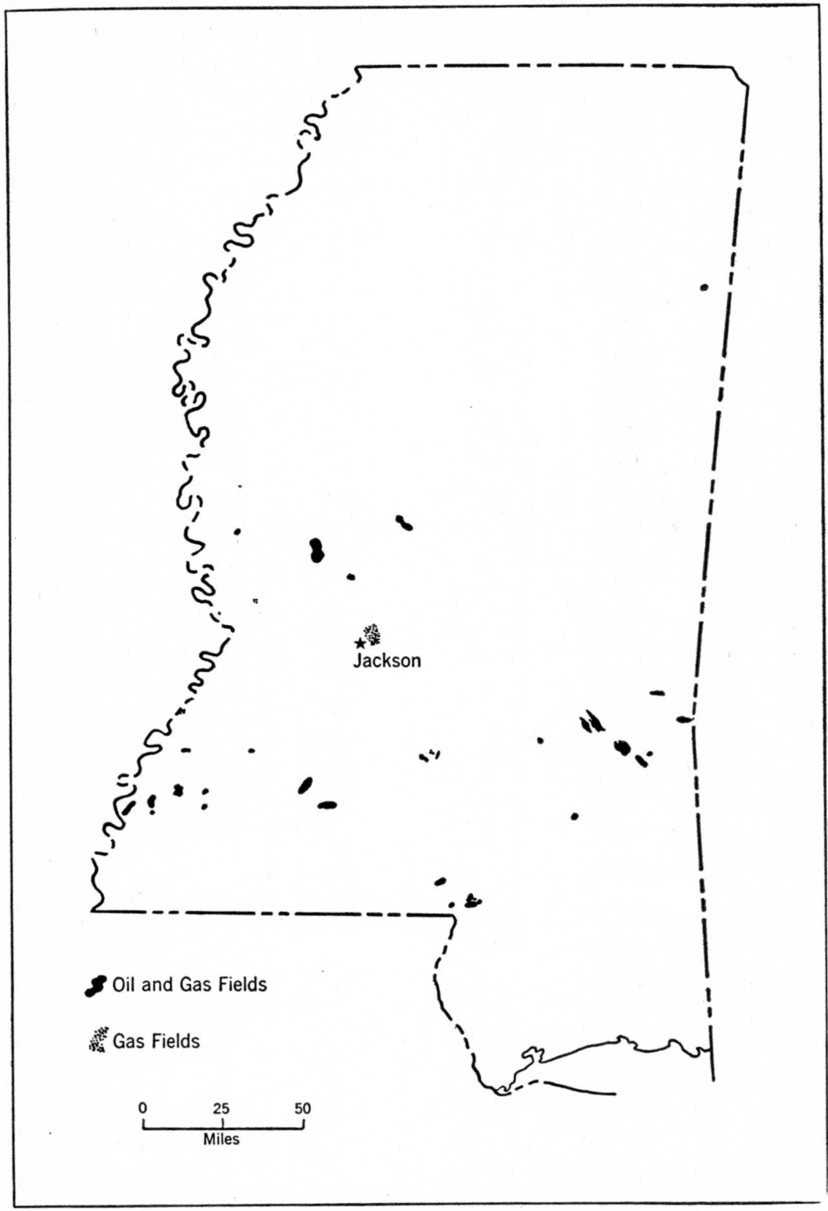

Fig. 138. Mississippi. Oil and gas fields.

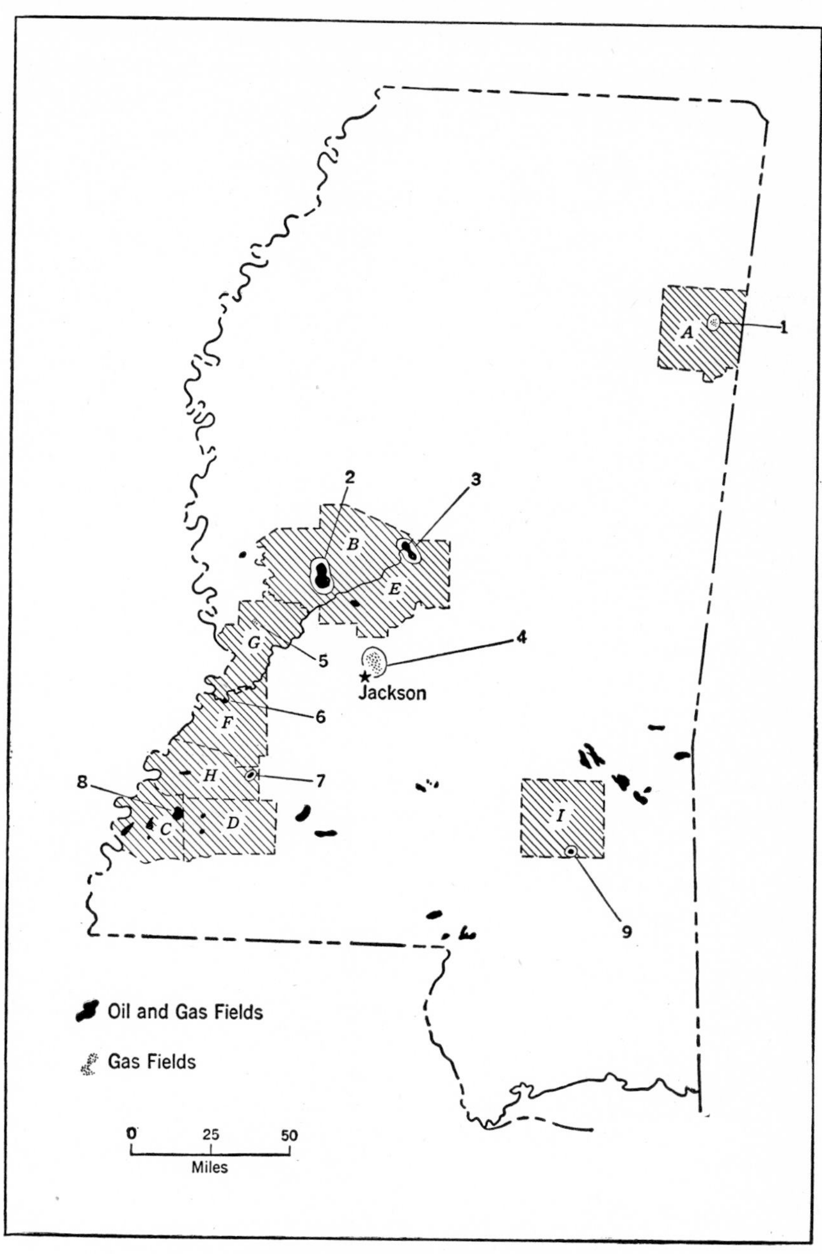

FIG. 139. Mississippi index map.

A, Monroe County.
B, Yazoo County.
C, Adams County.
D, Franklin County.
E, Madison County.
F, Claiborne County.
G, Warren County.
H, Jefferson County.
I, Jones County.

1, Amory gas field.
2, Tinsley oil field.
3, Pickens oil field.
4, Jackson gas field.
5, Kings gas field.
6, Bruinsberg gas field.
7, McBride gas field.
8, Cranfield oil field.
9, Ovett oil field.

addition, it is rather generally assumed that the oil fields producing from structural domes (and this constitutes a large proportion of those in Mississippi) overlie deep-seated salt cores, the intrusion of which was responsible for the doming.[209]

The reservoir rocks in Mississippi are mainly sandstones and sands. In the embayment area they range in age from middle Eocene to early Comanchean. The gas sand in the Amory field of Monroe County in northeastern Mississippi is Paleozoic in age, perhaps Mississippian. The most productive formations in the embayment area are the Tuscaloosa, Austin, and Eagle Ford, all Upper Cretaceous in age. The Eocene Wilcox is becoming increasingly important as an oil reservoir, however. A sandstone at the top of the Selma chalk of Upper Cretaceous age is the gas reservoir in the Jackson gas field and an oil reservoir in several other fields. The Comanchean reservoirs include the Glen Rose and the Travis Peak. The Travis Peak has only recently been found to be productive in Mississippi.[210]

Geologically, Mississippi can be divided into two and perhaps three potential oil- and gas-producing districts. The northernmost of these is the Paleozoic district, in which the reservoir rocks lie below the veneer of embayment deposits. Although represented only by an abandoned gas field, further discoveries may be made here in the future. The rest of Mississippi lies in the embayment district in which the reservoirs as well as the surface strata were deposited during the overlap of the Gulf of Mexico in Cretaceous and Tertiary times. The Gulf Coast of Mississippi may in time become a third district, corresponding to the Louisiana Gulf Coast district, if Miocene production is obtained in this belt.

Paleozoic Area. The Amory gas field, the first accumulation of hydrocarbons in commercial quantities to be found in Mississippi, was discovered in 1926 and abandoned in 1937 after having furnished nearby communities with almost a billion cubic feet of gas. This field was in east central Monroe County not far west of the Alabama boundary. The Paleozoic reservoir rocks, which are generally assumed to be of Chester (Mississippian) age, lie at a depth of about 2400 feet. So far, very little attempt has been made to find other fields in the Paleozoic rocks beneath the embayment sediments, but the Mississippi Geological Survey is currently investigating the possibilities.

209 Shreveport Geol. Soc., *op. cit.*

210 Anon., "Mississippi Gets Travis Peak Oil," *Oil and Gas Jour.*, Vol. 48 (Feb. 16, 1950), p. 149.

Embayment Area. The Jackson gas field [211] was discovered in 1930 and was approaching abandonment thirteen years later. The gas field occupies the very top of the large Jackson dome, with water underneath the gas. The trapping is obviously anticlinal. The reservoir rock is a porous zone at the top of the Upper Cretaceous Selma chalk and immediately beneath the unconformable Midway (Eocene) chalk. The core of the Jackson dome is igneous rock of syenitic composition, which has been found beneath the chalk by some of the field wells.

The Tinsley field of Yazoo County in west central Mississippi is not only the first oil field to be discovered in the state, but it is also far ahead of the fields subsequently discovered in cumulative production. It ranked second in output for 1949. Accumulation has taken place in an irregular and complexly faulted anticline.[212] This structure was discovered originally on the surface by the Mississippian Geological Survey during a locally sponsored county mineral survey, but before the discovery well was drilled, the dome was checked by a reflection seismograph survey. The discovery well for the field found oil in a sandstone facies of the Selma chalk or "Jackson gas rock," the term applied locally to the producing zone in the Jackson gas field. Production from this reservoir is restricted to some extent by the pinching out of the sand on the west flank of the Tinsley anticline. Subsequent wells located oil in several Upper Cretaceous reservoirs below the Selma.

The largest field in terms of annual production in 1949 was Cranfield, which lies in eastern Adams and western Franklin counties.[213] This field produces from both the Eocene Wilcox and the Upper Cretaceous Tuscaloosa. The latter formation produces both oil and distillate. The trap is a dome almost perfectly circular in plan. The distillate in the Tuscaloosa occurs across the top of the dome; the oil is beneath, occupying the flanks of the structure in a doughnut-shaped ring about 3000 feet in width.

Several of the Mississippi oil fields are fault traps similar to those in northern Louisiana. The strike of the faults parallels the strike of the embayment sediments, which varies from east-west, parallel to the coast line, to north-west in western Mississippi, owing to the regional structure created by the Mississippi embayment. Regardless of the direction of fault line, the downside is always the interior side.

[211] Donald J. Munroe, "Jackson Gas Field, Hinds and Rankin Counties, Mississippi," *Geology of Natural Gas* (Am. Assoc. Petrol. Geol., 1935), pp. 881–896.

[212] Shreveport Geol. Soc., *op. cit.*, Vol. 1, p. 300.

[213] Shreveport Geol. Soc., *op. cit.*, Vol. 1, pp. 249–253.

Accumulation takes place in the up-block on the Gulf side of the fault. The oil has moved up-dip from the south until trapped by the fault barrier. A typical example of this type of trap is the Pickens field, in Madison and Yazoo counties, which is illustrated and described in Chapter 8 (Fig. 65). The Pickens discovery was due to surface mapping, followed by a detailed geophysical survey.

In addition to the many fields that are assumed to overlie salt cores, Mississippi has one oil field and three gas fields, all minor in size, which produce from the strata arched over salt cores that have been penetrated by drilling. For several years relatively small amounts of gas have been obtained from the Bruinsburg salt dome in Claiborne County (the first interior salt dome to produce in Mississippi), the Kings dome in Warren County, and the McBride dome in Jefferson County.

The salt-dome oil field is the Ovett, in south-central Jones County, which was discovered early in 1948. The discovery well drilled into salt at a depth of 13,152 feet, but on its way down it had found several oil "shows" in both Upper and Lower Cretaceous rocks, and it was finally completed as a commercial oil well by perforating the casing in the Glen Rose section.

Alabama

(Figures 140–141)

Alabama is a relative newcomer among oil-producing states. The discovery of oil in Mississippi in 1939 stimulated prospecting in southern Alabama, and in 1944 the discovery well for the Gilbertown field was completed. This field produced approximately 0.02 per cent of the domestic oil output during 1949. In July, 1950, the Alabama State Geologist [214] reported the completion of the discovery well for a new field in Clarke County, southwestern Alabama. The producing formation is the Upper Cretaceous Tuscaloosa, and the pay zone lies at a depth of 5419 to 5429 feet.

In June of 1948 the first and so far the only known Alabama salt dome was discovered at a depth of only 410 feet, near the southeastern corner of Washington County, due north of Mobile. This is on approximately the same latitude as the easternmost salt dome so far discovered in Mississippi.

[214] Walter B. Jones, "Oil and Gas Progress and Prospects in Alabama," *World Oil*, Vol. 131 (July 1, 1950), pp. 57–64.

Alabama is far enough east of the Mississippi embayment so that only the west side and the southern half of the state lie in the Coastal

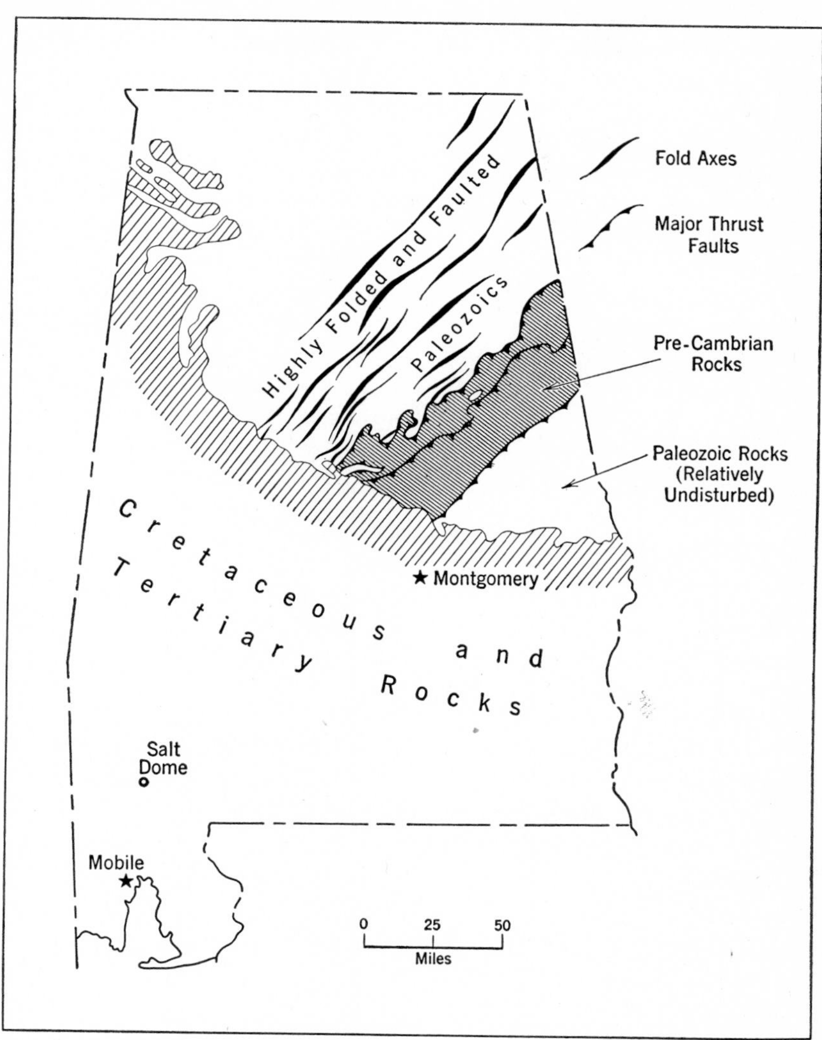

FIG. 140. Alabama. Tectonic map.

Plain. Northern and northeastern Alabama is floored with Paleozoic sediments, and in east central Alabama the pre-Cambrian crystallines lie at the surface. In central Alabama the highly folded and faulted Paleozoic sediments of the Appalachian geosyncline disappear beneath

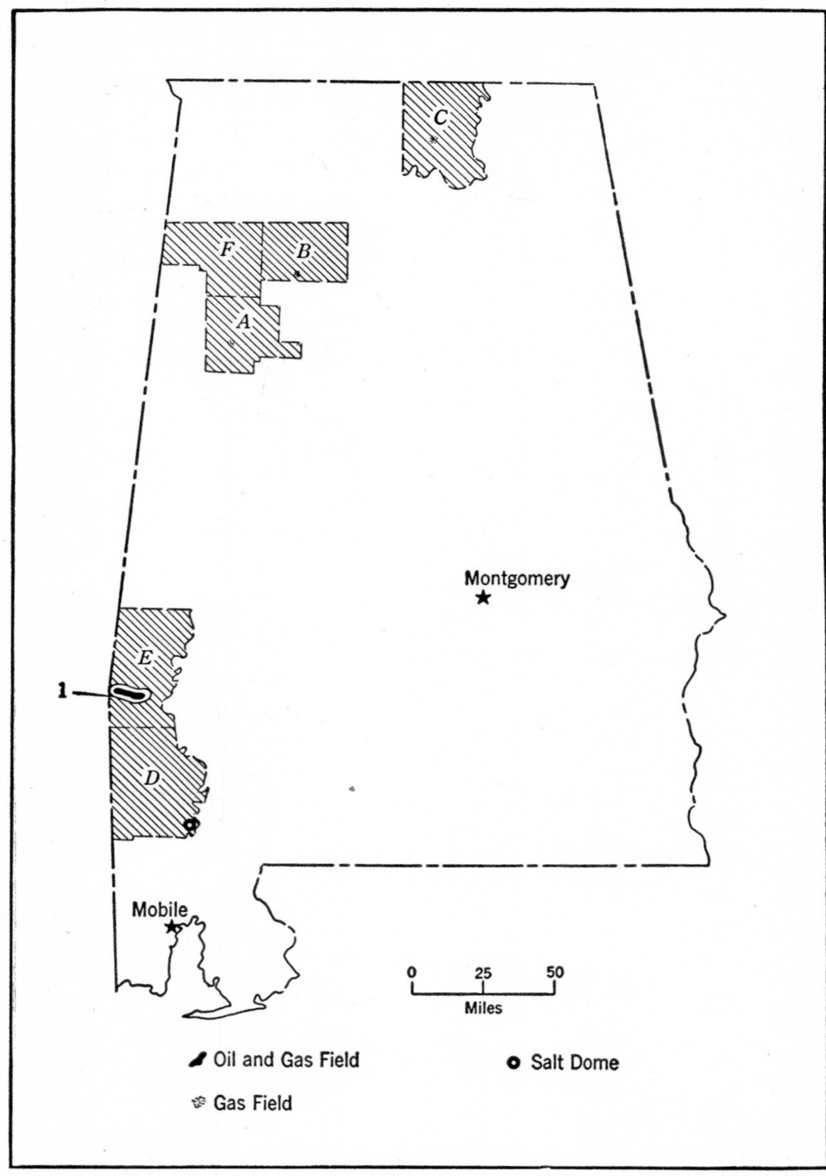

Fig. 141. Alabama index map. *A,* Fayette County; *B,* Winston County; *C,* Madison County; *D,* Washington County; *E,* Choctaw County; *F,* Marion County; 1, Gilbertown oil field.

the overlapping Cretaceous formations. Between this point and the Gulf, the Upper Cretaceous and Tertiary formations crop out in relatively narrow bands, with Quaternary sediments occupying the shoreline zone.

Northwestern Alabama lies in the Black Warrior basin.[215] This basin is bounded on the east by the highly folded Paleozoic sediments of the Appalachian geosyncline, on the south and southwest (beneath the embayment overlap) by the southeasterly extension of the Ouachita Mountain system, and on the north by the Nashville dome on the axis of the Cincinnati arch.

So far no discoveries have been made in the Paleozoic rocks of Alabama except for some small gas finds in Fayette, Marion, Winston, and Madison counties [216] in northwestern and northern Alabama. However, this area is receiving some attention; of twenty wildcats drilled in Alabama in 1948 four were located in the Paleozoic area.[217]

The Gilbertown field [218] is in western Choctaw County, only a short distance east of the Mississippi line. It is illustrated and described in Chapter 8 (Fig 65) as an example of fault trapping.

Florida

(Figure 142)

Florida is so far a one-field state. The first producing well, the discovery well for the Sunniland field, was completed in September, 1943, at a total depth of 11,626 feet. The initial production was about 100 barrels a day of black asphaltic oil of 20° gravity, which was adequate to win the $50,000 reward that had been posted by the state for Florida's first commercial well. Seven years later the field consisted of twelve producing wells, six of which were pumping and six flowing.[219] The discovery well has been abandoned and converted to a salt-water-disposal well. The newest producing well lies about 4 miles northwest of Sunniland in the same pool. It was completed on Jan. 3, 1950. The

[215] F. F. Mellen, "Black Warrior Basin, Alabama and Mississippi," *Bull. Am. Assoc. Petrol. Geol.,* Vol. 31 (October, 1947), pp. 1801–1816.

[216] Douglas R. Semmes, "Oil and Gas in Alabama," *Alabama Geological Survey, Special Report* 15, July, 1929, 408 pages.

[217] R. M. Harris and W. M. Payne, "Developments in Southeastern States in 1948," *Bull. Am. Assoc. Petrol. Geol.,* Vol. 33 (June, 1949), pp. 1002–1010.

[218] A. M. Current, "Gilbertown Field, Choctaw County, Alabama," *Structure of Typical American Oil Fields,* Vol. 3 (Am. Assoc. Petrol. Geol., 1948), pp. 1–4.

[219] Herman Gunter, "Exploration in Florida," *World Oil,* Vol. 129 (September, 1949), pp. 69–72; "Oil Exploration in Florida during 1949," *Oil and Gas Jour.,* Vol. 49 (June 22, 1950), pp. 310–312.

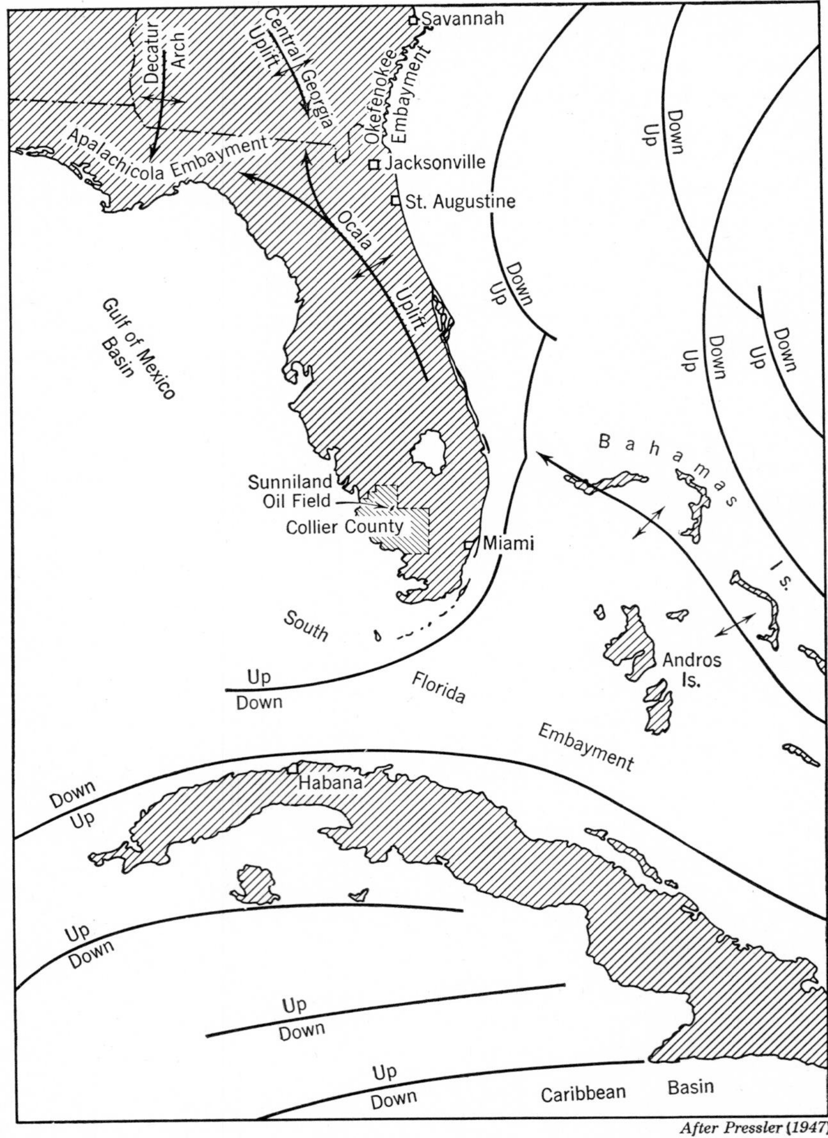

FIG. 142. Florida and environs. Tectonic and index map. *Courtesy American Association of Petroleum Geologists.*

Florida production during 1949 was roughly the same as that of Alabama, or about 0.02 per cent of the United States output.

Exploration has been very active in Florida both before and since the discovery of the Sunniland field. More than 240 wells have been drilled in the state since 1900. About 56 wells were drilled during the biennium 1947 to 1948, and one reached a depth of 15,455 feet before being abandoned as a dry hole. These wildcat tests are being drilled in all parts of the state. Several have had shows of oil of sufficient magnitude to warrant testing, but it was not possible to complete any of them as commercial producers.

The entire state of Florida is floored with Tertiary and Quaternary sediments. The most prominent structural feature in the state is an arch that forms the backbone of the northern half of the peninsula. Southern Florida, south and west of the uplift, has been designated the "south Florida embayment." [220] The sedimentary section there is up to 20,000 feet thick in embayment sediment alone, which is almost entirely carbonate rock. Western or panhandle Florida contains the Apalachicola embayment, in which the sediments are mainly clastic.

The Sunniland field lies in Collier County on the west side of Florida near the southern tip. The reservoir rock is called the Sunniland limestone, and it is probably approximately Glen Rose (Lower Cretaceous) in age. The trap is a dome with minimum uplift of 200 feet. The Sunniland limestone has a maximum effective porosity thickness of 40 feet. It is highly porous through this zone and may be a reef. Anhydrite occurs in the overlying sediments, and some rock salt has been penetrated below the Sunniland limestone in a few wells.

New Mexico [221]

(Figures 143–145)

During 1949 New Mexico produced about 2.7 per cent of the total output of oil in the United States. This amounted to slightly more than the Wyoming production. During the same year, the New Mexico yield was about 1.4 per cent of that for the entire world. The oil and gas fields of New Mexico occur in two districts in opposite corners of the state. About 99 per cent of the state's oil comes from

220 E. D. Pressler, "Geology and Occurrence of Oil in Florida," *Bull. Am. Assoc. Petrol. Geol.,* Vol. 31 (October, 1947), pp. 1851–1862.

221 Robert L. Bates *et al.,* "The Oil and Gas Resources of New Mexico," 2nd ed., *N. Mex. School Mines, Bull.* 18 (1942).

two counties, Lea and Eddy, in the southeastern corner of New Mexico. The remainder comes from San Juan and McKinley counties in the northwest corner of the state.

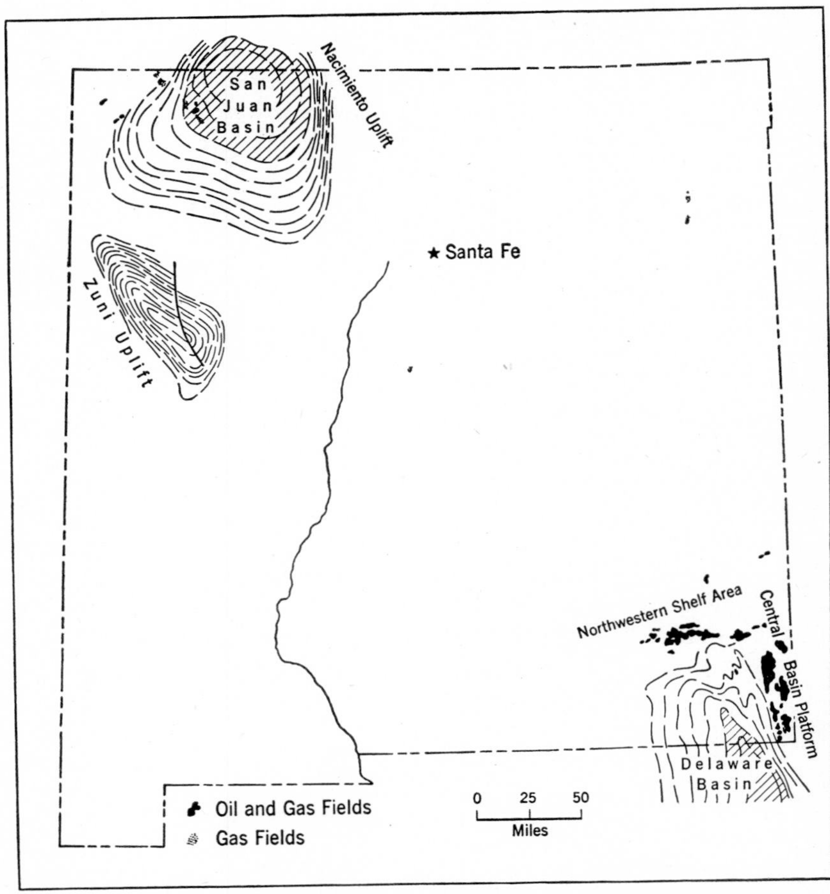

Fig. 143. Northwestern and southeastern New Mexico. Major structural features and oil and gas fields.

In southwestern and north central New Mexico, diastrophic activity in the geologic past was intense, and uplifted pre-Cambrian cores have been exposed by erosion in numerous places. In addition, considerable igneous activity in Tertiary time resulted in many intrusions, which have subsequently been unroofed, and extensive lava flows that have covered thousands of square miles, especially in the southwestern quadrant of the state. Geologists are beginning to consider the oil possibilities of the lava-covered sediments.

Southeastern New Mexico. Recorded production began in southeastern New Mexico in 1912 in what was then known as the Dayton

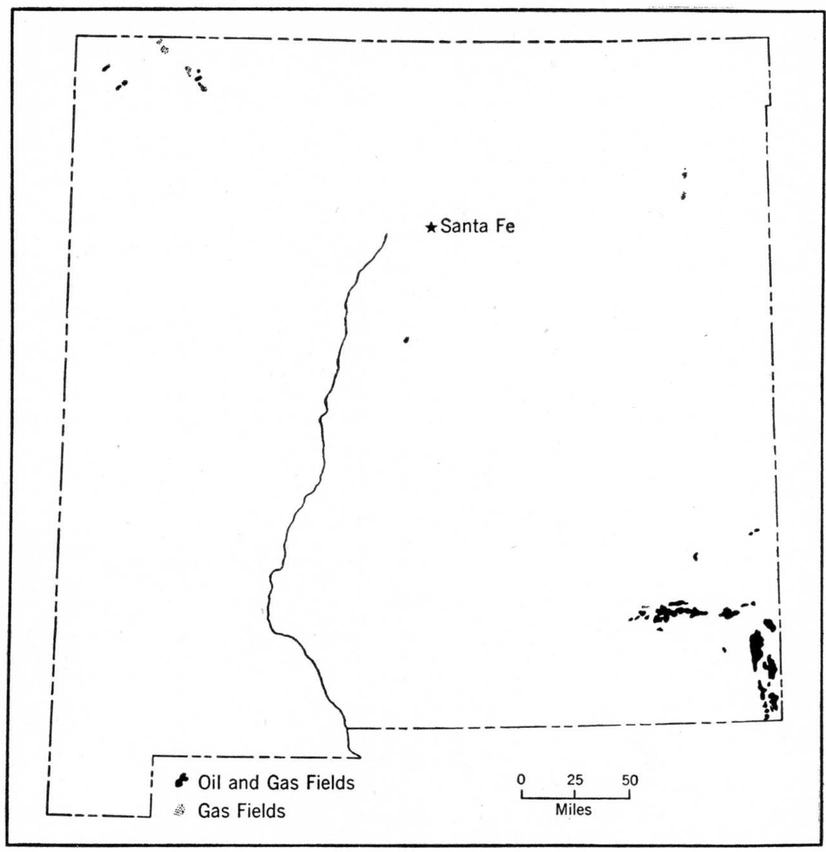

FIG. 144. New Mexico. Oil and gas fields.

pool but which later became a part of the Artesia field. The output remained insignificant until 1923, when the Artesia field was more extensively developed. The first major strike in this area was the Hobbs pool in 1928, leading to an extensive exploration program that is still in progress. During 1948 the Crossroads field in northeastern Lea County was discovered at a depth of 12,215 feet, at that time the deepest production in the district. A few months later, however, a well in eastern Lea County, some distance to the south of the Crossroads field, struck oil between a depth of 12,500 and 12,600 feet.

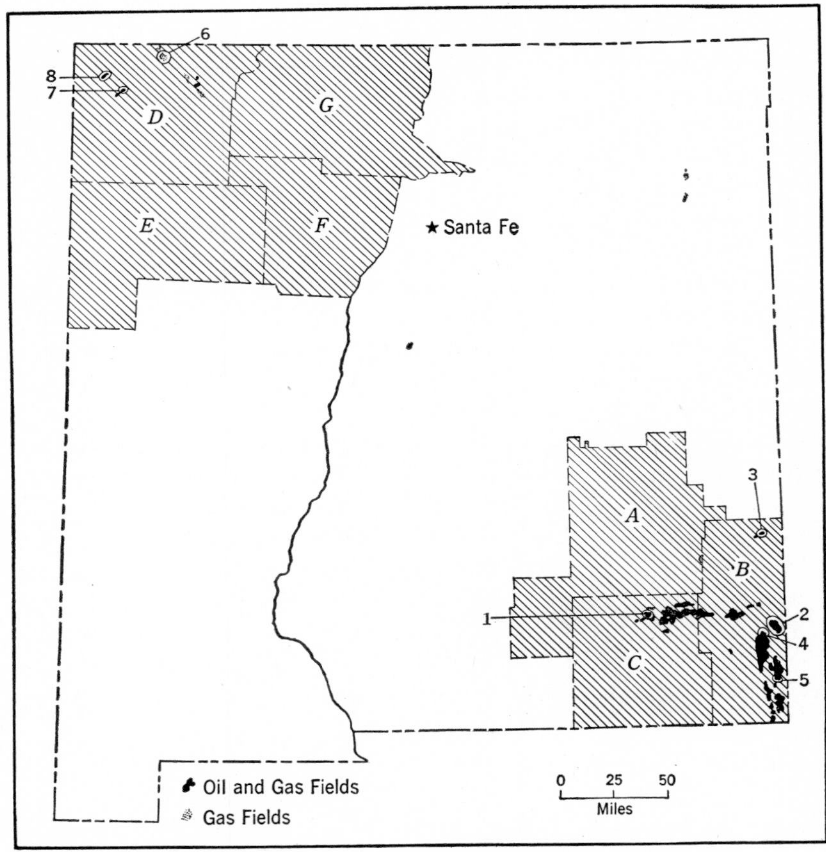

Fig. 145. New Mexico index map.

A, Chaves County.
B, Lea County.
C, Eddy County.
D, San Juan County.
E, McKinley County.
F, Sandoval County.
G, Rio Arriba County.

1, Artesia oil field.
2, Hobbs oil field.
3, Crossroads oil field.
4, Monument oil field.
5, Drinkard oil field.
6, Ute gas field.
7, Hogback oil field.
8, Rattlesnake oil field.

Geologically, southeastern New Mexico is an integral part of the West Texas district. Although to date the production is confined to Lea and Eddy counties, with one Lea County field overlapping into Chaves County, the Permian basin covers additional counties to the west, northwest, and north. The fields in the extreme southeastern corner of New Mexico lie on the northwest rim of the Central basin platform; the fields of northern Eddy and central Lea counties are on the Northwestern shelf.[222] The northern end of the Delaware basin extends into southern Eddy and southwestern Lea counties, but so far no significant production has been developed on this flank.

The oil and gas reservoirs in southeastern New Mexico are generally similar to those in the neighboring fields in Texas, but there have been some differences in the discovery history. Only since 1940 has oil been produced from the lower Permian Yeso and Abo formations and from the Ordovician Ellenburger limestone, and it was not until 1948 and 1949 that oil was found in Pennsylvanian and Devonian reservoirs. Another discovery of 1948 was oil in the Montoya limestone of upper Ordovician age.

The leading fields of New Mexico all lie within the Southeastern district. In cumulative production Hobbs, at the northernmost tip of the Central basin platform, stands first, and Monument, at the northwest corner of the platform, second. During 1949 the Drinkard pool, which lies to the southeast of the Monument field, was first and the Monument field second in production for the year.

The Hobbs field[223] was discovered by geophysical surveys. The main reservoir is a porous Permian limestone about 200 feet thick. The trap is an elongate anticline with a northwest-southeast trend. The porosity appears to increase toward the crest of the fold, and at the very top of the structure the limestone is even cavernous. Obviously the development of this porosity is connected in some way with the tectonic history of the Hobbs anticline.

The fields in eastern Lea County to the south of Hobbs are at the northern end of the "sand belt" area of Winkler and Ward counties, Texas,[224] described earlier in the section on West Texas. Accumulation is due to a favorable combination of structure and facies change to the east, where the reservoir rock grades into anhydrite.

Northwestern New Mexico. The Ute gas field in northern San Juan County was discovered in 1921, and the Hogback oil field, 20

[222] John E. Galley and G. S. Corey, "Developments in West Texas and Southeast New Mexico in 1949," *Bull. Am. Assoc. Petrol. Geol.*, Vol. 34 (June, 1950), pp. 1129–1143.

[223] Ronald K. DeFord and E. A. Wahlstrom, "Hobbs Field, Lea County, New Mexico," *Bull. Am. Assoc. Petrol. Geol.*, Vol. 16 (January, 1932), pp. 51–90.

[224] R. L. Denham and W. E. Dougherty, " 'Sand Belt' Area of Ward and Winkler Counties, Texas, and Lea County, New Mexico," *Stratigraphic Type Oil Fields* (Am. Assoc. Petrol. Geol., 1941), pp. 750–759.

miles to the southwest, in 1922. The anticlines are practically naked in this country, and the discovery of Hogback was followed by the testing of other domes, which led to the discovery of the Rattlesnake field in 1924. Subsequently, other fields were discovered in this district, but so far all have been relatively small accumulations. The entire "Four Corners" area was the scene of considerable activity in 1949–1950. A compilation [225] published in 1949 listed eighty traps, almost all anticlines, in the San Juan basin, of which fifty-nine are in northwestern New Mexico. Of the latter, twenty were still untested at the time the compilation was made.

The controlling tectonic feature in northwestern New Mexico is the San Juan basin. The deepest part of this basin is in northern San Juan County. It covers all San Juan County, northern McKinley County to the south, northwestern Sandoval County to the southeast, and the western half of Rio Arriba County to the east. It also extends across the line into southwestern Colorado. The basin is bounded on the east by the Nacimiento uplift, on the southwest by the Zuni uplift, and on the west (northeastern Arizona) by the Defiance uplift. The reservoir rocks are mainly sandstones of the Upper Cretaceous, including especially the Dakota. In addition, two fields produce gas from the Paradox formation of Pennsylvanian age, and oil was at one time obtained from the Pennsylvanian Hermosa formation in the Rattlesnake field. Wells drilled to a depth of 6700 feet at Rattlesnake have developed a helium reserve in the Ouray limestone of Mississippian-Devonian age.

Thirteen oil and gas fields are producing in northwestern New Mexico.[226] Two are in McKinley County and the others in San Juan County. Both the McKinley County fields are oil fields, but in San Juan County four of the ten fields are gas fields.

Dobbin [227] shows in tabular form the nature of the oil and gas trapping in northwestern New Mexico. In three-fourths of the fields the trapping is anticlinal. Several of the anticlines and domes are faulted, but the faults do not appear to have played a role of any prominence in the accumulation of the hydrocarbons. In four fields

225 Frank C. Barnes, "Structures of the San Juan Basin," *Oil and Gas Jour.*, Vol. 47 (March 31, 1949), pp. 98–99.

226 Paul H. Umbach, "Developments in Arizona, Western New Mexico, and Northern New Mexico in 1949," *Bull. Am. Assoc. Petrol. Geol.*, Vol. 34 (June, 1950), p. 1146.

227 C. E. Dobbin, "Structural Conditions of Oil and Gas Accumulation, Rocky Mountain Region, United States," *Bull. Am. Assoc. Petrol. Geol.*, Vol. 27 (April, 1943), p. 456.

the traps are in monoclines, owing to varying permeability of the reservoir rock. In these the reservoirs are sandstone lenses in shale.

The Rattlesnake field [228] was described and illustrated in Chapter 8 (Fig. 40) as an example of anticlinal trapping.

Colorado [229]

(Figures 146–148)

The state of Colorado was credited with 1.3 per cent of the domestic production of petroleum during 1949. This was 0.7 per cent of the world production and roughly the equivalent of that of British Borneo.

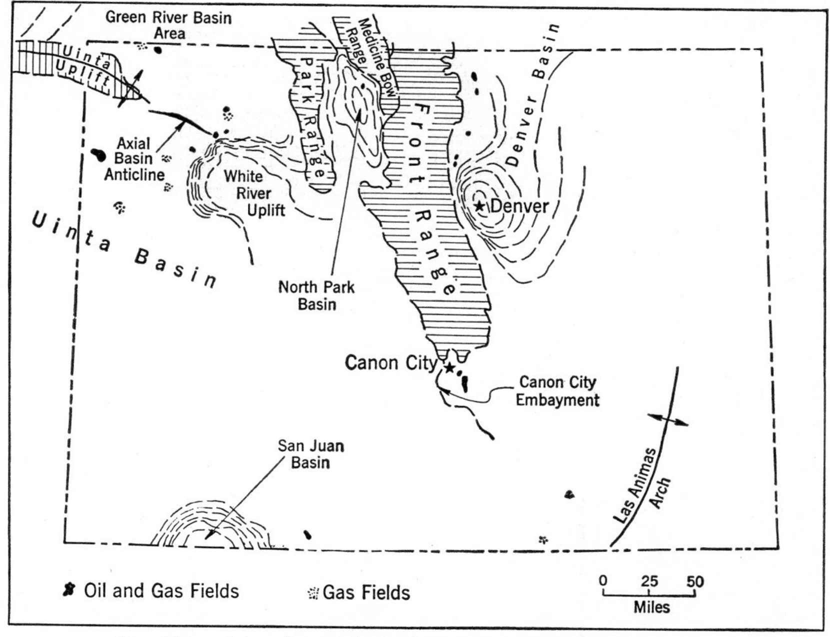

FIG. 146. Colorado. Principal basins and oil and gas fields.

Oil seepages near Cañon City in Fremont County, Colorado, first excited interest in 1862, and some of this oil was exploited by dug

[228] H. H. Hinson, "Reservoir Characteristics of Rattlesnake Oil and Gas Field, San Juan County, New Mexico," *Bull. Am. Assoc. Petrol. Geol.*, Vol. 31 (April, 1947), pp. 731–771.

[229] Clark F. Barb, "The Oil and Gas Industry of Colorado," *Quarterly Colo. School of Mines,* Vol. 37 (April, 1942); J. Harlan Johnson, "Selected Bibliography on Colorado Petroleum Geology and Stratigraphy," *Mines Mag.,* Vol. 35 (April, 1945), pp. 167–173.

and drilled wells. However, it was not until 1886, when the nearby Florence pool was developed, that Colorado began continuous oil production. The modern era began in 1923 with the discovery of several fields in northwestern Colorado and in the Fort Collins area of eastern Colorado, but it was not until 1944, when exploitation of the deep

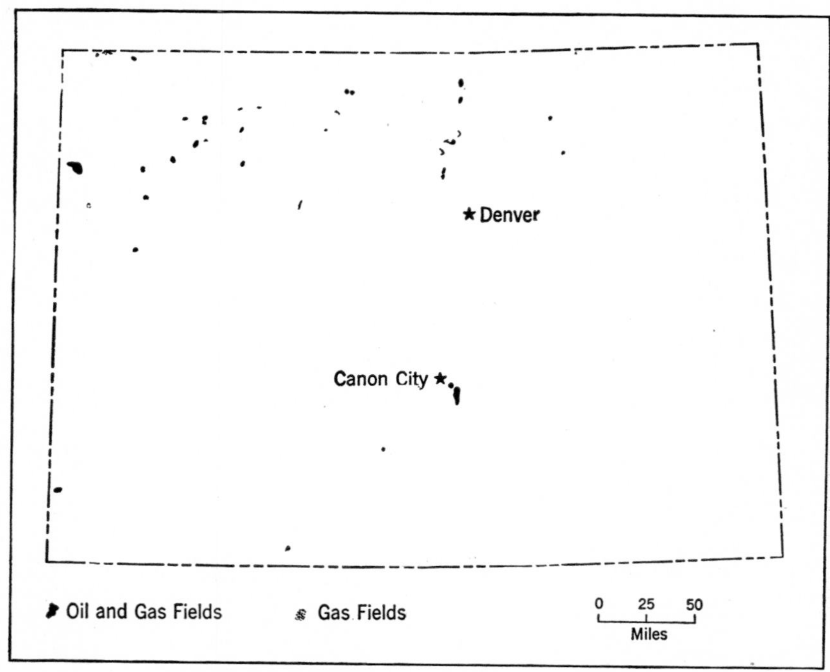

FIG. 147. Colorado. Oil and gas fields.

Weber reservoir at Rangely got under way, that Colorado became a relatively important oil-producing state.

The most recent discoveries have been (1) the Dove Creek pool in Montezuma County, southwestern Colorado, by a well completed in 1948 in the Hermosa-Paradox formation of Pennsylvanian age, with an estimated initial production of 200 barrels per day of 66° gravity distillate and 5 million cubic feet of gas; [230] (2) the Gurley field in Cheyenne County, southwest Nebraska, in 1949, which brought about a considerable revival of interest in the Denver basin of northeastern

[230] C. L. Dorn, "Developments in Rocky Mountain Region in 1948," *Bull. Am. Assoc. Petrol. Geol.*, Vol. 33 (June, 1949), p. 835.

Colorado; and (3) the Oak Creek field in Routt County, northwestern Colorado, in August, 1949.[231]

The western two-thirds of Colorado lies within the Cordilleran geosyncline province and consists of a series of uplifts, some of great

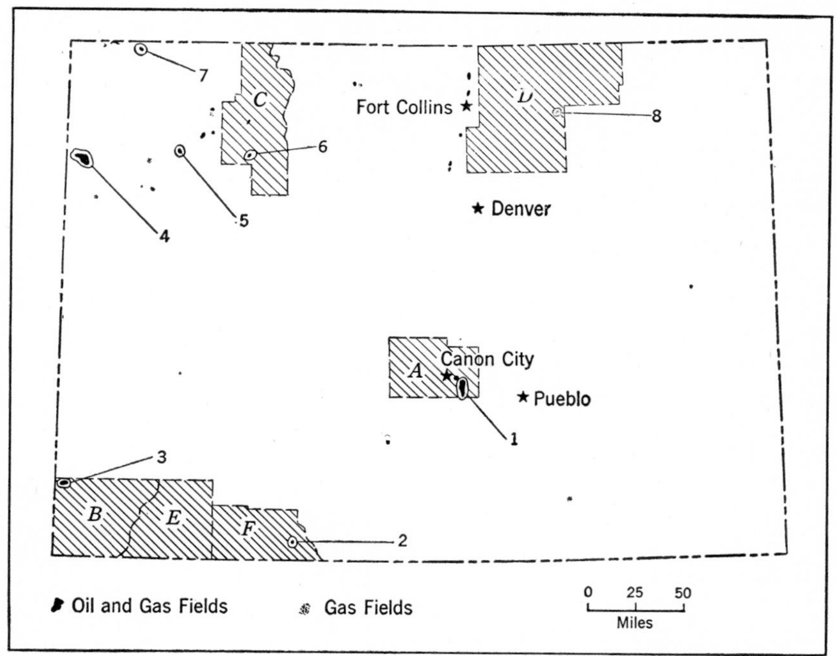

FIG. 148. Colorado index map.

A, Fremont County.	*F*, Archuleta County.	4, Rangely oil field.
B, Montezuma County.		5, Wilson Creek oil field.
C, Routt County.	1, Florence oil field.	6, Oak Creek oil field.
D, Weld County.	2, Gramps oil field.	7, Powder Wash oil field.
E, Plata County.	3, Dove Creek oil field.	8, Greasewood oil field.

magnitude, with intervening basins or "parks," which are floored with sedimentary rock. East of the Front Range, and constituting about one-third of the state in area, is the district hereinafter referred to as eastern Colorado, which is a part of the High Plains physiographic province and in which the tectonic features resemble more closely those of the Mid-Continent than they do those of the Rocky Mountain Cordillera.

[231] Gilbert M. Wilson, "Oak Creek Discovery," *World Oil,* Vol. 130 (January, 1950), pp. 65–66.

The pre-Cambrian basement rocks are exposed in the cores of the major uplifts, where they create the mountain ranges for which Colorado is famed. The sedimentary rocks are confined to the basins. Two basins in eastern Colorado, the Denver and the Cañon City, and four of the western Colorado basins, the North Park, Green River, Uinta, and San Juan basins, have been found so far to contain oil or gas accumulations.

The reservoir rocks range in age from the Eocene to the Pennsylvanian. The Eocene reservoir is the Wasatch formation, which is unusual in that it is of continental rather than marine origin. The Upper Cretaceous is represented by the Dakota and other sandstones, and the Jurassic by the Morrison basal sand and the Sundance sandstone. The Weber sandstone of Pennsylvanian age is the most prolific reservoir because it is the source of the major part of the Rangely oil.

Almost all the Colorado fields produce from typical anticlinal traps.[232] Some of the anticlines are faulted, but usually the faults have had no effect whatsoever on accumulation. An exception is the Gramps field, a fault trap in the San Juan basin of southwestern Colorado. It is described in a later paragraph. Colorado is also a well-known locality for fissure accumulation, especially in the Florence field of Fremont County. So far, very little oil trapped by varying permeability has been found in Colorado.

The Rangely field in northwestern Colorado is the major field of the state in both cumulative and recent annual production. The second field in cumulative production is Wilson Creek, which lies to the east of Rangely.

Eastern Colorado. The most prominent structural features of eastern Colorado are the Las Animas arch and the Denver basin. The highest part of the Las Animas arch is in northeastern New Mexico, immediately south of the Colorado line, from which point it plunges to the northeast across eastern Colorado, losing its identity near the northwestern corner of Kansas. The Denver basin lies to the northwest of the Las Animas arch. This basin is asymmetric, with the deepest part immediately in front of the Front Range between Denver and Cheyenne, Wyoming. It is estimated that the pre-Cambrian floor lies at an elevation of about −15,000 feet at Denver, which means a total thickness to the sedimentary section in that immediate vicinity of more than 20,000 feet. The northeastern flank of the Denver basin not only extends across northeastern Colorado, but it also covers much

[232] C. E. Dobbin, "Structural Conditions of Oil and Gas Accumulation in Rocky Mountain Region of United States," *Bull. Am. Assoc. Petrol. Geol.*, Vol. 27 (April, 1943), pp. 452–453.

of southwestern and western Nebraska, as well as the southeastern corner of Wyoming.

The Denver basin is currently having a revival of interest because of the previously mentioned discovery in western Nebraska. However, this district has had a number of small fields for many years. The Greasewood field [233] at the eastern boundary of Weld County was discovered in 1930. Small production has been obtained from the Greasewood sand of Dakota age at a depth of about 6650 feet. The trap is a low anticline, with lensing of the reservoir sand controlling the distribution of oil on the structure.

At the southwest corner of the Denver basin is a local offshoot, sometimes referred to as the Cañon City embayment but better described as the Cañon City basin. This is a small structural pocket occupying a re-entrant into the Front Range between Pueblo and Cañon City. It is in this re-entrant that the oil discoveries of 1862 were made. The accumulation of oil in fissures in the Pierre shale in the Florence and Cañon City fields in the Cañon City basin was described in Chapter 8.

Western Colorado. Along the north edge of central Colorado is North Park, a small basin lying between the Park Range and the Medicine Bow Range. Some oil and considerable carbon dioxide-bearing gas have been found in two anticlines in this area. The reservoir rock is a sandstone in the Dakota formation.

To the west in northwestern Colorado is the southeastern corner of the Green River basin, which covers much of southwestern Wyoming. The southeastern rim of this basin is formed by the Park Range, and the southwestward limit is the Uinta Mountain uplift and its southeasterly extension, the Axial basin anticline-White River uplift. Half a dozen small fields lie within the Colorado part of the Green River basin. Accumulation is entirely controlled by anticlines.[234] One domal trap contains the Powder Wash field,[235] which has produced as much as 1000 barrels per day and 34 million cubic feet of gas from non-marine sediments of the Eocene Wasatch formation. Some irregularity in distribution of hydrocarbons occurs on this structure owing to lenticularity of the reservoir sand. The oil and gas are thought to be indigenous to the continental sediments.

[233] Charles S. Lavington, "Greasewood Oil Field, Weld County, Colorado," *Stratigraphic Type Oil Fields* (Am. Assoc. Petrol. Geol., 1941), pp. 19–42.

[234] Ross L. Heaton, "Relation of Accumulation to Structure in Northwestern Colorado," *Structure of Typical American Oil Fields* (Am. Assoc. Petrol. Geol., 1929), Vol. 2, pp. 93–114.

[235] W. T. Nightingale, "Petroleum and Natural Gas in Non-Marine Sediments of Powder Wash Field in Northwest Colorado," *Bull. Am. Assoc. Petrol. Geol.,* Vol. 22 (August, 1938), pp. 1020–1047.

The Uinta basin lies to the south of the Uinta uplift, covering a part of northwestern Colorado and a large part of northeastern Utah. This basin contains the great Rangely anticline and oil field, which were described and illustrated in Chapter 8 (Fig. 38) as an example of anticlinal accumulation. The second field in cumulative production in Colorado, the Wilson Creek, also lies in the Uinta basin. The trap here is a triangular, asymmetrical dome with closure of about 1000 feet but with the oil confined to the crestal area.[236]

The San Juan basin, previously described in connection with northwestern New Mexico, extends northward into southern Montezuma, Plata, and Archuleta counties in southwestern Colorado. It was in Montezuma County that the previously mentioned Dove Creek gas-distillate field was discovered in 1948. The reservoir rock is a Permian sandstone lying at a depth of nearly 6000 feet. To the eastward in Archuleta County, near the northeastern boundary of the San Juan basin, is the Gramps field.[237] This field was discovered in 1935, but geological details were withheld until 1946. The reservoir rock is the Upper Cretaceous Dakota sandstone, and the oil has accumulated against an east-west fault that crosses a north-south anticlinal axis. Not only has the fault provided a barrier to the oil in the upthrown block but also it has displaced the fold axis nearly a mile westward on the downthrown block. Gramps field is unique in that it is entirely privately owned and therefore free from many governmental operating regulations.

The San Juan basin is currently the scene of active investigation. Barnes [238] lists twenty anticlines, of which ten are untested, in the Colorado part of this basin.

Wyoming [239]

(Figures 149–151)

Wyoming is the leading Rocky Mountain state in oil production, with an output during 1949 amounting to 2.6 per cent of the domestic

[236] C. E. Dobbin, "Structural Conditions of Oil and Gas Accumulation in Rocky Mountain Region of United States," *Bull. Am. Assoc. Petrol. Geol.*, Vol. 27 (April, 1943), p. 454.

[237] W. A. Waldschmidt, "Gramps Field, Archuleta County, Colorado," *Structure of Typical American Oil Fields* (Am. Assoc. Petrol. Geol., 1948), Vol. 3, pp. 110–131.

[238] Frank C. Barnes, "Structures of the San Juan Basin," *Oil and Gas Jour.*, Vol. 47 (March 31, 1949), pp. 98–99.

[239] Eleanor K. Keefer, R. M. Larsen, J. D. Love, and Maxine W. Allen, "Map of Wyoming Showing Test Wells for Oil and Gas, Anticlinal Axes, Oil and Gas

yield. This was 1.4 per cent of the world production, somewhat less than that of Mexico for the same period.

The first successful well was drilled in Wyoming in 1883, but since there was no outlet for the oil, commercial production did not begin until 1895. The great Salt Creek field, discovered in 1908, became an important producer in 1913. Subsequently, no year has passed without

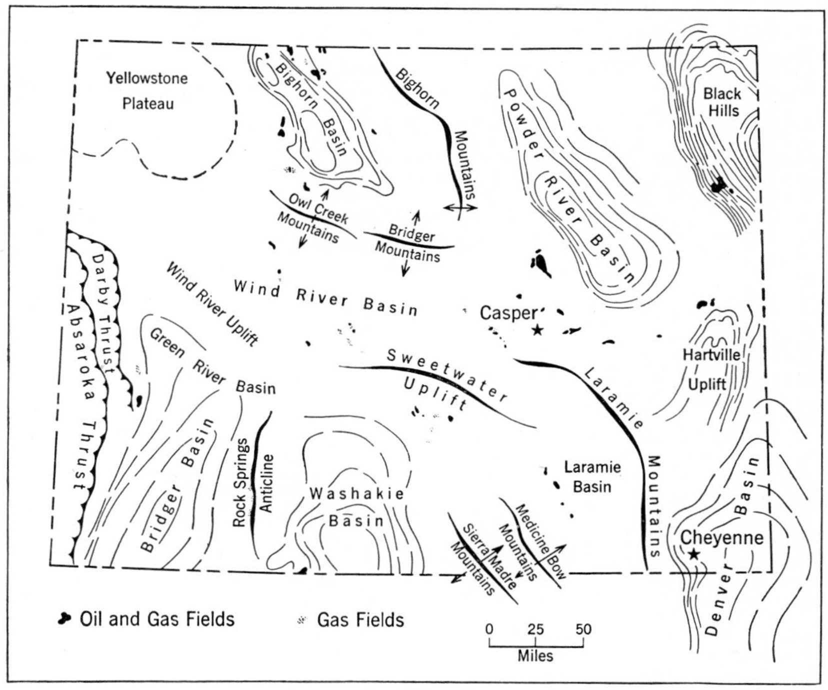

FIG. 149. Wyoming. Major structural features.

the discovery of one or more new oil fields, and in 1943 Wyoming led all states in the finding of new oil, mainly because of new discoveries in the Elk Basin field.

The broader tectonic features of Wyoming have a marked influence on the topography. The structural uplifts have been of such magni-

Fields, Pipe Lines, Unit Areas, and Land District Boundaries," *U. S. Geol. Survey, Oil and Gas Investigation, Preliminary Map* 107 (1949); Horace D. Thomas, "Geology and Petroleum Resources of Wyoming," *Petrol. Eng.*, Vol. 20 (November, 1948), pp. 128–138; C. L. Dorn, "Developments in Rocky Mountain Region in 1948," *Bull. Am. Assoc. Petrol. Geol.*, Vol. 33 (June, 1949), pp 827–836; C. E. Dobbin, "Structural Conditions of Oil and Gas Accumulation in Rocky Mountain Region, United States," *Bull. Am. Assoc. Petrol. Geol.*, Vol. 27 (April, 1943), pp. 417–478.

tude that partial erosion has uncovered the pre-Cambrian crystalline cores, which have become mountain ranges. Between the uplifts are the regional synclinal belts, which contain thick series of sediments representing all eras and all periods except the Silurian. These broad and thick sedimentary rock deposits occupy basins, which are both

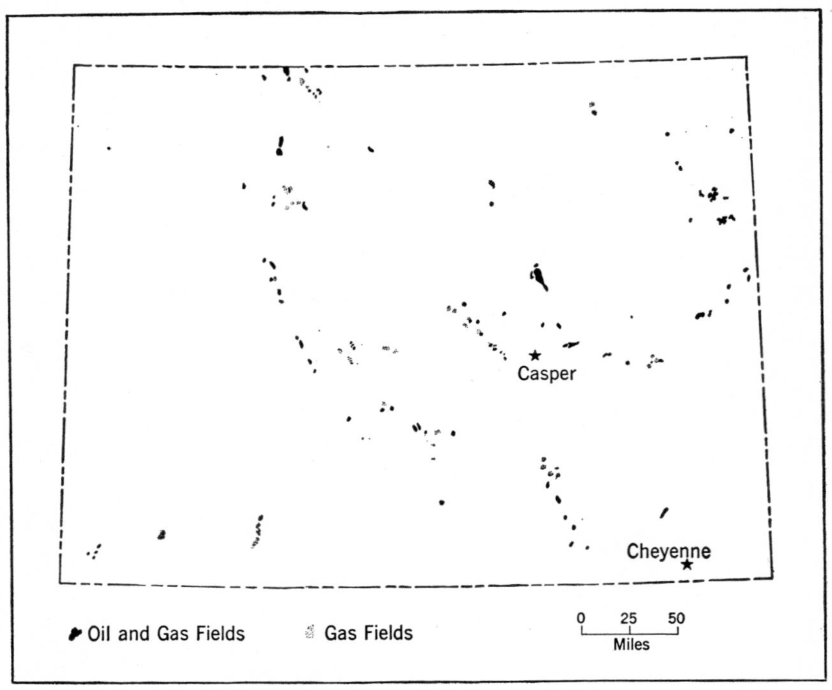

Fig. 150. Wyoming. Oil and gas fields.

structural and topographic features. It is here that the oil and gas fields of Wyoming occur. The marine Mesozoic and Paleozoic rocks are exposed, as a general rule, only around the edges of the basins; these rocks are masked toward the centers of the basins by thick deposits of continental Tertiary and Quaternary sediments.

The major uplifts from west to east across the northern third of Wyoming are the Yellowstone Plateau and Absaroka Range, the Big Horn Mountains in north central Wyoming, and the Black Hills, which extend from South Dakota into northeastern Wyoming. South of the Yellowstone Plateau, in western Wyoming, are the great Absaroka and Darby overthrusts, crustal breaks along the Salt River and Wyoming ranges. Trending east-west across north central Wyoming is the Owl Creek-Bridger Mountain chain, and in southwest-central Wyoming are the Wind River Mountains and to the east the Granite Ranges of central Wyoming. Southeastern Wyoming has

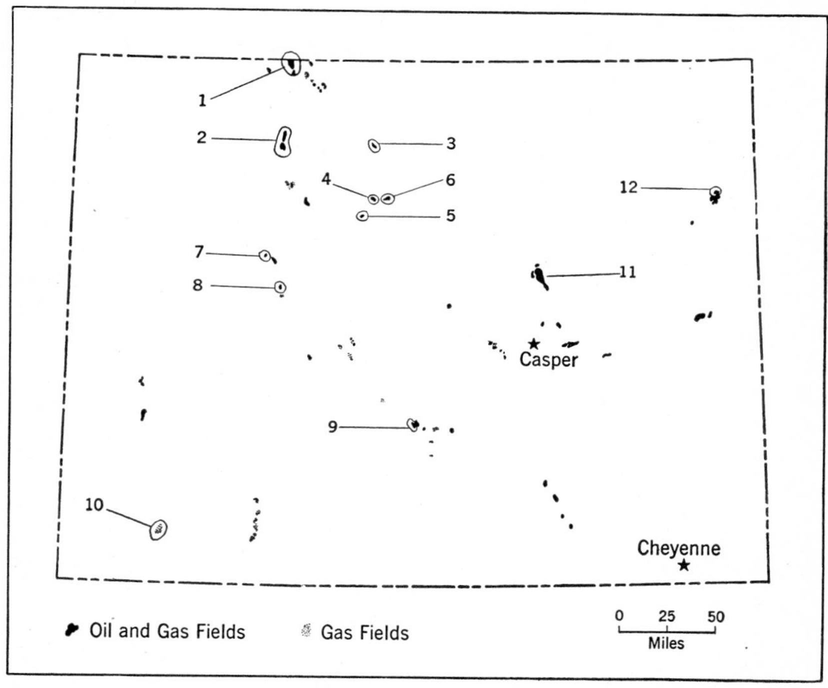

Fig. 151. Wyoming index map.

1, Elk Basin oil field.
2, Oregon Basin oil field.
3, Worland oil field.
4, South Fork oil field.
5, Nieber oil field.
6, Sand Creek oil field.
7, Circle Ridge oil field.
8, Steamboat Butte oil field.
9, Lost Soldier oil field.
10, Church Buttes gas field.
11, Salt Creek oil field.
12, Osage oil field.

four uplifts with northerly trends. These are, from west to east, the Sierra Madre, the Medicine Bow, the Laramie, and the Hartville. The Hartville is a structural ridge trending northeasterly which ties the Black Hills to the Front Ranges of the Rockies.

The two greatest basins in area are the Powder River basin, occupying most of the northeast quarter of the state, and the Green River basin in the opposite corner. The Powder River basin is outlined by the Black Hills and Hartville uplift on the east, by the northwest end of the Laramie Mountains on the south, and by the Big Horn Mountains on the west. The Green River basin lies east of the overthrust zone, west of the Sierra Madre, and south of the Wind River-Sweetwater uplifts. It is divided into the Bridger basin on the west and the Washakie and Red Desert basins on the east by the Rock Springs uplift.

Next in size is the Big Horn basin, which is enclosed on three sides by the Yellowstone Plateau, the Owl Creek-Bridger Mountain chain, and the Big Horn Mountains. The Wind River basin lies in central Wyoming, with the Owl Creek-Bridger Mountains on the north and the Wind River-Sweetwater uplift on the south. The Laramie basin lies between the Medicine Bow and the Laramie Mountains. East and southeast of the Laramie Mountains and the Hartville uplift is the northern end of the Denver, or Julesberg, basin.

All the earlier discoveries in the Wyoming basins were near the peripheries, where the pre-Tertiary sedimentary rocks are beautifully exposed and the anticlines so striking that in many places they can be easily recognized by laymen. Steep dips and large closures are the rule rather than the exception throughout the Rocky Mountain province. It was at first assumed that out toward the centers of the basins, beneath the thick cover of Tertiary continental deposits, the folds died out and no oil accumulations would be found. However, the application of geophysical instruments to Rocky Mountain exploration, plus the vastly increased depths reached by exploratory wells, has shown this assumption to be fallacious, and oil and gas fields have been found toward the basin centers. According to Thomas, in a paper published in November, 1948: "It has been in the past two years only that oil and gas fields have been found in the central parts of the basins. The Church Buttes field lies in the exact center of the Green River basin. Four fields have been found well out toward the axial part of the Big Horn basin; Worland, South Fork, Nieber, and Sand Creek." [240] Furthermore, the Paleozoic formations, which carry only heavy black oil in the periphery fields as a general rule, have been found to contain high-gravity crude oil in the deep basin accumulations.

The producing formations of Wyoming range in age from Tertiary to Cambrian. The Tertiary formation is the continental Wasatch of Eocene age which carries oil in the Green River basin in Wyoming and Colorado. The most important period from a standpoint of pro-

[240] Horace D. Thomas, *op. cit.*, p. 138.

lific reservoir sands is the Cretaceous, mainly the Upper Cretaceous.[241] The greater part of the Wyoming oil produced to date has come from the Frontier sands of the Upper Cretaceous. Other important Cretaceous reservoirs are the Muddy and Dakota sands. The Sundance sandstone of Jurassic age is an important reservoir in some fields. Upper Paleozoic reservoirs include the Phosphoria lime (Permian), the Tensleep and Amsden of the Pennsylvanian, and the Mississippian Madison limestone. The completion of a 700-barrel well in the Deadwood sandstone of Cambrian age, in June, 1948, in the Lost Soldier field [242] extended the potential reservoir section for the Rocky Mountain area to the very bottom of the sedimentary section.

The Salt Creek field has produced over one-third of a billion barrels of oil and has no competition as the principal field of Wyoming in cumulative production. For the year 1949 Salt Creek was second only to Elk basin in annual yield.

Almost all the oil and gas so far produced in Wyoming have come from anticlinal accumulations.[243] Some of these anticlines are faulted, but in most of them it is the fold and not the fault that has been responsible for trapping the oil. In the list of approximately a hundred Wyoming oil fields compiled by Dobbin,[244] eighty-eight are listed as anticlinal or domal accumulations, and twelve are classified as being due to sand lensing and other types of "stratigraphic" trapping. However, none of these twelve fields are large, and their total contribution to the cumulative production of Wyoming has been insignificant. Most of them occur either in northeastern Wyoming on the west flank of the Black Hills or near the southwestern corner of the state.

The Elk Basin field, large in area, in closure, and in current production, was illustrated and described as an example of anticlinal accumulation in Chapter 8 (Fig. 42). The older Salt Creek field has been described by Beck [245] and others. This field is in the southwestern

[241] J. David Love, "Oil and Gas Possibilities in Post-Frontier Cretaceous Rocks of Wyoming," *Am. Assoc. Petrol. Geol., Program Annual Meeting* (1950), p. 23.

[242] E. W. Krampert, "Commercial Oil in Cambrian Beds, Lost Soldier Field, Carbon and Sweetwater Counties, Wyoming," *Bull. Am. Assoc. Petrol. Geol.*, Vol. 33 (December, 1949), pp. 1998–2010.

[243] H. D. Thomas, "Geology and Petroleum Resources of Wyoming," *Petrol. Eng.*, Vol. 20 (November, 1948), p. 136.

[244] C. E. Dobbin, "Structural Conditions of Oil and Gas Accumulation in Rocky Mountain Region, United States," *Bull. Am. Assoc. Petrol. Geol.*, Vol. 27 (April, 1943), pp. 440–446.

[245] Elfred Beck, "Salt Creek Oil Field, Natrona County, Wyoming," *Structure of Typical American Oil Fields* (Am. Assoc. Petrol. Geol., 1929), Vol. 2, pp. 589–603.

part of the Powder River basin. The Salt Creek structure is an elliptical anticline with a much steeper dip on the west side, toward the Big Horn Mountains. It has approximately 1600 feet of closure, but the structural relief into the basin to the east is much greater. Beck has estimated that the potential drainage area extends northeastward from Salt Creek for a distance of 40 miles.[246] By far the greatest production at Salt Creek has come from the Second Wall Creek sandstone of Frontier (Cretaceous) age. Other reservoirs of importance, all sandstones, are the First Wall Creek of the Frontier, the deeper Cretaceous Lakota, the Third Sundance of the Jurassic, and the Pennsylvanian Tensleep.[247]

The Steamboat Butte oil field [248] is a large, relatively new field discovered in 1943 in the Wind River basin. The trap is an elongate anticline with a north-south trend and a fault on the west flank, limiting production in that direction. The estimated closure is 350 to 400 feet. The first reservoir discovered is the Nugget sandstone of Jurassic age, but the oil reserve in the deeper Tensleep, which was discovered about a year later, is much greater. The maximum thickness of oil-saturated Tensleep sand is 300 feet.

The Oregon Basin field [249] lies on the west side of the Big Horn basin, not far west of the basin axis, which is considerably west of the geographic axis. Accumulation here is also anticlinal. The Oregon basin structure has a closure of about 1600 feet; the anticlinal axis sags in the center, dividing the fold into two domes with intervening saddle. Black heavy oil is produced in quantity from the Permian Phosphoria limestone, the Pennsylvanian Tensleep sandstone, and the Mississippian Madison limestone.

The Osage field [250] is an example of trapping due to varying permeability. The reservoir rock is the Newcastle sandstone member of the Graneros (Cretaceous) shale, which occurs here as a lens of irregular shape, completely surrounded by shale, lying upon the flank of a monocline (Fig. 152). The oil has been trapped in this porous

246 Elfred Beck, *op. cit.,* pp. 591–594.

247 R. W. Mallory, "The Salt Creek Oil Field," *Wyo. Geol. Assoc. Guide Book Fourth Annual Field Conference* (1949), pp. 89–91.

248 H. E. Barton, "Steamboat Butte Oil Field, Fremont County, Wyoming," *Structure of Typical American Oil Fields* (Am. Assoc. Petrol. Geol., 1948), Vol. 3, pp. 480–513.

249 Paul T. Walton, "Oregon Basin Oil and Gas Field, Park County, Wyoming," *Bull. Am. Assoc. Petrol. Geol.,* Vol 31 (August, 1947), pp 1431–1453.

250 C. E. Dobbin and J. C. Miller, "Osage Oil Field, Weston County, Wyoming," *Stratigraphic Type Oil Fields* (Am. Assoc. Petrol. Geol, 1941), pp. 847–857.

and permeable rock. Other exceptional accumulations in Wyoming and other Rocky Mountain states have been described elsewhere.[251]

The Wyoming Geological Association has published descriptions of several Wyoming oil fields.[252] These are all anticlinal accumula-

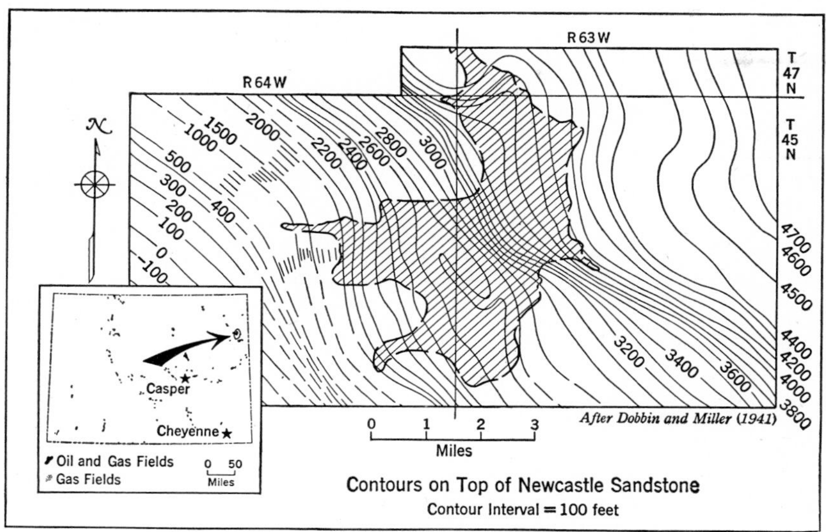

Fig. 152. Osage field, Wyoming. Lenticular sandstone trap. *Courtesy American Association of Petroleum Geologists.*

tions, although in one field, the Circle Ridge,[253] the producing dome lies in an overthrust block.

Montana [254]

(Figures 153–155)

The state of Montana contributed during 1949 about 0.5 per cent of the domestic production. This was approximately equal to the

[251] C. E. Dobbin, "Exceptional Oil Fields in the Rocky Mountain Region of the United States," *Bull. Am. Assoc. Petrol. Geol.,* Vol. 31 (May, 1947), pp. 797–823.

[252] Wyoming Geological Association, *Guide Book Third Annual Field Conference, Wind River Basin, Wyoming, Aug. 11–14, 1948; Guide Book Fourth Annual Field Conference, Powder River Basin, Wyoming, Aug. 9–13, 1949.*

[253] W. G. Olson, *Wyoming Geol. Assoc. Guide Book Third Annual Field Conference* (1948), pp. 178–185.

[254] C. E. Dobbin and C. E. Erdmann, "Geologic Occurrence of Oil and Gas in Montana," *Problems of Petroleum Geology* (Am. Assoc. Petrol. Geol., 1934), pp. 695–718; Eugene S. Perry, "Natural Gas in Montana," *Mont. Bur. Mines and Geol., Mem.* 3 (1937).

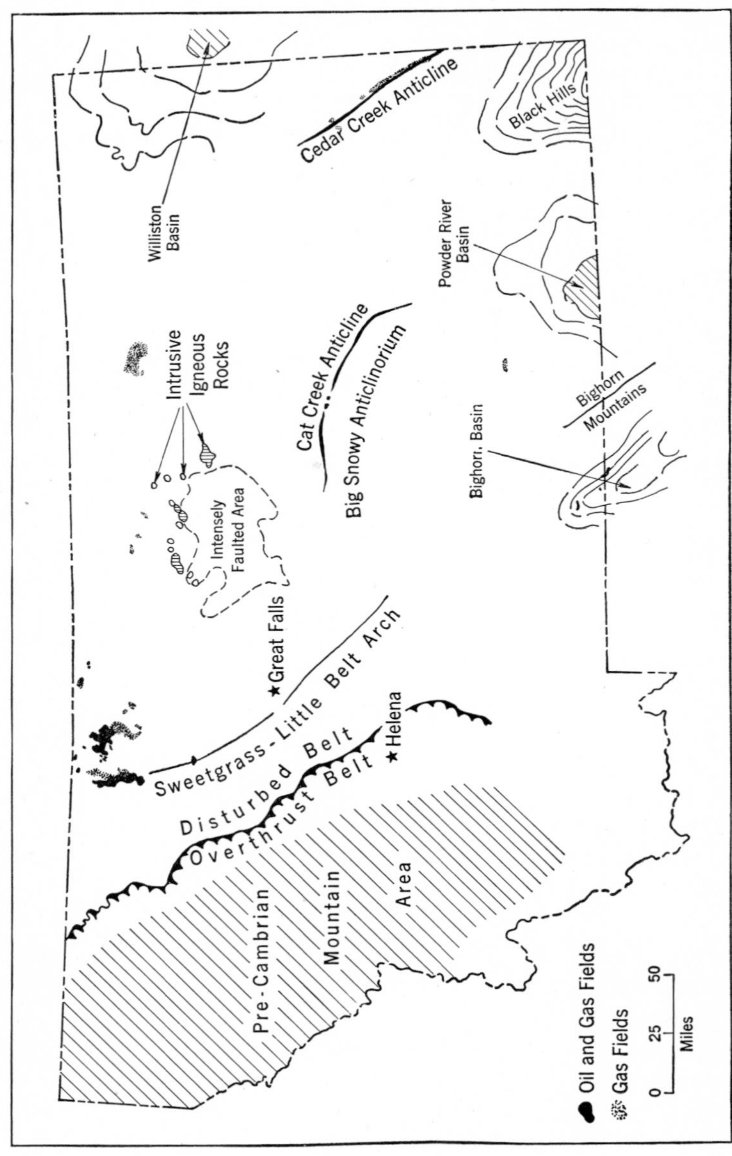

Fig. 153. Montana. Major tectonic features and oil and gas fields.

Indiana output. In terms of world production, the Montana share for the year was 0.29 per cent, which was about the same as the annual yield of Canada before the discovery of the Leduc and other reef accumulations beneath the plains of Alberta.

The first hydrocarbon discovery in Montana was the Glendive gas field in Dawson County on the eastern edge of the state in 1913. Two years later the first oil was struck on the Montana side of the Elk Basin oil field, which lies mainly in Wyoming. The first exclusively

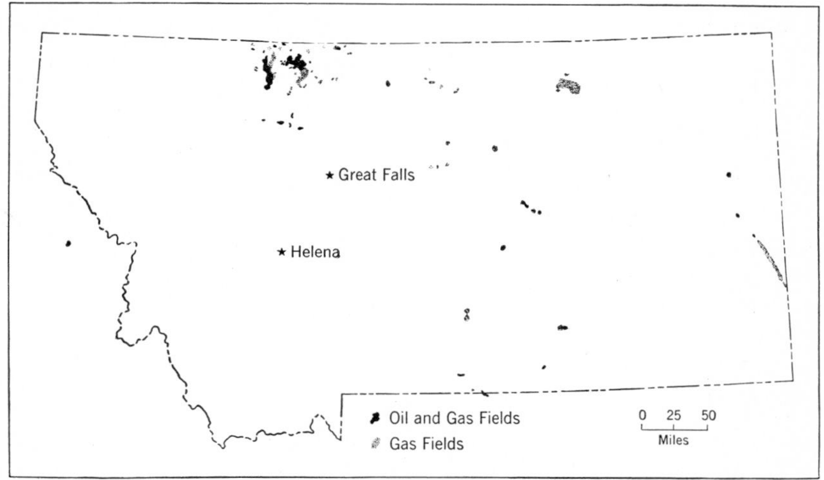

FIG. 154. Montana. Oil and gas fields.

Montana oil discovery was at Cat Creek in 1920, and other major discoveries were the Kevin-Sunburst field in 1922 and the Cut Bank field in 1929. Late in 1947 new discoveries in Musselshell County in central Montana stimulated interest in the state. By the end of 1948 Montana was being explored more actively than at any other time in its history. This paid dividends during 1949 when one gas-condensate and three oil pools were discovered. The finding of the prolific reef accumulations to the north in Alberta has also stimulated the search for oil in Montana.

The eastern two-thirds of Montana, that part east of the Rocky Mountain front, is floored mainly with sedimentary rock and is prospective oil- and gas-producing territory. The eastern border zone of the Rockies in northern Montana is marked by a series of overthrust faults which has carried pre-Cambrian sediments over Cretaceous in some places, notably at Glacier Park. East of the overthrust zone is the "disturbed belt," 8 to 10 miles wide, in which the upturned sediments parallel to the Rocky Mountain front are strongly folded and faulted. In approximately the central third of the state the tectonic pattern is a hybrid between that of the Rocky Mountains proper and that of the plains area to the eastward. In northwestern Montana, east of the disturbed belt and extending from Alberta to west central Montana, near Great Falls, is the Sweetgrass arch. North central

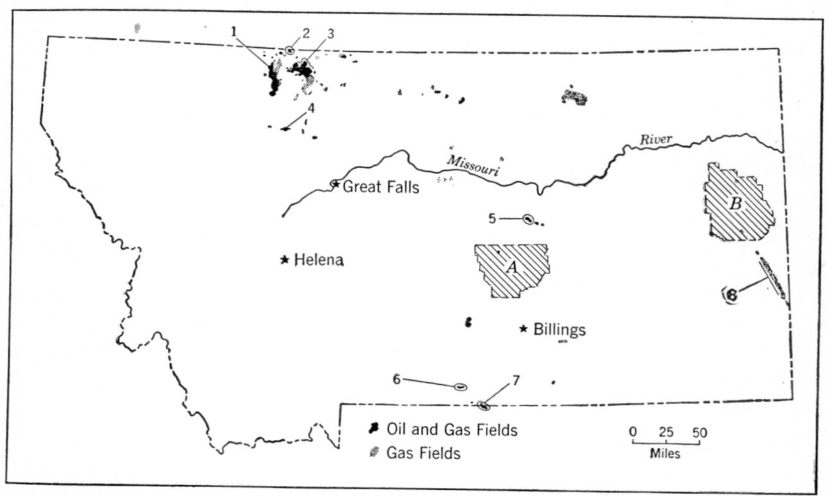

FIG. 155. Montana index map. *A*, Musselshell County; *B*, Dawson County; 1, Cut Bank oil field; 2, Border-Red Coulee oil field; 3, Kevin-Sunburst oil field; 4, Pondera oil field; 5, Cat Creek oil field; 6, Dry Creek oil field; 7, Elk Basin oil field; 8, Cedar Creek (Glendive) gas field.

Montana is floored with Cretaceous sediments interrupted by laccolithic mountains and local thrust faults. To the south in central Montana are the Little Belt-Big Snowy anticlinorium, an east-west uplift containing the laccolithic Judith Mountains, and the anticlinal Big Snowy Mountains. An eastward extension to the anticlinorium is the Porcupine dome. South central Montana contains the northwesterly extension of the Big Horn Mountains and the northernmost tip of the Big Horn basin.

The eastern third of Montana is part of the High Plains physiographic province. Crossing the eastern border of the state immediately north of the North Dakota-South Dakota boundary line is the Cedar Creek (Baker-Glendive) anticline, which is a very elongate structural ridge with a northwest-southeast trend. It separates the Williston basin of northeastern Wyoming and northwestern South

Dakota from the northern end of the Powder River basin of northeastern Wyoming. The very southeastern corner of Montana contains the northern flank of the Black Hills uplift.

The reservoir rocks range in age from Upper Cretaceous to early Mississippian. The leached upper surface of the Madison limestone of Mississippian age is especially important as an oil reservoir in Montana.

The leading field in both cumulative production and in output for 1949 is the Cut Bank. The older Kevin-Sunburst field is second in cumulative and third in recent annual production. The Elk Basin field was the second Montana field in 1949, although it produced over 2½ times as much oil on the Wyoming side of the line.

Of the twenty-seven Montana fields listed by Dobbin in 1943,[255] twenty produced from faulted and non-faulted domes or anticlines. However, among the seven fields in which accumulation has been due to varying permeability is the Cut Bank field, the largest oil accumulation so far discovered in the state.

The Cut Bank field [256] is one of several lying near to or upon the Sweetgrass arch.[257] It is 31 miles long and up to 10 miles wide. It lies 20 miles down the west flank of the Kevin-Sunburst dome, a node on the Sweetgrass arch. The main oil and gas reservoir rock is the Cut Bank sand at the base of the Kootenai formation (Lower Cretaceous). The trap is formed by the up-dip pinching out of this sandstone. Oil and gas are also found in two discontinuous lenses in the overlying Sunburst sand zone (middle part of Kootenai), as well as in the Madison limestone. Cut Bank is the largest stratigraphic-type accumulation so far discovered in the Rocky Mountain province.

The older Kevin-Sunburst [258] field, which lies to the east of Cut Bank, is irregularly distributed on the northwest flank of the Kevin-Sunburst dome. The principal reservoir is the leached top of the Madison (Mississippian) limestone, and the irregular distribution of the hydrocarbons is due to the erratic porosity of this reservoir. Some production is also obtained from the Kootenai sand which likewise has variable thickness and permeability.

[255] C. E. Dobbin, "Structural Conditions of Oil and Gas Accumulation in Rocky Mountain Region, United States," *Bull. Am. Assoc. Petrol. Geol.*, Vol. 27 (April, 1943), pp. 438–439.

[256] John E. Blixt, "Cut Bank Oil and Gas Field, Glacier County, Montana," *Stratigraphic Type Oil Fields* (Am. Assoc. Petrol. Geol., 1941), pp. 327–381.

[257] C. E. Dobbin, "Exceptional Oil Fields in Rocky Mountain Region of United States," *Bull. Am. Assoc. Petrol. Geol.*, Vol. 31 (May, 1947), p. 799.

[258] W. F. Howell, "Kevin-Sunburst Field, Toole County, Montana," *Structure of Typical American Oil Fields* (Am. Assoc. Petrol. Geol., 1929), Vol. 2, pp. 254–268.

Another nearby field on the Sweetgrass arch is the Border-Red Coulee.[259] The fact that this field straddles the international boundary led to an unusual development history, including the non-drilling of a strip 525 feet wide along the boundary line. Oil has accumulated in Kootenai sands, which lens out up-dip on the north flank of the Kevin-Sunburst dome. The third most important field in the arch is the Pondera, which lies on a structural terrace, or nose, west of Conrad.

Elsewhere in the state, as at Dry Creek, which is perhaps the northernmost of the Big Horn basin structures, and at Cat Creek[260] in central Montana, the trapping is anticlinal, although complicated by numerous faults striking across the folds. At Dry Creek one fault is reported to have a displacement of 1000 feet, and several others offset the strata 500 feet or more.[261] The Cedar Creek field,[262] also referred to as the Baker-Glendive field, produces mainly gas from an asymmetric anticline more than 100 miles long. The gas is confined to nodes along the axis of this extremely elongate fold.

Utah[263]

(Figure 156)

The total production of oil and gas in Utah to date has been insignificant. Some recent discoveries, however, lead to the belief that this state may one day begin to produce its share of the Rocky Mountain annual output. Most of the eastern half of Utah is underlain by a thick series of sedimentary rocks, and it is here that the chances of finding new oil deposits appear best. Some interest is being shown also at the present time in the Basin and Range province of western Utah, in the hope that beneath the floors of Pleistocene and Recent sediment the basins contain an adequate, and oil-bearing, stratigraphic section. The search is complicated by the presence of abundant igneous rocks and involved faulting.

259 Charles E. Erdmann and John R. Schwabrow, "Border-Red Coulee Oil Field, Toole County, Montana, and Alberta, Canada," *Stratigraphic Type Oil Fields* (Am. Assoc. Petrol. Geol., 1941), pp. 267–326

260 C. E. Dobbin, "Exceptional Oil Fields in Rocky Mountain Region of United States," *Bull. Am. Assoc. Petrol. Geol.*, Vol. 31 (May, 1947), pp. 806–807.

261 C. E. Dobbin, "Structural Conditions of Oil and Gas Accumulation in Rocky Mountain Region, United States," *Bull. Am. Assoc. Petrol. Geol.*, Vol. 27 (April, 1943), p. 439.

262 C. E. Dobbin, *op. cit.*, Vol. 31 (May, 1947), pp. 821–823.

263 George H. Hansen and Mendell M. Bell, "Oil and Gas Possibilities of Utah," *Utah Geol. Min. Survey*, 1950 (reviewed by the *Oil Reporter*, March 11, 1950).

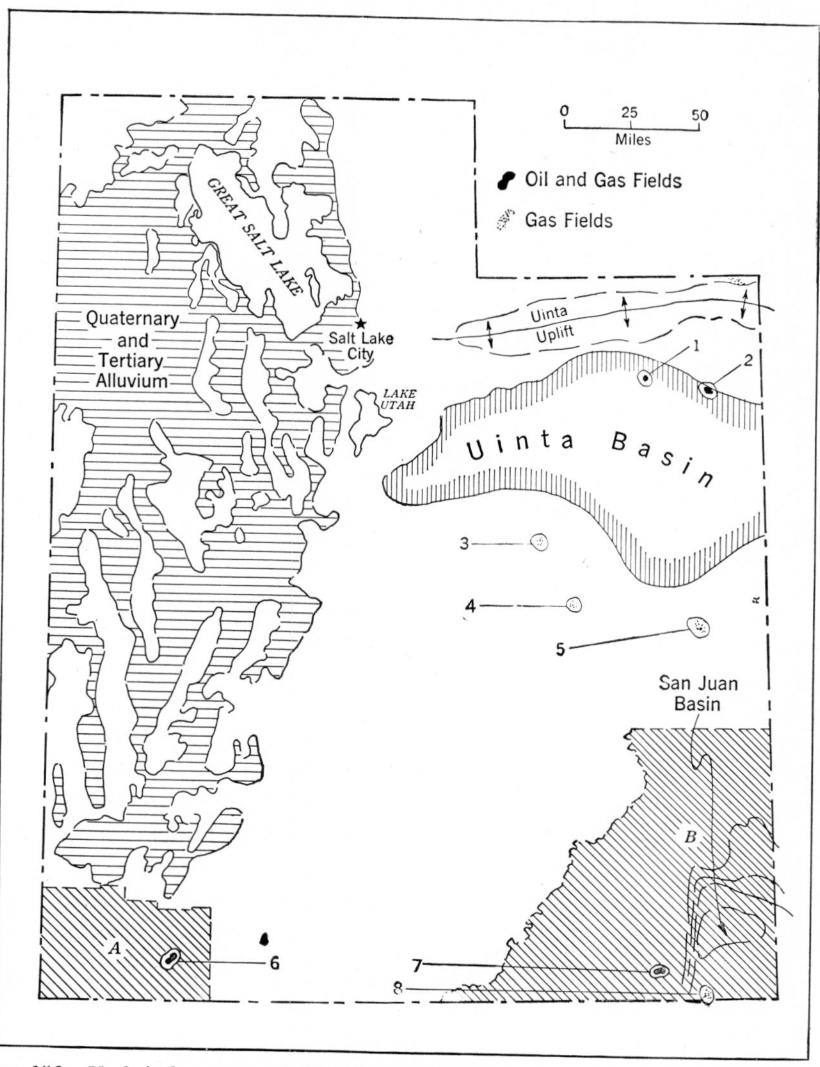

FIG. 156. Utah index map. *A*, Washington County; *B*, San Juan County; 1, Roosevelt oil field; 2, Ashley Valley oil field: 3, Farnham gas field; 4, Woodside gas field; 5, Cisco gas field; 6, Virgin River oil field; 7, San Juan oil field; 8, Boundary Buttes gas field.

The major structural and sedimentary basin is the Uinta, which lies south of the Uinta Mountains in east central Utah. The large Rangely field of Colorado is near the easternmost end of the Uinta basin. The San Juan basin of northwestern New Mexico and southeastern Colorado also overlaps a short distance into southeastern Utah.

Utah has been producing gas intermittently since 1886 and oil since 1907. The gas was discovered in the Salt Lake basin near Salt Lake City. The reservoir rock, and probably the source rock also, is the fresh-water Pleistocene sediment with which this basin is floored. The oil discovery in 1907 was in a small intermontane basin near the southwestern corner of the state on the Virgin River in Washington County. The first oil well in the Utah part of the San Juan basin was drilled in 1908. The Cisco gas field, which was exploited for the manufacture of carbon black, was discovered in 1924. In 1931 gas was rediscovered in the Great Salt Lake basin, this time 35 to 40 miles north of the earlier discovery.[264]

Until recently the only oil production came from the two small fields in the southwestern and southeastern corners of the state. By 1943 the oil output had dwindled to almost nothing. In 1948 the first substantial oil production was obtained by drilling deeper in the Ashley Valley field in Uinta County and testing the Weber sandstone of Pennsylvanian age.[265] During the same year further testing of the Boundary Butte field of San Juan County in southeastern Utah led to the discovery of oil in the Coconino (Permian) sand at a depth of about 1500 feet and the discovery of gas with an estimated yield of 28 million cubic feet daily from the underlying Pennsylvanian Hermosa formation. Based on a seismograph survey, the discovery well for a new field in the Uinta basin was completed in mid-1949. This new field, which has been named the Roosevelt, lies approximately 110 miles east of Salt Lake City. The reservoir rock is a fractured dolomitic Eocene shale lying at a depth of nearly 9400 feet. Although the oil is of excellent quality, with a gravity of 32.6°, it contains so much paraffin that it solidifies at 90° F. Its temperature as it emerges from the well is 94°.[266]

[264] Virgil R. D. Kirkham, "Natural Gas in Washington, Idaho, Eastern Oregon, and Northern Utah," *Geology of Natural Gas* (Am. Assoc. Petrol. Geol., 1935), pp. 240–243.

[265] C. L. Dorn, "Developments in Rocky Mountain Region in 1948," *Bull. Am. Assoc. Petrol. Geol.,* Vol. 33 (June, 1949), p. 835.

[266] Anon., "Carter Finds Unusual Oil in Utah," *The Link,* Vol. 14 (July, 1949), p. 10.

The traps[267] of the gas fields so far discovered in Utah are anticlines. Some are domes and others are very elongate. They may or may not be faulted. Closures range up to 800 feet. The Woodside gas contains 1.31 per cent helium, and the Farnham gas runs 98.3 per cent carbon dioxide.

The two oldest oil fields, the Virgin and the San Juan, produce from varying-permeability traps on the flanks of monoclines.

Reservoir rocks so far explored in Utah range in age from Upper Cretaceous to Mississippian.

California[268]

(Figures 157–159)

California is second only to Texas in its annual production of petroleum. During 1949 the California share of the domestic output was 18.6 per cent, which was 9.8 per cent of the world's production. California produced more oil during 1949 than any foreign country except Venezuela.

Oil and gas seeps are abundant in parts of California, and the early search for buried hydrocarbon deposits was guided by the presence of these natural outcrops. That famous animal trap, Rancho La Brea, is but one of many tarry surface accumulations which are found from southern California as far north as Humboldt County, in the Coast Ranges some 200 miles north of San Francisco. A very active search for oil carried on by many individuals and companies took place during the two decades 1854–1874. The search extended from Los Angeles County to Humboldt County, and some small production was obtained in Ventura County. In 1874 two successful wells were drilled in Pico Canyon near Newhall, Los Angeles County. Commercial production started in 1875, and fields in this vicinity have been continuously productive ever since.

Between 1875 and 1905, some thirty fields were opened up in southern California. These were all situated near seeps, and because of

[267] C. E. Dobbin, "Structural Conditions of Oil and Gas Accumulation in Rocky Mountain Region, United States," *Bull. Am. Assoc. Petrol. Geol.,* Vol. 27 (April, 1943), p. 457; Dean E. Winchester, "Natural Gas in Colorado, Northern New Mexico, and Utah," *Geology of Natural Gas* (Am. Assoc. Petrol. Geol., 1935), pp. 363–384.

[268] Olaf P. Jenkins, *et al.,* "Geologic Formations and Economic Developments of the Oil and Gas Fields of California," *Calif. Div. Mines, Bull.* 118, 1943; Graham B. Moody, "Developments in West Coast Area in 1949," *Bull. Am. Assoc. Petrol. Geol.,* Vol. 34 (June, 1950), pp. 1015–1031.

these seeps, they were explored and discovered. Included among the fields discovered between 1899 and 1905 were such production giants as Coalinga, McKittrick, Sunset, Midway, Kern River, and the old

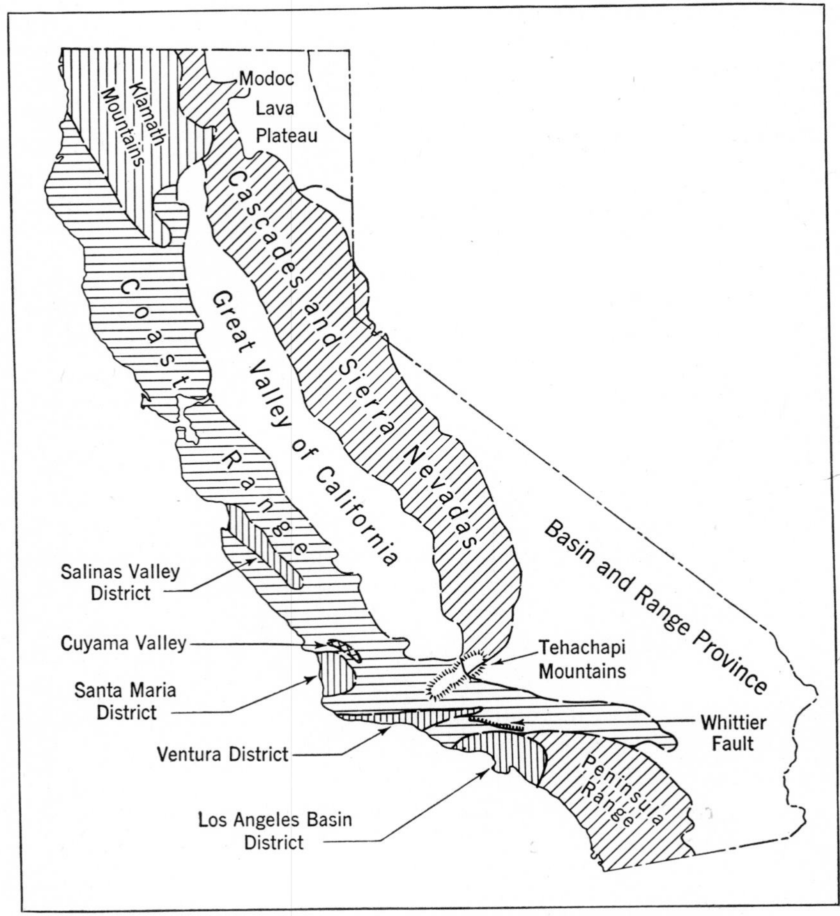

FIG. 157. California. Geological provinces and oil districts.

Santa Maria field. At the same time, the value of geology to oil questing was recognized, and company geological staffs were initiated.

Another great spurt in discovery took place between 1920 and 1924 when the Los Angeles basin fields of Huntington Beach, Santa Fe Springs, Long Beach, Torrance, Dominguez, and Inglewood were found.

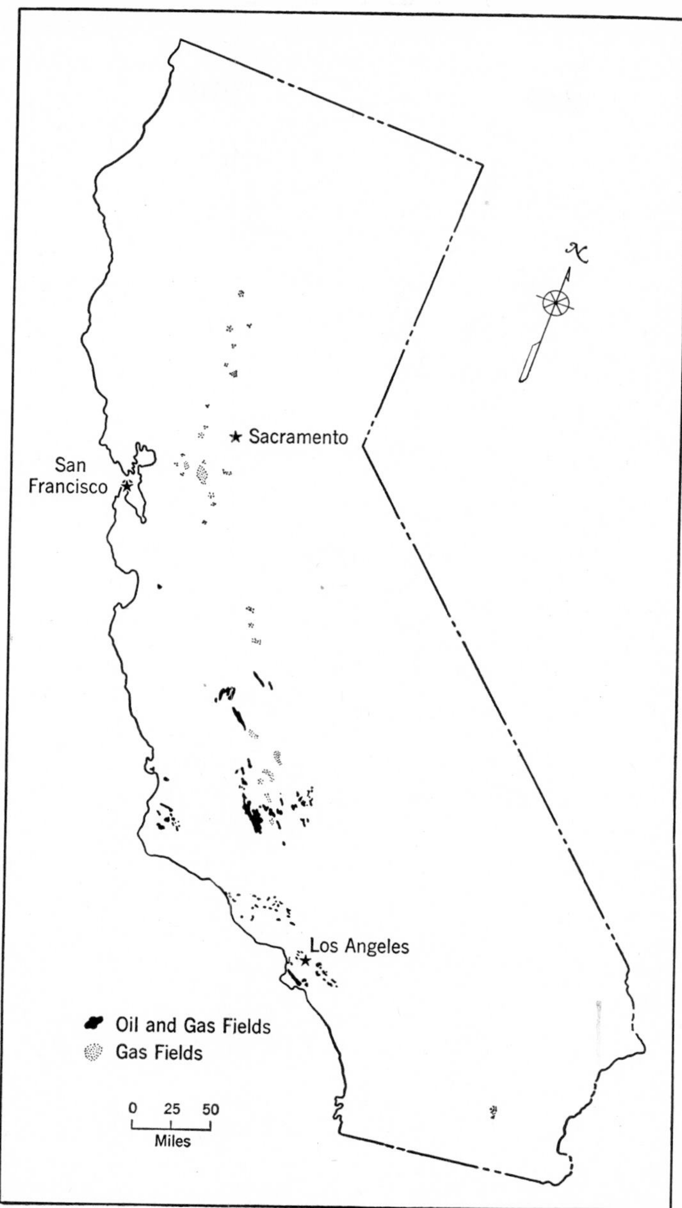

FIG. 158. California. Oil and gas fields.

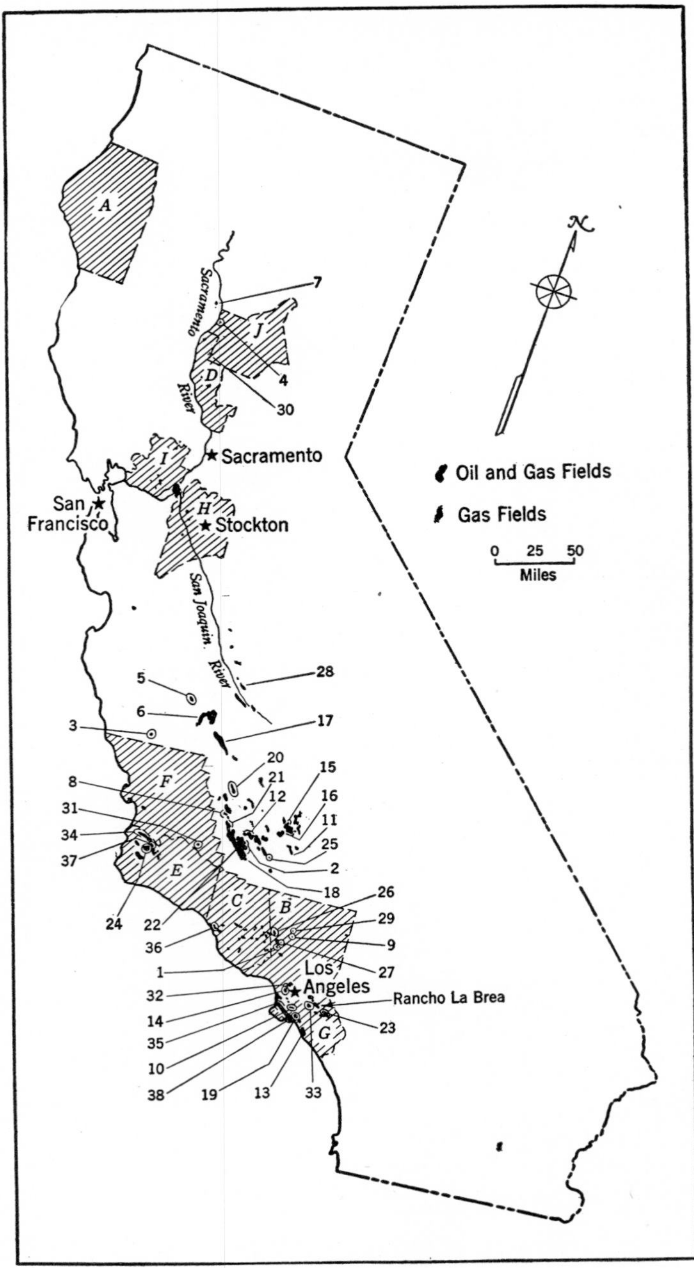

See legend on page 493.

Although still not important oil-producing territory, northern California has produced gas for many years. Gas was first struck in water wells in Stockton in 1854, and beginning in 1889 this gas was marketed until the field was exhausted. Between 1891 and 1933, northern California was the scene of scattered small gas discoveries. In 1933 the first high-pressure gas discovery was made at Marysville Buttes in Sutter County. New gas finds have continued ever since, the largest one being the discovery of Rio Vista, California's greatest gas field, in 1937.

The outstanding event in recent years was the discovery of oil in the Cuyama Valley on both sides of the Santa Barbara-San Luis Obispo County line. This new district lies about midway between the nearest fields in the San Joaquin Valley and those of the Santa Maria district. The first field, the Russell Ranch, was discovered in June, 1948. The South Cuyama field, 4 miles to the southeast, was found in May, 1949, and a third field 3 miles northwest of Russell Ranch was discovered in April, 1950.

California pioneered in the development of offshore fields many years ago, and the search for such deposits is continuing. In 1948 two new offshore oil fields, one in Orange County and the other in Santa Barbara County, were discovered.

Four of the seven main geologic provinces of California consist of either crystalline rocks or ancient sedimentary rocks, or both, and so

---

FIG. 159. California index map.

A, Humboldt County.
B, Los Angeles County.
C, Ventura County.
D, Sutter County.
E, Santa Barbara County.
F, San Luis Obispo County.
G, Orange County.
H, San Joaquin County.
I, Solano County.
J, Butte County.

1, Aliso Canyon oil field.
2, Buena Vista oil field.
3, Campbell oil field.
4, Chico gas field.
5, Ciervo oil field.
6, Coalinga oil field.
7, Corning gas field.
8, Cymric oil field.
9, Del Valle oil field.
10, Dominguez oil field.
11, Edison oil field.
12, Elk Hills oil field.
13, Huntington Beach oil field.
14, Inglewood oil field.
15, Kern Front oil field.
16, Kern River oil field.
17, Kettleman Hills oil field.
18, Lakeview oil field.
19, Long Beach oil field.
20, Lost Hills oil field.
21, McKittrick oil field.
22, Midway-Sunset oil field.
23, Olinda oil field.
24, Orcutt oil field.
25, Paloma oil field.
26, Pico Canyon oil field.
27, Placerita oil field.
28. Raisin City oil field.
29, Ramona oil field.
30, Rio Vista gas field.
31, Russell Ranch oil field.
32, Salt Creek oil field.
33, Santa Fe Springs oil field.
34, Santa Maria Valley oil field.
35, Torrance oil field.
36, Ventura Avenue oil field.
37, West Cat Canyon oil field.
38, Wilmington oil field.

they are not likely to be oil-bearing. These are the Klamath Mountains of northern California, the Modoc lava plateau of northeastern California, the Sierra Nevada, which forms the backbone of most of eastern California, and the Peninsular Range, which extends into southern California from Lower California. One of the remaining three, the Basin and Range province of western Utah, Nevada, and southeastern California, contains no oil or methane gas fields as yet, but it is an object of oil company interest at the present time.

All the California oil and gas fields so far discovered lie in either the Great Valley or the Coast Range province. The Great Valley is a topographic and tectonic trough lying between the Sierra Nevada and the Coast Ranges. It has been an area of sedimentation and downwarp throughout later geologic time. It drains into San Francisco Bay by means of the southward-flowing Sacramento River and the northward-flowing San Joaquin River. At the present time all the Great Valley oil fields are in the upper part of the San Joaquin Valley.

The Coast Range province includes both the Coast Ranges proper and the Transverse Ranges. The Coast Ranges are not continuous but are offset one from the other, and the intervening re-entrants have, like the Great Valley, been areas of downwarp and sedimentation through a considerable span of Tertiary and Quaternary history. Three of these re-entrants, the Los Angeles basin, the Ventura basin, and the Santa Maria basin, contain many oil fields, and a fourth, the Salinas Valley, has recently become productive.[269]

The Great Valley and the Coast Range re-entrants were washed by shallow seas during much of the Tertiary and, in places, into the Quaternary. From the organic characteristics of much of the sediment deposited in these seas and from the enormous quantities of oil stored within these sediments, one is justified in concluding that the Tertiary and early Quaternary seas were teeming with aquatic life. At the same time, clastic sediment, including potential reservoir sands, was being washed in from nearby mountain areas. For these reasons, the sedimentary sections in the California oil districts contain many reservoir beds, and there is abundant oil within the reservoirs.

The reservoir rocks of California range in age from Pleistocene to pre-Cretaceous. The Kern River formation, which is productive in San Joaquin Valley, extends from the Upper Pliocene into the Pleistocene. Other Pliocene reservoirs of note are the Pico, Repetto, and Etchegoin. The Pliocene and the Miocene have so far produced

[269] J. E. Kilkenny, "Geology and Exploration for Oil in Salinas Valley, California," *Bull. Am. Assoc. Petrol. Geol.*, Vol. 32 (December, 1948), pp. 2254–2268.

most of California's oil. Important Miocene reservoirs include the Monterey, Temblor, and Vaqueros. The Oligocene Sespe produces considerable oil in the Ventura-Santa Clara district, but the Oligocene is not important as yet in other areas. The Eocene was a very minor source of California oil until the discovery of the Gatchell zone at Coalinga, from which considerable oil has been obtained. One field in the Valley produces an insignificant quantity of oil from an Upper Cretaceous reservoir. The oldest reservoir rock is pre-Cretaceous schist and other metamorphosed basement rocks in which an estimated 15,000 barrels per day is now being produced.[270]

It has been estimated that sand or sandstone is the reservoir rock for 98 per cent of California's oil.[271] The remaining 2 per cent comes from fractured chert, shale, and schist, or from conglomerate composed of schist fragments. In addition, some gas is produced from siltstone and sandy shale. Five per cent, or more, of the oil produced in California comes from reservoirs which are non-marine in origin. In some places these formations grade laterally into marine facies, but in many it is probable that the source material, as well as the reservoir rock, was deposited in fresh water.

Practically every type of hydrocarbon trap except those peculiar to carbonate rock reservoirs has been found in California.[272] The anticline is the most important in terms of volume of oil (about two-thirds of the state total) so far produced. Second in importance is sealing by truncation and overlap. Faulting is common in California, and it has controlled the distribution of oil across anticlines in numerous fields. In addition, there are some fields where the trap has been created by the faulting of a plunging anticline. Some trapping has been brought about by lensing of the sandstone reservoirs, but most of the producing sandstones of California are sheet sands, and wedge-out traps have been due to truncation and sealing rather than to original depositional lenticularity. Although California is the best known locality for brea sealing, the actual volume of oil impounded below solid hydrocarbon barriers is relatively insignificant. An even more freakish type of accumulation, in one of the reservoirs

[270] W. S. Eggleston, "Summary of Production from Fractured Rock Reservoirs in California," *Bull. Am. Assoc. Petrol. Geol.*, Vol. 32 (July, 1948), pp. 1352–1355.

[271] Harold W. Hoots, "Origin, Migration and Accumulation of Oil in California," "Oil and Gas Fields of California," *Calif. Div. Mines, Bull.* 118 (1943), p. 267.

[272] J. C. Hazzard, R. R. Simonson, P. H. Dudley, H. W. Weddle, and D. M. Davis, "Oil and Gas Traps in California," *Am. Assoc. Petrol. Geol., Program Annual Meeting* (1950), p. 17; E. H. McCollough, "Structural Influence on the Accumulation of Petroleum in California," *Problems of Petroleum Geology* (Am. Assoc. Petrol. Geol., 1934), pp. 735–760.

at East Coalinga, has been described by Hoots as follows: "The Temblor reservoir sand crops out up the plunge of the fold. The oil, however, extends to, and seeps from, the outcrop and commercial production has been obtained from shallow wells nearby. According to Max Birkhauser (personal communication), who has devoted considerable study to the geology of this area, it is probable that accumulation occurred when the outcrop of the 'Temblor' sand was overlapped by impermeable lower Pliocene strata, and that subsequent late Quaternary elevation and erosion of the Coalinga anticline has stripped away the Pliocene seal. Apparently the reservoir fluid pressure since that time has not been high enough to flush all of the oil from the sand." [273]

The oil fields of California can be divided readily into two major districts, the Great Valley and the Coast Range. The Coast Range district can be subdivided into the Los Angeles basin, Ventura basin, and Santa Maria basin.

In cumulative production through 1949, the Los Angeles basin was a few thousand barrels ahead of the San Joaquin Valley district. The Ventura and the Santa Maria districts rank third and fourth respectively. In annual production for 1949, the San Joaquin Valley stood ahead of the Los Angeles basin but with no change of rank for the other two districts. The leading California field in total production is Midway-Sunset, with Long Beach second. Before East Texas, the Midway-Sunset field had the largest cumulative production of any field in the United States. Third and fourth in cumulative production in California are the Coalinga pools and Santa Fe Springs. During 1949 the Wilmington field in the Los Angeles basin produced the most oil, followed by the group of pools producing from the Coalinga anticline. Ventura Avenue and Huntington Beach were practically tied for third place.

Los Angeles Basin District. Although the Los Angeles City field was discovered in 1892, it was not until the early 1920's that this district assumed world importance as a source of oil. Three of the four leading fields, Long Beach, Santa Fe Springs, and Huntington Beach, were discovered during that time. The fourth and currently the largest field in California, Wilmington, was discovered in 1932.

According to Driver,[274] the Los Angeles basin covers about 1200 square miles. It is bounded on the north by the San Gabriel Moun-

[273] Harold W. Hoots, *op. cit.*, p. 269.

[274] Herschel L. Driver, "Genesis and Evolution of Los Angeles Basin, California," *Bull. Am. Assoc. Petrol. Geol.*, Vol. 32 (January, 1948), pp. 109–125.

tains; beyond the mountains is the Ventura Valley district. Topographically, the Los Angeles basin is a plains area containing, however, various hills and knolls that reflect underlying anticlinal structures. Many of these hills, such as Signal Hill (Long Beach), are now covered with oil fields. Most of the oil has accumulated within sandstones of Lower Pliocene and Upper Miocene age. There has been some accumulation in weathered or fractured metamorphic rocks belonging to the basement complex.

The Long Beach field was illustrated and discussed in Chapter 8 (Fig. 33) as an example of an elongate anticline. The Santa Fe Springs field was also treated in Chapter 8 (Fig. 44) as an example of accumulation in a structural dome. The Wilmington oil field, with a production in 1949 of nearly 44 million barrels of oil, making it second only to East Texas among the fields of the United States in output for the year, has not been described heretofore in this book. It is 20 miles south of Los Angeles, on the coast midway between San Pedro and the city of Long Beach. Unlike the nearby Long Beach and Torrance anticlines, the Wilmington anticline is not obvious at the surface. The topography is only very slightly elevated, and the bed-rock structure is obscured by a thick deposit of Quaternary alluvium. The first explorations were carried out in this area in an attempt to extend the Torrance field to the southeast. Subsurface studies based on the information obtained during the drilling of these earlier wells, plus a seismograph survey, resulted in the discovery of the Wilmington field in January, 1932. The Wilmington anticline is a large and irregular dome with the strata dipping off the axis at angles ranging from 2° to 15°. The structure is cut by major faults. Most of the folding and the faulting took place before the deposition of the Upper Pliocene sediments. The trapping is entirely anticlinal, but in some of the faulted areas production is confined to the upblock. The oil comes from eight producing zones in the Lower Pliocene Repetto formation, in the underlying Upper Miocene Puente formation, and in the basement schist.

Although not so large, most of the other Los Angeles basin accumulations are similar to Wilmington, Long Beach, and Santa Fe Springs. Trapping is largely anticlinal. An exception is along the Whittier fault, but even there only the Olinda pool (Chapter 8) actually demonstrates fault trapping; elsewhere along the fault, accumulation has taken place in anticlines paralleling the fault.

Ventura-Santa Clara Valley District. This district occupies a long and narrow re-entrant with an east-west trend between two transverse ranges in the Coast Range system. Most of the district is in Ventura County, but the eastern end is in Los Angeles County, 30 to 40 miles north of the city of Los Angeles. The Ventura Avenue field [275] is by far the largest in the district, both in cumulative production and in recent annual output. It is destined to produce before abandonment somewhere between ½ and ¾ billion barrels of oil. The Ventura Avenue field lies 2½ miles north of the city of Ventura on the California coast. Production is obtained from a very elongate anticline 16 miles long with trend almost exactly east. The dips to the north and south are relatively steep, ranging from 30° to 60°. The fold is cut by several thrust faults, which have permitted some transverse migration and which have affected accumulation in several of the reservoir zones. Six oil-bearing zones lie within the Pico formation of Upper Pliocene age. According to Thoms and Bailey,[276] the Pico zones yield a relatively light oil; the underlying Repetto, of Lower Pliocene age, produces a thick heavy oil.

The Aliso Canyon field [277] lies near the eastern end of the district about 30 miles northwest of the city of Los Angeles and 4 miles southeast of Pico Canyon, where oil was first struck in 1874. The Aliso Canyon field was discovered in 1938. Here the district is a region of intense folding and thrust faulting. The reservoir rocks are in the stationary block beneath the folded Santa Susana thrust block (Fig. 160). The Pliocene, Miocene, and Eocene rocks each contain one productive zone. Because of the presence of an erosional unconformity between the different rock series, the area of closure differs from one level to the next, and so the productive limits are different for each oil zone.

In the same general area are the Del Valle [278] and the Ramona [279] oil fields. The Del Valle field lies immediately to the southeast of the Ramona field. In both fields accumulation has taken place in

[275] F. W. Hertel, "Ventura Avenue Oil Field, Ventura County, California," *Structure of Typical American Oil Fields* (Am. Assoc. Petrol. Geol., 1929), Vol. 2, pp. 23–24.

[276] C. C. Thoms and William C. Bailey, "Ventura Avenue Oil Field," *Calif. Div. Mines, Bull.* 118, p. 392.

[277] Claude E. Leach, "Geology of Aliso Canyon Field, Los Angeles County, California," *Structure of Typical American Oil Fields* (Am. Assoc. Petrol. Geol., 1948), Vol. 3, pp. 24–37.

[278] L. A. Tarbet, "Geology of Del Valle Oil Field, Los Angeles County, California," *Bull. Am. Assoc. Petrol. Geol.,* Vol. 26 (February, 1942), pp. 188–196.

[279] Loyal E Nelson, "Preliminary Report on Ramona Field, Los Angeles and Ventura Counties, California," *Bull. Am. Assoc. Petrol. Geol.,* Vol. 32 (August, 1948), pp. 1658–1663.

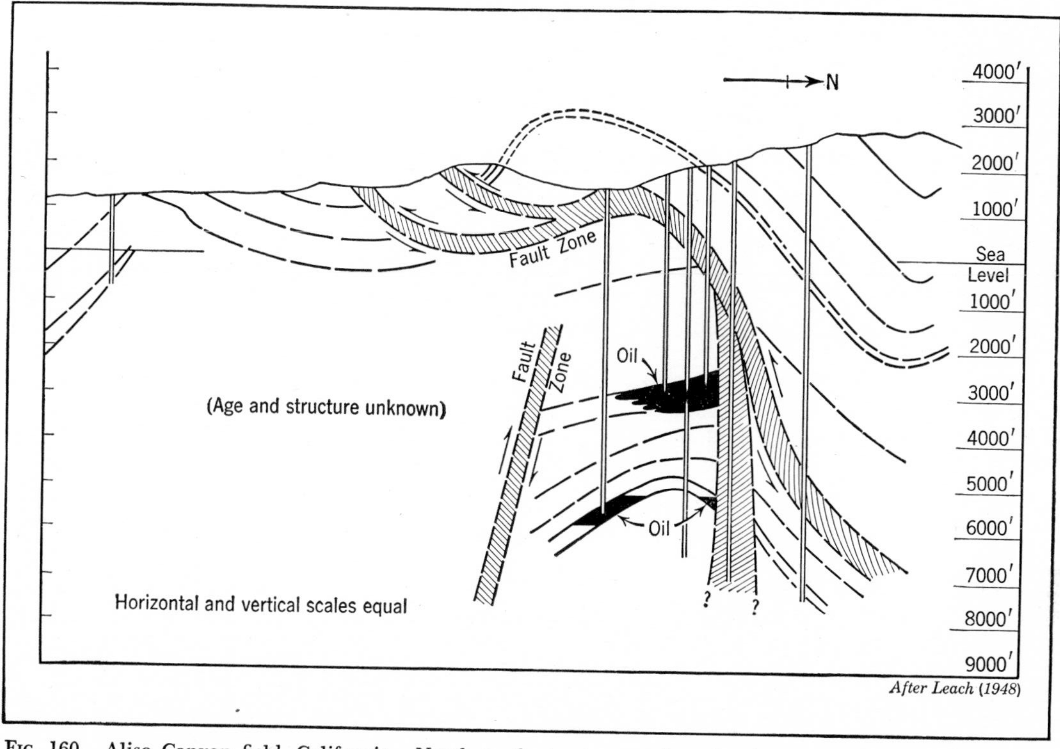

FIG. 160. Aliso Canyon field, California. North-south structure section, showing complicated fault and anticlinal trapping. *Courtesy American Association of Petroleum Geologists.*

anticlines and drag folds in an overthrust fault block (Fig. 161). Closure is completed in some of the reservoirs by lensing of the sandstones.

The latest occurrence in the long and eventful petroleum history of the upper Santa Clara Valley was the discovery of oil in quantity in the Placerita field [280] 2 miles east of Newhall. This field had been producing a few barrels daily since 1920, but a well drilled a mile from the old field in 1948 flowed an estimated 70 to 100 barrels daily from a depth of only 717 feet and brought about a wasteful town-lot drilling campaign. The reservoir sands lie in the upper Pliocene section. Accumulation has been due to a combination of plunging anticlinal structure, faults, and up-dip wedging.

Santa Maria District.[281] The Santa Maria district occupies a wedge-shaped re-entrant into the Coast Ranges, with the mouth of the Santa Maria River forming the northwest corner of the triangle and the river itself the northeast edge of the producing district. All the fields lie within 30 miles of the coast line. Of the six major fields, the old Orcutt field (formerly known as the Santa Maria) is the largest in cumulative production, but it will probably be surpassed within two or three years by the much newer Santa Maria Valley field. This field leads the district in recent annual production, with West Cat Canyon a close second.

The Santa Maria Valley field [282] lies out in the valley, where the bed rock is obscured by 400 to 1600 feet of alluvium and stream gravels. That is one reason why it was not discovered until 1934, whereas the Orcutt field was opened up in 1902. Perhaps another reason for the delay in discovery is the fact that, unlike the other fields in the Santa Maria district, the Orcutt does not overlie any part of a sharp anticlinal fold. On the contrary, it lies on the north limb of the Santa Maria Valley syncline. Closure of the Miocene reservoir rocks is brought about by abutment against the basement rock, with overlap by younger formations. Along the north side of the field, the Miocene rocks have pinched out completely.

In the other five major fields, accumulation has taken place in anticlines and domes with closures of several hundred feet. Distribution

280 Gordon B. Oakeshott, "Geology of the Placerita Oil Field, Los Angeles County, California," *Calif. Jour. Mines and Geol.*, Vol. 46 (January, 1950), pp. 43–80.

281 R. E. Collom, "Oil Accumulation and Structure of the Santa Maria District, Santa Barbara County, California," *Structure of Typical American Oil Fields* (Am. Assoc. Petrol. Geol., 1929), Vol. 2, pp. 18–22.

282 Charles R. Canfield, "Santa Maria Valley Oil Field," *Calif. Div. Mines, Bull.* 118 (1943), pp. 440–442.

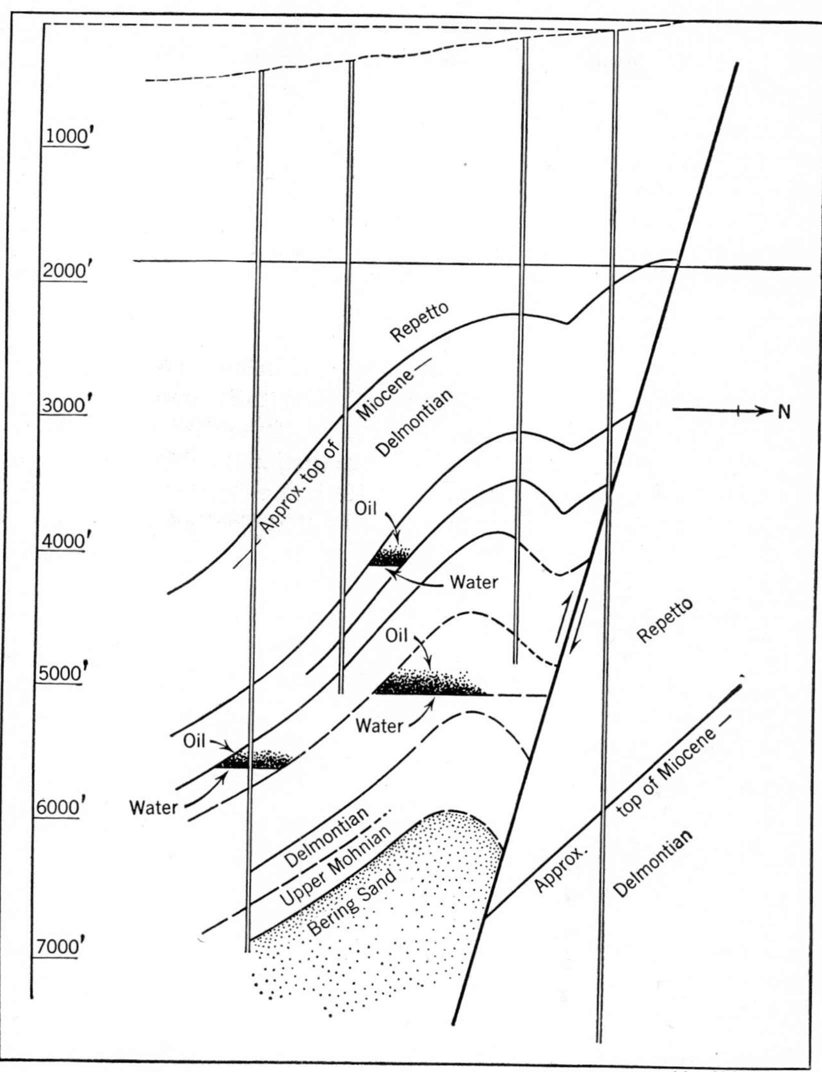

After Nelson (1948)

FIG. 161. Ramona oil field, California. South-north cross section. *Courtesy American Association of Petroleum Geologists.*

has been affected to some extent by faulting, but of greater import has been the development of fractures in which an estimated 77 per cent of the district's oil so far produced was stored.[283] Two per cent of the total oil has accumulated in fractures in the Knoxville basement rocks where these fractured sandstones lie above the level of the oil-water interface for the field. With this relatively minor exception, the fractured reservoirs are cherts, calcareous shales, and siliceous shales. Since the principal fracture zones have fairly wide distribution, accumulation is largely structurally controlled.

San Joaquin Valley District.[284] The San Joaquin Valley district lies at the southern end of the Great Valley. To the east is the Sierra Nevada, to the west the Coast Range, and to the south the transverse Tehachapi Range. The north side of the district has no fixed boundary. Geologically and tectonically, it continues for several hundred miles, first down the San Joaquin Valley to its mouth and then up the Sacramento Valley to the headwaters of the Sacramento River. For many years the oil (but not gas) production to the north ended with the Coalinga field. However, in 1931, the Raisin City field was discovered farther down the valley, proving that Coalinga, at least, was not the northern limit of oil production. Most of the Great Valley is floored with Quaternary deposits washed in from the neighboring mountain ranges. Therefore, the bed rock is exposed, as a general rule, only around the periphery of the valley, and most of the earlier oil discoveries were confined to folds visible at the surface in this belt. In 1939 the discovery of the Paloma field [285] out in the valley, where the bed rock is mantled by the bed of ancient Buena Vista Lake, led to the opening up of the covered area for exploration and discovery. The initial well of the Paloma field was located on evidence obtained by the reflection seismograph. It produced at the rate of 1100 barrels per day of 51° oil, unusually light for California, plus 10 million cubic feet of gas.

The first six fields in cumulative production in the San Joaquin Valley are the Midway-Sunset, Coalinga, Buena Vista, Kettleman Hills, Kern River, and Elk Hills. The ranking for 1949 is Coalinga first,

[283] Louis J. Regan, Jr., and Aden W. Hughes, "Fractured Reservoirs of Santa Maria District, California," *Bull. Am. Assoc. Petrol. Geol.*, Vol. 33 (January, 1949), pp. 32–51.

[284] G. M. Cunningham and W. D. Kleinpell, "Importance of Unconformities to Oil Production in the San Joaquin Valley, California," *Problems of Petroleum Geology* (Am. Assoc. Petrol. Geol., 1934), pp. 785–805.

[285] Robert W. Clark, "Paloma Oil Field, Kern County, California," *Bull. Am. Assoc. Petrol. Geol.*, Vol. 24 (April, 1940), pp. 742–744.

followed by Buena Vista, Midway-Sunset, and Kettleman Hills. If Buena Vista is added to Midway-Sunset, with which it connects, the total cumulative production comes to over 1 billion barrels, and the combined fields become a close second to Coalinga in current annual production.

Most of the great accumulations of oil in the San Joaquin Valley are the result of anticlinal trapping. These anticlines are elongate folds many miles in length and thousands of feet in closure. Most of those so far discovered occur in the peripheral belt, where differential erosion has carved the outcropping folded beds into ridges and valleys which show by their elliptical patterns the character of the structure. Because of the greater resistance to erosion of some of the truncated layers in these anticlines, they tend to create hilly areas. As a result, many of the Valley oil wells are to be found in relatively rugged country.

One excellent example of anticlinal accumulation in the San Joaquin Valley is the Elk Hills field,[286] which was discovered in 1911. The Elk Hills anticline at the surface is an elongate dome with a closure of 450 feet. It has eroded into an isolated ridge 17 miles long and 7 miles wide at the widest point, rising out of the floor of San Joaquin Valley. Between the surface and the reservoir formation, the dip and the closure increase greatly, and three separate nodes appear along the axis of the fold. Although trapping is entirely anticlinal, the thickness and porosity of the reservoir sands determine the volume of production from one well to the next.

The Kettleman Hills field[287] occupies the middle section of the Coalinga anticline, which extends from the Coalinga field southeastward through Kettleman Hills to Lost Hills. The Kettleman Hills segment of the Coalinga anticline consists of three nodes, North dome, Middle dome, and South dome, which are slightly en echelon from each other. The greater part of the Kettleman Hills oil has come from the North dome. This anticline is about 18 miles long and 5 miles wide. The dips at the surface range up to 43°. The total closure of the Kettleman Hills structure is in the neighborhood of 3000 feet. North dome rises about 1600 feet above the saddle between it and Middle dome. The anticline is cut by many faults, but trapping is

[286] J. R. Pemberton, "Elk Hills, Kern County, California," *Structure of Typical American Oil Fields* (Am. Assoc. Petrol. Geol., 1929), Vol. 2, pp. 44–61.

[287] W. P. Woodring, Ralph Bentley Stewart, and R. W. Richards, "Geology of the Kettleman Hills Oil Field, California, Stratigraphy, Paleontology and Structure," *U. S. Geol. Survey, Professional Paper* 195 (1940), 170 pages.

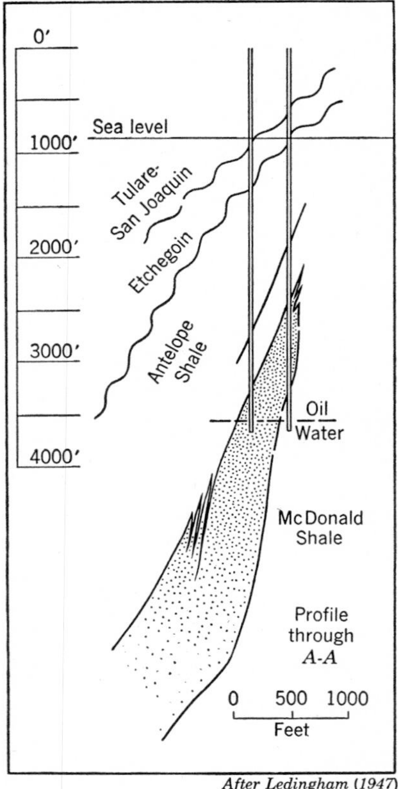

After Ledingham (1947)

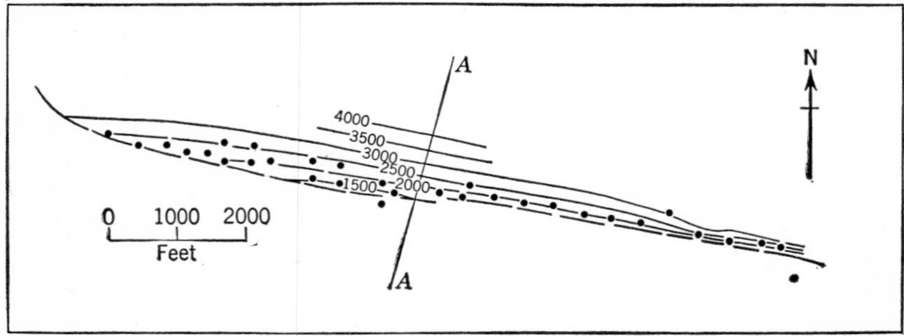

FIG. 162. Santiago pool, California. Lower: structure map, contoured on top of Leutholtz sand. Figures are below sea level. Upper: transverse structure section. *Courtesy American Association of Petroleum Geologists.*

entirely anticlinal. The oil and gas come from Miocene sands ranging from 1500 to 2000 feet in thickness. The most important reservoir formation is the Temblor.

Accumulation at the Cymric oil field in Kern County is anticlinal in some reservoirs and is caused by pinch-outs in others. This field is described in Chapter 8 (Fig. 37). The Salt Creek field [288] illustrates accumulation in a plunging anticline, with an up-dip fault supplying the necessary closure.

An unusual accumulation is that of the Santiago pool [289] (Fig. 162), where a near-vertical sandstone reservoir pinches out upward between two shales. The oil-water interface lies about 1200 feet below the point of pinch-out, but because of the steep dip, the field is only about 500 feet wide at its widest point.

The wedge-out of the Lakeview sand in the Lakeview pool,[290] a part of the Midway-Sunset field, takes place at a much gentler slope and therefore covers a wider area (Fig. 163). The development history of this pool is quite unusual. The discovery well, drilled in 1910, blew out and produced an estimated 8,250,000 barrels of oil in 544 days of uncontrolled flow. The underlying water is under no great pressure, and the wild well robbed the reservoir of the greater part of its gas pressure. As a consequence, the field produces under gravity drive. The first wells to fail were those at the apex of the sand body, and presumably the last to be abandoned will be those closest to the oil-water interface.

The Kern Front field [291] lies a short distance north of Bakersfield in the same county. The structure is entirely monoclinal, and the oil is obtained from non-marine sands which thin out and are faulted up-dip to the east. Closure to the south is due to the presence of a plunging anticline, but to the north a facies change from permeable to impermeable rock appears to close the reservoir in that direction. The reservoir sands in the Edison oil field [292] illustrate not only fault seal up-dip to the east but also sealing by onlap and overlap of reservoirs against the basement complex. A third type of accumulation at Edison

[288] J. H. Beach, "Preliminary Report on Salt Creek Field, Kern County, California," *Bull. Am. Assoc. Petrol. Geol.,* Vol. 31 (September, 1947), pp. 1674–1677.

[289] Glenn W. Ledingham, "Santiago Pool, Kern County, California," *Bull. Am. Assoc. Petrol. Geol.,* Vol. 31 (November, 1947), pp. 2063–2067.

[290] W. P. Sims and W. G. Frailing, "Lakeview Pool, Midway-Sunset Field," *Am. Inst. Min. Met. Engineers, Technical Paper* 2779 (1950).

[291] Everett C. Edwards, "Kern Front Oil Field, Kern County, California," *Stratigraphic Type Oil Fields* (Am. Assoc. Petrol. Geol., 1941), pp. 9–18.

[292] Everett C. Edwards, "Edison Oil Field and Vicinity, Kern County, California," *idem,* pp. 1–8.

is the trapping of oil in permeable basement rock schist and felsite.[293] The discovery well in the basement rock was completed in June, 1945, with a production of 528 barrels per day from a permeable zone 80 feet within the schist. Since then many other wells have been drilled and a productive area of about 1500 acres of basement rock has been outlined. The successful wells penetrate as much as 1350 feet of

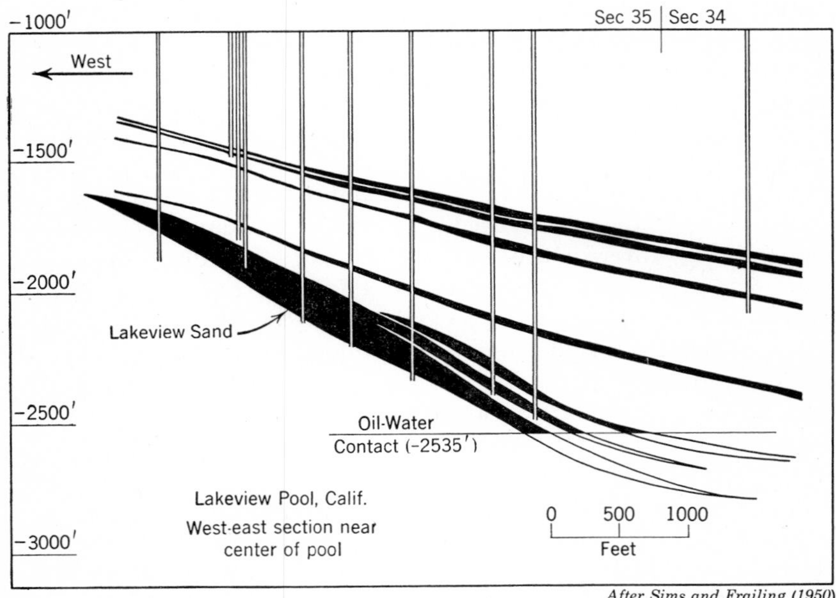

Fig. 163. Lakeview pool, Midway-Sunset field, California. West-east section near center of pool, showing pinch-out of reservoir sands. *Courtesy American Institute of Mining and Metallurgical Engineers.*

oil-bearing crystalline rock. Without doubt this oil, which is confined to the topographically highest points of the basement rock, migrated into the fracture reservoirs from adjacent, topographically lower, sedimentary layers.

Miscellaneous Districts. The Sacramento Valley first became a producer of gas many years ago. In the intervening years other gas

[293] J. H. Beach, "Geology of Edison Oil Field, Kern County, California," *Structure of Typical American Oil Fields* (Am. Assoc. Petrol. Geol., 1948), Vol. 3, pp. 58–85; J. H. Beach and Arthur S. Huey, "Geology of Basement Complex, Edison Field, California," *Am. Assoc. Petrol. Geol., Program Los Angeles Meeting* (1947), p. 26; J. C. May and R. L. Hewitt, "The Nature of the Basement Complex Oil Reservoir, Edison Oil Field, California," *Bull. Am. Assoc. Petrol. Geol.,* Vol. 31 (December, 1947), pp. 2239–2240.

pools have been discovered north of the San Joaquin oil district, especially in San Joaquin, Solano, and Sutter counties. The northernmost gas field so far discovered is Corning in Tehama County. The search for gas deposits in "northern" California continues, and three gas wells, each capable of producing several million cubic feet of gas daily, were completed during 1948.

The Rio Vista field, discovered in 1937, has become California's largest gas field, producing more during 1948 than Kettleman North dome and Wilmington combined. The discovery well was drilled about 2 miles west of the town of Rio Vista on the right bank of the Sacramento River in Solano County. It flowed at an estimated rate of 81 million cubic feet of gas daily from a depth of 4485 feet. Subsequently, the field was extended east of the river into Sacramento County. The reservoirs are Middle Eocene sands. Trapping has taken place in a broad faulted dome.

In addition to the Santa Maria Valley, the Coast Ranges contain other synclinal valleys with known oil deposits. The newest discoveries have been in the Cuyama Valley. Three fields were found there between June, 1948, and April, 1950. The discovery field for the valley, the Russell Ranch, is about 4½ miles long and ½ mile wide.[294] The oil, unusually light for California, lies in two sand zones in the Vaqueros formation of lower Miocene age. It has been impounded by a normal strike fault cutting a monocline. Accumulation at South Cuyama is in a faulted dome.

The next major re-entrant to the north is Salinas Valley.[295] The San Ardo field was discovered in this area in November, 1947, and six months later a second pool, the Campbell, 3½ miles to the southeast, was found. The reservoirs so far developed in the Salinas Valley are Miocene sandstones. Exploration is continuing here and in other favorable localities to the north of the older oil districts.

Washington [296]

(Figure 164)

Washington has had two small, but commercial, gas fields. They are both very shallow, and in both accumulation has taken place under

[294] Rollin Eckis, "Geology of Russell Ranch and South Cuyama Oil Fields, Cuyama Valley, California" (Abstract), *Bull. Am. Assoc. Petrol. Geol.,* Vol. 33 (December, 1949), pp. 2058–2059.

[295] J. E. Kilkenny, "Geology and Exploration for Oil in Salinas Valley, California," *Bull. Am. Assoc. Petrol. Geol.,* Vol. 32 (December, 1948), pp. 2254–2268.

[296] Sheldon L. Glover, "Preliminary Report on Petroleum and Natural Gas in Washington," *Wash. Div. Geol., Rept. of Investigations No.* 4 (1936), 24 pages.

unusual circumstances. The larger of these fields, the Rattlesnake Hills,[297] is on the Columbia River lava plateau of eastern Washington. For over 20 years as many as sixteen wells produced gas from one or two zones of porous basalt. Intercalated between the flows are thin beds of lake clays which may have been the source rocks, but which now function as cap rocks. The original reservoir pressure was

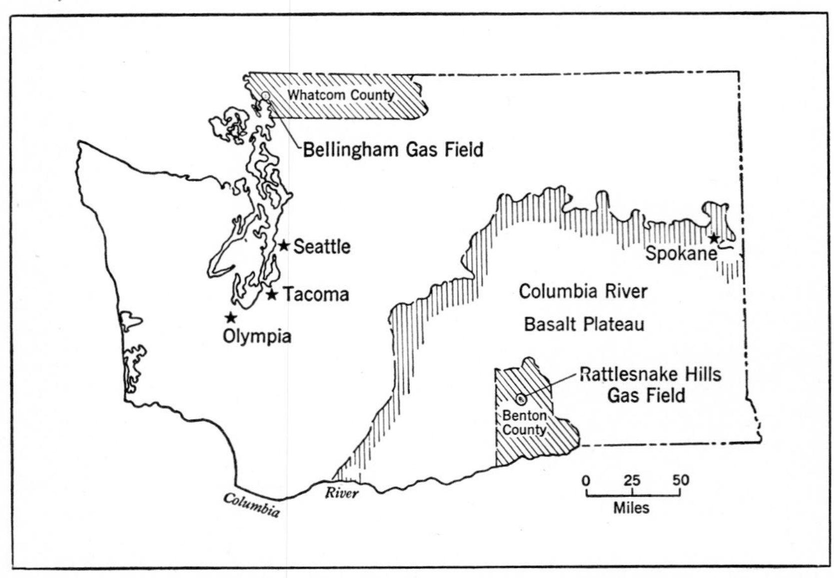

Fig. 164. Washington index map.

only slightly over 2 pounds per square inch. The average depth to the reservoir rocks is between 700 and 800 feet. Trapping within the lava reservoirs was due to the presence of a faulted anticline, which is a part of the belt of anticlinal folding that created the Rattlesnake Range of hills.

The other field lies 6 miles north of Bellingham in Whatcom County of western Washington. At one time (1934) it contained six producing wells. Most of the wells were completed in mantle rock reservoirs lying at depths between 166 and 193 feet. Presumably the gas migrated from underlying Tertiary formations and became trapped in sand lenses in the glacial sediments.

297 A. A. Hammer, "Rattlesnake Hills Gas Field, Benton County, Washington," *Bull. Am. Assoc. Petrol. Geol.,* Vol. 18 (July, 1934), pp. 847–859.

Alaska [298]

(Figure 165)

Although it has failed so far to produce hydrocarbons in any significant quantities, the territory of Alaska does contain some enormous thicknesses of sedimentary rock and a few provocative seepages. Inter-

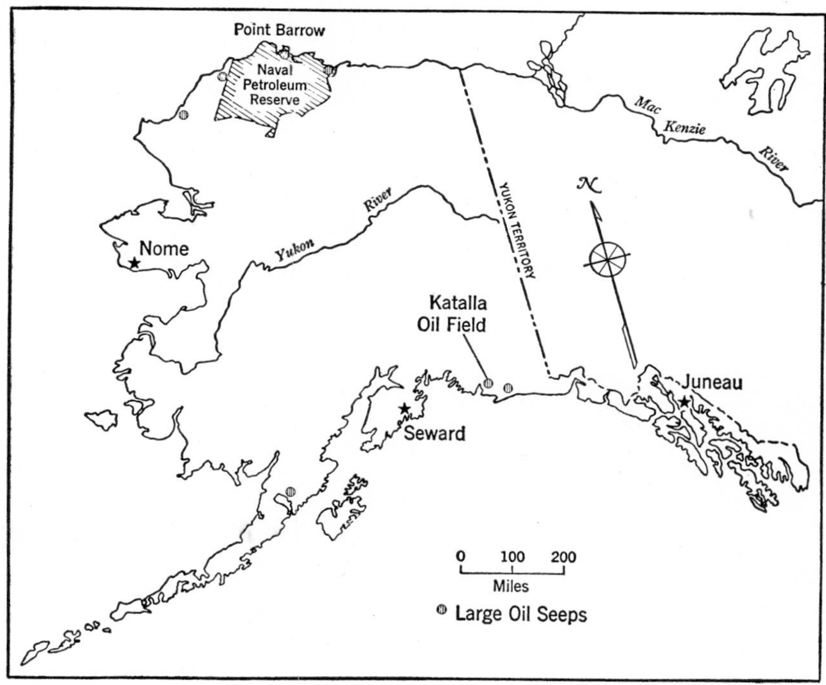

Fig. 165. Alaska. Oil seeps, Katalla field, and Naval Petroleum Reserve.

mittently since the 1900's, oil has been produced in small quantities at Katalla on the coast to the east of Seward. This is the only commercial oil field in Alaska to date. It has had as many as fourteen producing wells, ranging in depth from 366 feet to 1130 feet.[299] At least two large seeps have been known for many years in southwestern Alaska on the west shore of Cook Inlet and farther out on the penin-

[298] John C. Reed, "Recent Investigations by United States Geological Survey of Petroleum Possibilities in Alaska," *Bull. Am. Assoc. Petrol. Geol.*, Vol. 30 (September, 1946), pp. 1433–1443; Ralph L. Miller, "Developments in Alaska in 1949," Bull. 34 (June, 1950), pp. 1226–1234.

[299] W. A. Ver Wiebe, *Oil Fields in North America* (1949), p. 231.

sula at Cold Bay. Drilling in these areas has so far been unsuccessful. A large seep near Point Barrow at the northernmost tip of Alaska led to the setting aside by the government of a large block of land as a Naval Petroleum Reserve.[300] During and since World War II, the Navy has conducted a vigorous exploration program in this Arctic area, using surface geology, the gravity meter, and the seismograph to locate test wells and then drilling to depths, in at least two places, in excess of 6000 feet. In mid-July of 1949 the National Military Establishment announced that the second well drilled about 6 miles south of Point Barrow had struck gas at a depth of 2500 feet with an estimated potential production of 4 to 5 million cubic feet per day. The search for oil is continuing.

[300] Anon., "Intensive Exploration Program Mapped for Navy's Alaskan Petroleum Reserve," *Oil and Gas Jour.,* Vol. 47 (Jan. 20, 1949), pp. 45–47.

Chapter 10

DISTRIBUTION OF OIL AND GAS FIELDS—EXCLUSIVE OF THE UNITED STATES

Canada [1]

During 1949 the Canadian production amounted to about 0.6 per cent of the world oil output. This was slightly less than that of Colorado for the same period, but it was a 90 per cent increase over the preceding year, and as soon as pipe-line outlets for the new Alberta discoveries have been completed Canada (Figs. 166–168) will become a much more important source of world oil.

The Canadian oil history is contemporaneous with that of the United States. A natural seep at Oil Springs in southwestern Ontario was exploited by dug shafts in 1860, and in 1861 the first commercial oil well was drilled in this area. Four years later the nearby Petrolia field, which is still producing, was discovered. Other discoveries followed in the southwestern Ontario peninsula, and new deposits of oil and gas are still being found in this area.[2] In New Brunswick, where the first drilling for oil took place in 1858, a small oil and gas field, the Stony Creek, was discovered near Moncton in 1909.

Much newer and much bigger are the oil and gas discoveries in western Canada. The first strike was made at Turner Valley, near Calgary, in 1914. A deeper and more prolific reservoir was discovered there in 1924, and a third great strike was made in 1936. In 1920 the discovery well of the Norman Wells field, 90 miles south of the Arctic

[1] G. S. Hume, "Petroleum Geology of Canada," *Can. Geol. Survey, Economic Geology Series,* No. 14 (1944); G. S. Hume, "Canada," *Science of Petroleum,* Vol. 1 (Oxford Univ. Press, 1938), pp. 96–99; J. G. Gray and W. A. Roliff, "Developments in Canada in 1949," *Bull. Am. Assoc. Petrol. Geol.,* Vol. 34 (June, 1950), pp. 1235–1259.

[2] Zoe Pauline Trotter, "Search for Oil in Ontario," *World Oil,* Vol. 128 (December, 1948), pp. 227–228, 230.

Circle on the Mackenzie River in Northwest Territories, was drilled. This field was completely developed during the war years as a part of

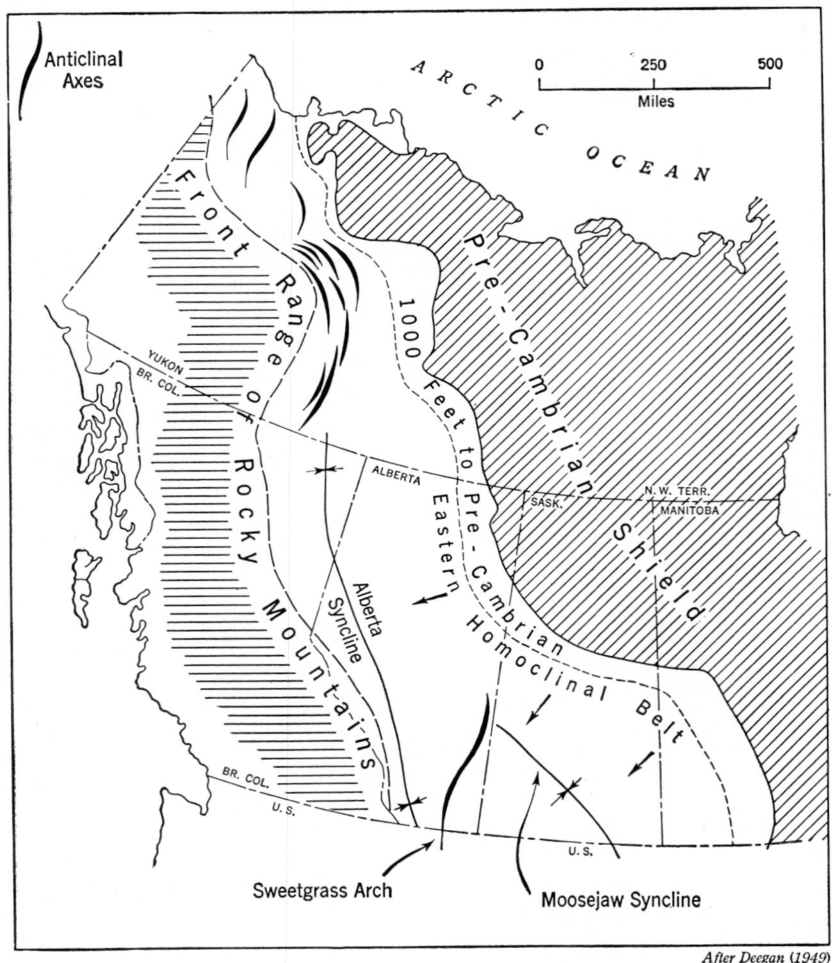

After Deegan (1949)

Fig. 166. Western Canada. Major tectonic features. *Courtesy Oil and Gas Journal.*

the Canol project. Another facet of this project was the search for new deposits of oil elsewhere in the Arctic and sub-Arctic, a search that is still continuing.

The modern era in western Canada oil development began in February, 1947, when the discovery well of the Leduc field was completed.

This well flowed at the rate of 1000 barrels a day from near the top of a Devonian carbonate and evaporite rock series. The second well, which came in for a flush production of 2000 barrels a day, discovered the deeper, extremely porous, *D*-2 reef dolomite, and the scramble to find other reef accumulations in the Devonian section beneath the plains of western Canada was under way. The Leduc field has had

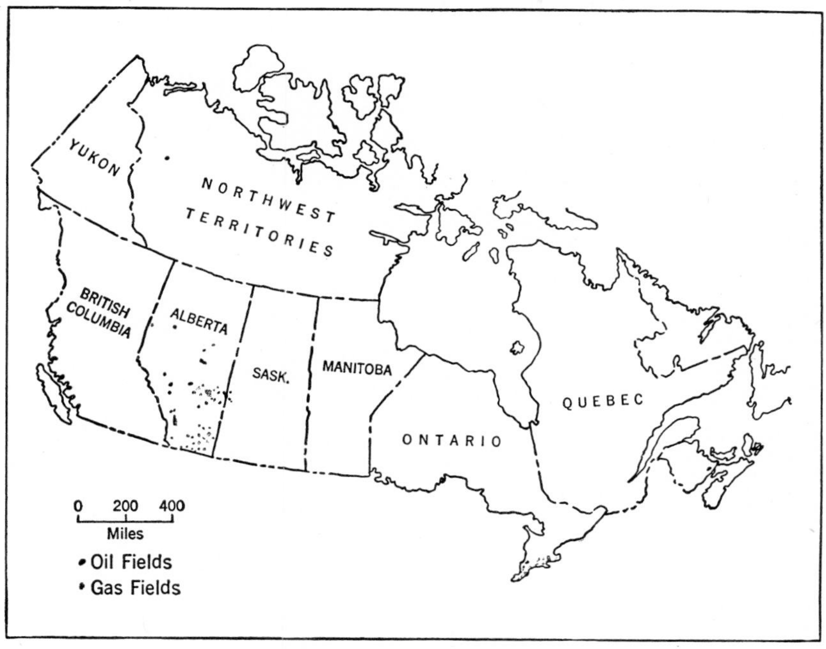

FIG. 167. Canada. Oil and gas fields.

three extensions since the initial drilling. Other discoveries include the Redwater field, 30 miles northeast of Edmonton in 1948, the Golden Spike field early in 1949, the Excelsior field in December, 1949, and three recent finds 90 miles southeast and 200 miles northwest of Edmonton.

The Canadian oil and gas deposits fall naturally into two geographic divisions, eastern Canada and western Canada. The eastern Canada district is separated from the western by the pre-Cambrian shield belt north of Lake Superior. Most of the oil and gas production in eastern Canada is in the southwestern Ontario peninsula. The western Canada district includes Alberta, Saskatchewan, and the Northwest Territories. In cumulative oil production, Turner Valley, the oldest of the Alberta fields, is in first place, with about 93 million barrels through 1949. The aggregate for all the Ontario fields has been about 30 million barrels, and Leduc in the thirty-four months since discovery produced 10 million barrels. In daily production in 1949, Leduc was considerably ahead of all other pools, with Redwater second and Turner Valley third.

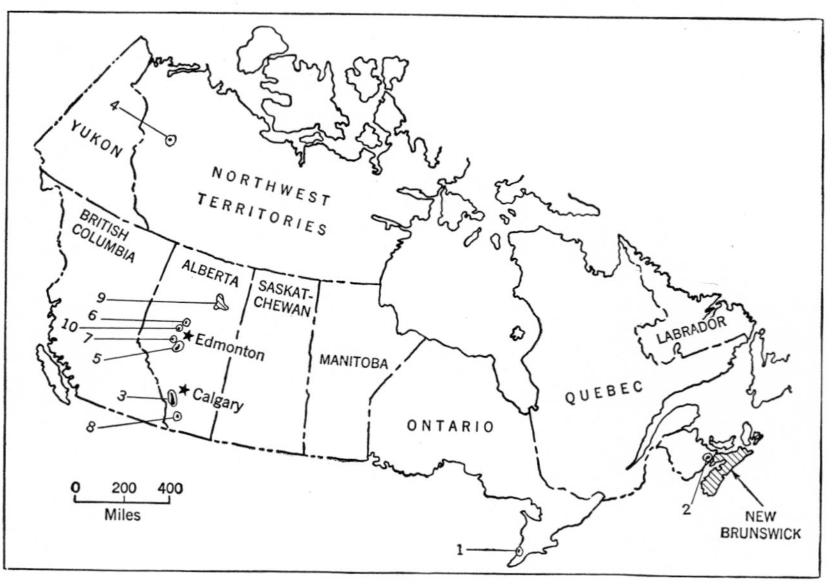

FIG. 168. Canada index map. 1, Petrolia oil field; 2, Stony Creek oil field; 3, Turner Valley oil field; 4, Norman Wells oil field; 5, Leduc oil field; 6, Redwater oil field; 7, Golden Spike oil field; 8, Pincher Creek oil field; 9, Athabaska heavy oil ("tar sand") area; 10, Excelsior oil field.

WESTERN CANADA DISTRICT.[3] A great sedimentary belt extends the length of western Canada from the International Boundary northwest to the Arctic Ocean. Topographically, this is the Interior Plains province, the northwestern extension of the Great Plains province of the United States. It lies between the pre-Cambrian shield on the east and the Front Range of the North American Cordillera

[3] Theo. A. Link, "The Western Canada Sedimentary Basin Area," *World Oil,* Vol. 129 (December, 1949), pp. 230 *et seq.;* Theo. A. Link, "Alberta's Oil Development and Problems," *World Oil,* Vol. 129 (July 1, 1949), pp. 205 *et seq.;* Charles J. Deegan, "Exploration in Western Canada Today," *Oil and Gas Jour.,* Vol. 8 (June 23, 1949), pp. 92 *et seq.;* Benjamin F. Zwick, "Development of the Oil and Gas Industry in Western Canada," *Mines Mag.,* Vol. 39 (December, 1949), pp. 55–61; Alberta Symposium, *Bull. Am. Assoc. Petrol. Geol.,* Vol. 33 (April, 1949).

on the west. Figure 169 shows the geologic section across the Canadian Interior Plains near the International Boundary. The sedimentary strata sag twice, once for the Moose Jaw syncline, which is the northern extension of the Williston basin, and again for the much deeper Alberta syncline. The intervening positive area is the northern end of the Sweetgrass arch of northwestern Montana. Between the axis of the Alberta syncline and the Front Range of the Rocky Mountains is the foothills belt in which the sediments are highly disturbed. The

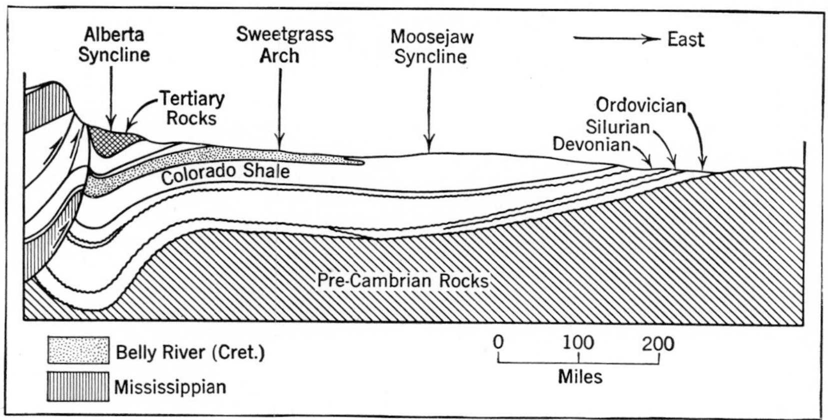

After Deegan (1949)

Fig. 169. Western Canada. Structure section across southern plains. *Courtesy Oil and Gas Journal.*

Turner Valley field is in this belt, but the reef fields are farther east on the relatively undisturbed east flank of the Alberta syncline.

The reservoir rocks of western Canada range from the Lower Cretaceous to the Devonian. Hydrocarbons are produced from Lower Cretaceous, Jurassic, and Mississippian sandstones and from Mississippian and Devonian limestones. Devonian limestone is much the most important reservoir rock.

The complicated structure at Turner Valley [4] is best illustrated by cross sections (Fig. 170). Accumulation has taken place in an overthrust block that has many subsidiary faults. The principal reservoir rock is the Madison (Mississippian) limestone, which has a general

[4] G. S. Hume, "Petroleum Geology of Canada," *Can. Geol. Survey, Economic Geology Series,* No. 14 (1944), pp. 37–43; A. J. Goodman, "Limestone Reservoir Conditions in Turner Valley Oil Field, Alberta, Canada," *Bull. Am. Assoc. Petrol. Geol.,* Vol. 29 (August, 1945), pp. 1156–1168.

westward dip of 20° to 25°. Goodman believes that the upper surface of the Mississippian limestone was leached by meteoric waters during a pre-Jurassic emergence of the Paleozoic rocks. This porous zone was subsequently covered by Jurassic and younger sediments during later

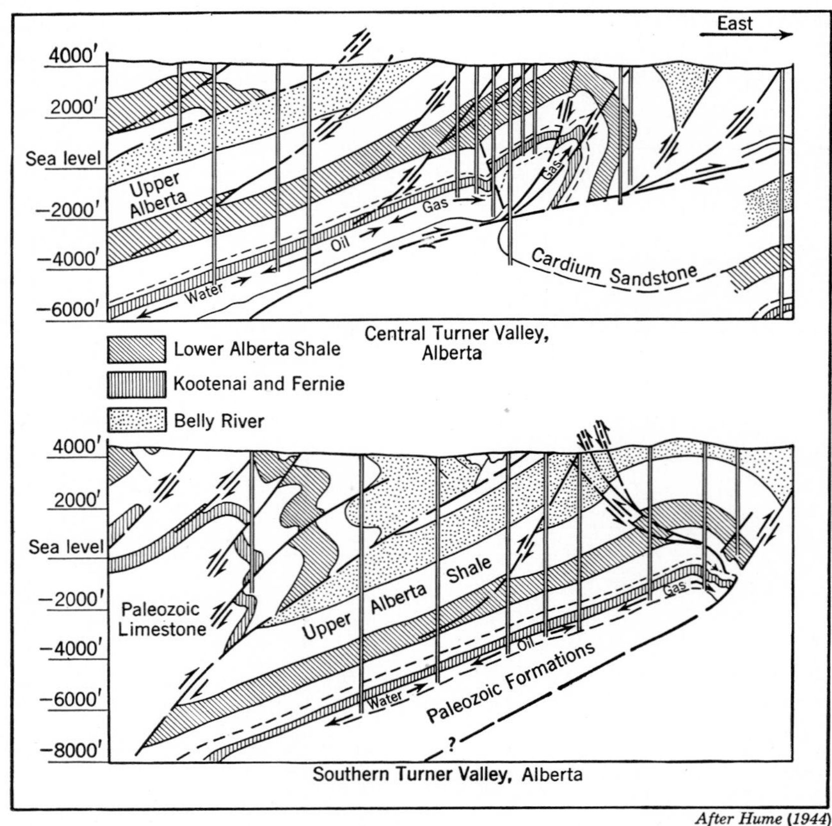

After Hume (1944)

Fig. 170. Turner Valley field, Canada. Two transverse structure sections. *Courtesy Canadian Geological Survey.*

submergences. At its upper end, the reservoir rock abuts against the underthrust block; a fairly well-developed drag fold is present in the contact zone. Trapping has been due to the truncation of a plunging anticline on a monoclinal dip by a major fault. Another Madison producer is the Pincher Creek field, a recent discovery 15 to 20 miles north of the International Boundary. This field produces gas and distillate from a depth of 12,250 feet.

The Leduc field was illustrated and described in Chapter 8 (Fig. 68) as an example of reef trapping. The Redwater field is probably the largest of the reef fields so far discovered. It is at least 10 miles long and 2 miles wide. The top 170 feet of the *D*-3 reservoir is saturated with oil; beneath the oil is bottom water. The discovery well of the Golden Spike field, drilled 4½ miles northwest of the Woodbend pool, a Leduc outlier, had an estimated initial production of 12,000 barrels daily. Here the uppermost 546 feet of the *D*-3 reservoir is saturated with oil. Below this zone the limestone is tight and contains neither oil nor water. The Norman Wells field [5] occupies parts of two islands and the right bank of the Mackenzie River in Northwest Territories, about 55 miles below Fort Norman. The reservoir rock is a reef limestone surrounded by shales of upper Devonian age. The reef lies on a monocline that has a southwest dip of about 5°. Water underlies the oil down-dip; closure up-dip and to the sides is the result of the pinching-out of the reef rock.

The great reserves of petroleum products present in the heavy oil deposits of the Athabaska area are discussed in Chapter 11.

EASTERN CANADA.[6] Except for the Stony Creek field in New Brunswick, which produces from fresh-water sediments of Mississippian age, the eastern Canada oil fields are confined to the southwestern Ontario peninsula, especially that part of the peninsula lying between Lake Erie and Lake St. Clair-St. Clair River. Tectonically, this area is the Chatham sag between the Findlay and the Ontario arches. To the northwest is the Michigan basin and to the southeast the Ohio basin, the northwest flank of the Appalachian geosyncline. The reservoirs range in age from the Devonian to Ordovician, but in terms of hydrocarbon production, especially gas, the Silurian reservoirs are the most important.

Roliff [7] has described the occurrence of oil and gas in Silurian dolomites. He believes that trapping in the Guelph-Lockport reservoirs has been due in the main to the presence of reefs. Faults are common and may have contributed to the trapping. In the fields producing

[5] J. S. Stewart, "Norman Wells Oil Field, Northwest Territories, Canada," *Structure of Typical American Oil Fields* (Am. Assoc. Petrol. Geol., 1948), Vol. 3, pp. 86–109.

[6] G. S. Hume, "Oil and Gas in Eastern Canada," *Can. Geol. Survey, Economic Geology Series,* No. 9 (1932), pp. 1–88; J. F. Caley, "Paleozoic Geology of the Brantford Area, Ontario," *Can. Geol. Survey, Mem.* 226 (1941), "Geology of the London Area, Ontario," *Mem.* 237 (1943), "Paleozoic Geology of the Windsor-Sarnia Area, Ontario," *Mem.* 240 (1945).

[7] W. A. Roliff, "Salina Guelph Fields of Southwestern Ontario," *Bull. Am. Assoc. Petrol. Geol.,* Vol. 33 (February, 1949), pp. 153–188.

from the overlying Salina rocks, on the other hand, a combination of anticlinal structure and porosity is necessary. These carbonate rocks are quite erratic in the distribution of porosity, and many wells in structurally high positions fail to find adequate permeability. The anticlinal traps range in shape from elongate anticlines to quaquaversal domes. Most of the folds have closures between 25 and 50 feet.

Mexico [8]

During 1949 Mexico produced approximately 1.8 per cent of the world's petroleum output. This was slightly less than the production for the state of Illinois for the same period. The Mexican output for 1949 was about 61 million barrels, not quite one-third of its production in 1921, when Mexico ranked second only to the United States among the oil-producing countries of the world.

As in many other parts of the world, the Mexican oil districts (Figs. 171–174) contain abundant seeps, some of large size. These were exploited for decades and even centuries before the drilling of the first oil wells, and they were used as a guide for the location of oil deposits when drilling became active. The first successful oil well was drilled in the Tampico area in the early 1880's, but it was not until the early 1900's that Mexico began producing oil in important quantities. The Panuco, or Northern, field was discovered in 1904, and the "Golden Lane" field, south of Tampico, in 1910. Exploration along the Golden Lane resulted in a series of gushers as large as any the world has ever seen. One of these had an estimated initial production of 100,000 barrels a day.

The first successful oil well in the Isthmus of Tehuantepec district was completed in 1921, and the Poza Rica field, currently the largest in Mexico, was discovered by exploration to the south of the Golden Lane in 1930.

After many years of inactivity in the way of new discoveries, Mexico began to open up new fields again in 1946. The first discovery was

[8] Jorge L. Cumming, "Deep Discoveries Increase Mexico's Oil Reserves," *World Oil,* Vol. 130 (March, 1950), pp. 225–226; Antonio García Rojas, "Mexican Oil Fields," *Bull. Am. Assoc. Petrol. Geol.,* Vol. 33 (August, 1949), pp. 1336–1350; J. M. Muir, "Geology of the Tampico-Tuxpan Oil Field Region," *Science of Petroleum* (Oxford Univ. Press, 1938), Vol. 1, pp. 100–105; Manuel Santillan, "Synopsis of the Geology of Mexico," *Bull. Am. Assoc. Petrol. Geol.,* Vol. 20 (April, 1936), pp. 394–402; Eduardo J. Guzmán, Federico Mina Uhink, and Stewart H. Folk, "Developments in Mexico in 1949," *Bull. Am. Assoc. Petrol. Geol.,* Vol. 34 (June, 1950), pp. 1260–1282.

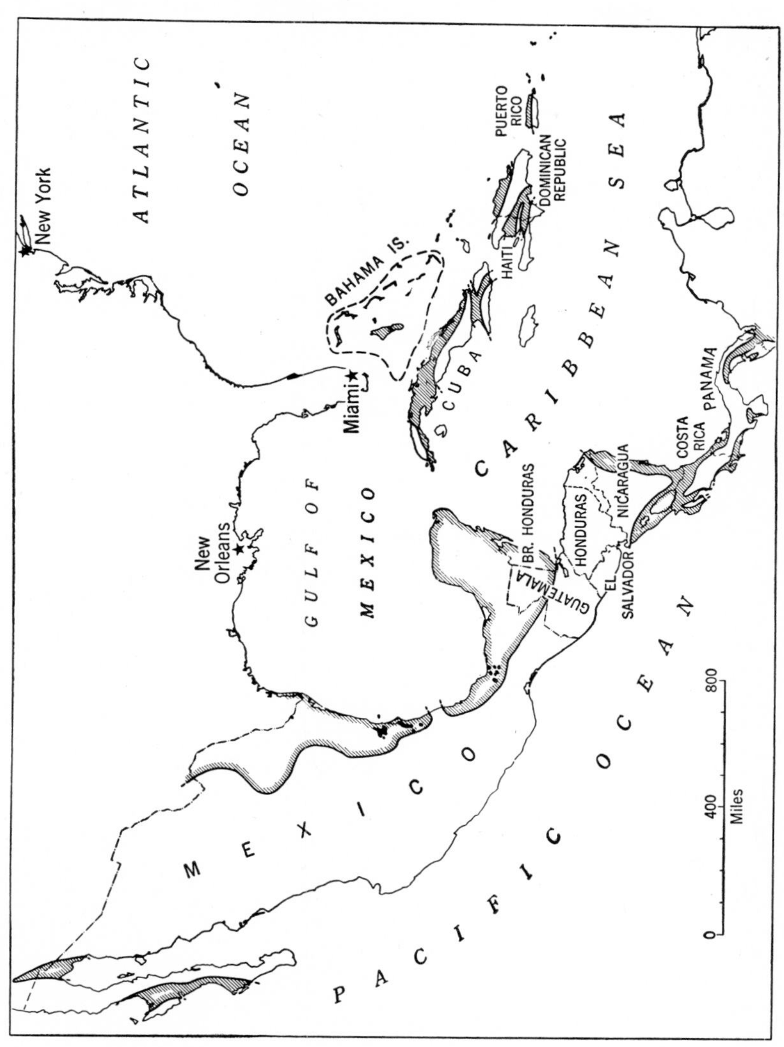

FIG. 171. Sedimentary basins and oil fields in Mexico, Central America, and West Indies. *Courtesy L. G. Weeks and American Association of Petroleum Geologists.*

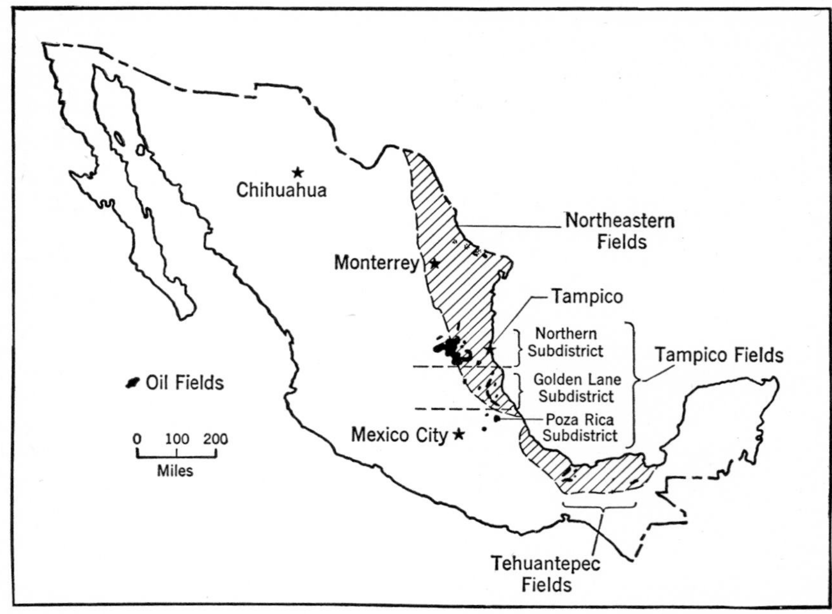

Fig. 172. Mexico. Oil and gas field districts.

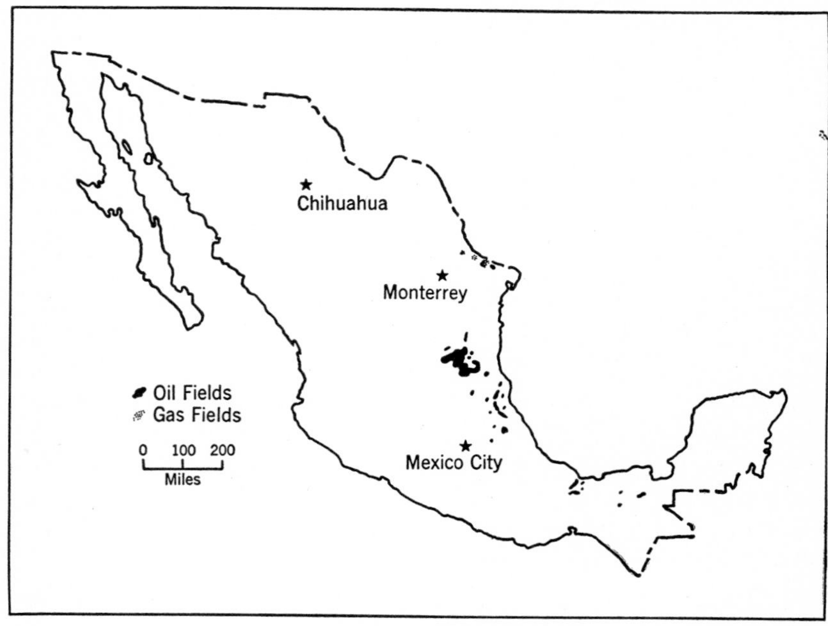

Fig. 173. Mexico. Oil and gas fields.

the Mision gas field in northeastern Mexico, immediately across the Rio Grande River from Hidalgo County, Texas. During the first half of 1948, the Reynosa oil field was discovered a few miles down river from the Mision field. This was the first discovery of oil between the International Boundary and the Tampico area. Other discoveries have included some new production in the Moralillio field, west of the

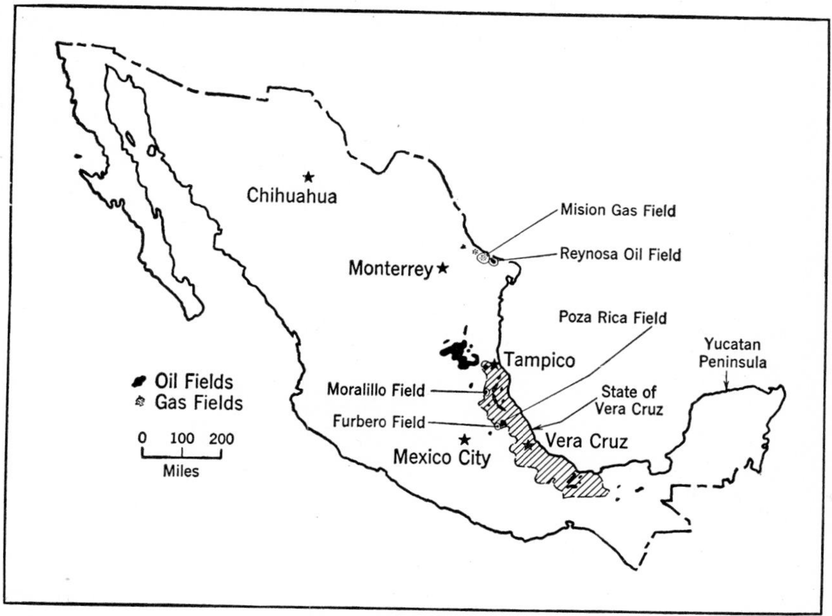

Fig. 174. Mexico index map.

Golden Lane, and two new fields in southern Veracruz in the Isthmus region.

The Mexican oil fields so far discovered are confined to the Gulf Coastal plain, a continuation of the same physiographic and tectonic province in the southern United States. Owing to the presence of the Rio Grande syncline, the coastal plain extends far into the interior along the International Boundary, but in the Tampico area the plain is only about 75 miles wide. It pinches out altogether north of Veracruz, but then it reappears and continues southeastward and eastward, occupying about half of the Isthmus area and the entire Yucatan peninsula. The Mexican coastal plain is the west, southwest, and south rim of the great Gulf of Mexico sedimentary basin; the north rim is the Gulf Coastal plain of the United States. Salt-cored structures occur in the Isthmus of Tehuantepec area but have not been found as yet in other parts of the Mexican coastal plain.

The Mexican oil fields fall naturally into three districts: the northeastern, the Tampico, and the Isthmus of Tehuantepec. The Tampico district is further subdivided into the Northern or Panuco area, the Southern or Golden Lane area, and the Poza Rica field, which lies still farther to the south. The Golden Lane fields lead in cumulative production. This area has produced over 1 billion barrels of oil since its discovery in 1908. The Northern fields have produced more than 800 million barrels since 1901, and Poza Rica 345 million barrels since 1930. In 1949, Poza Rica was the leading field in Mexico, with a daily production averaging 95,000 barrels. The Northern area was second, with a daily average of 26,000 barrels, and the Golden Lane district third, with 18,000 barrels daily. The aggregate production for the various fields in the Isthmus district during 1949 was about 17,000 barrels daily. The Isthmus fields produce from Miocene sands; the reservoirs in the Tampico district are Lower Cretaceous limestones.

NORTHEASTERN MEXICO DISTRICT.[9] In early 1950, the northeastern Mexico district consisted of the Mision gas field, four other, and smaller, gas fields to the west, and the Reynosa oil field. The reservoir rock at Mision is a sandstone lying within the Vicksburg of Lower Oligocene age. Accumulation has taken place in a dome faulted on the west flank. However, trapping is due mainly to the wedging-out of the reservoir sands on the eastern flank before they reach the apex of the fold. At Reynosa the oil has been trapped in an elongate anticline with a north-northwest trend, a length of 5 miles, and a maximum width of 3 miles. The closure, according to a seismograph survey, is about 150 feet. Production has been found in two oil sands and three intervening gas sands, all within the Frio formation of Oligocene age.

TAMPICO DISTRICT.[10] The Gulf Coastal plain in the Tampico district contains literally thousands of heavy oil seepages. Also present

[9] Eduardo J. Guzmán, "New Petroleum Development by Petróleos Mexicanos in Northeastern Mexico," *Bull. Am. Assoc. Petrol. Geol.,* Vol. 33 (August, 1949), pp. 1351–1384; William G. Kane, "Structural Geology of Border Province of Northeastern Mexico Adjacent to Zapata and Starr Counties, Texas," *Bull. Am. Assoc. Petrol. Geol.,* Vol. 20 (April, 1936), pp. 403–416; Eduardo J. Guzmán, "Report of Pemex Activities in Northeastern Mexico," *Oil and Gas Jour.,* Vol. 47 (March 17, 1949), pp. 165 *et seq.*

[10] John M. Muir, "Limestone Reservoir Rocks in the Mexican Oil Fields," *Problems of Petroleum Geology* (Am. Assoc. Petrol. Geol., 1934), pp. 377–398; Earl A. Trager, "The Geologic History of the Panuco River Valley and Its Relation to the Origin and Accumulation of Oil in Mexico," *Bull. Am. Assoc. Petrol. Geol.,* Vol. 10

in this district are many occurrences of igneous intrusions, mainly dikes and volcanic plugs. DeGolyer [11] has pointed out that a considerable number of the oil seepages are in the igneous-sedimentary contact zone, probably because "the fractured, fissured, and metamorphosed plane of contact provides easy channels of migration along which the oil from deep reservoirs of sedimentary rocks is forced to the surface." In one relatively small oil field, the Furbero near Poza Rica, most of the oil accumulated in the contact zone between a sill of gabbro and the overlying metamorphosed Tertiary shale.

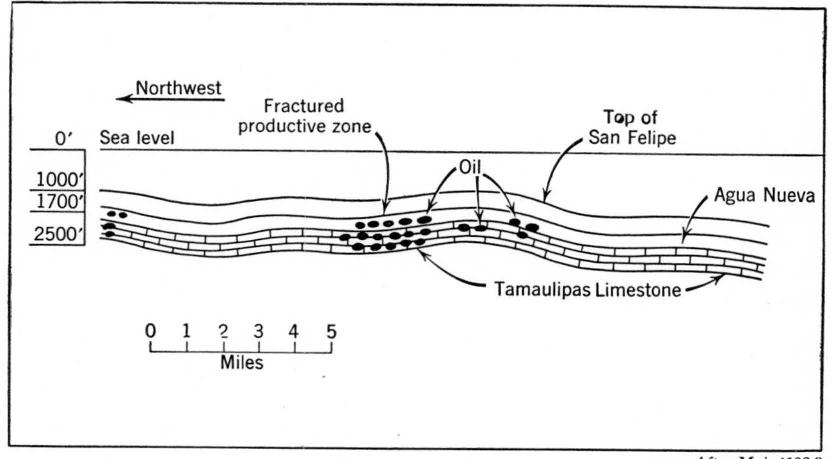

After Muir (1934)

FIG. 175. Northern subdistrict, Mexico. Northwest-southeast cross section of Cocalilao anticline. *Courtesy American Association of Petroleum Geologists.*

The oil fields in the northern part of the Tampico district occupy a roughly circular area a short distance to the west of Tampico. They lie upon a southward-plunging regional anticline cored by the Tamaulipas (Cretaceous) limestone. This limestone and the immediately overlying San Felipe limestone are the reservoir rocks throughout the northern area. Both limestones are compact, and accumulation has taken place only where they are fractured. Some of the fractures are due to jointing, but most appear to be the result of the shattering of the brittle limestones during faulting. Trapping has taken place

(July, 1926), pp. 667–696; Ben C. Belt, "Stratigraphy of the Tampico District of Mexico," *Bull. Am. Assoc. Petrol. Geol.,* Vol. 9 (January–February, 1925), pp. 136–144.

[11] E. L. DeGolyer, "Oil Associated with Igneous Rocks in Mexico," *Bull. Am. Assoc. Petrol. Geol.,* Vol. 16 (August, 1932), pp. 799–818.

either at the top, where fracturing is present, or on the flanks of local anticlines (Fig. 175) superimposed upon the southward-plunging regional fold. The oil in the northern fields is unusually heavy (gravity 12.8°) and flows through the lines at the surface with difficulty.

In the southern or Golden Lane subdistrict, the fields occupy a very narrow belt about 51 miles long with an average width less than 1 mile. The reason for the long and narrow shape of the producing area is that the oil has accumulated along the crest of a sharp anticline with a steep, probably faulted, west flank (Fig. 176). This fold

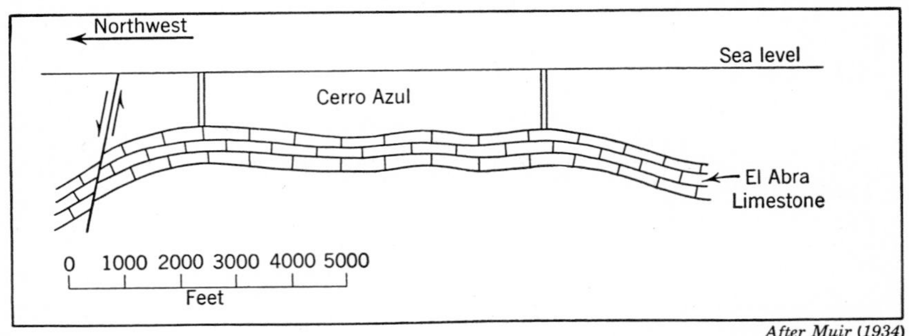

After Muir (1934)

Fig. 176. Golden Lane, Mexico. Northwest-southeast cross section. *Courtesy American Association of Petroleum Geologists.*

is not adequately reflected in the surface geology, and the early discoveries were made by drilling close to oil seepages. The reservoir rock is the El Abra reef facies of the Tamaulipas limestone of Cretaceous age. Because it is extremely porous and even cavernous, almost every producer drilled was a large gusher. Salt water under high pressure underlies the oil.

The Poza Rica [12] field lies about 160 miles south of Tampico and has been the leading producer of Mexico since 1935. Trapping is anticlinal, and the main producing formation is the Tamabra limestone of Lower Cretaceous age. It is highly porous.

ISTHMUS OF TEHUANTEPEC DISTRICT. Unlike the other fields of Mexico, those in the Isthmus area produce from sandstones of Miocene age. Furthermore, the structures are all salt-cored; in some the salt lies close to the surface and in others the cap rocks are buried to considerable depths. About four fields, now abandoned, produced

[12] Guillermo P. Salas, "Geology and Development of Poza Rica Oil Field, Veracruz, Mexico," *Bull. Am. Assoc. Petrol. Geol.*, Vol. 33 (August, 1949), pp. 1385–1409.

from the cap rock itself. Most of the current production is coming from upfolds on the flanks of the salt domes, which are probably by-products of the salt piercement.

Cuba [13]

Currently Cuba is producing about 300 barrels of oil daily from two fields.[14] During 1949 the total Cuban production amounted to about 0.004 per cent of the world's oil output. This was slightly

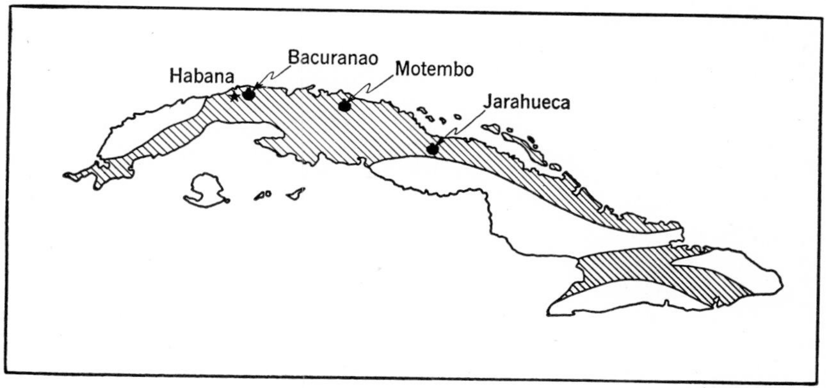

FIG. 177. Cuba. Sedimentary basins and oil fields. *Courtesy American Association of Petroleum Geologists.*

more than that of Brazil and slightly less than the Burma production. The fields now producing are the Motembo, which was discovered in 1881, and the Jarahueca, which began producing in 1943. A third field, the Bacuranao, discovered in 1915, is now inactive. Oil and gas seeps and asphalt deposits have been found in practically all parts of Cuba. In at least four localities asphalt is being, or has been, mined.

The island of Cuba is structurally an asymmetric geanticline with the older rock core exposed in the central part. Jurassic, Cretaceous,

[13] J. E. Kastrop, "Cuba's Oil Outlook," *World Oil,* Vol. 130 (May, 1950), pp. 219–226; J. Whitney Lewis, "Occurrence of Oil in Igneous Rocks of Cuba," *Bull. Am. Assoc. Petrol. Geol.,* Vol. 16 (August, 1922), pp. 809–818; Arthur H. Redfield, "Petroleum Reserves of the West Indies," *Trans. Am. Inst. Min. Met. Engineers,* Vol. 68, No. 1166-P (June, 1922).

[14] L. G. Weeks, "Highlights on 1948 Developments in Foreign Petroleum Fields," *Bull. Am. Assoc. Petrol. Geol.,* Vol. 33 (June, 1949), p. 1049.

and Tertiary sedimentary rocks occur on the anticlinal flanks in northern and southern Cuba (Fig. 177). The three oil fields so far discovered are in the sedimentary basin on the north flank of the geanticline. The sedimentary rocks are intruded by basic igneous rocks, most of which have been serpentinized. In all three of the Cuban oil fields, the oil has been found not in the sedimentary rocks but in cracks and fissures in serpentine. These fields were discovered by drilling alongside gas or light oil seeps.

The oil at Motembo is a colorless naphtha, perhaps because of the filtration through clay of heavy petroleum migrating into the reservoir serpentine. The source of the oil is undoubtedly either the subjacent Jurassic sediment or the adjacent Cretaceous beds.

South America

The sedimentary basins and oil fields of South America are shown on Fig. 178. Although a large part of South America, including the Andes ranges and the Brazil-Guiana shield, is floored with crystalline rock, there are, nonetheless, areas of considerable size which contain an adequate thickness of sedimentary rock for the commercial occurrence of petroleum. The most prolific of the basins so far explored are the two at the northern extremity of the continent, which cover eastern and western Venezuela. The eastern Venezuela basin extends across southern Trinidad, which geologically is a part of South America and which will be considered in the following section.

Venezuela has been the second country in the world in oil production in recent years, and the first in South America, producing about sixteen times more oil than the second South American country, Colombia. Argentina is third, Trinidad fourth, and Peru fifth. Smaller amounts of oil are obtained in Ecuador, Bolivia, and Brazil.

General References. L. G. Weeks, "Highlights on 1948 Developments in Foreign Petroleum Fields," *Bull. Am. Assoc. Petrol. Geol.,* Vol. 33 (June, 1949), pp. 1029–1124; *Oil and Gas Jour., Annual Review Number,* Vol. 48 (January 26, 1950); *Oil and Gas Jour., International Number,* Vol. 48 (December 22, 1949); *World Oil, International Operations Issue,* Vol. 131 (July 15,1950); Max W. Ball, *This Fascinating Oil Business* (Bobbs-Merrill, New York, 1940); Joseph T. Singewald, Jr., "Bibliography of Economic Geology of South America," *Geol. Soc. Am., Special Paper* 50 (1943); John L. Rich, "Oil Possibilities of South America in the Light of Regional Geology," *Bull. Am. Assoc. Petrol. Geol.,* Vol. 29 (May, 1945), pp. 495–563.

After Weeks (1949)

FIG. 178. South America. Sedimentary basins and oil fields. *Courtesy L. G. Weeks and American Association of Petroleum Geologists.*

Trinidad [15]

The oil production for Trinidad during 1949 amounted to approximately 0.6 per cent of that for the entire world. This was slightly less than the Colorado production and slightly more than the Michigan production for the same period. Heretofore, Trinidad has been one of the leading oil producers in the British Empire, but Canada caught up with it in 1949 and surpassed it in 1950.

Although Sir Walter Raleigh calked the vessels of his fleet with asphalt from the Trinidad pitch lake in 1595, and exploitation of this semisolid hydrocarbon deposit has been continuous since 1867, it was not until 1908 that Trinidad commenced commercial production of liquid petroleum. In a relatively short time after the drilling of the first successful oil well, nearly a score of additional fields was discovered, and the cumulative production to date amounts to over ⅓ billion barrels. Several deep wells have been drilled in recent years in an attempt to discover new Tertiary and perhaps Cretaceous reservoirs. These probings have not as yet been successful. Gravity surveys have been made across the Gulf of Paria between the oil fields of Trinidad and those of eastern Venezuela, but offshore drilling of promising structures awaits the granting of the necessary licenses.

The island of Trinidad (Fig. 179) is about 50 miles long, north and south, and 30 miles wide. It can be divided physiographically and tectonically into five east-west provinces, of which three are ranges and two are intervening lowland zones. The Northern Range exposes Cretaceous and older metamorphic rocks. The Central Range has a Cretaceous core, and in the Southern Range, lower Tertiary rocks are exposed along the axis. Almost all the Trinidad oil fields so far discovered are in the lowland belt between the Central Range and the Southern Range, especially in the western half, where upper Tertiary rocks lie at the surface. Structurally, the southern lowlands is a wide synclinal trough, but along the edges adjacent to the ranges the sediments are close-folded and thrust-faulted.

Most of the reservoir rocks in Trinidad are Miocene sands. Recently considerable oil has been discovered in an Oligocene reservoir in several fields. No older rocks have been found to be productive as yet.

About 90 per cent of the production has come from a belt extending

[15] V. C. Illing and Hans G. Kugler, "Eastern Venezuela and Trinidad," *Science of Petroleum* (Oxford Univ. Press, 1938), Vol. 1, pp. 106–110; G. A. Waring and C. G. Carlson, "Geology and Oil Resources of Trinidad, British West Indies," *Bull. Am. Assoc. Petrol. Geol.,* Vol. 9 (September, 1925), pp. 1000–1008.

across the southwestern Trinidad peninsula from Brighton on the north shore to Palo Seco near the south shore. The leading field in both cumulative production and yield during 1949 was the Forest Reserve, which lies about midway across the peninsula. This field was discovered in 1914. The second and third fields in both cumulative and current production are the Point Fortin and the Penal.

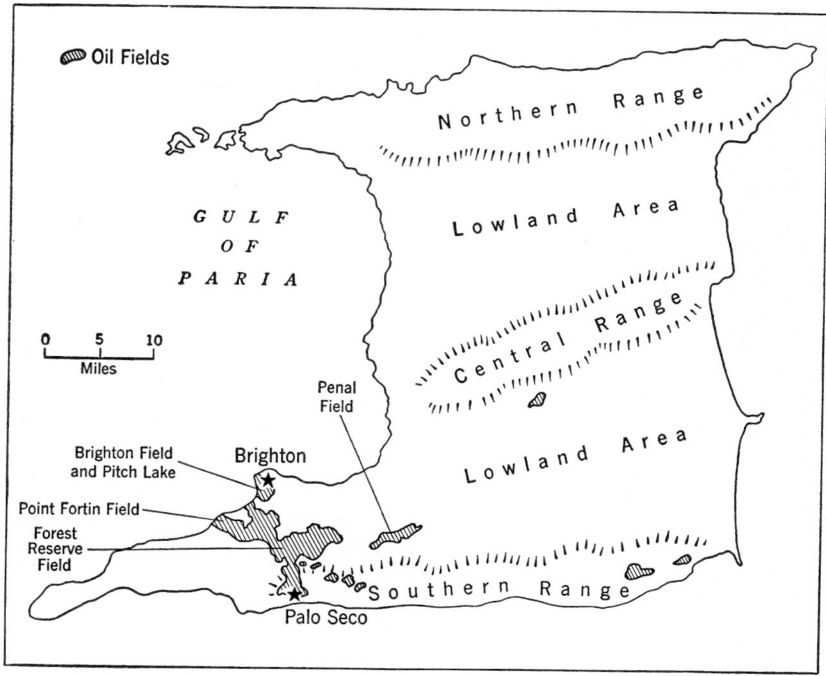

FIG. 179. Trinidad index map.

Most of the trapping in the Trinidad oil fields is anticlinal. In some fields, such as Penal, the anticline is faulted, and in a few fields true fault traps exist. To some extent the distribution of oil in the anticlines, and a relatively small amount of actual trapping, are due to varying permeability of the reservoir sand.

The northernmost field on the southwestern Trinidad peninsula is the Brighton. The oil brought to the surface by wells in the Brighton field has accumulated in a structural dome about 2 miles in diameter. On the crest of this dome at the surface is the famous pitch lake, which is nearly circular and about $\frac{1}{3}$ mile in diameter. Although millions of tons of asphalt have been removed from this lake and shipped to all parts of the world since 1867, this activity has lowered the lake level only about 16 feet. Continuous upward seepage of heavy oil that hardens upon contact with the air has replenished the greater part of the asphalt removed.

Venezuela [16]

In 1949 Venezuela (Figs. 180–182) was second only to the United States, producing 14 per cent of the oil output of the world. The

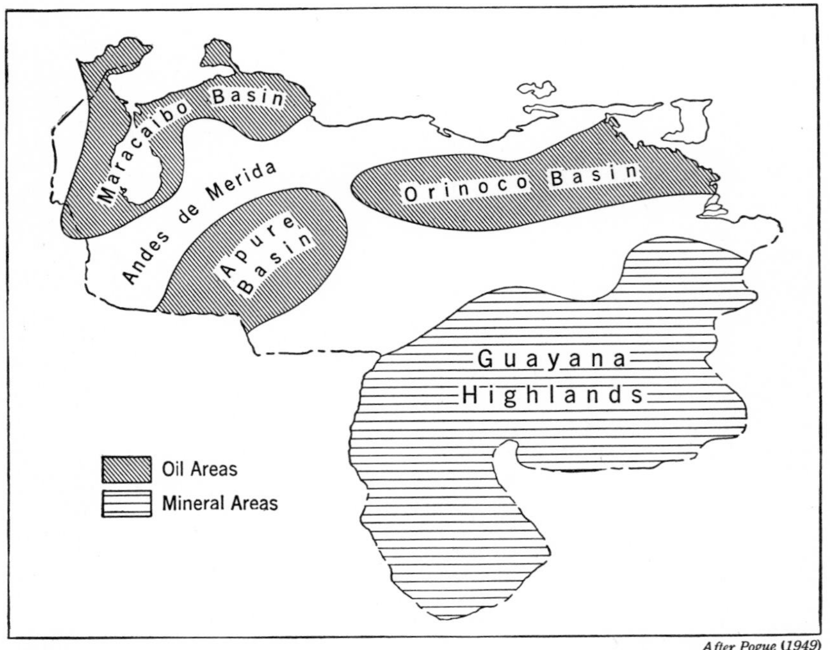

FIG. 180. Venezuela. Sedimentary basins. *Courtesy Chase National Bank.*

United States produced 54 per cent during the same year. The Venezuelan output is approximately equal to that of California and Oklahoma combined. The market situation in Venezuela is quite different from that in the United States, for that country exports

[16] Ralph Alexander Liddle, *The Geology of Venezuela and Trinidad* (Paleontological Research Institution, Ithaca, N. Y., 1946), reviewed by E. Mencher, *Bull. Am. Assoc. Petrol. Geol.*, Vol. 32 (March, 1948), pp. 382–383; Venezuelan number *World Petrol.*, Vol. 10 (December, 1939); Joseph E. Pogue, *Oil in Venezuela* (Chase National Bank, New York, June, 1949).

nearly 99 per cent of its annual oil production. In recent years, about one-third of Venezuelan oil has gone to Europe, another third to the United States, and the remaining third has been distributed among other South American countries, Canada, Central America, and nearby marine fueling stations. The marketing of Venezuelan oil is simplified considerably by the strategic geographic position of this country. The

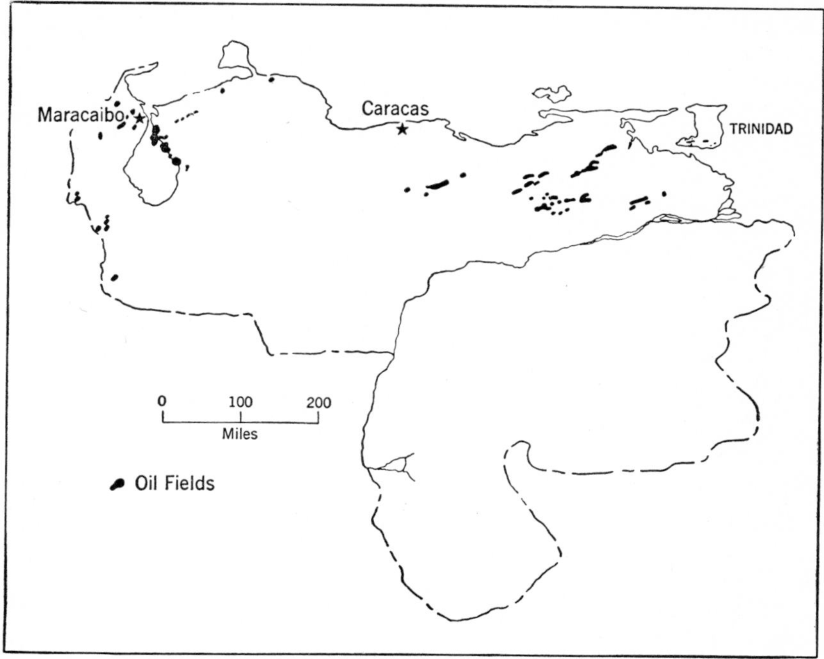

FIG. 181. Venezuela. Oil and gas fields.

great oil fields of Lake Maracaibo are closer to New York City than are the oil-shipping ports of the Texas Gulf Coast.

Although petroleum has been known in Venezuela for centuries, the country is a relative newcomer among oil-producing commonwealths. It was not until 1912 that any serious effort was made to find oil in Venezuela, and the first field, the Mene Grande, which lies to the east of Lake Maracaibo, was discovered in 1913. During the two years following, other fields were found southwest of the lake, and in 1917 the first of the great Bolivar Coastal fields along the east shore of Lake Maracaibo was discovered. The largest of the Venezuelan fields, the Lagunillas on the Bolivar Coast, began producing in 1926. The first major oil field of eastern Venezuela, the Quiriquire, was opened up in 1928.

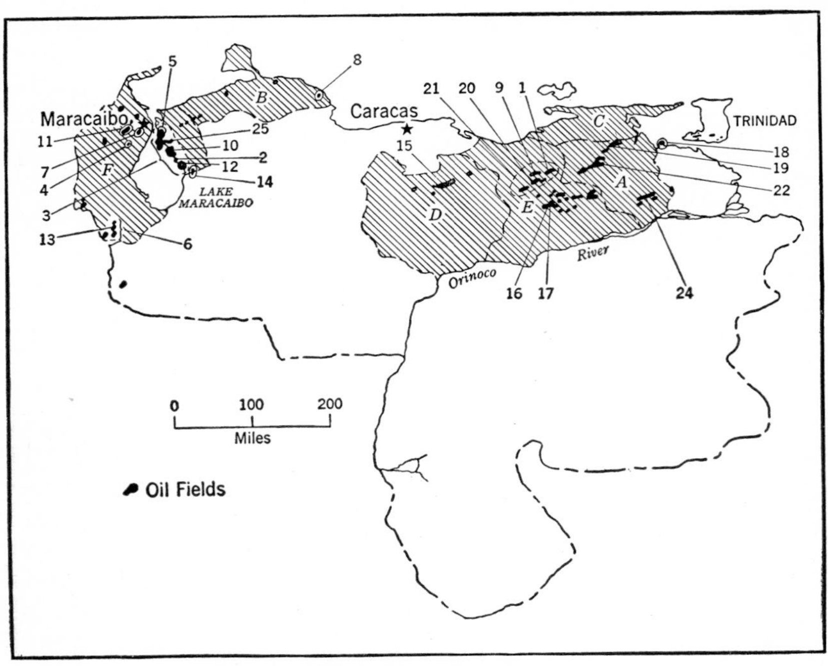

FIG. 182. Venezuela index map.

A, Monagas state.
B, Falcon state.
C, Sucre state.
D, Guarico state.
E, Anzoategui state.
F, Zulia state.

1, Anaco group oil fields.
2, Bachaquero oil field.
3, Bolivar Coast group oil fields.
4, Boscan oil field.
5, Cabimas oil field.
6, Colon district oil fields.
7, Concepcion oil field.
8, El Mene de Acosta oil field.
9, El Roble oil field.
10, Lagunillas oil field.
11, La Paz oil field.
12, Las Cruces oil field.
13, Manueles oil field.
14, Mene Grande oil field.
15, Mercedes group oil fields.
16, Oficina group oil fields.
17, Oficina oil field.
18, Pedernales oil field.
19, Quiriquire oil field.
20, San Joaquin oil field.
21, Santa Ana oil field.
22, Santa Barbara-Jusepin oil field.
23, Tarra group oil fields.
24, Temblador-Tucupita oil field.
25, Tia Juana oil field.

Venezuela is notable for the quantity and size of its oil and asphalt seepages. Sometimes described as the largest seepage in the world is Bermudez, or Guanoco, Lake in eastern Venezuela, an asphalt deposit larger in area, but perhaps not in depth, than the pitch lake of Trinidad. Seepages are especially common around the edges of

Maracaibo basin, and their presence aided materially in finding the earlier oil fields. At Mene Grande hundreds of seepages occur, covering an area of about 1 square mile with asphalt.

After the initial discoveries in both western and eastern Venezuela, the search spread to other parts of these districts and many new fields were found. In recent years the emphasis has been on greater exploration of the third dimension, depth, and this search has also been extremely successful. Early production in the Lake Maracaibo area was confined to Oligocene-Miocene sands, but more recently rich Eocene reserves have been found under the lake by deeper drilling. In 1944 oil was discovered in quantity in Cretaceous limestones (heretofore practically all the production had been from Tertiary sandstones) west of Lake Maracaibo, and new discoveries are continuing in that area. Some Cretaceous limestone wells are producing over 20,000 barrels daily, and the average is about 6000 barrels. A Cretaceous oil deposit recently discovered in the outskirts of the city of Maracaibo is one of the deeper oil fields of the world, lying below 12,200 feet.

With the exception of the Cretaceous limestone reservoirs now being exploited west of Lake Maracaibo, practically all the Venezuelan production comes from Tertiary sandstones. Miocene and Miocene-Oligocene formations are of great importance in both western and eastern Venezuela. Eocene sandstones have produced a major portion of the oil in many western Venezuelan fields and constitute a huge reserve in the Lake Maracaibo area. The Eocene-Oligocene Merecure formation has become an important source of oil in the Anaco group of fields in eastern Venezuela.

As regards types of traps, the Bolivar Coastal fields of western Venezuela and the Quiriquire field of eastern Venezuela are largely due to up-dip wedge-out of reservoir beds against an unconformity surface. The fields on the southern edge of the eastern Venezuela basin are mainly the result of fault accumulations. Fields of the Anaco trend in eastern Venezuela and such western Venezuelan fields as Mene Grande, Concepcion, and La Paz are dominantly anticlinal.

Venezuela is divided into two tectonic basins (Fig. 180) by the Venezuelan Andes and Caribbean Ranges. To the north and west of these mountains is the Maracaibo-Falcon basin. To the south and east are the Apure basin, extending into Colombia, and the Orinoco basin, opening eastward to Trinidad and the Atlantic Ocean. So far most of the Venezuelan oil has come from the Maracaibo part of the Maracaibo-Falcon basin and from the Orinoco basin. Some oil has been found in the Apure basin, but no outlet has yet been provided for it. It is customary to classify the oil fields of Venezuela into two principal districts, eastern and western.

So far Venezuela has produced approximately 5 billion barrels of oil, with about 9 billion barrels of known crude reserve remaining. About three-fourths of that total production has come from the Bolivar Coast and Mene Grande on the east side of Lake Maracaibo. The leading individual fields in cumulative production are Lagunillas, Cabimas (La Rosa), Tia Juana, Mene Grande, and Quiriquire. However, the production-ranking of an individual oil field may be as misleading as the population-ranking of a city, since both may commonly be restricted by arbitrary areal limits placed about them early in their history. For this reason, a possibly more significant areal evaluation of Venezuelan production is that made by general producing areas or groups of fields as tabulated.

	Average Daily Production 1949	*Cumulative Production to End* 1949
Western Venezuela		
Bolivar coastal fields	631,500	3,155,200,000
Mara-Maracaibo fields	220,800	249,000,000
Mene Grande	46,300	339,000,000
Colon fields	12,200	113,700,000
Falcon fields	5,000	68,500,000
Boscan	3,700	1,700,000
Eastern Venezuela		
Greater Oficina fields	183,700	359,800,000
Sta Barbara-Jusepin	73,700	252,000,000
Quiriquire	63,700	326,400,000
Anaco fields	34,300	72,500,000
Temblador-Tucupita fields	16,000	38,400,000
Mercedes	15,600	7,800,000
Eastern Guarico fields	11,700	5,200,000
Pedernales	5,800	12,500,000

Western Venezuela.[17] The oil fields of western Venezuela lie in the Maracaibo-Falcon basin, which is a V-shaped topographic depres-

17 Caribbean Petroleum Company Staff, "Oil Fields of Royal Dutch-Shell Group in Western Venezuela," *Bull. Am. Assoc. Petrol. Geol.*, Vol. 32 (April, 1948), pp. 517–628; F. A. Sutton, "Geology of Maracaibo Basin, Venezuela," *Bull. Am. Assoc. Petrol. Geol.*, Vol. 30 (October, 1946), pp. 1621–1741; H. B. Schaub, "Outline of Sedimentation in Maracaibo Basin, Venezuela," *Bull. Am. Assoc. Petrol. Geol.*, Vol. 32 (February, 1948), pp. 215–227; V. R. Garfias and Theodore Chapin, "Colombia and Maracaibo Basin," *Science of Petroleum* (Oxford Univ. Press, 1938), Vol. 1, pp. 111–117.

sion bounded by the Andes de Merida on the southeast, the Sierra de Perija on the west, and a foreland (not a part of the Andes orogeny) and the Caribbean Sea to the north. This part of South America passed through a series of orogenies that culminated in the late Pliocene by the uplift of the two Andes ranges, at which time the final shaping of the Maracaibo-Falcon basin took place. Simultaneously, anticlinal folds were formed on the eastern and western flanks of the basin parallel to the bordering highlands. The Maracaibo basin, in which most of the oil fields of western Venezuela are located, was a basin of sedimentation. It is occupied at the center by Lake Maracaibo, which is in reality a very large bay of the Caribbean. The basin extends to the southwest a short distance across the boundary into eastern Colombia, and five oil fields have been discovered so far in the Colombia part of the Maracaibo basin (Barco concession).

About 85 per cent of the basin is covered by either lake water or Quaternary deposits. Successively older formations, locally extending to the pre-Cambrian, are exposed around the basin edge. Oil in commercial quantities has been found in all but two of the seventeen formations which comprise the 23,000-foot stratigraphic section from the top of the middle Miocene down to the base of the middle Cretaceous.

Accumulation of oil in western Venezuela is chiefly structural around the periphery, but toward the center of the basin it has been controlled in large part by permeability variations. Faulting is quite common and has contributed to the closure necessary for trapping in several fields.

The oil fields of western Venezuela may be divided into six groups. First and foremost of these producing areas is the Bolivar Coastal fields on the east shore of Lake Maracaibo and extending out into the lake for varying distances. (Some producing wells have been drilled in 100 feet of water and more than 10 miles from shore.) A second area is that of the Mene Grande field, south of the Bolivar Coastal fields and 12 miles inland from the east shore of the lake. This is the oldest major field in the country. A third producing area is in the Colon district, southwest of the lake and near the eastern border of Colombia. A fourth area is on the west side of the lake, northwest of the city of Maracaibo, in the districts of Mara and Maracaibo. A fifth is the recently discovered Boscan field, southwest of the city of Maracaibo, and a sixth group includes the fields of the State of Falcon, northeast of the lake.

According to the Caribbean Petroleum Company Staff,[18] most of the oil so far produced in the Bolivar Coastal fields has come from Miocene sandstone reservoirs, which have a regional dip lakeward. Trapping on the monoclinal dip has been due to a combination of structural and stratigraphic conditions. Low plunging anticlines are sealed up-dip by facies changes which involve decrease in permeability, by wedging-out of lenticular sands (Fig. 183), and, especially in the

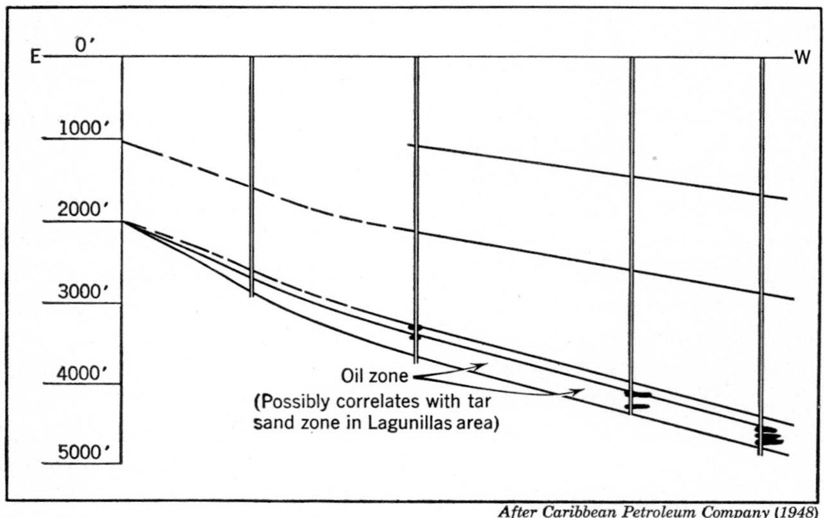

Fig. 183. Bachaquero field, Venezuela. East-west cross section showing updip wedge-out of producing sands. *Courtesy American Association of Petroleum Geologists.*

Cabimas field, by strike faults. Another interesting occurrence in the Cabimas field is a general decrease in the specific gravity of the oil down-dip. This appears to be due to near-surface asphaltization of the oil, which further aided trapping.

At Mene Grande the oil has accumulated in a much-faulted dome. The Las Cruces and Manueles fields in the Colon district southwest of Lake Maracaibo are the result of trapping in nodes along the Tarra anticline, a north-south fold which has been traced at the surface for a distance of 46 miles. This structure is thrust-faulted, and oil has accumulated in domes in the overthrust block.

The area west of Maracaibo City and northwest of Lake Maracaibo (districts of Mara and Maracaibo) has become prominent because of

[18] *Op. cit.*, p. 543.

the discovery of oil in relatively deep Cretaceous limestone reservoirs. Production is from anticlinal traps, but faulting has played a part in controlling accumulation. The Concepcion field in this same area (Fig. 184) produces largely from the Eocene on a strongly folded anticline with several longitudinal and cross faults. As a result, the anticline is broken into five main blocks. The highest of these, at the apex of the fold, was the one in which oil was first discovered and the earliest development took place. However, the thickest reservoir sand section is on the Ramillete flank, and so this structural block has provided the greater part of the Concepcion oil. The oil moving up-dip on the Ramillete flank was impounded below the strike fault, which cuts the anticline just below its crest. In the La Paz field to the west of Concepcion, accumulation has taken place in both Eocene sands and Cretaceous limestones in an elongate anticline shattered along its crest by a series of longitudinal faults. The deepest well outside the United States was reported drilling below 17,000 feet in April, 1950, in the state of Zulia west of Lake Maracaibo. It was planned to test the Cretaceous limestones in that area.

The fields so far discovered in the Falcon subdistrict to the northeast of Lake Maracaibo are, with the exception of the Cumarebo field, relatively minor accumulations compared with those to the west and southwest. One of these, the El Mene de Acosta field,[19] has been abandoned. The oil occurred on the south flank of an anticline truncated by erosion. Each one of the three reservoir sands is lenticular and dies out before reaching the erosion surface. Most of the oil in the fields of West Buchivacoa [20] has accumulated where buried unconformity surfaces have been warped into fairly sharp anticlines. Trapping is due to both anticlinal structure and impounding below the unconformity.

EASTERN VENEZUELA.[21] The present oil fields of the eastern Venezuela district lie to the east of the meridian passing through Caracas. The Orinoco sedimentary basin is bordered on the north in Sucre state by the Caribbean Range, the westward extension of the

[19] H. H. Suter, "El Mene de Acosta Field, Venezuela," *Bull. Am. Assoc. Petrol. Geol.*, Vol. 31 (December, 1947), pp. 2193–2206.

[20] G. W. Halse, "Oil Fields of West Buchivacoa, Venezuela," *Bull. Am. Assoc. Petrol. Geol.*, Vol. 31 (December, 1947), pp. 2170–2192.

[21] Willard Miller, "The Relationship of Structure to Petroleum Production in Eastern Venezuela," *Econ. Geol.*, Vol. 34 (August, 1939), pp. 524–536; V. C. Illing and Hans G. Kugler, "Eastern Venezuela and Trinidad," *Science of Petroleum* (Oxford Univ. Press, 1938), Vol. 1, pp. 106–110.

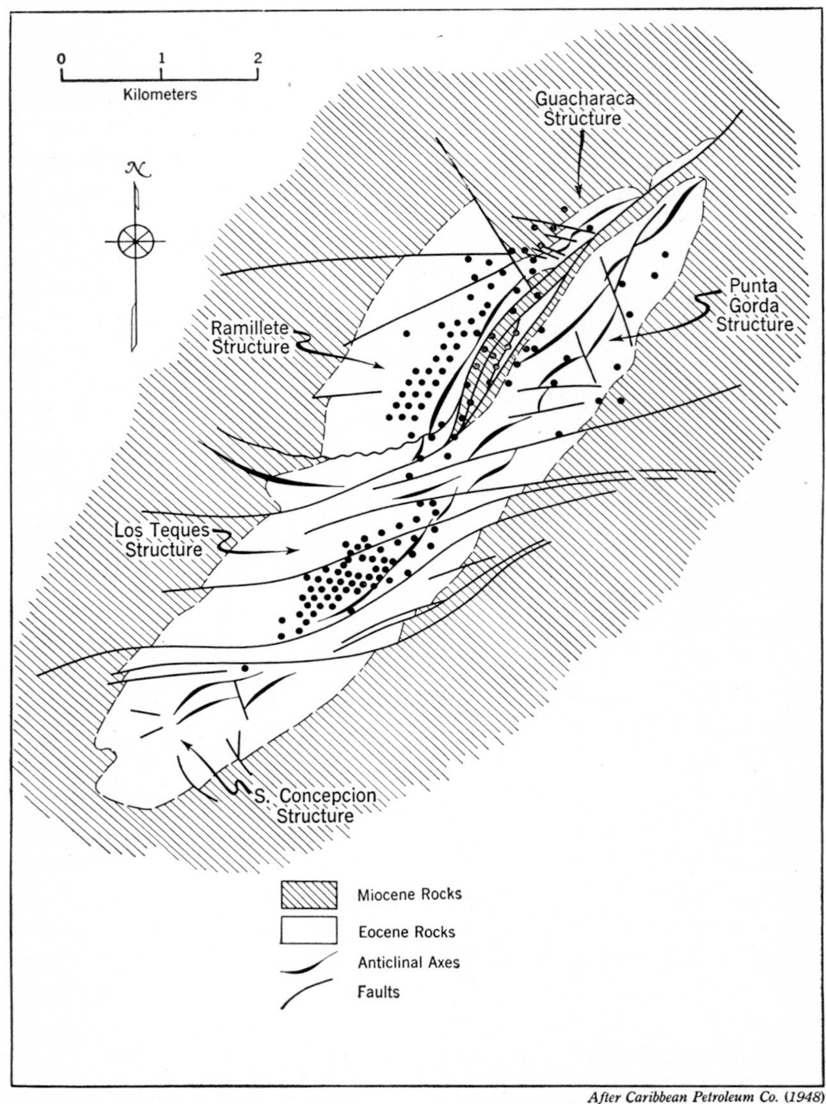

After Caribbean Petroleum Co. (1948)

Fig. 184. La Concepcion field, Venezuela. Areal geology and major structural features. *Courtesy American Association of Petroleum Geologists.*

Northern Range of Trinidad. The Orinoco River runs along the south side of the basin, and beyond it to the south is the Guiana Highland province. Within the basin, the topography varies from flat in the Orinoco delta region to rolling plains farther west. The basin is covered by a thick blanket of Pleistocene and Recent sediments except along the northern edge, where the Tertiary and Cretaceous formations crop out. The rocks exposed along the southern border of the basin in the banks of the Orinoco River are metamorphosed sediments and intrusive igneous rocks.

The fields of eastern Venezuela fall into about eight different groups. The westernmost (Mercedes group) is in northern Guarico state. Another group of shallow production fields is in eastern Guarico. In Anzoátegui are two groups, the Oficina, near the center of the state, and the Anaco group to the north. Monagas state has two groups of fields near the northern edge of the basin (Santa Barbara-Jusepin and Quiriquire) and another on the same parallel as the Oficina group but farther east (Temblador-Tucupita). Still farther east is the Pedernales field at the mouth of the Orinoco.

Trapping in eastern Venezuela is mostly anticlinal, but in the Quiriquire field accumulation has taken place on a monocline, owing in part to the up-dip lensing-out of the Pliocene sandstone and conglomerate reservoirs and in part to a strike fault. Eastern Venezuelan reservoir rocks are almost entirely Tertiary sandstones with Miocene and Miocene-Oligocene formations predominating.

The petroleum geology of both the Oficina and the Anaco groups of fields has been described in considerable detail by Hedberg, Sass, and Funkhouser.[22] The San Joaquin field of the Anaco group is illustrated (Fig. 46) and described in Chapter 8 as an example of accumulation in a structural dome. The oldest field in this group is the Santa Ana, discovered in 1937. Five other domes were subsequently drilled and found to be productive. All six fields are in a northeast-southwest line extending for a distance of 30 miles. The southwest domes are mappable at the surface because of outcrops of Middle Miocene inliers surrounded by Upper Miocene and Pliocene rocks. To the northeast, however, the structure is hidden by a blanket

[22] H. D. Hedberg, L. C. Sass, and H. J. Funkhouser, "Oil Fields of the Greater Oficina Area, Central Anzoátegui, Venezuela," *Bull. Am. Assoc. Petrol. Geol.*, Vol. 31 (December, 1947), pp. 2089–2169; H. J. Funkhouser, L. C. Sass, and H. D. Hedberg, "Santa Ana, San Joaqúin, Guario, and Santa Rosa Oil Fields (Anaco Fields), Central Anzoátegui, Venezuela," *Bull Am. Assoc. Petrol. Geol.*, Vol. 32 (October, 1948), pp. 1851–1908.

of unconformable younger sediments. Immediately to the southeast of the row of domes is a parallel zone of thrust faulting. The dip of the fault zone is to the northwest; the domes are in the overthrust block and may have been formed by drag. Unlike so many Venezuelan fields, there were no hydrocarbon clues at the surface, such as asphalt deposits or oil and gas seeps. Discovery was the result of air-photograph study, surface geological reconnaissance, detailed surface mapping, and reflection seismograph checking. Accumulation in all the Anaco domes is due to structural closure, but sand lenticularity has had some control on the distribution of oil across the anticlines.

The Oficina fields are also in a region in which seepages are lacking. Furthermore, the area is completely covered by a blanket of Quaternary and uppermost Tertiary deposits. The discovery well was started in 1933 as a result of torsion balance and seismograph work. Subsequently, some twenty fields have been developed in this area. Regionally, the Greater Oficina district lies on the southern limb of the eastern Venezuelan basin, and the dips are less than 5° to the north, with very little folding. Trapping has been due largely to the presence of normal strike faults which cut across the regional basinward dip and, through their arcuate form assisted by cross faults and mild compaction folds, impound the oil, which has been migrating southward and upward from the deeper parts of the basin. Locally, sand lenticularity has also been responsible for some oil accumulation. The reservoir section lies entirely within the Oficina formation of Oligocene-Miocene age. Sixty-five distinct producing sands have been found within this section at depths ranging from 4000 to 7000 feet. As much as 550 feet of productive sand may be found in a single well.

Colombia [23]

During 1949 Colombia (Figs. 185–186) produced 0.9 per cent of the world's oil. It ranks a low second to Venezuela (14 per cent) among South American oil-producing countries. The Colombia yield during 1949 was slightly more than that of Arkansas for the same period.

The Infantas field in the Magdalena River valley was discovered in 1918, but it was not until 1921 that Colombia had its first recorded

[23] J. L. Anderson, "Petroleum Geology of Colombia, South America," *Bull. Am. Assoc. Petrol. Geol.*, Vol. 29 (August, 1945), pp. 1065–1142; V. R. Garfias and Theodore Chapin, "Colombia and the Maracaibo Basin," *Science of Petroleum* (Oxford Univ. Press, 1938), Vol. 1, pp. 111–117; John W. Butler, Jr., "Geology of Honda District, Colombia," *Bull. Am. Assoc. Petrol. Geol.*, Vol. 26 (May, 1942), pp. 793–837.

output, and large-scale production did not commence until the completion of the first pipe-line outlet in 1926.

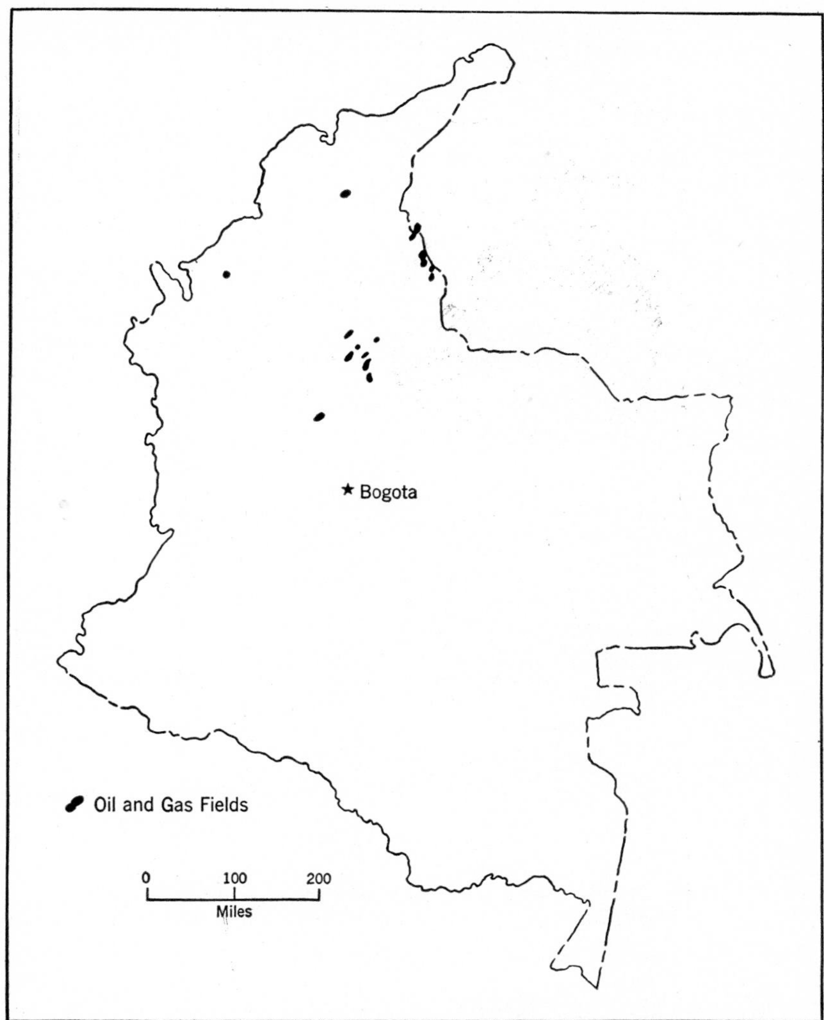

Fig. 185. Colombia. Oil and gas fields.

Oil seeps and asphaltic accumulations are abundant in areas of Tertiary rock outcrop. Of unusual prominence in Colombia are the mud volcanoes, which mark seeps of natural gas.[24]

[24] F. M. Anderson, "Original Source of Oil in Colombia," *Bull. Am. Assoc. Petrol. Geol.,* Vol. 10 (April, 1926), pp. 388–389.

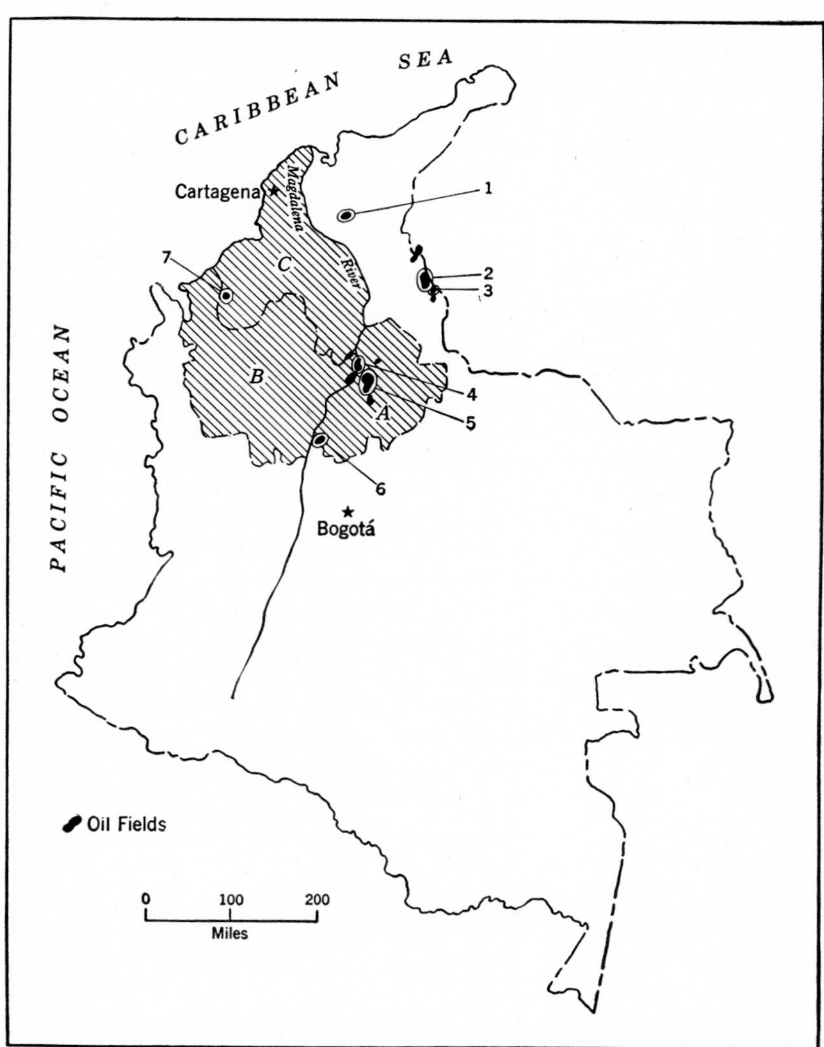

FIG. 186. Colombia index map. *A,* Santander state; *B,* Antioquia state; *C,* Bolivar state; 1, Dificil oil field; 2, Tibu oil field; 3, Petrolea oil field; 4, Casabe oil field; 5, Infantas-La Cira oil field; 6, Velasquez oil field; 7, Sinu oil field (abd).

Colombia is dominated by the three Andes ranges and the plains ("Llanos") to the east. The three ranges are called the Cordillera Occidental, the Cordillera Central, and Cordillera Oriental. The Occidental and Central Andes merge in northern Colombia and continue northward into Panama as a single range. The Cordillera Oriental splits near the Venezuelan border into two forks, the Sierra de Perijo on the left (west) and the Sierra de Merida on the right. The Maracaibo basin of western Venezuela, which lies within the V formed by the two ranges, extends a short distance into eastern Colombia. The Apure basin makes the low plains east of the mountains in eastern Colombia. The Bolivar geosyncline lies between the Cordillera Oriental and its left-hand fork, the Sierra de Perijo, and the Cordillera Central-Occidental. It is occupied in part by the valley of the Magdalena River. A fourth sedimentary basin overlaps the north coast of Colombia, adjacent to the Caribbean.

Most of the commercial accumulations of oil in Colombia are anticlinal. With few exceptions, these oil-bearing anticlines are considerably broken by faults which may control distribution across the structures, but the initial trapping has been due to the presence of an upfold.

The sedimentary section proved to be oil-bearing has an aggregate thickness of 25,000 feet. The producing formations range in age from Pliocene to Cretaceous. So far the greater part of the oil has come from Oligocene-Eocene reservoirs. Sandstones predominate, but one Oligocene reservoir and the Cretaceous reservoirs are limestones.

Tectonically, the oil fields of Colombia lie in two districts, the Colombian sector of the Maracaibo basin and the Magdalena River-Bolivar geosyncline. No commercial oil deposits have been found as yet in the other two sedimentary areas, the Llanos and the north coast. The north coast area did have at one time the Sinu field in western Bolivar state, but it has been abandoned.

The greatest concentration of fields is in the upper Magdalena River valley in western Santander, northeastern Antioquia, and southeastern Bolivar. In the state of Santander near the right bank of the Magdalena are La Cira and the Infantas fields. La Cira is the leading field in Colombia in cumulative production, and the Infantas, the discovery field for the country, stands second. The two together have produced nearly 84 per cent of the total Colombian output. Currently, the largest field in annual production is the Casabe, which lies across the Magdalena in northeastern Antioquia state. La Cira is a close second in current production.

The only other concentration of fields is in what is known as the Barco concession along the Colombian rim of the Maracaibo basin. In addition, there are two isolated fields, the Velasquez about 80 miles up-river from the Casabe-La Cira group, and, in the opposite direction, the Dificil in west central Magdalena state but still in the Bolivar geosyncline.

Large seeps led to the discovery of Infantas in 1918. The field is about 7 miles long and nearly 1 mile wide. It occupies an anticline

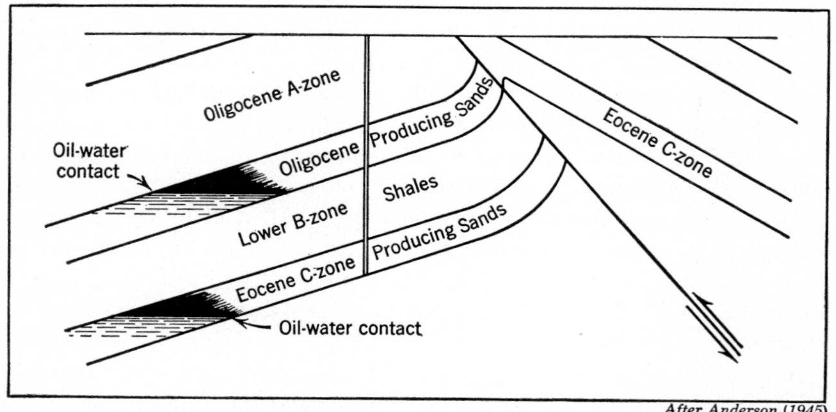

FIG. 187. Infantas oil field, Colombia. Generalized cross section of anticline. *Courtesy American Association of Petroleum Geologists.*

(Fig. 187) which is overthrust along the axis. Fourteen cross faults divide the anticline into a series of blocks. The oil occurs below the fault plane in the underthrust block in Oligocene and Eocene sandstones; the Eocene are more important in terms of yield.

The La Cira anticline was discovered in 1926 after vertical strata of oil-stained sand had been observed in a railroad excavation. This was the nearest thing to a seepage in the La Cira vicinity. The field is now 5 miles long and 4 miles wide; trapping has taken place in a relatively wide anticline. This fold is also faulted, but the faults are of minor importance compared with those at Infantas.

The producing structure in the Casabe field on the left bank of the Magdalena is more like that at Infantas. It is extensively faulted and produces from several different reservoir zones.

The fields in the Barco concession [25] lie high on the southwest flank

[25] Frank B. Notestein, Carl W. Hubman, and James W. Bowler, "Geology of the Barco Concession, Republic of Colombia, South America," *Bull. Geol. Soc. Am.*, Vol. 55 (1944), pp. 1165–1216.

of the Maracaibo basin. The Tarra anticline, previously mentioned in the Venezuela discussion, extends about 40 miles into Colombia. The Petrolea field of Colombia occupies a node along the axis of this regional anticline. The closure at Petrolea is approximately 4000 feet. The fold is complexly faulted, and oil and gas seeps are numerous at the surface. A gathering system was installed in 1940 at a seep near Petrolea, and in the first year over 21,000 barrels of 40° oil were recovered. Six reservoir zones lying in the Lower Cretaceous and lowermost Upper Cretaceous have been discovered in exploiting the Petrolea oil field.

The leading field in current production in the Barco area is the Tibu. This field lies immediately to the west of the Venezuelan boundary north of the Petrolea field. Trapping at Tibu has taken place in a large anticline that is separated from the Cira anticline by a structural depression. According to seismic data, the Tibu anticline has a closure on the La Luna limestone at the base of the Upper Cretaceous of more than 1100 feet.

Argentina [26]

Argentina (Figs. 188–189) is the third South American country in oil production, with a yield during 1949 slightly greater than that of Trinidad and amounting to 0.6 per cent of the world total. Although oil seepages have been known in northern and western Argentina for many decades, it was not until 1907 that this country became a consistent producer of oil. The first commercial discovery was due to an accident; relatively deep drilling during the search for water in the village of Comodoro Rivadavia on the east coast of Patagonia found oil instead of water, and the development of the Comodoro Rivadavia group of oil fields followed. Subsequently, oil was discovered in other parts of the country, including the Mendoza and Salta areas, where oil seeps are abundant. The most recent activity has been at the southernmost tip of South America in Tierra del Fuego, where an exploratory well drilled during 1939 struck gas at a depth of 6300 feet in the Argentine part of the island, and a 62-barrel oil discovery well was reported in October, 1950.

[26] Enrique Fossa-Mancini, "The Argentine Republic," *Science of Petroleum* (Oxford Univ. Press, 1938), Vol. 1, pp. 120–123; Anon., "Elements of Argentine Petroleum Geology," *World Petrol.*, Vol. 12 (September, 1941), pp. 77–79; John L. Rich, "Oil Possibilities of South America in the Light of Regional Geology," *Bull. Am. Assoc. Petrol. Geol.*, Vol. 29 (May, 1945), pp. 495–563.

The sedimentary basins of Argentina are shown on the map of South America (Fig. 178). Northern and northeastern Argentina are covered by the great sedimentary basin, the Sub-Andean trough, which lies between the easternmost Andes Range and the Brazilian shield.

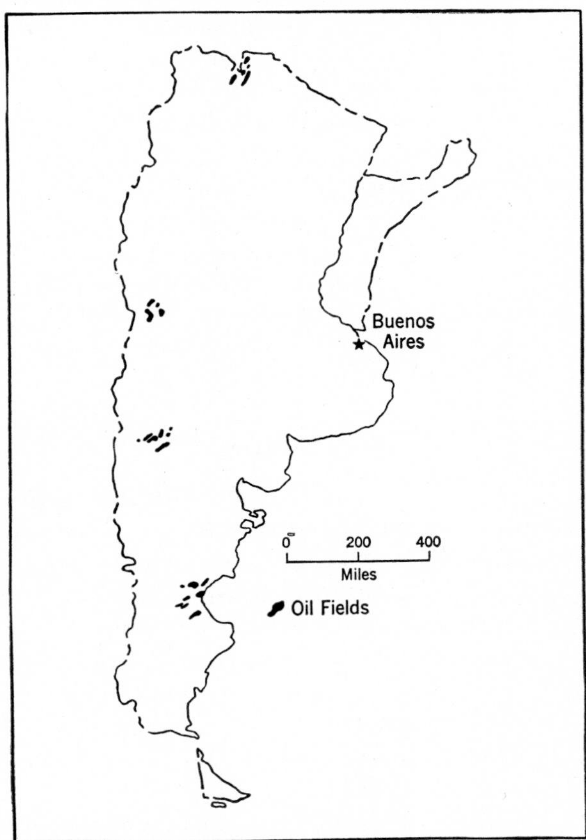

FIG. 188. Argentina. Oil and gas fields.

A second basin occupies parts of southern Argentina, extending to the Atlantic coast across sags in the Patagonian shield. The oil fields lie in three districts, of which one, in northern Argentina, is in the Sub-Andean trough. The other two districts are in the southern basin. The Mendoza-Neuquen group of fields is in western Argentina. The Comodoro Rivadavia district is on the Atlantic coast in the San Jorge basin, an eastward offshoot of the main basin. The Mendoza area is unusual in the close association in some fields between oil (both seeps and buried accumulations) and igneous intrusions.[27] In one small oil field, the Cerro Alquitrán, the oil accumulation is "intimately associated" with andesitic intrusions. Veins of solid hydrocarbon are

FIG. 189. Argentina index map.

found in fault fissures which intercept volcanic dikes and plugs in this area.

The government oil agency, the Yacimientos Petroliferos Fiscale (YPF), produces about two-thirds of the Argentine oil, and its statistics on output have been a state secret since 1948. So far as is known the

[27] Enrique Fossa-Mancini, *op. cit.*, p. 122; F. H. Lahee, "Oil Seepages and Oil Production Associated with Volcanic Plugs in Mendoza Provinces, Argentina," *Bull. Am. Assoc. Petrol. Geol.*, Vol. 16 (August, 1932), pp. 819–824.

Comodoro Rivadavia group of thirteen or more fields is outstanding in both cumulative production and current daily output. This group has produced nearly three-fourths of the Argentine total. It also has large gas reserves. The Mendoza fields are second, and the Neuquen and Salta fields are approximately tied for third place. However, according to available statistics, the San Pedro field in the Salta district is currently second only to Comodoro Rivadavia in daily output.

The reservoir rocks range in age from Tertiary to Devonian. Most of the Comodoro Rivadavia oil is obtained from Upper Cretaceous sandstones. The San Pedro field produces from Permian reservoirs, as do most of the other fields in the Salta district. The reservoirs in the Mendoza area are Triassic in age, and the Neuquen fields produce from Jurassic rocks. Except for two of the smaller Salta fields, the Argentine reservoir rocks are sand or sandstone.

Fossa-Mancini,[28] in his classification of fault traps in Argentina, states that he could find no example of accumulation in simple anticlines. He describes the traps at Comodoro Rivadavia as "faulted, tabular structures." Most of the other Argentine fields produce from faulted anticlines. The accumulation at San Pedro in the Salta district was illustrated and discussed in Chapter 8 (Fig. 34). The surface structure of the Tupungato oil field[29] in Mendoza is a dome with a faulted west flank, but it becomes complicated at depth by a series of low-angle thrust faults. The first production at Tupungato was obtained from Pliocene rocks, in which accumulation had taken place in fractures. The major oil-producing formation at present is an upper Triassic series of volcanic tuffs, but here also the oil appears to be stored almost entirely in cracks.

Peru

During 1949 Peru (Figs. 190–191) produced 0.4 per cent of the world's petroleum output. This was a little less than the production for the state of Michigan during the same period. Peru now ranks fifth among South American countries in oil production, but it was the leading country until 1924, when Venezuela forged to the front. The exploitation of seep oil in Peru extends back into prehistory. Pits where the Incas mined asphalt are abundant at Pta. Parina, northwestern Peru, which is the westernmost point of South America. These

28 *Op. cit.*, pp. 122–123.

29 Harry L. Baldwin, "Tupungato Oil Field, Mendoza, Argentina," *Bull. Am. Assoc. Petrol. Geol.*, Vol. 28 (October, 1944), pp. 1455–1484.

seeps were still being exploited by the Indians when Pizarro landed there in 1527. However, the discovery well for Peru was drilled in the Zorritos field, another seep area farther north, sometime between 1867 and 1873. The first recorded production was in 1884. The

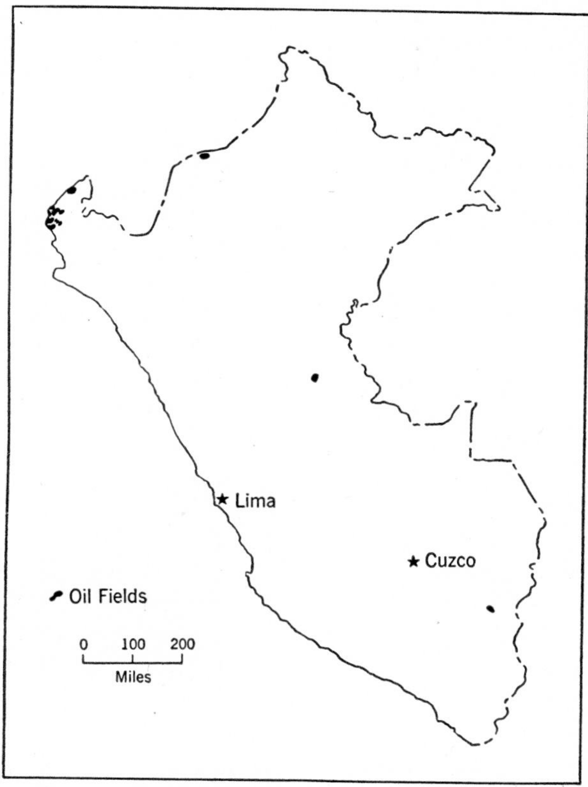

FIG. 190. Peru. Oil and gas fields.

La Brea-Parinas field in the Pta. Parina seep area was discovered in 1889. The Agua Caliente field east of the Andes was opened up in 1932.

Most Peruvian oil still comes from the Pta. Parina area in northwestern Peru. This part of Peru, and the adjacent southwestern corner of Ecuador, is coastal plain and is underlain by basin sediments. Of relatively minor importance in both current and cumulative production is the Agua Caliente field, which is in the Amazon drainage basin. It lies in the Sub-Andean trough, an elongate sedimentary basin east of the Andes which extends from southern Colombia across Ecuador, eastern Peru, central Bolivia, and parts of Paraguay, Argentina, Brazil, and Uruguay (Fig. 178). The Sub-Andean trough is also productive much farther to the southeast on both sides of the Bolivia-

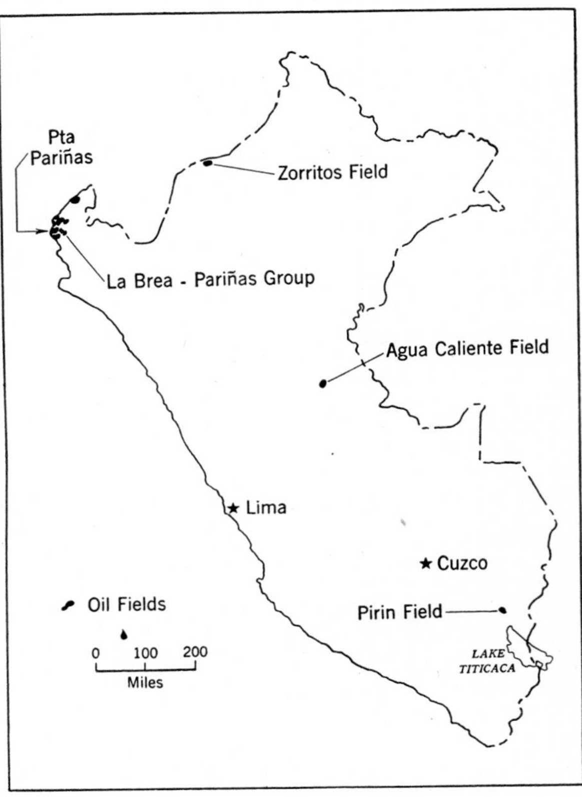

Fig. 191. Peru index map.

Argentina international boundary. Still another area of sedimentation is the intermontane basin, in which Lake Titacaca lies, which extends from northwestern Bolivia into southern Peru. For some years the Pirin field at the north end of Lake Titicaca produced oil, but it has been abandoned since 1915.

All the reservoir rocks so far discovered in Peru are sands and sandstones. The coastal plain fields produce from Tertiary (mainly Eocene) sediments; at Agua Caliente the reservoir is Cretaceous in age. Faulting plays a most important role in the trapping of oil beneath the coastal plain. In some fields the faults cut across plunging anticlines on monoclinal flanks, and in others they cut through anticlinal folds. Accumulation at Agua Caliente is in a structural dome.

Miscellaneous South American Countries

ECUADOR (Fig. 192).[30] The production of oil in Ecuador during 1949 was 0.08 per cent of the total output of the world for that year.

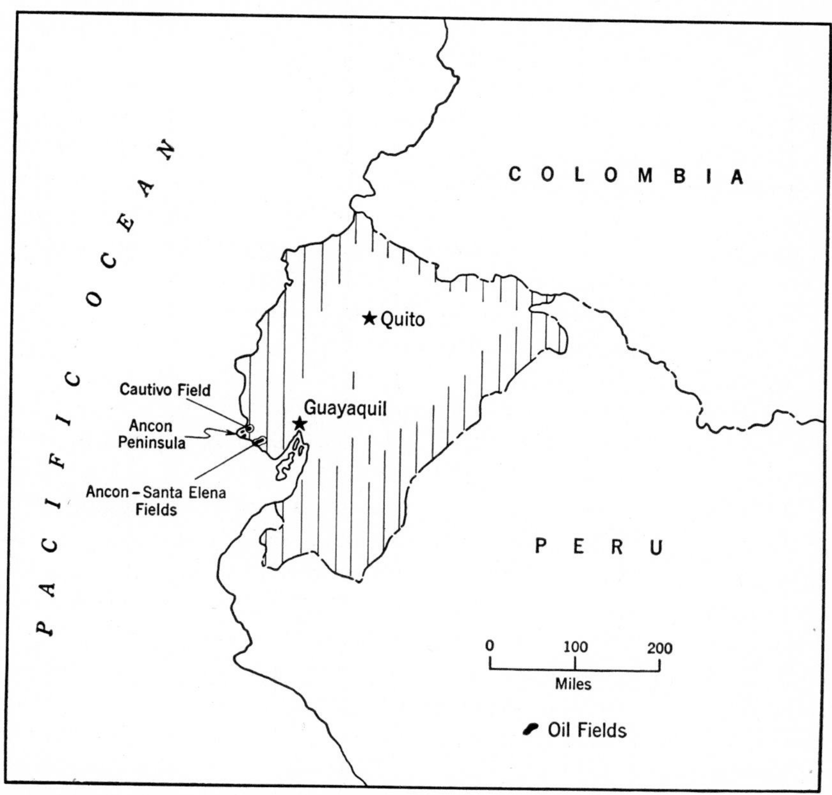

Fig. 192. Ecuador index map.

This is approximately the equivalent of the oil production of West Virginia. All the Ecuadorian oil fields are on Ancón peninsula in the southwestern part of the country. So far attempts to find com-

[30] H. G. Busk, "Ecuador," *Science of Petroleum* (Oxford Univ. Press, 1938), Vol. 1, pp. 118–119; Kenneth B. Barnes, "Ecuador Has Small but Lively Integrated Petroleum Industry," *Oil and Gas Jour.*, Vol. 46 (Aug. 30, 1947), pp. 46–48.

mercial deposits in the Sub-Andean sedimentary basin in eastern Ecuador around the headwaters of the Amazon have not been successful.

Parts of three sedimentary basins lie in Ecuador. The Sub-Andean trough occupies the eastern half of the country, and the other two lie along the coast line. The Ancón peninsula is a part of the same narrow coastal plain on which lie the oil fields of northwestern Peru. Northwestern Ecuador is overlapped by the southern end of the Colombian coastal plain.

The Ancón-Santa Elena peninsula is floored on the south side by nearly flat-lying, but nonetheless faulted, Eocene strata and in the center and on the north side by steeply dipping and otherwise much-disturbed sediments which have been intruded by basic igneous magmas. The largest field in both cumulative and current production is the Ancón-Sta. Elena, which is on the southern side of the peninsula in the zone of relatively undisturbed sediments. The second field is the Cautivo, lying near the north shore in the zone of intense deformation. The reservoirs in both areas are Eocene sandstones, but much of the accumulation has taken place in fissures rather than in intergranular openings. In the southern part of the peninsula, most of the trapping has been due to impounding by strike faults, but the smaller and scattered fields on the north side produce from the most fractured of the local fault blocks.

BOLIVIA (Fig. 193). The oil production of Bolivia during 1949 amounted to approximately 0.02 per cent of the world output. This came from three fields in the Sub-Andean trough in southern Bolivia immediately to the north of the Salta fields of northern Argentina. The largest is Camiri, which is also the farthest north. It produces from a Devonian sandstone reservoir. The other two fields produce from Permo-Triassic sandstones. In all three fields accumulation has taken place in elongate anticlines. Oil seepages are common throughout this area.

BRAZIL (Fig. 194).[31] Oil was first found in Brazil in commercial amounts in 1939. The initial discovery was in the Bahia district on the Atlantic coast, and the six fields that are currently producing lie

[31] Avelino Ignacio de Oliveira, "Brazil Has Four Oil Fields with Twenty-Five Producing Wells," *World Petrol.,* Vol. 16 (September, 1945), pp. 74–75; Fróes Abreu, "Brazilian Oil Fields and Oil-Shale Reserves," *Bull. Am. Assoc. Petrol. Geol.,* Vol. 33 (September, 1949), pp. 1590–1599.

within a few miles of the city of Bahia. They occupy the southern corner of a small triangular basin of sedimentation (Fig. 178) that is a re-entrant into the Brazilian pre-Cambrian shield. Three other re-entrants, two much larger, lie to the north and northwest. In

Fig. 193. Bolivia index map.

addition, a bulge of the Sub-Andean trough extends across a part of Paraguay into southern Brazil. So far none of the attempts to find petroleum in these other basins have been successful.

The reservoir rocks in the Bahia district are Cretaceous sandstones. Trapping has been anticlinal in most fields, but in the largest, the Candeias, the oil has been impounded by the up-dip wedging out of lenticular sands. In the Lobato-Joanes field immediately to the north of the city of Bahia (Salvador), which was the discovery field for the district, oil has been trapped by a strike fault on a monoclinal flank.

CHILE (Fig. 195).[32] In spite of the fact that Chile has an adequate section for commercial hydrocarbon occurrence in only two places, each of relatively limited area, it does have one oil field. This is on

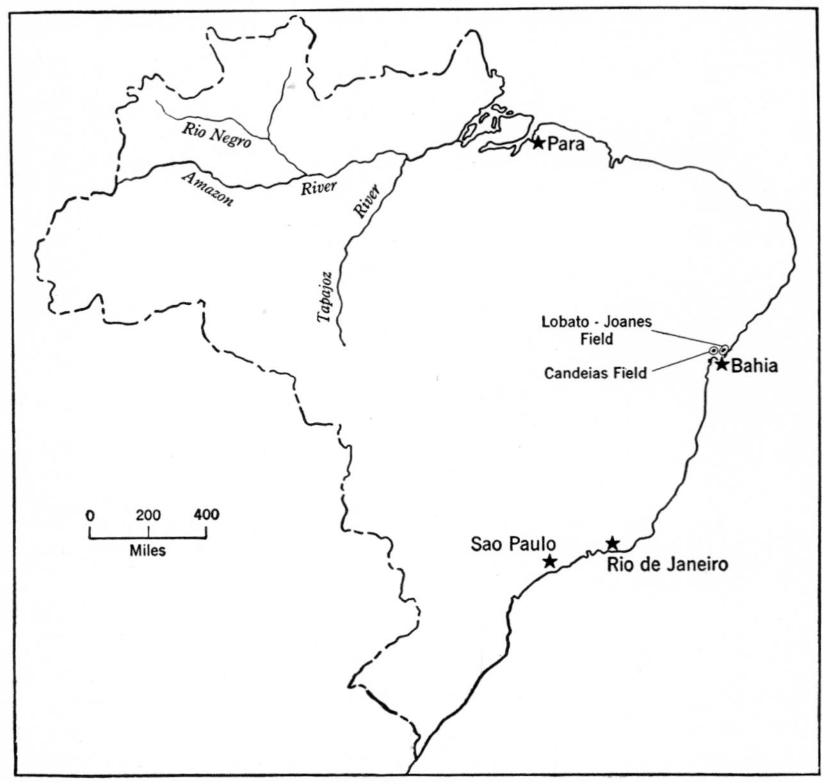

Fig. 194. Brazil index map.

Tierra del Fuego in the Magallanes basin, the southernmost extension of the sedimentary trough in which the Comodoro Rivadavia, Neuquen, and Mendoza fields of Argentina occur. The Magallanes basin covers the northern part of the island of Tierra del Fuego, as well as the mainland to the north and northwest. The single oil field, now known as Manantiales but formerly called the Spring Hill, lies near

[32] C. R. Thomas, "Geology and Petroleum Exploration in Magallanes Province, Chile," *Bull. Am. Assoc. Petrol. Geol.*, Vol. 33 (September, 1949), pp. 1553–1578; C. R. Thomas, "Manantiales Field, Magallanes Province, Chile," *ibid.*, pp. 1579–1589.

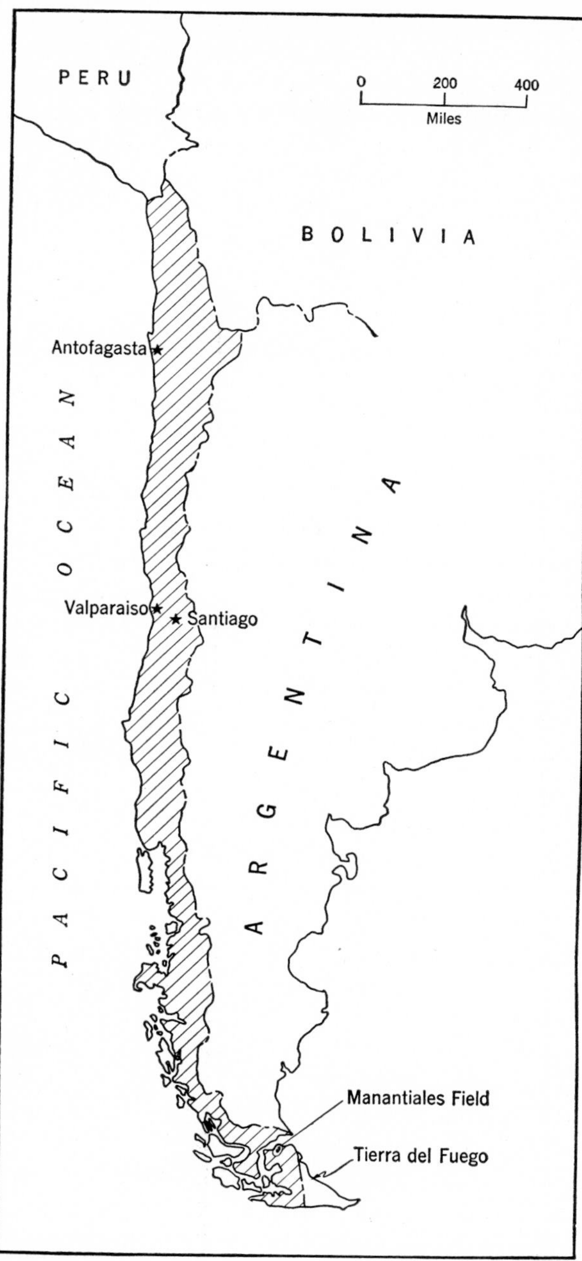

FIG. 195. Chile index map.

the northern tip of the island and the Straits of Magellan. Although it was discovered in 1945, it did not begin commercial production until late 1949, after the completion of a pipeline to the Straits. The oil is high gravity, about 42°. It has accumulated in an anticlinal trap that was mapped by seismograph surveys. The reservoir rock is a sandstone lying near the base of the Upper Cretaceous. Out of twenty-five wells drilled by late 1949, fifteen were successful oil wells and five were gas wells. In addition, one well that struck gas and distillate has been drilled on another anticline about 7 miles to the north of Manantiales.

EUROPE

Many sedimentary basins (Fig. 196) occupy parts of the European continent south of the Fennoscandian shield. Most are relatively small and as yet unproductive. A notable exception is eastern Europe, where the greater part of Russia west of the Ural Mountain front is floored by basin sediments. The largest basin in western Europe lies to the south of the Baltic, extending from the North Sea eastward across northern Germany into Poland. Of considerable importance as a source of oil is the arcuate sedimentary basin, lying beyond the convex front of the Carpathians, which covers parts of southern Poland, eastern Rumania, and northern Bulgaria. To the westward, across the Carpathians, is the Central Hungarian basin. Italy, Spain, France, and England are also occupied in part by small sedimentary basins.

Russia, producing mainly from the southern end of the great Russian basin, is the outstanding oil-producing country of the European continent. Rumania, the oldest oil-producing country in the world, is a poor second, and the eleven other European countries together produce but a fraction of 1 per cent of the world's oil (Fig. 197).

General References. L. G. Weeks, "Highlights on 1948 Developments in Foreign Petroleum Fields," *Bull. Am. Assoc. Petrol. Geol.*, Vol. 33 (June, 1949), pp. 1070–1095; *Oil and Gas Jour., Annual Review and Forecast Number,* Vol. 48 (Jan. 26, 1950); *Oil and Gas Jour., International Number,* Vol. 48 (Dec. 22, 1949); *World Oil, International Operations Issue,* Vol. 131 (July 15, 1950); Max W. Ball, *This Fascinating Oil Business* (Bobbs-Merrill, New York, 1940); O. Stutzer, *Erdöl* (Gebrüder Borntraeger, Berlin, 1931); H. Stille and H. Schlüter, "European Oil and Gas Occurrences and Their Relationship to Struc-

FIG. 196. Europe. Sedimentary basins and oil fields. *Co*

. G. Weeks and American Association of Petroleum Geologists.

FIG. 197. Europe index map.

tural Conditions," *Bull. Am. Assoc. Petrol. Geol.*, Vol. 18 (June, 1934), pp. 736–745.

Rumania [33]

Production statistics are no longer available for Rumania (Fig. 198), but according to estimates, the recent oil output for this country

[33] G. D. Hobson, "Roumania," *Science of Petroleum* (Oxford Univ. Press, 1938), Vol. 1, pp. 167–171; Ray P. Walters, "Oil Fields of Carpathian Region," *Bull. Am. Assoc. Petrol. Geol.*, Vol. 30 (March, 1946), pp. 319–336; Ionel I. Gardescu, "Geology of Natural Gas in Roumania," *Bull. Am. Assoc. Petrol. Geol.*, Vol. 18 (July, 1934), pp. 871–891; S. L. Mason, "Rumanian Oil Fields," *Bull. Am. Assoc. Petrol. Geol.*, Vol. 9 (January–February, 1925), pp. 145–157.

amounts to about 0.9 per cent of that of the world. This is roughly the equivalent of the production of Colombia or Arkansas for 1949. The exploitation of oil deposits in Rumania extends back many years. Oil was produced from dug wells as early as 1650, and in 1860 the first successful oil wells were drilled. Three years later oil was discovered in the Ploesti area, which has been the leading source of western European oil ever since. For some years now the trend in

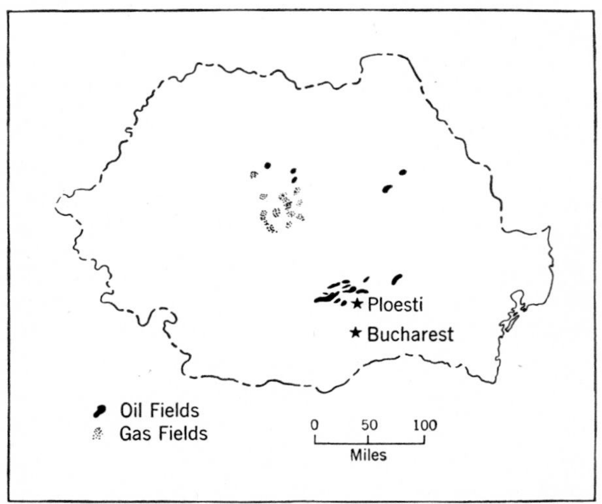

Fig. 198. Rumania. Oil and gas fields.

Rumanian production has been downward. No new fields of importance have been found since 1935. A discovery in Transylvania was reported in 1949, but the importance of this find is not yet known.

Topographically and structurally, Rumania is dominated by the Carpathian Mountains, which make a great arc to the eastward in crossing central Rumania from south to north. On the outside of the arc is a depressed zone forming the forelands of the Carpathian Mountain Range; within is the Transylvanian basin. The outer belt was a basin of subsidence during the Tertiary, in which 10,000 feet or more of sediment was deposited. During the late Tertiary, these formations were strongly folded. In addition, salt masses were intruded in many places (Fig. 199) into the Tertiary sediments in the late Pliocene or early Pleistocene. At least eleven of the many salt cores have been exploited for salt.[34] Furthermore, many of the oil and gas deposits are associated with the salt intrusions.

Gas occurs in the Transylvania basin, and both oil and gas fields occur in two districts lying in the outer arc. One of these districts, in the province of Walachia south of the Carpathians, produces most of Rumania's oil. The other district lies to the east of the Carpathians in the province of Moldavia. Although oil was first exploited in this area, the district is now of relatively minor importance.

The reservoir rocks of Rumania are sandstones, mostly of Pliocene age although some older Tertiary rocks carry oil, especially in Moldavia.

WALACHIA DISTRICT. This district has been referred to also as the Ploesti, the Prahova, and the southern sub-Carpathian district. In addition to providing the greater part of the Rumanian oil, it also produces five-sixths of that country's gas. In proceeding southward across the district, the intensity of the diastrophism as reflected by the oil-bearing structures decreases considerably. Close to the Carpathian front the folds are highly compressed with some overthrusting; farther south is a zone of salt-cored uplifts, with the salt either at the surface or at shallow depth, and toward the southern edge of the district the anticlines are simple but have deep salt cores which have been penetrated in some places. Trapping is anticlinal except in the zone of shallow salt cores, where the oil occurs toward the top of the Tertiary sandstones dragged up on the flanks of salt intrusions.

MOLDAVIA DISTRICT. The Moldavia area is sometimes referred to as the Bacau district, Bacau being the largest city. Tectonically, the district lies in the eastern Carpathian Flysch zone. This is a region of intense overthrust faulting, with the oil fields concentrated along the fault lines. The petroleum tends to accumulate in the structurally higher parts of the faulted, dragged, contorted, and even overturned and fractured reservoir beds. Oil seepages are fairly common.

TRANSYLVANIA DISTRICT. Oil seepages occur on the fringes of the Transylvanian basin, and most of the marginal folds have salt cores. The gas fields lie closer to the center of the basin, but the anticlinal traps in which the gas has accumulated also are assumed to have salt cores at depth. The reservoirs are Miocene sandstones. This district produces about one-sixth of the annual Rumanian gas output.

[34] I. P. Voitesti, "Geology of the Salt Domes in the Carpathian Region of Roumania," *Bull. Am. Assoc. Petrol. Geol.*, Vol. 9 (November, 1925), p. 1165.

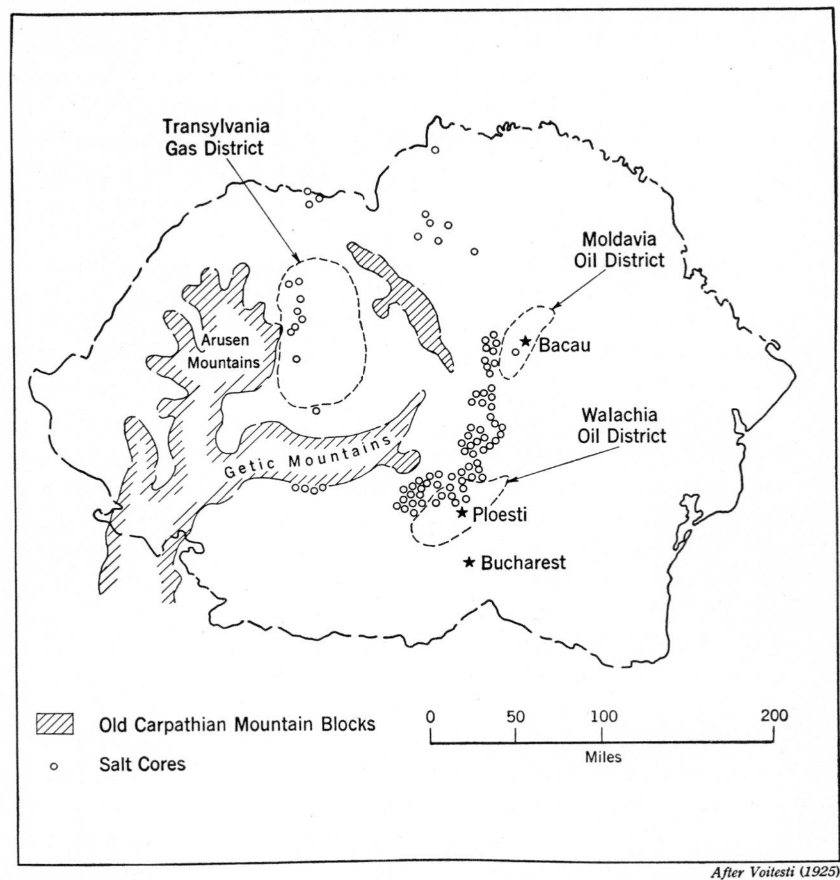

FIG. 199*a*. Rumania. Known salt-cored structures and oil and gas districts. *Courtesy American Association of Petroleum Geologists.*

Union of Soviet Socialist Republics [35]

Although production figures for Russia (Figs. 200–202) are no longer available, it is estimated that the oil fields of Soviet Europe and Soviet Asia produced about 7.4 per cent of the world output during 1949. This is less than the yield of California (9.8 per cent) for the same period. At one time Russia led the world in petroleum production,

[35] F. Julius Fohs, "Petroliferous Provinces of Union of Soviet Socialist Republics," *Bull. Am. Assoc. Petrol. Geol.,* Vol. 32 (March, 1948), pp. 317–350; G. D. Hobson, "U.S.S.R.," *Science of Petroleum* (Oxford Univ. Press, 1938), Vol. 1, pp. 165–166; I. M. Goubkin, "Tectonics of Southeastern Caucasus and Its Relation to the Pro-

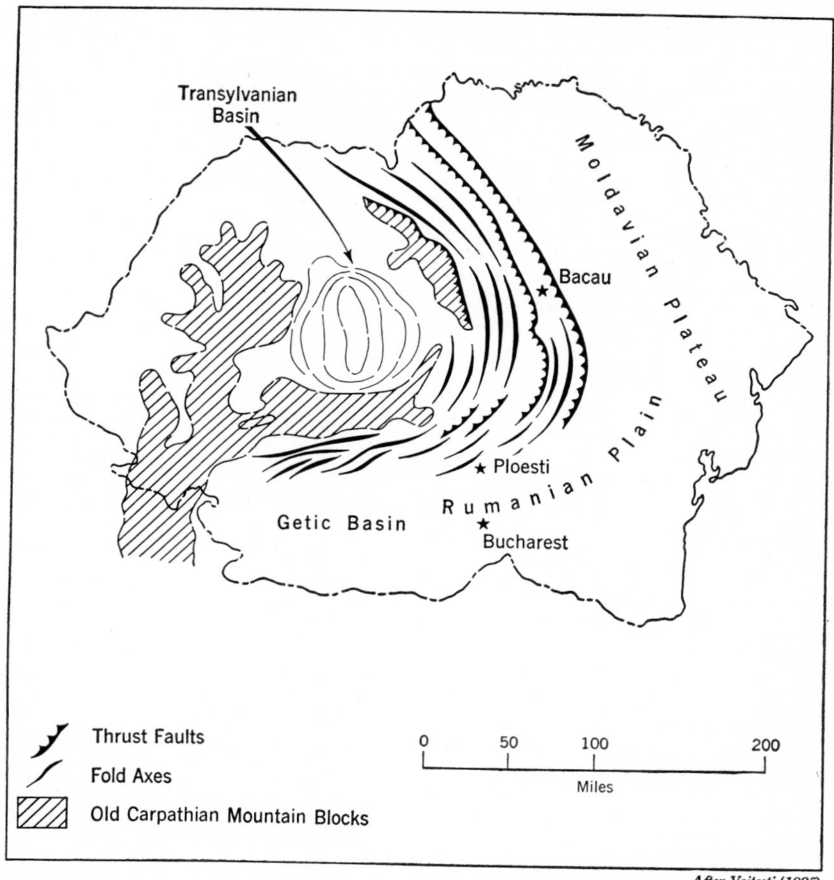

FIG. 199*b*. Rumania. Principal tectonic features. *Courtesy American Association of Petroleum Geologists.*

and for many years it was second only to the United States. Recently, however, this area has produced but little more than half as much oil as Venezuela.

Early exploration for oil and gas was aided greatly by the presence of oil seeps, asphalt deposits, gas seeps, and mud volcanoes, especially on the Apsheron Peninsula which juts into the Caspian at Baku, elsewhere in the Caucasian region, and in the Ferghana basin in Asiatic Russia. Ignited gas seeps gave rise to the cult of fire worship, and

ductive Oil Fields," *Bull. Am. Assoc. Petrol. Geol.*, Vol. 18 (May, 1934), pp. 603–671; Charles Bohdanowicz, "Natural Gas Occurrences in Russia (U.S.S.R.)," *Bull. Am. Assoc. Petrol. Geol.*, Vol. 18 (June, 1934), pp. 746–759.

temples built for this purpose on Apsheron Peninsula date from ancient times. Far back in history, seep oil was obtained from hand-dug pits. The first successful drilled well was bored in this area in 1871, and exploitation of oil deposits by means of wells has largely, but not entirely, supplanted production from surface pits. After the initial discoveries in the Baku area, the industry spread westward the

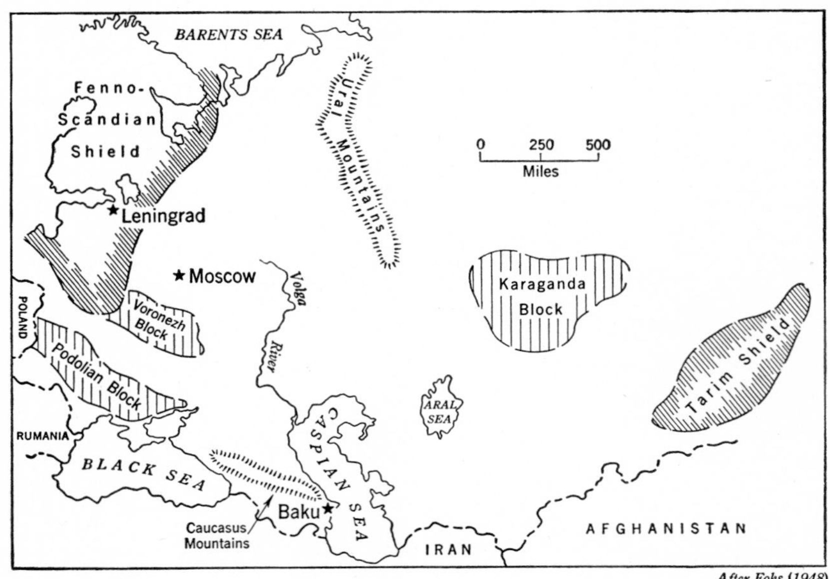

Fig. 200. Western U.S.S.R. tectonic map.

length of the Caucasus belt, northward nearly to the Arctic, and east across the Caspian to the Ferghana area. The occurrence of oil on Sakhalin Island in the Pacific will be discussed subsequently. With the decline of the Caucasian fields, the trend in recent years has been to intensify exploration for new fields in the Paleozoic reef limestones of the Ural-Volga district.

Most of European Russia is occupied by sedimentary basins. An exception is the west side, where the Fennoscandian shield extends from the Arctic to northern Ukraine. Extending eastward into south central Russia from the southern end of the Fennoscandian shield is the Voronezh block. Crossing the Ukrainian basin parallel to the Voronezh block is the Podolian block, another positive feature. Also the greater part of the land area between the Crimea and the Caspian is occupied by the east-west Caucasian Range of folded Paleozoic and younger sediments. North of the Caspian, and separating European Russia from Asiatic Russia, is still another positive feature, the Ural Mountains. The sedimentary basins of western Asiatic Russia are bordered by the Karaganda block, east of the southern end of the

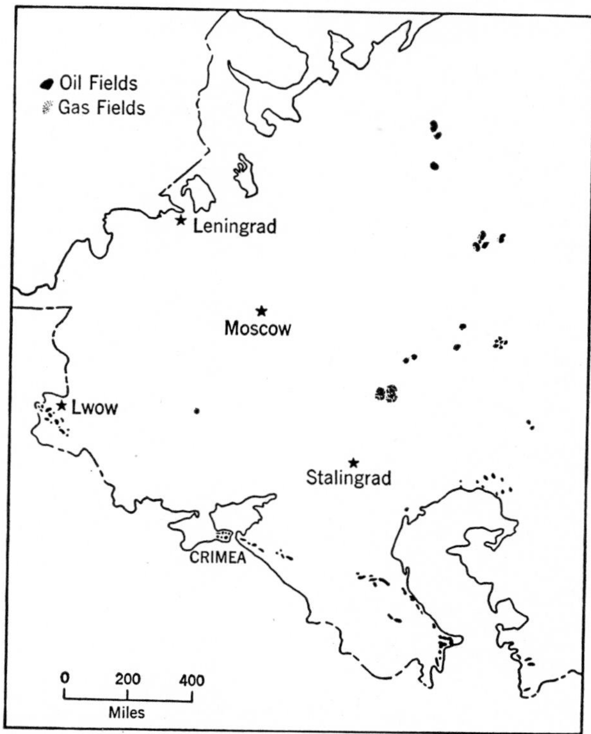

FIG. 201. European U.S.S.R. oil and gas fields.

Urals, and by the Tarim shield, which lies across westernmost China and eastern Afghanistan.

The major basin of European Russia covers all that country between the Urals and the Fennoscandian shield except for the Voronezh and Podolian blocks, the Caucasus Range, and some lesser ranges in the northern part of the country. Western Asiatic Russia east of the Urals is covered by a major basin, except for the Karaganda block and the Tarim shield and some mountain offshoots of these positive tectonic features. The western Asiatic basin connects with the Russian basin south of the Urals.

Local basins [36] occur either within the major basins or as tongues extending outward from these basins. Examples of the first type are the Moscow, Pechora, and east Russian basins in the northern part

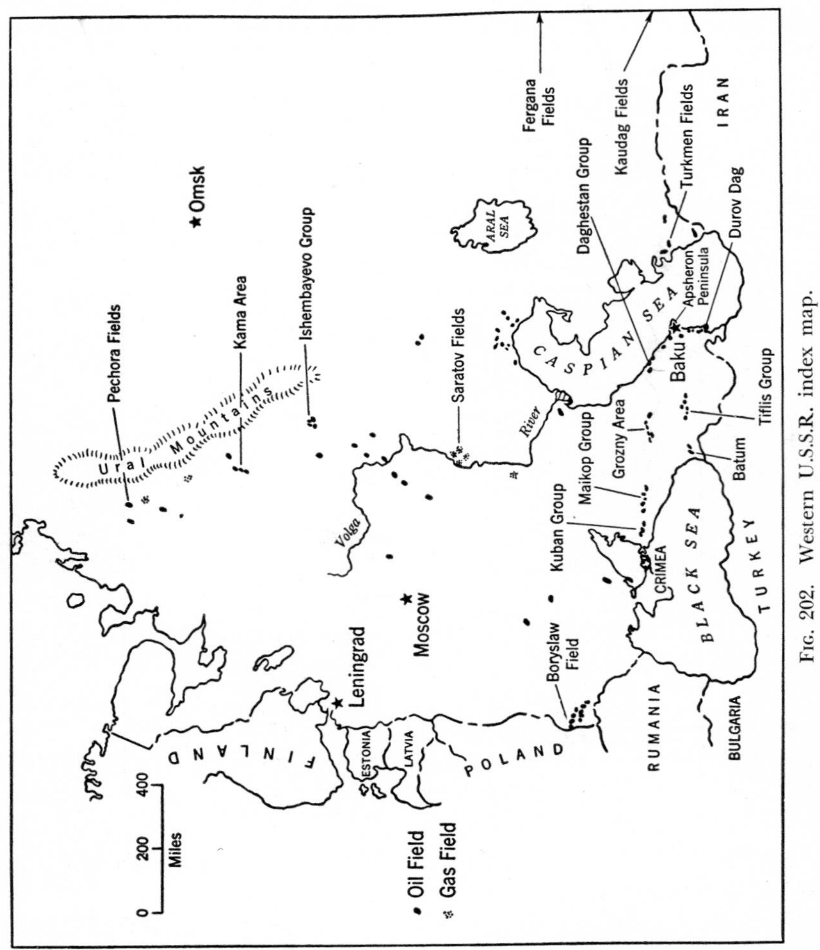

Fig. 202. Western U.S.S.R. index map.

of European Russia. The south Russian, or Ukrainian, basin is a tongue extending westward from southern Russia between the Voronezh and Podolian blocks. The elongate Kuban basin or syncline trends eastward from Crimea on the north shore of the Black Sea

[36] Arthur H. Redfield, "The Petroleum Resources of Russia," *Bull. Am. Assoc. Petrol. Geol.,* Vol. 11 (May, 1927), pp. 493–513.

along the north flank of the Caucasus to the Caspian and beyond into southwestern Asiatic Russia. At the eastern end of this depressed zone are the Ferghana and Turkmen tongues. South of the Caucasus in the province of Georgia and on the Apsheron Peninsula is the Kura River-Baku basin. Between the north end of the Caspian and the south end of the Urals is Russia's largest salt basin, the Emba.[37] Salt domes are also known, but with a lesser development, in the Ukraine basin and on the Arctic coast of Siberia.

Geographically and tectonically, the Russian oil fields can be separated into seven major districts (Fig. 200). These are, first and foremost, the Caucasian district, which includes all the fields between the Caspian and the Crimea on both sides of the Caucasus Range; the Carpathian district, acquired from Poland at the end of World War II; the trans-Caspian district of Asiatic Russia; the Ukraine; the Emba salt basin; eastern Russia; and northern Russia. Before World War II, the Caucasian district produced over 90 per cent of Russia's oil. The leading field outside this district was the Ishembayevo in eastern Russia, which annually accounted for about 3 per cent of the Russian production. During and since the war, the Caucasian production has decreased significantly. This was in part compensated by the acquisition of the rich Boryslaw and other fields in sub-Carpathian Poland. Also there has been an increase in production since the war in the Ural-Volga areas in eastern Russia and in some of the fields in the trans-Caspian district.

CAUCASIAN DISTRICT. The Caucasian district contains at least six producing areas. The greatest of these is Baku, on the Apsheron Peninsula, which extends out into the Caspian beyond the western terminus of the Caucasus Mountains. Proceeding counterclockwise around the Caucasus mountain core are, on the north side, the Daghestan, Grozny, Maikop, and Kuban-Crimea areas. Between the Black Sea and the Caspian, south of the Caucasus, are the Batum, Tiflis, and Durov Dag areas. The 90 per cent of the Russian production from the Caucasus district before World War II came mainly from three areas, Baku (75 per cent), Grozny (10 per cent), and Maikop (5 per cent).

The reservoir rocks in the Caucasian district are mainly Pliocene sands at Baku, Pliocene-Miocene sands in the south Caucasus areas, Miocene at Grozny, and Miocene-Oligocene at Daghestan, Maikop,

[37] C. W. Sanders, "Emba Salt-Dome Region, U.S.S.R., and Some Comparisons with Other Salt-Dome Regions," *Bull. Am. Assoc. Petrol. Geol.*, Vol. 23 (April, 1939), pp. 492–516.

and in the Kuban-Crimea area. The Tertiary basins surrounding the Caucasus Range have been subjected to severe diastrophic activity during and since the deposition of the later Tertiary sediments. In addition to overturned folds and overthrust faults, this belt contains diapiric folds in which the cores have flowed upward under pressure. This is the "piercing core" type of structure, which is common in salt basins but fairly rare in clastic rock areas such as Caucasia.

With the exception of the fields in the Maikop area, trapping in the Caucasus district has been anticlinal, as a general rule. Accumulation has taken place in the internally ruptured diapiric anticlines, in faulted anticlines, and, in less disturbed areas, in normal anticlines and domes. The prolific Baku district contains accumulations of all three types. In this area, which has been the mainstay of Russian production for many decades, the more shallow sands are approaching exhaustion, necessitating the exploration and development of reservoirs as deep as 9000 feet.

The regional structure in the Maikop district is monoclinal, and the oil has been trapped in sand lenses beneath unconformities. The richest accumulations occur where post-Middle Oligocene erosion carved valleys in the Lower and Middle Oligocene strata, which subsequently were filled with gravels and coarse sand of the basal Maikop (upper Oligocene and lower Miocene) formations. Thick deposits of these coarse valley-filling clastics yield prolific quantities of oil.

OTHER DISTRICTS. The recently acquired fields in the Carpathian district are described under the section on Poland. The trans-Caspian district includes three oil-producing areas. On the eastern shore of the Caspian Sea is the Turkmen group of fields, in which the oil is obtained from Pliocene sandstone reservoirs where they have been folded into anticlines. Trapping is also anticlinal at the west side of the district in the Khaudag and Fergana areas. Oligocene reservoirs produce in the Khaudag district and Eocene reservoirs in the more important Fergana area. Oil production to date in the Ukraine fields has been relatively insignificant. Accumulation has taken place owing to the presence of salt domes in reservoir rocks of Mesozoic age. Emba, at the north end of the Caspian, is a much more important salt dome district. Here the reservoir rocks are Jurassic.

The eastern Russian district extends from the Saratov area, which has Pliocene production, westward through the Volga region to the Ural area. The Volga and Ural fields produce from Permian carbonate rock reefs. This district appears to be the most active at the present time. The fields of the northern Russian district are small.

They occur in two areas, the Kama and, still farther north, the Pechora. Trapping is anticlinal. The reservoir rocks are Permian and Carboniferous at Kama, and Devonian at Pechora.

Miscellaneous European Countries

GERMANY (Fig. 203).[38] The production of oil in Germany during 1949 amounted to about 0.16 per cent of the world production. This was slightly more than that of New York state for the same period.

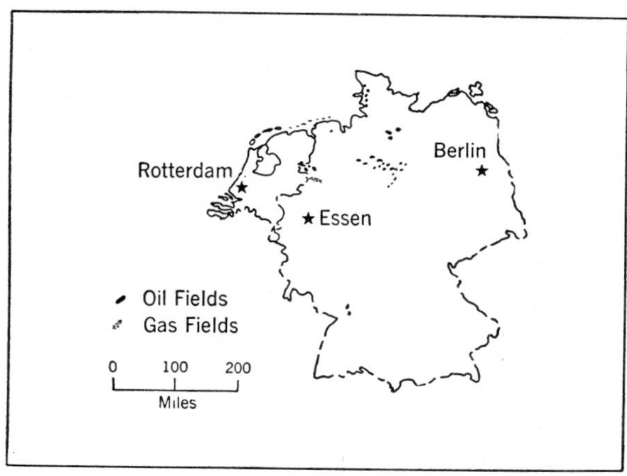

Fig. 203. Germany and Netherlands. Oil and gas fields.

Although oil has been produced in Germany since 1860, the greatest activity has taken place since 1935. Between that year and 1945, mainly because of Germany's desperate need for additional oil supplies, twenty-eight new fields were discovered. Discoveries have continued since the war; during 1949 nine new fields or field extensions were discovered, and the production was greater than it had been in the preceding year. While the war was in progress, three small fields were found along the Dutch border in the Emsland area. Additional discoveries have been made there since, and the greater part of the current German reserve is credited to the Emsland district. Two of

[38] S. E. Coomber, "Germany," *Science of Petroleum* (Oxford Univ. Press, 1938), Vol. 1, pp. 184–188; Frank Reeves, "Status of German Oil Fields," *Bull. Am. Assoc. Petrol. Geol.,* Vol. 30 (September, 1946), pp. 1546–1584; W. A. J. M. van Waterschoot van der Gracht, "Occurrence and Production of Petroleum in Germany," *Bull. Am. Assoc. Petrol. Geol.,* Vol. 16 (November, 1932), pp. 1144–1151; H. Stille and H. Schlüter, "Natural Gas Occurrences of Germany," *Bull. Am. Assoc. Petrol. Geol.,* Vol. 18 (June, 1934), pp. 719–735.

the discoveries made in 1949 were deep anticlinal accumulations in the old Hannover district, where practically all the oil found heretofore has been in piercement-type salt domes. The present trend is toward exploration beyond the boundaries of the salt-dome area, as at Emsland, and within the salt basin for non-piercement structures such as those recently discovered. The search for new deposits involves extensive seismic and other geophysical surveys, as well as core drilling and intensive geological studies.

Parts of three sedimentary basins extend into German territory, and a fourth, the Permian salt basin of Thuringia, is entirely within Germany. One basin, lying to the north of the Alps in southern Bavaria, has not produced any commercial oil as yet. Another, the Rhine graben, has produced a little oil, especially at Pechelbronn, which is now on the French side of the boundary. One field in the Thuringia basin, discovered while salt was being mined, has produced a little oil. With these minor exceptions, all the German oil is obtained from beneath the north German plain. Reeves [39] groups the fields into the following districts: Schleswig-Holstein, Oldenburg, west Hannover, north Hannover, and central Hannover. Formerly, more than four-fifths of the German oil came from three fields, Nienhagen and Wietze, in central Hannover, and Reitbrook, in the north Hannover district. During recent months, the Emsland area, which is in the west Hannover district, has produced over 25 per cent of the German output.

Practically all the older German production came from Lower Cretaceous and Jurassic formations on the flanks of salt structures.[40] The actual trapping has been due to the sealing of the dragged up reservoir beds by unconformities and faults. In addition to supplying most of Germany's oil for many years, the salt domes which underlie the Hamburg-Hannoverian plain have been the world's chief source of potash and have also furnished a large volume of salt.

The Emsland fields, on both sides of the German-Dutch border, appear to be beyond the zone of salt intrusives, and accumulation there has taken place largely in simple anticlinal folds, but in one recently discovered field, the Scheerhorn, accumulation is credited to a stratigraphic trap.[41] The oil in the Emsland district is obtained from

[39] Frank Reeves, "Status of German Oil Fields," *Bull. Am. Assoc. Petrol. Geol.*, Vol 30 (September, 1946), p. 1546.

[40] Lester S. Thompson, "Salt Domes Are Source for Almost Entire German Oil Production," *Oil and Gas Jour.*, Vol. 47 (Feb. 17, 1949), pp. 78–80.

[41] Anon., "Pickup in Germany," *Oil and Gas Jour.*, Vol. 49 (May 11, 1950), pp. 56–57.

a Lower Cretaceous sandstone, and gas is derived from a Permian dolomite some 2000 feet deeper.

FRANCE (Fig. 197).[42] The two principal sedimentary basins in France are the Paris basin in northern France and the Aquitaine basin in the southwestern corner of the country. The Rhine graben, a long, narrow trough of sedimentation, extends into northeastern France from Germany. Other small basins lie in southeastern France, especially immediately to the east of the Central Massif.

Most of the French oil comes from one field, Pechelbronn.[43] This field lies in the Rhine graben and has been operated under the German flag as well as under the French. The beginning of exploitation of Pechelbronn is dated differently by different historians, ranging from 1498 to 1813. Apparently systematic exploitation did not begin until 1735, and the first well was drilled in 1813. However, up until 1882 all drilling was for the purpose of exploring the reservoir ahead of underground development, and even as late as 1948, 44 per cent of the Pechelbronn output was still coming from underground galleries. Most of the oil has been obtained from Oligocene sands, but deeper pays of Jurassic and Triassic age have also been found. During late 1949 a well rated at 600 barrels daily, nearly two-thirds as much as the entire normal Pechelbronn production, was completed within the boundaries of the field in deep, highly cavernous, Triassic carbonate rock.[44] The sedimentary layers in the Rhine graben at Pechelbronn are cut by many faults, and these appear to be responsible for most of the trapping, although sand lenticularity may also be a factor in accumulation in the Oligocene reservoirs.

Considerable gas and a little oil are obtained from the Saint Marcet field in the Aquitaine basin of southwestern France immediately north of the Pyrenees. This field lies upon an anticline which is simple in the surface rocks but which develops into a highly disturbed diapiric

42 Daniel Schneegans, "Gas-Bearing Structures in Southern France," *Bull. Am. Assoc. Petrol. Geol.*, Vol. 32 (February, 1948), pp. 198–214; A. J. Eardley, "Petroleum Geology of Aquitaine Basin, France," *Bull. Am. Assoc. Petrol. Geol.*, Vol. 30 (December, 1946), pp. 1517–1545; Stanislav Zuber, "France," *Science of Petroleum* (Oxford Univ. Press, 1938), Vol. 1, pp. 193–195; Frederick G. Clapp, "Oil and Gas Possibilities of France," *Bull. Am. Assoc. Petrol. Geol.*, Vol. 16 (November, 1932), pp. 1092–1143.

43 René Schnaebele *et al.*, "Monographie Géologique du champ pétrolifère de Pechelbronn," *Mémoires du Service de la Carte Géologique d' Alsace et de Lorraine*, No. 7 (1948), reviewed by H. de Cizancourt, *Bull. Am. Assoc. Petrol. Geol.*, Vol. 34 (March, 1950), pp. 457–458.

44 Anon., "French Discovery Well Tests Six Hundred Barrels Daily," *Oil and Gas Jour.*, Vol. 48 (Nov. 3, 1949), p. 50.

fold at depth. Trapping is anticlinal. Gas condensate is produced from an Upper Cretaceous breccia or conglomerate, but the principal reservoir rock is a Middle Jurassic dolomite. To the eastward, a short distance inshore from the Mediterranean, is the Gabian field,[45] discovered in 1945 and virtually abandoned in 1949.

POLAND (Fig. 197).[46] The same sedimentary basin that occupies the convex side of the Carpathian arc in Rumania continues for 200 miles in a westerly direction across southern Poland. Similarly, the zone of highly disturbed rock next to the Carpathian front contains numerous oil seepages which were exploited by dug pits for many centuries before the drilling of the first oil well. Pre-war Poland contained three oil districts in this elongate basin of sedimentation. These are, from east to west, the Bitkow, Boryslaw, and Jaslo-Krosno. The middle district, Boryslaw, was by far the largest both in cumulative and current production. At the close of World War II, eastern Poland, including both the Bitkow and Boryslaw districts, was incorporated into Soviet Russia. This shift in the international boundary took with it 75 per cent of the Polish oil production.

The Bitkow and Boryslaw districts are in the Flysch zone of strongly thrust-faulted and highly disturbed strata. In this area are three overthrust sheets, one above the other, and oil is found in each one, chiefly in Oligocene formations. In the Boryslaw district Eocene and Cretaceous sandstones are also productive. The trapping is anticlinal, but the structure is so complicated that it is a considerable feat to locate a well at the surface that will be structurally high at the reservoir level. For example, in drilling through the overturned folds in one section of the Boryslaw field, "wells passed through, from top down, Upper Cretaceous, Lower Cretaceous, Eocene, Upper Cretaceous, Lower Cretaceous, Mio-Oligocene, and finally lower Oligocene." [47] The Jaslo-Krosno district, the only one remaining in Poland, is west

[45] Weldon Hill, "New Field in France Being Developed," *Oil Weekly*, Vol. 117 (May 28, 1945), pp. 46–48.

[46] Ray P. Walters, "Oil Fields of Carpathian Region," *Bull. Am. Assoc. Petrol. Geol.*, Vol. 30 (March, 1946), pp. 319–336; Hugo Burstin, "Polish Oil Industry—Today's Position, Tomorrow's Prospects," *Oil and Gas Jour.*, Vol. 46 (Jan. 1, 1948), pp. 26 *et seq.;* S. E. Coomber, "Poland," *Science of Petroleum* (Oxford Univ. Press, 1938), Vol. 1, pp. 177–183; K. Tolwinski, "Natural Gas in Poland," *Bull. Am. Assoc. Petrol. Geol.*, Vol. 18 (July, 1934), pp. 892–907; Charles Bohdanowicz, "Geology and Mining of Petroleum in Poland," *Bull. Am. Assoc. Petrol. Geol.*, Vol. 16 (November, 1932), pp. 1061–1091; Henry de Cizancourt, "Geology of Oil Fields of Polish Carpathian Mountains," *Bull. Am. Assoc. Petrol. Geol.*, Vol. 15 (January, 1931), pp. 1–41.

[47] Ray P. Walters, *op. cit.*, p. 325.

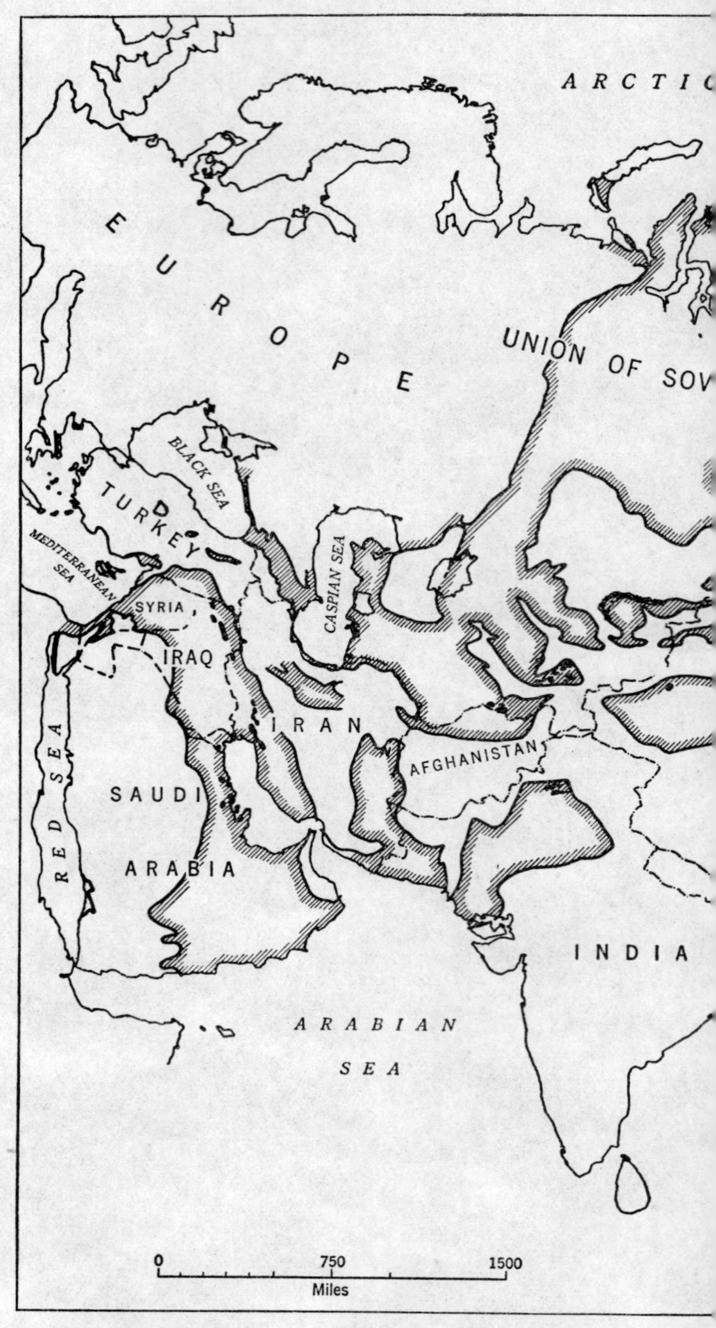

FIG. 204. Asia. Sedimentary basins and oil fields. *Courtesy*

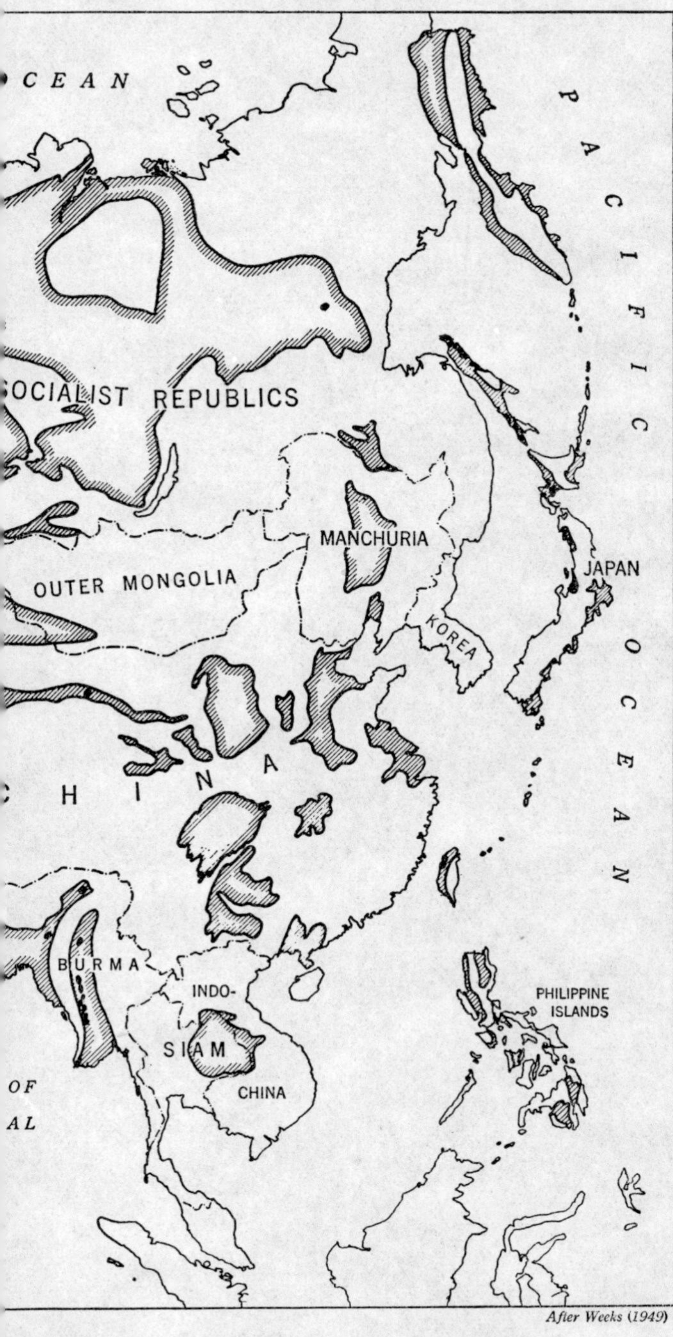

Weeks and American Association of Petroleum Geologists.

of the Flysch zone, and accumulation has taken place there in the more normal type of anticline. These fields are relatively small, however.

OTHER COUNTRIES (Fig. 197). Although there have been sporadic attempts to find oil in *Great Britain* [48] for some time, the first consistent production was obtained in 1939, when oil was discovered in the Midlands in Nottinghamshire. By 1944 Britain had more than 200 producing wells, mostly in the Eakring-Dukeswood field north of Nottingham but also in two other fields in the Midlands and one at Formby near Liverpool. These fields are all in the western end of the same sedimentary basin that produces in northern Germany and Holland. Another and much narrower basin crosses southern Scotland; one field was discovered there, but it is no longer productive. A third basin that crosses southernmost England contains no oil fields as yet discovered. The Nottinghamshire fields produce from faulted domes. The reservoir rocks are mainly Carboniferous sandstones. No new discoveries have been made since 1943, and although production is declining, it is being maintained to some extent by artificial water drive.

The Netherlands (Fig. 203),[49] entered the producing column in 1943 with the discovery of the Schoonebeek field on the Dutch side of the Emsland district of northwestern Germany. As of December, 1949, this field had seventy-nine pumping wells and was producing nearly 12,000 barrels daily from a Lower Cretaceous sandstone at a depth of about 2500 feet. This is currently the largest field in western Europe. The trapping is anticlinal. According to a recent report, another Emsland field, the Ruehlertwist-Ruehlermoor, has been extended into Dutch territory by a successful outpost well.[50]

The impetus of approaching war, and the war itself, led to extensive exploration in the Vienna basin of *Austria,* with the result that about eight fields were discovered between 1938 and 1944; it is reported that the Russians found two additional fields during 1949. Accumulation has taken place in faulted anticlines and buried hills. All the reservoir beds are sands and sandstones of Miocene age. The Vienna sedi-

48 H. R. Lovely, "Geological Occurrence of Oil in United Kingdom with Reference to Present Exploratory Operations," *Bull. Am. Assoc. Petrol. Geol.,* Vol. 30 (September, 1946), pp. 1444–1516.

49 W. Th. B. Reimering, "Schoonebeek, Western Europe's Largest Field, Now Producing 11,300 Barrels Daily," *Oil and Gas Jour.,* Vol. 48 (June 2, 1949), pp. 112 *et seq.*

50 Anon., "Outpost Extends New German Field into Dutch Territory," *Oil and Gas Jour.,* Vol. 48 (Oct. 27, 1949), p. 50.

mentary basin extends northward into central *Czechoslovakia*,[51] and two small fields have been developed on the Czech side of the border.

The Pannonian depression, a sedimentary basin of considerable size, occupies much of *Hungary* and northern *Yugoslavia*. The oil fields found in this basin are largely concentrated in southwestern Hungary and in the neighboring border zone of Yugoslavia. The largest field is the Lovaszi in Hungary. Trapping in this district is in anticlines, and the principal reservoir rock is a Pliocene sandstone.

Albania [52] has had small oil production since 1933 from fields in the vicinity of Devoli and Pahtoso. Accumulation has taken place in folded Tertiary reservoirs. A sedimentary basin occupies the Po valley and the Adriatic coast of *Italy*.[53] The upper Po valley contains four producing oil fields, of which the oldest and largest, the Valaezza, was discovered in 1909. The principal reservoir rock is an Oligocene sandstone. Considerable gas is also produced in the upper Po valley, but more than half of Italy's gas comes from the lower end of the valley, where the Quaternary deposits in which the dry gas reservoirs occur reach great thickness. Exploration for additional deposits in the Po valley has been active in recent years.

ASIA

The sedimentary basins which cover much of Asia are shown in Fig. 204. The largest basin is bordered on the west by the Urals. It covers most of western Siberia north of Outer Mongolia. The oil fields so far discovered in this basin are near the southwestern corner in the trans-Caspian area. Although in Asia, the trans-Caspian district is a continuation of the Caucasus district and was discussed briefly with the fields of European Russia. The second largest basin in Asia extends from the Mediterranean to the Arabian Sea through Syria, Iraq, western Iran, and eastern Saudi Arabia. The Persian Gulf lies within this sedimentary basin. Other basins occur to the east clear to the Pacific, especially in India, China, and Manchuria. The islands in the western Pacific off the Asiatic mainland are occupied by sedi-

[51] Stanislav Zuber, "Czechoslovakia," *Science of Petroleum* (Oxford Univ. Press, 1938), Vol. 1, pp. 175–176.

[52] Stanislav Zuber, "Albania," *Science of Petroleum* (Oxford Univ. Press, 1938), Vol. 1, pp. 172–174.

[53] Dahl M. Duff, "State Company Sets up Development Program for Upper Po Valley Area," *Oil and Gas Jour.*, Vol. 48 (Sept. 1, 1949), pp. 30–31; George O. Ives, "Po Valley Gas Vital to Italy's Fuel Economy," *World Oil*, Vol. 128 (January, 1949), pp. 200–204.

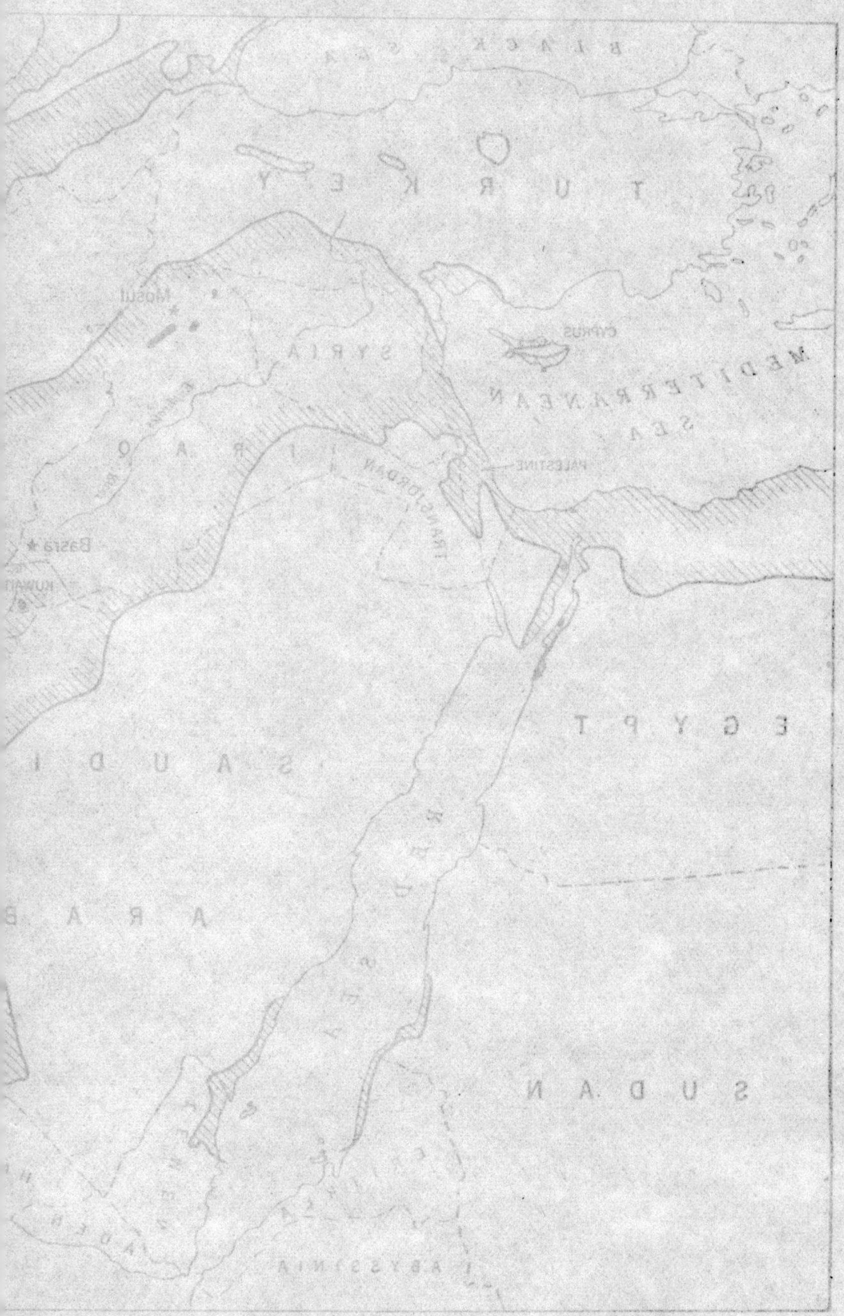

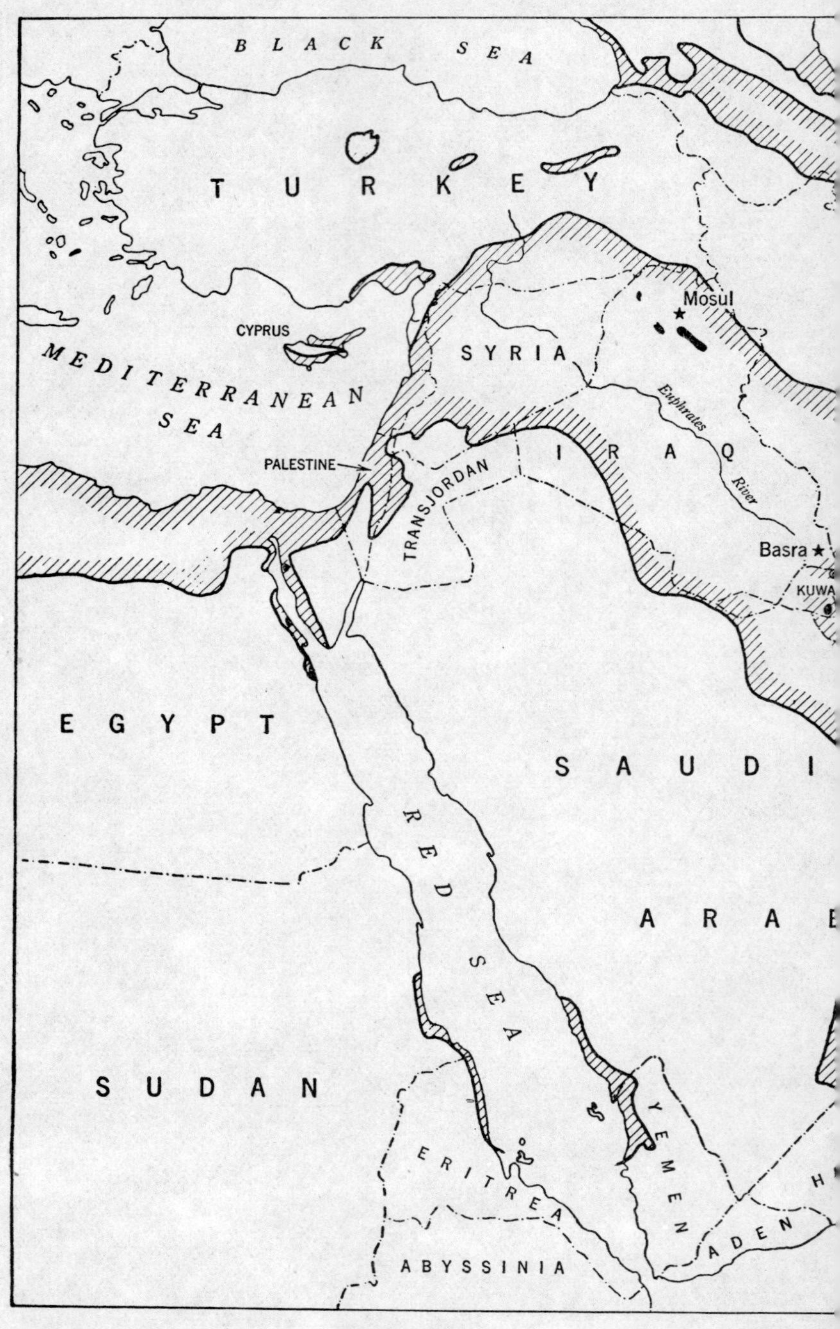

FIG. 205. Middle East. Sedimentary basins and oil fields. Co

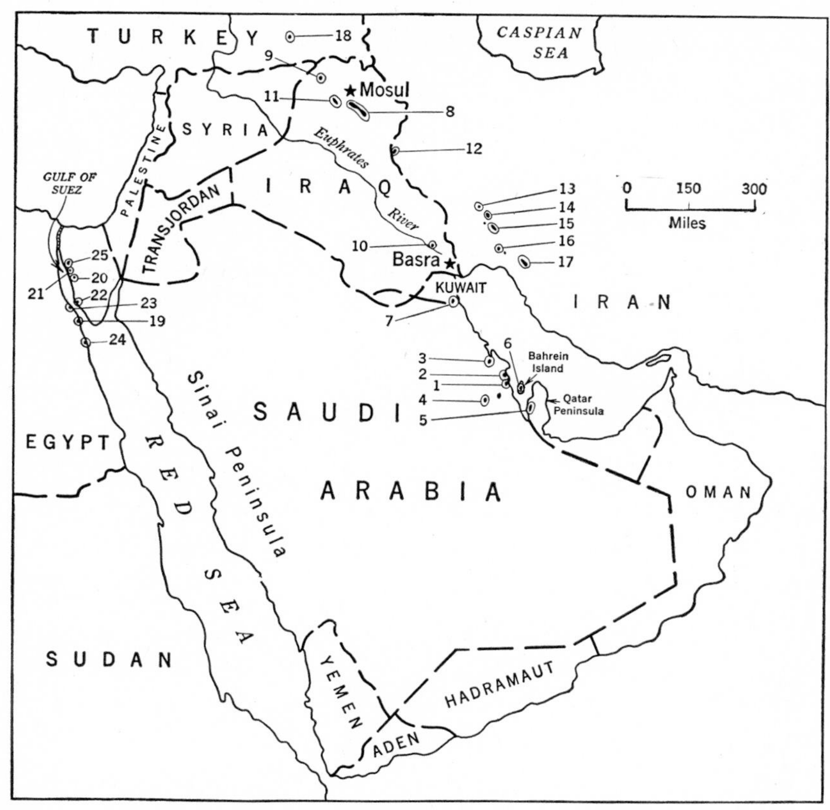

FIG. 207. Middle East index map.

Saudi Arabia fields

1, Damman oil field.
2, Qatif oil field.
3, Abu Hadriya oil field.
4, Ain Dar oil field.
5, Dukhan oil field.
6, Bahrein oil field.
7, Burghan oil field.

Fields in Turkey

18, Ramandag oil field.

Fields in Iraq

8, Kirkuk oil field.
9, Ain Zalah oil field.
10, Nahr Umr oil field.
11, Qaiyarah oil field.

Fields in Egypt

19, Ras Gemsa oil field.
20, Asl oil field.
21, Rasmataima oil field.
22, Wadi Feiran oil field.
23, Ras Gharib oil field.
24, Hurghada oil field.
25, Sudr oil field.

Fields in Iran

12, Naft-i-Shah oil field.
13, Lali oil field.
14, Masjid-i-Sulaiman oil field.
15, Haft Kel oil field.
16, Agha Jari oil field.
17, Gach Saran oil field.

mentary basins only here and there around the shores. An exception is Sakhalin, the greater part of which is underlain by basin sediments.

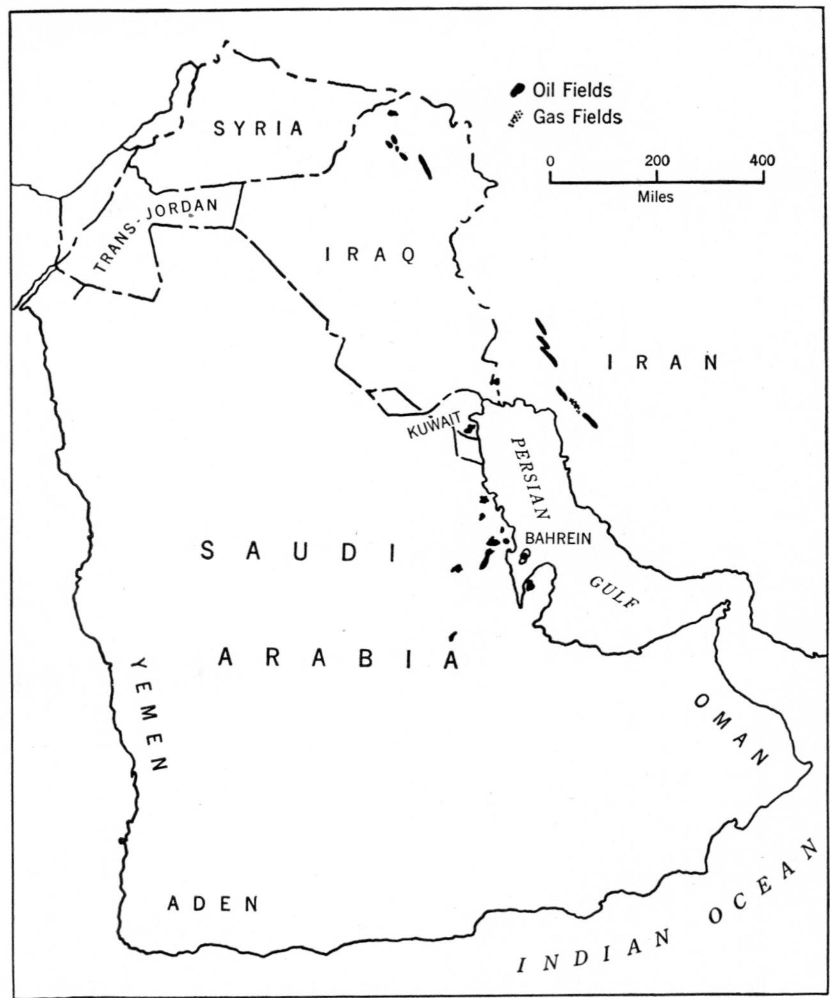

Fig. 206. Middle East. Oil and gas fields.

In terms of past production, and excluding the Russian fields of the trans-Caspian and Sakhalin for which statistics are not available, over 99 per cent of Asia's oil comes from the sedimentary basin of the Middle East (Figs. 205–207) and especially from fields lying within

. G. Weeks and American Association of Petroleum Geologists.

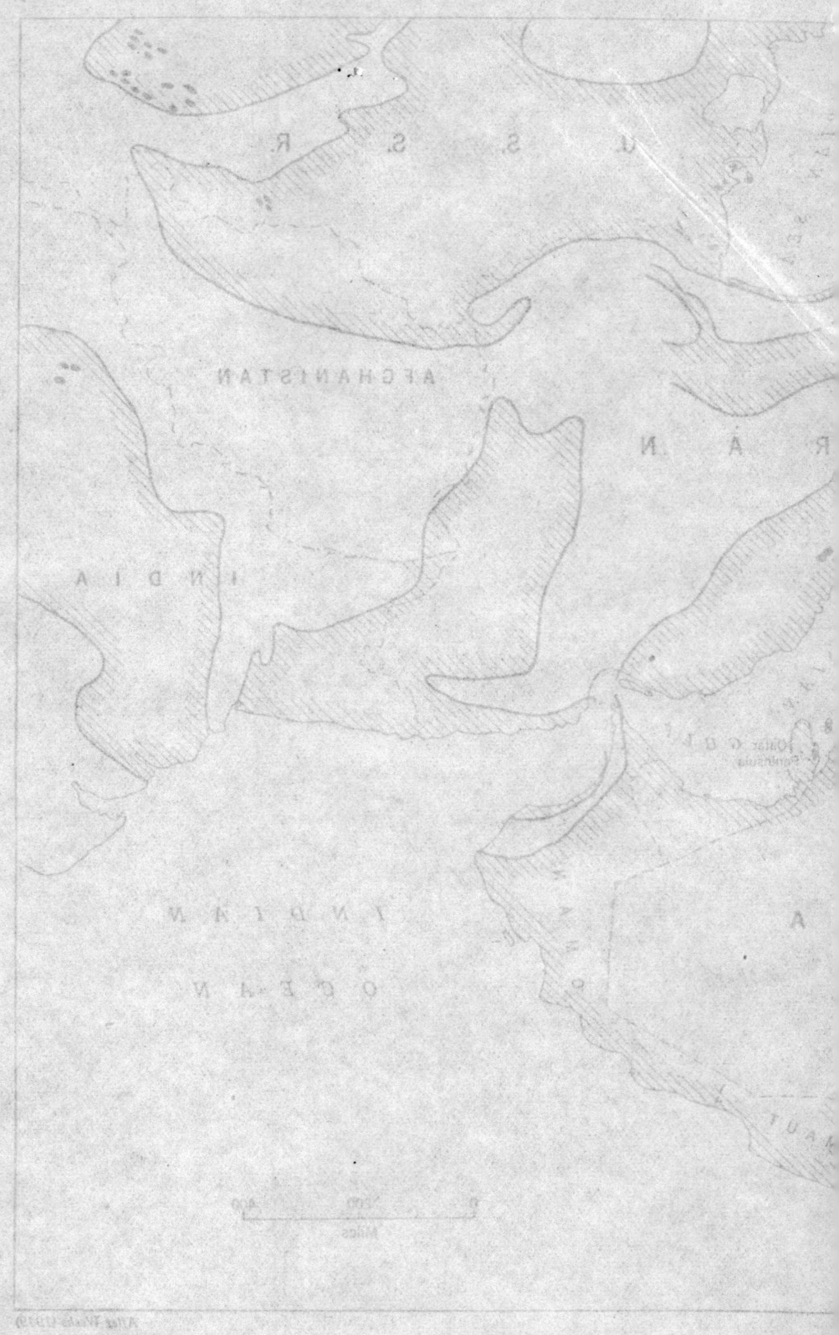

a few miles of the Persian Gulf and from islands out in the Gulf. The producing countries of the Middle East are, in decreasing order of output for 1949, Iran, Saudi Arabia, Kuwait, Iraq, and Bahrein. To this list shortly will be added Qatar. The remaining 1 per cent of the non-Soviet Asiatic production is scattered among India, Pakistan, Burma, China, and Japan.

General References. L. G. Weeks, "Highlights on 1948 Developments in Foreign Petroleum Fields," *Bull. Am. Assoc. Petrol. Geol.*, Vol. 33 (June, 1949), pp. 1103–1115; *Oil and Gas Jour., Annual Review and Forecast Number,* Vol. 48 (Jan. 26, 1950); *Oil and Gas Jour., Annual International Number,* Vol. 48 (Dec. 22, 1949); *World Oil, International Operations Issue,* Vol. 131 (July 15, 1950), *Arabian-American Oil Company, Summary of Middle East Oil Developments,* 2nd. ed. (1948); *Petroleum Times, Review of Middle East Oil* (June, 1948).

Saudi Arabia

The discovery well for Saudi Arabia was the well that discovered the Damman field in 1938. Eleven years later Saudi Arabia was producing over 5 per cent of the world's annual oil output. This was a little less than the Louisiana production; it was also considerably less than Saudi Arabia can produce as soon as more facilities for transportation to market become available. Two new fields were discovered during 1949, and exploration is continuing both on land and in the shoal areas offshore.

Western and central Saudi Arabia is an uplift area with granite and other pre-Cambrian crystalline rocks at the surface. Eastern Arabia, from the Iraq border to the Indian Ocean, is a part of the great Middle East sedimentary basin in which Mesozic limestones, which are now oil-bearing, were deposited in considerable thickness. This basin was continually sinking from the Permian through the Cretaceous.

The seven pools so far discovered in Saudi Arabia lie on the eastern coastal plain within a few miles of the shoreline of the southern Persian Gulf. Four of the pools were shut in during 1949, awaiting pipe-line outlets. Of the three currently producing, the Abqaiq field is the largest, with cumulative production of more than ¼ billion barrels of oil. The Damman pool, the first to be discovered, is the second in both cumulative and current production, and the Qatif field is third. By the end of 1949, the average daily production from these three fields totaled more than ½ million barrels of oil.

Windblown sand completely hides the surface structure at Abqaiq. This field was discovered by core drilling to the base of the Eocene formations.

The reservoir rock in all but one of the Saudi Arabia fields is the so-called Arab zone in a Jurassic limestone sequence. The exception is the Abu Hadriya field, the northernmost field so far discovered in this country, where the reservoirs are other Jurassic limestones about 3000 feet below the Arab zone. In all seven fields the trapping is anticlinal, and in one of the anticlines, the Damman, faulting is also present.

The Damman field is the result of accumulation in a nearly circular dome almost 4 miles in diameter in one direction and 3 miles in the other. This structure is readily recognizable at the surface. An inlier of Eocene rock is completely surrounded by a rim of Miocene limestone. The limestone is relatively resistant to erosion, and so the outcrop area is hilly. There is 300 feet of closure at the reservoir level. The oil-bearing limestones are separated by beds of anhydrite. The Damman structure shows a negative gravity anomaly and may be a salt dome. Thick beds of salt are known to occur within the Cambrian sequence in the basin which surrounds the Persian Gulf, where the Cenozoic and Mesozoic rock cover has been stripped off by erosion. Piercement salt domes are fairly numerous.

The Abqaiq field occupies an elongate anticline that has been proved over a length of 30 miles. It is 5 to 6 miles wide and has a closure of 1400 feet at the reservoir level. The Abu Hadriya field, 100 miles north of Damman, also may be a salt dome. This structure was located by a seismic survey. The Ain Dar field, discovered in 1948, had 250 feet of pay section in the Arab limestone in the first well drilled. The second well, which was equally good, was drilled 18,000 feet to the south of the discovery well.

Miscellaneous Persian Gulf Producing Areas

QATAR. The Qatar Peninsula extends northward into the Persian Gulf from the Saudi Arabia coast south of the present producing area. On this peninsula is the Dukhan anticline, which at the surface is 50 miles long, and up to 5 miles wide, and has some 300 feet of closure. It was discovered in 1940, and the first two wells flowed at the rate of 5000 barrels daily. Activity ceased during the war, and the seven wells that had been drilled by the end of 1949 were still shut in, awaiting completion of a loading station. The reservoir formation is

Middle Jurassic in age, probably the equivalent of the Arab zone of Saudi Arabia, and consists of four limestones with intervening anhydrite layers.

BAHREIN. Bahrein Island lies at the mouth of the bay between Qatar Peninsula and the mainland of Saudi Arabia. Its one field, which is also named Bahrein, produced 0.3 per cent of the world oil output during 1949. This is approximately the same as the yield from Indiana or Montana during the same period. Bahrein was discovered in 1932 and was the first field to be found in the southern Persian Gulf. Exploration was encouraged by the presence of a gas seep.

Accumulation at Bahrein has taken place in a "textbook" anticline which is striking from the air. The anticline is elliptical in plan, and an outcropping, resistant limestone of Cretaceous age has been eroded into a ridge that surrounds the field. Most of the rest of the island is the dip slope of this limestone. The reservoir formation is the same sequence of Jurassic limestones, with interbedded anhydrites which produce at Qatar and in the nearby fields on the Arabian mainland.

Kuwait

Kuwait is a triangular-shaped country bordering the west side of the head of the Persian Gulf. Iraq lies to the north and Saudi Arabia to the south. The one field so far found in Kuwait, the Burghan (Fig. 208), was discovered in 1938. During 1949 it produced 2.6 per cent of the world's oil, nearly that of the entire state of Kansas (3 per cent). This field is considered by many to be the world's largest known single oil accumulation. Estimates of its reserves range from 9 billion to 40 billion barrels. Even if it proves up to only the minimum figure, it will be the largest oil field so far discovered. The average daily production in 1949 from this one field was more than ¼ million barrels.

Accumulation in the Burghan field is anticlinal, and only a relatively small part of the probable total productive area has been tapped by wells as yet. As a part of the development program, twenty-four wells were drilled during 1948; all were flowing wells.

The crest of the anticline is marked at the surface by great tar and asphalt seepages. The reservoir rocks are Middle Cretaceous sandstones, and the productive section is about 1100 feet in thickness. Most of the wells are completed in two separate oil sands.

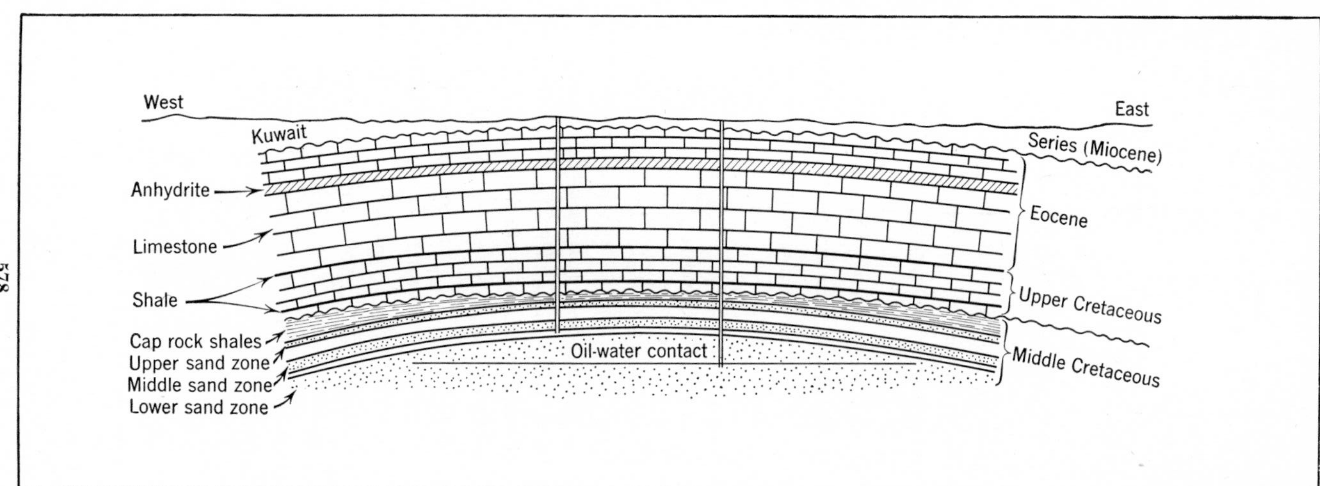

After Petroleum Times (June, 1948)

FIG. 208. Burghan field, Kuwait. Diagrammatic cross section (not to scale). *Courtesy Petroleum Times.*

Iraq [54]

The petroleum production for Iraq in 1949 was 0.8 per cent of the total output for the world during that year. This is approximately the same as the Rumanian production for the same period and a little less than that of the state of Arkansas. At present the production of Iraq is limited by pipe-line capacity; it could produce much more oil than it does. Furthermore, one of the two pipe-line outlets is through Palestine and has been closed down much of the time in recent years because of political disturbances.

Although the presence of oil and gas seeps were known to the ancients, the first successful drilled wells were not completed until 1927, when the Kirkuk and Qaiyarah fields were discovered almost simultaneously. The Ain Zalah field in the northern tip of Iraq was discovered in 1940, and in 1949 two discoveries were made on the Euphrates floodplain near the southeastern corner of the country. High-gravity oil was found at Nahr Umr, a few miles above Basra, and another well 25 miles to the south, between Basra and the northern border of Kuwait, struck high-pressure gas at a depth of more than 11,000 feet and had to be killed. Seepages have played an important role in every field discovery in Iraq, including the two latest ones on the Euphrates floodplain, except at Ain Zalah, where such surface manifestations of the presence of oil are absent.

All the reservoir rocks so far developed in Iraq are limestones. They range in age from Miocene to Upper Cretaceous. All the traps so far discovered in this country are anticlines.

The only oil field from which oil has been shipped as yet is Kirkuk in northern Iraq. This field is south of the Turkish border, with Syria on the west and Iran on the east. Seep oil has been refined at Kirkuk and used for lamp oil for over two centuries. However, the gas seeps 5 miles north of Kirkuk along the crest of the great anticlinal fold have had an even longer history. "Except during the war when it was extinguished as an air raid precaution, gas from the principal seepage has burned continuously since the time of King Nebuchadnezzar . . . at night the scene is one of impressive and exotic beauty: dancing whisps of bright blue flame, like brandy burn-

[54] C. T. Barber, "The Kirkuk Field," *Petroleum Times Review of Middle East Oil* (June, 1948), pp. 48–61; N. E. Baker, "The Structural Conditions of the Kirkuk Oil Field, Iraq," *Science of Petroleum* (Oxford Univ. Press, 1938), Vol. 1, p. 149; William T. Foran, "Oil from the Garden of Eden," *Petrol. Engineer,* Vol. 14 (October, 1942), pp. 85–95; G. M. Lees and F. D. S. Richardson, "The Geology of the Oil Field Belt of Southwestern Iran and Iraq," *Geol. Mag.,* Vol. 77 (May–June, 1940), pp. 227–252.

ing on a huge Christmas pudding."[55] The discovery well for the Kirkuk field was completed on Oct. 13, 1927. It flowed 4000 barrels a day from a depth of 780 feet. Two days later a second well came in which gushed at an estimated rate of 70,000 to 90,000 barrels per day. In spite of protracted shutdown periods during the war and marketing difficulties throughout most of its brief history, Kirkuk has already produced over 400 million barrels of oil. All the producing wells are less than 3500 feet deep. The gravity is 36°.

The trap for the Kirkuk oil and gas is an elongate anticline 60 miles in a northwest-southeast direction and 2 miles across. It parallels the trend of the Iranian mountain range to the east. The northeast flank of the fold is marked at the surface by a 200-foot scarp of Pliocene sandstone. The top of the fold is eroded into an anticlinal valley. The present producing area covers only about 80 miles of the potential 60-mile length.

Drilling has shown that the structure on the southwest flank of the fold, above the reservoir limestone, is complicated by overthrusting and flowage in the Miocene evaporite section (Fig. 209). This does not affect the structure in the reservoir limestones except to shift the crest of the fold some distance to the northeast. There is also cross faulting and an unusual amount of fissuring.

The main reservoir at Kirkuk is the Qarah Chauk group of limestones, ranging in age from Oligocene to Eocene. These rocks are reefs and nummulite and globigerina limestones. They are highly fractured, and the productive section averages 1000 feet in thickness. A high degree of interconnection exists between the various reservoir limestones. This condition even extends upward into the partially oil-bearing limestones of the Miocene Transition beds. No gas cap overlies the oil; it has probably been dissipated through centuries of seepage.

The Qaiyarah area near Mosul, northwest of Kirkuk, contains four oil fields, the first of which was discovered practically simultaneously with the Kirkuk discovery in 1927. The reservoirs are limestones of Miocene to Upper Cretaceous age lying at depths between 700 and 1800 feet. The trapping in each is anticlinal. Oil in the Mosul district is very heavy (16°) and has a high sulfur content. Because of the marketing difficulties involved with this type of oil, all four fields are shut in except for an insignificant yield for local consumption.

[55] C. T. Barber, *op. cit.*, p. 48.

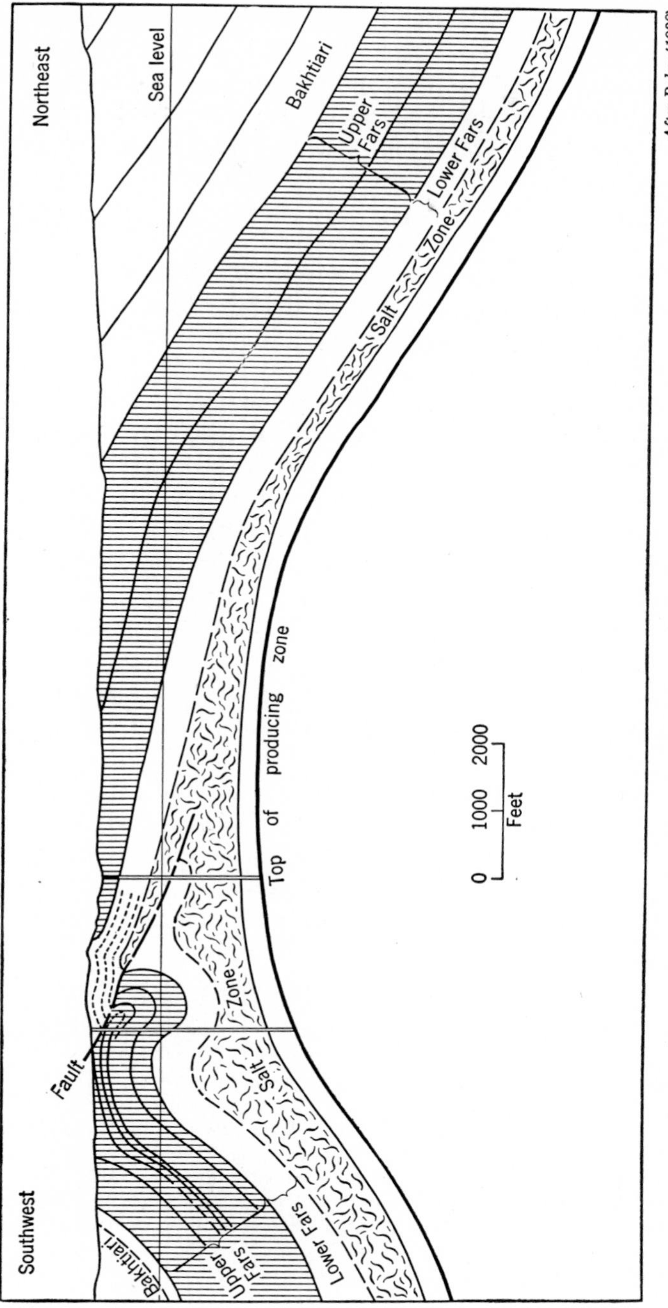

After Baker (1938)

FIG. 209. Kirkuk oil field, Iraq. Southwest-northeast cross section. *From Science of **Petroleum**; permission to publish purchased from Oxford University Press.*

The Ain Zalah field, near the Turkish border, has seven wells but no production as yet owing to lack of pipe-line outlet. However, the oil is much better than that of Mosul, with a gravity of 32°. It lies at depths between 5000 and 6000 feet. Trapping is in an east-west anticline, 8 miles long and 2 miles wide. The closure is approximately 1000 feet.

Iran [56]

During 1949 Iran was the fourth country of the world in oil production, with a yield of 5.9 per cent of the world output. This was a little more than that of the state of Louisiana for the same period. The first successful well in Iran was drilled in 1908 in what became known as the Masjid-i-Sulaiman field. Commercial production did not start, however, until 1911. The second field was discovered in 1923, and the newest field so far found was opened in 1946.

Most of the Iranian oil fields lie in a northwest-southeast trending belt immediately north of the head of the Persian Gulf in southwestern Iran. A much smaller district is in western Iran very close to the Iraq boundary southeast of Kirkuk. Both Iranian districts and the oil fields of northern Iraq lie along the northeast side of the sedimentary basin that extends from southern Turkey and Syria southeast to the Indian Ocean. Throughout this belt, the basin is floored with highly folded Tertiary strata. Differential erosion of the upturned strata has produced a rugged foothills topography. The main range, the Zagros Mountains, lies to the northeast. In this range, Mesozoic and Paleozoic sediments are exposed. The tectonic features and the geologic formations in the foothills belt strike northwest-southeast parallel to the trend of the Zagros Mountains.

Southeast of the oil fields, the Persian Gulf coastal plains and the Tertiary foothills contain over 100 known salt plugs.[57] These intrusive stocks have an average diameter of about 4 miles; most are circular or elliptical, although a few follow fault lines and are much more elongate. In most places, the salt itself does not crop at the surface, but its presence can be assumed by the presence of inliers of highly

[56] C. T. Barber, "Review of Middle East Oil—Iran," *Petroleum Times Review of Middle East Oil* (June, 1948), pp. 10–15; G. M. Lees, "The Geology of the Oil Field Belt of Iran and Iraq," *Science of Petroleum* (Oxford Univ. Press, 1938), Vol. 1, pp. 140–148; H. W. Lane, "Oil Production in Iran," *Oil and Gas Jour.*, Vol. 48 (Aug. 18, 1949), pp. 127–136; H. S. Gibson, "Oil Production in Southwestern Iran," *World Oil*, Vol. 128 (May, 1948), pp. 271–280; (June, 1948), pp. 217–226.

[57] G. M. Lees, *op. cit.*, p. 142.

jumbled older rocks. However, some of the salt plugs do crop out, forming mountains of salt that rise as much as 5000 feet above the adjacent lowlands. The time of salt movement has varied between the Upper Cretaceous and the Recent. Perhaps the most unusual feature about the Iranian salt plugs is that, although there is abundant Miocene salt in the stratigraphic section, the great salt intrusions appear to have had their sources in Cambrian strata.

The oil fields of Iran have much in common. They all produce from Oligocene-Miocene limestones, and in every one trapping is anticlinal. Every field so far discovered has had oil seeps or gas seeps, or both, at the surface.

The reservoir rock is the Asmari limestone, which ranges in age from Lower Miocene to Upper Oligocene. The producing zone is about 1000 feet thick. No appreciable production is obtained in drilling a well until a fissure is penetrated. For this reason, it was formerly thought that practically all the storage in the Asmari limestone was in crevices. It is now believed that most of the actual storage is in pores in the limestone, with fissures supplying channels for migration and egress. Apparently, as the oil is removed from the fracture system by wells, it is replaced by bleeding from the limestone pores.

The southwestern Iran district contains six oil fields and one gas-condensate field. The wells in this district average 10,000 barrels per day, and in one field, Agha Jari, the average per well is 22,000 barrels. Two fields, the Masjid-i-Sulaiman and the Haft Kel, have produced nearly a billion barrels of oil each, which places them among the first half dozen oil fields of the world in cumulative production. The Haft Kel field, which was not discovered until 1928, twenty years after the Masjid-i-Sulaiman, is now slightly ahead of that field in total output. The Agha Jari is third and the Gach Saran fourth in cumulative production. In average daily production during 1949, the first four fields were, in descending order, Agha Jari, Haft Kel, Masjid-i-Sulaiman, and Gach Saran.

Western Iran, southeast of Kirkuk in Iraq, has one producing field, the Naft-i-Shah, and another field nearby that is not producing.

There is a remarkable similarity in the character of the anticlines in which the oil has been trapped, not only in the southwestern Iran fields but also in the western Iran and Kirkuk fields. A cross section of the Kirkuk structure was shown above. The panel on page 584 (Fig. 210) shows similar cross sections for Naft-i-Shah in western Iran and for the Lali, Haft Kel, and Gach Saran structures in southwestern Iran. It will be noted that in every field the reservoir formation, the Asmari limestone, is folded into an anticline that may be asymmetric and even slightly overthrust on the southwest flank. However,

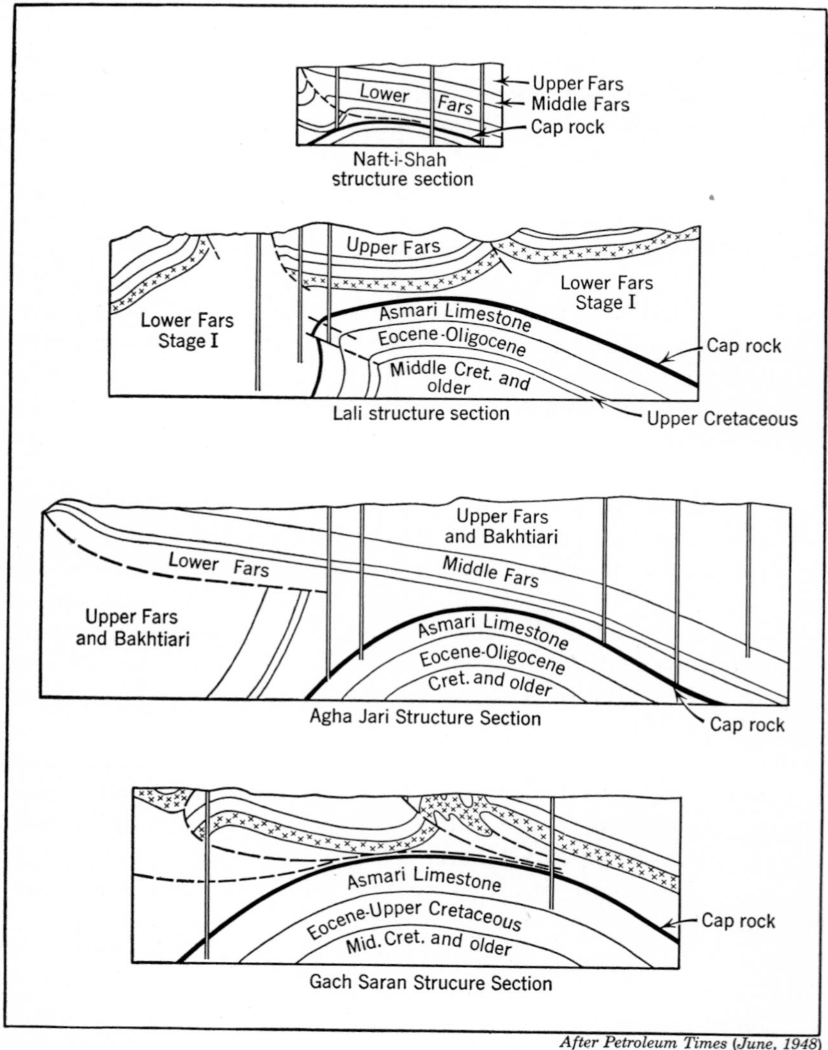

After Petroleum Times (June, 1948)

Fig. 210. Iran oil fields. Panel of transverse structure sections. *Courtesy Petroleum Times.*

the overlying lower Fars (Miocene) evaporite-containing sediment is strongly folded and thrust-faulted, and this diastrophism has been accompanied by plastic flowage of the salt layers. The still younger Fars rocks, and overlying Pleistocene sediments, are more competent, and the aptly termed "turbulence" of the lower Fars is not repeated in these relatively rigid younger formations. The intensity of the deformation in the lower Fars sediments is at the maximum on the southwest flank.

The Agha Jari field, currently the leading field in Iran with a daily production of $\frac{1}{4}$ million barrels of oil, lies on an anticline more than 50 miles long. The Agha Jari gas seep is 3 miles southwest of the anticlinal axis in the Asmari limestone, owing to escape by way of a low-angle overthrust fault plane.

Miscellaneous Asiatic Producing Countries

TURKEY.[58] Turkey's one oil field to date is the Ramandag, near the southeastern corner of Asiatic Turkey (Fig. 207). It is but a short distance north of the borders of Iraq and Syria, and it is in the same sedimentary basin as the other Middle Eastern oil fields. The nearest production is in the Ain Zalah field in northernmost Iraq.

The first successful well in the Ramandag area was drilled in 1940, but water soon came into the bore hole in such abundance that production ceased. Continued attempts to develop the field became successful in 1947, and production was resumed in 1948. By the end of 1949, four successful wells had been drilled to depths between 4400 and 4500 feet. The oil is heavy (15° to 20°). Until a pipe line is constructed to the Mediterranean coast, only enough oil is produced to satisfy the local demand. The present development of the field indicates a potential production of 3000 barrels daily. However, the Ramandag anticline, in which accumulation has taken place, is about 40 miles long and 7 miles wide. At the present time, an area of only about 4 square miles on this structure has been proven. The reservoir rock is the topmost section of an Upper Cretaceous limestone.

PAKISTAN (Fig. 211).[59] Oil is produced in the Punjab district of Pakistan, formerly northwest India. The yield during 1949 was

[58] Anon., "Turkey Schedules Ten Wells in Ramandag Field for 1950," *Oil and Gas Jour.*, Vol. 48 (Jan. 5, 1950), pp. 68–69.

[59] E. S. Pinfold, "Northwest India," *Science of Petroleum* (Oxford Univ. Press, 1938), Vol. 1, p. 138; D. Dale Condit, "Natural Gas and Oil in India," *Bull. Am. Assoc. Petrol. Geol.*, Vol. 18 (March, 1934), pp. 283–314.

0.02 per cent of the total world output. This was less than the Indian production but considerably more than that of Burma during the same period.

The Pakistan oil fields occur out in front of the Himalayan cordillera, where the diastrophism has been much less intense. The oil

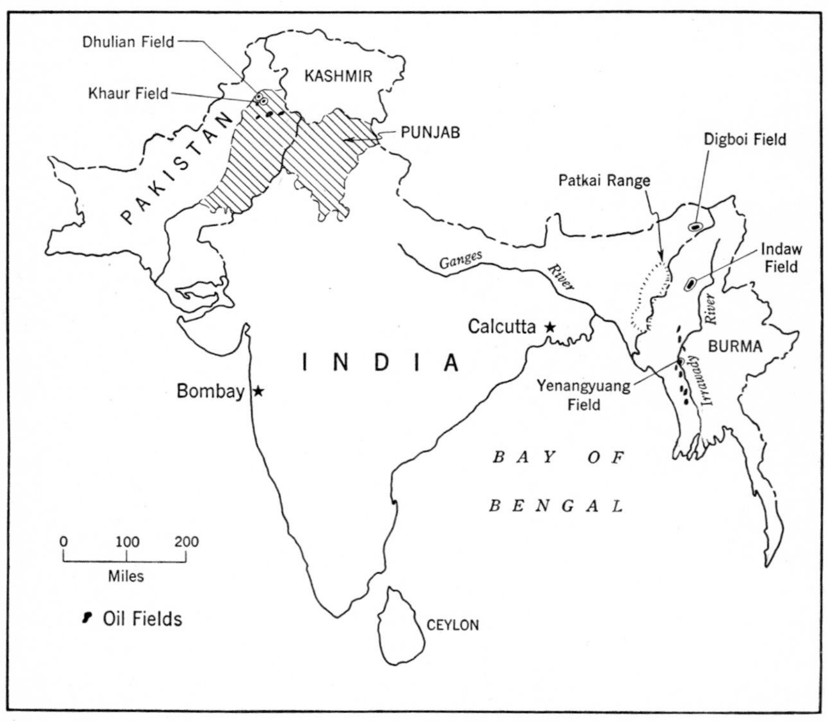

Fig. 211. Pakistan-India-Burma index map.

has been trapped in anticlines. Although seeps are common in Pakistan, the first successful well, which discovered the Khaur field, was not drilled until 1915. Here the oil occurs in fissures in an Upper Tertiary sandstone between the surface and depths below 5000 feet. Deeper drilling uncovered oil in the underlying Eocene limestone also. Twenty years after the Khaur discovery, oil was found in the Dhulian anticline 10 miles to the southwest. Production at Dhulian is largely from the Eocene limestone. Two more Eocene limestone fields were discovered in the Punjab district between 1944 and 1946, but the oil is considerably heavier than it is at Dhulian.

INDIA (Fig. 211).[60] The only active producing area in what is left of India is the Digboi field, which is currently producing a little more

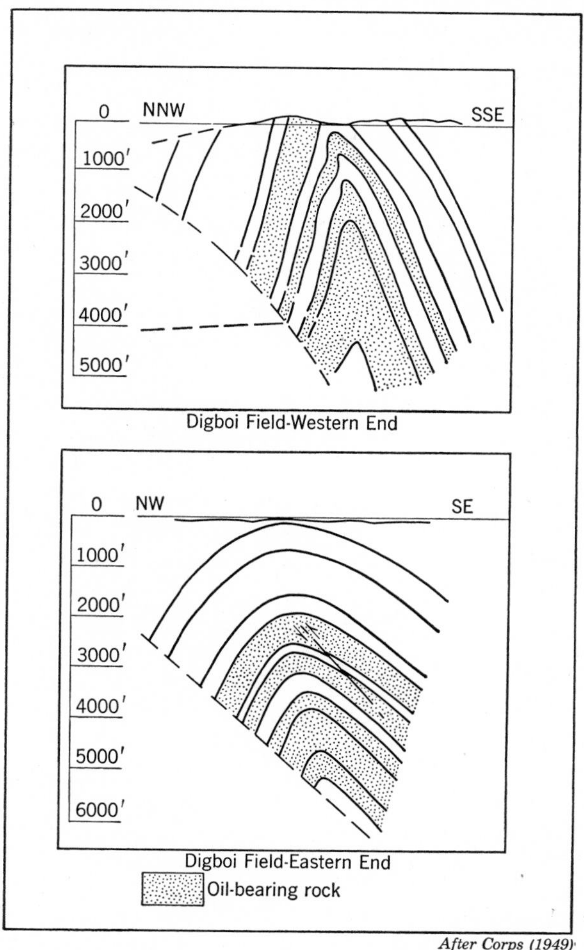

FIG. 212. Digboi oil field, India. Cross sections. *Courtesy American Association of Petroleum Geologists.*

than 5000 barrels daily and which has produced about 42 million barrels since its discovery in 1890. The Digboi daily production is nearly three times that of the fields in the Punjab district of Pakistan.

[60] E. V. Corps, "Digboi Oil Field, Assam," *Bull. Am. Assoc. Petrol. Geol.*, Vol. 33 (January, 1949), pp. 1–21; G. W. Lepper and P. Evans, "Burma and Assam," *Science of Petroleum* (Oxford Univ. Press, 1938), Vol. 1, pp. 133–136; D. Dale Condit, *op. cit.*

Digboi is located at the north end of the western of the two basins that lie at the head of the Bay of Bengal. The eastern basin is in Burma. An uplift area, which includes the Patkoi Range at the north end, separates the basins. Accumulation at Digboi has taken place in an elongate faulted anticline. Trapping has occurred in the upfold on the overthrust block (Fig. 212). The reservoir rocks are Miocene sandstones.

BURMA (Fig. 211).[61] Even by the end of 1949, the oil fields of Burma had not yet recovered from the ravages of war. Only about 500 barrels of oil daily are being produced in this country, whereas two of the leading fields together produced over 20,000 barrels of oil daily before the war.

The sedimentary basin in which the oil fields of Burma lie is very elongate in a northerly direction from the Bay of Bengal. It is also a topographic trough, with mountain ranges on both sides and the valley of Irrawaddy River occupying the central part. The Irrawaddy basin has been divided into three subsidiary basins, north, central, and south. The one field in the north basin, the Indaw, was discovered in 1918. The central basin contains eight fields, whose discovery dates range from 1889 to 1919. Among these are the largest of the Burmese oil fields. The south basin contains three fields discovered between 1922 and 1928. All produce a moderately light oil (36°) from Miocene and Oligocene sandstones. The Yenangyaung field, in the central basin, has from fifty to sixty separate reservoir sands, of which from ten to fifteen may be penetrated by a single well. Most of the oil produced in Burma has been trapped in anticlinal folds. Some of the anticlines are faulted.

CHINA (Fig. 213).[62] Scattered across the vast interior of China are several sedimentary basins (Fig. 204) in which a considerable thickness of sedimentary rock has accumulated. Three additional basins lie along the China coast, and still another occupies the western half of the island of Formosa. Although oil has been obtained from a number of small scattered fields in China in the past, the only commercial oil field today is the Yumen (Laochunmiao) field in Kansu province. Estimates of the production of this field range from 1000

[61] G. W. Lepper and P. Evans, *op. cit.;* L. Dudley Stamp, "Natural Gas Fields of Burma," *Bull. Am. Assoc. Petrol. Geol.,* Vol. 18 (March, 1934), pp. 315–326; H. R. Tainsh, "Tertiary Geology and Principal Oil Fields of Burma," *Bull. Am. Assoc. Petrol. Geol.,* Vol. 34 (May, 1950), pp. 823–855.

[62] K. C. Lu, "Post-War Progress in China's Northwestern Oil Field," *World Oil,* Vol. 128 (July, 1948), pp. 205–208; Martin J. Gavin, "Petroleum in Kansu Province, China," *Petrol. Engineer,* Vol. 17 (October, 1945), pp. 181–184.

to 2000 barrels daily, and the cumulative production since discovery in 1939 is approximately 3 million barrels. This field has produced about 0.02 per cent of the world's annual output in recent years, approximately the same as the production for Bolivia and Pakistan.

The discovery well at Yumen found oil in Tertiary sand at a depth of 460 feet. Subsequently, it was learned that the oil-bearing section

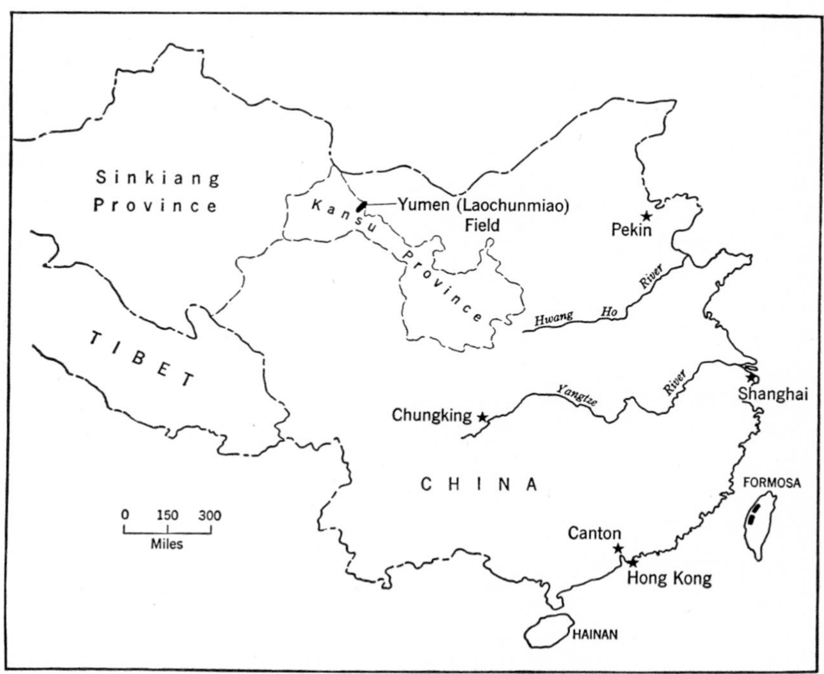

FIG. 213. China index map.

extends from 460 feet to about 3000 feet, but most wells are completed in the *L* sand, between 1400 and 1650 feet deep. The average sand thickness is 85 feet. The field is on a high plateau, with elevations ranging from 7800 to 8500 feet. Accumulation has taken place in a faulted asymmetric anticline.

Seven small fields, which have produced mainly gas, were discovered in western Formosa between 1904 and 1940. The estimated production of liquid hydrocarbons from this district at the present time is about 50 barrels per day. This figure includes the casinghead gasoline, a by-product of the gas production. Trapping is anticlinal; the folds tend to parallel the long axis of the island.

JAPAN (Fig. 214).[63] During 1949 the average daily production of petroleum in Japan was a little less than 4000 barrels. For the year this amounted to 0.04 per cent of the world output, or about half that of the state of West Virginia. Production of oil from dug wells began in Niigata Prefecture in 1874, and the first commercial exploitation by drilled wells began in 1891. In March of 1946 the Japanese Islands contained 50 fields and 4190 producing wells.[64]

The Japanese sedimentary basins (Fig. 204) lie along the southeastern and northwestern coasts of Honshu and on both the eastern and western sides of Hokkaido Island. None of these basins extends very far inland, and consequently the percentage of favorable territory for oil and gas occurrence is relatively small. All the reservoirs so far developed are Tertiary sandstones, but the deeper Cretaceous may also be oil-bearing.

The oil fields occur in the basins on the Japan Sea side of the island chain; the basins on the Pacific side are, in the main, not yet productive. The fields are in five prefectures, with the largest concentration in Akita Prefecture on the west side of northern Honshu. Here is the Yabase field, which is currently producing about 35 per cent of the total Japanese output. Two of the fields in Niigata Prefecture, the Niitsu and the Nishiyama, are, however, larger in cumulative production than Yabase. The Niigata district lies to the south of Akita in west central Honshu. The third prefecture in number of oil fields is Hokkaido. A few fields have also been found in Yamagata Prefecture and one in Shizuoka. With the exception of Yabase, most producing fields in Japan are completely drilled up and approaching depletion.

The Yabase structure[65] is a gentle anticline with a larger than usual gathering area. So far, twelve producing zones, lying between depths of 300 and 6275 feet, have been found in this field. Until 1949 most of the Yabase oil came from Zone VII at a depth of 3400 feet, but in that year a well drilled into Zone VIII flowed 272 barrels per day from a depth of 3800 feet. Later two new reservoirs were found beneath Zone VIII with one well (drilled in January, 1950) flowing

[63] Leo W. Stach, "Petroleum Exploration and Production in Western Pacific During World War II," *Bull. Am. Assoc. Petrol. Geol.*, Vol. 31 (August, 1947), pp. 1384–1403; Yoshinosuki Chitani, "Petroleum Resources of Japan," *Bull. Am. Assoc. Petrol. Geol.*, Vol. 18 (July, 1934), pp. 908–924.

[64] C. M. Pollock and L. W. Stach, "Production and Resources of Petroleum in Japan," *Bull. Am. Assoc. Petrol. Geol.*, Vol. 31 (January, 1947), pp. 156–158.

[65] Anon., "New Find in Japan," *Oil and Gas Jour.*, Vol. 48 (Dec. 1, 1949), pp. 47–48.

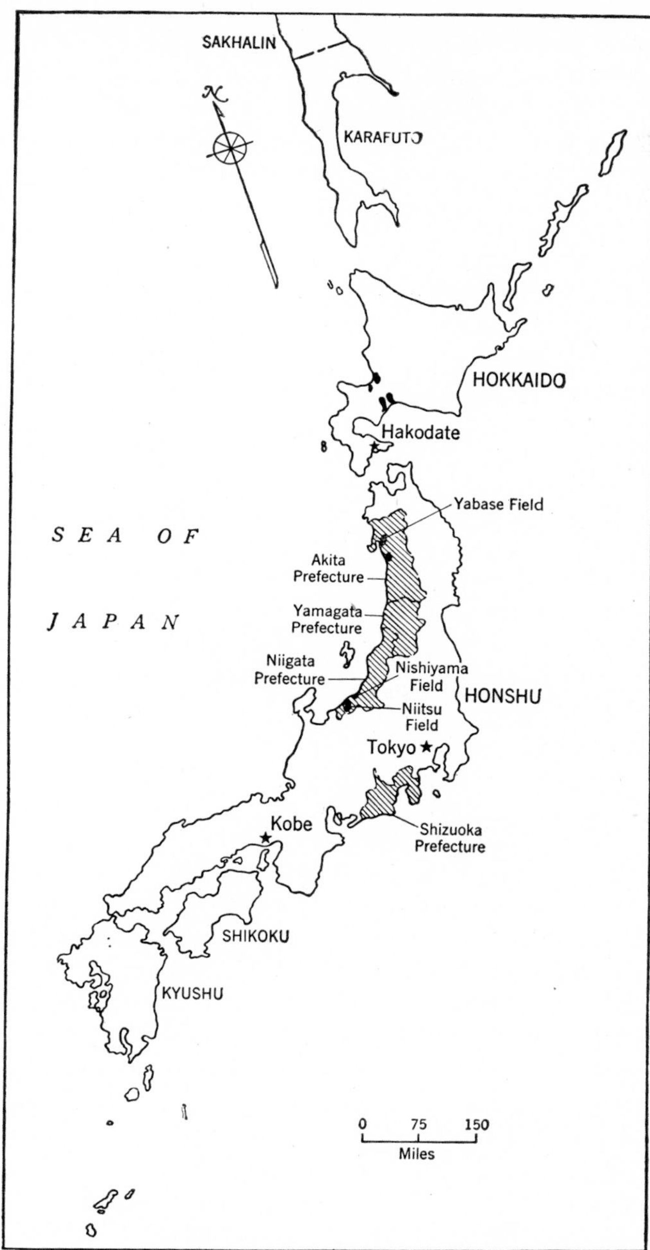

Fig. 214. Japan index map.

2000 barrels daily from a depth of 6275 feet. By the latter part of 1949, about one hundred geologists and geophysicists were engaged in the search for new oil deposits to replenish the almost exhausted Japanese reserves.

SAKHALIN (Fig. 214).[66] Before World War II, Japan owned the southern half (Karafuto) of Sakhalin, and Russia owned the northern half. When attempts to find oil in Karafuto were unavailing, the Japanese leased a part of northern Sakhalin. This area produced about 4 million barrels in 1940, but the current production is not known. From ten to twelve oil fields have been discovered, but most of the production has come from four fields. The district is about 25 miles wide and 250 miles long, extending south from the peninsula at the north end of Sakhalin Island. Unlike the Japanese Islands to the south, the greater part of Sakhalin is occupied by a sedimentary basin (Fig. 204). The oil district also differs from those to the south in that it lies on the Pacific rather than the interior sea side of the island. The anticlines tend to parallel the coast line; the folded structure is reflected, to some extent, in the topography of the tundra plain. Three of the fields apparently occupy local nodes along the crest of a single anticline, 150 miles long. All the known production to date has come from more than a dozen separate but shallow Miocene sandstone reservoirs. No deep tests were attempted by the Japanese during their period of operation. The Tertiary section may be as much as 30,000 feet thick.

AFRICA

Much the greater part of Africa is underlain by ancient crystalline rock. However, around the edges of the continent are a number of sedimentary basins that extend for varying distances inland (Fig. 215). The largest of these crosses the northern end of the continent from the head of the Red Sea to eastern Morocco. This is the only one of the African basins currently producing any oil, and Egypt is the only country with any significant output. A little oil is obtained in French Morocco and in Algeria. In recent years there has been considerable activity in searching for oil in various other parts of

[66] Leo W. Stach, *op. cit.,* pp. 1390–1400; Don L. Carroll, "Sakhalin Island Has Good Possibilities," *Oil Weekly,* Vol. 114 (Aug. 28, 1944), pp. 28–30; Giichiro Kobayashi, "Preliminary Report on the Geology of the Oil Fields in North (Russian) Sakhalin," *Bull. Am. Assoc. Petrol. Geol.,* Vol. 10 (November, 1926), pp. 1150–1162; I. P. Tolmachoff, "The Results of Oil Prospecting on Sakhalin Island by Japan in 1919–1925," *ibid.,* pp. 1163–1170.

Africa, including Ethiopia, Madagascar, Mozambique, Angola, French Equatorial Africa, Nigeria, Tunisia, and Spanish Morocco.

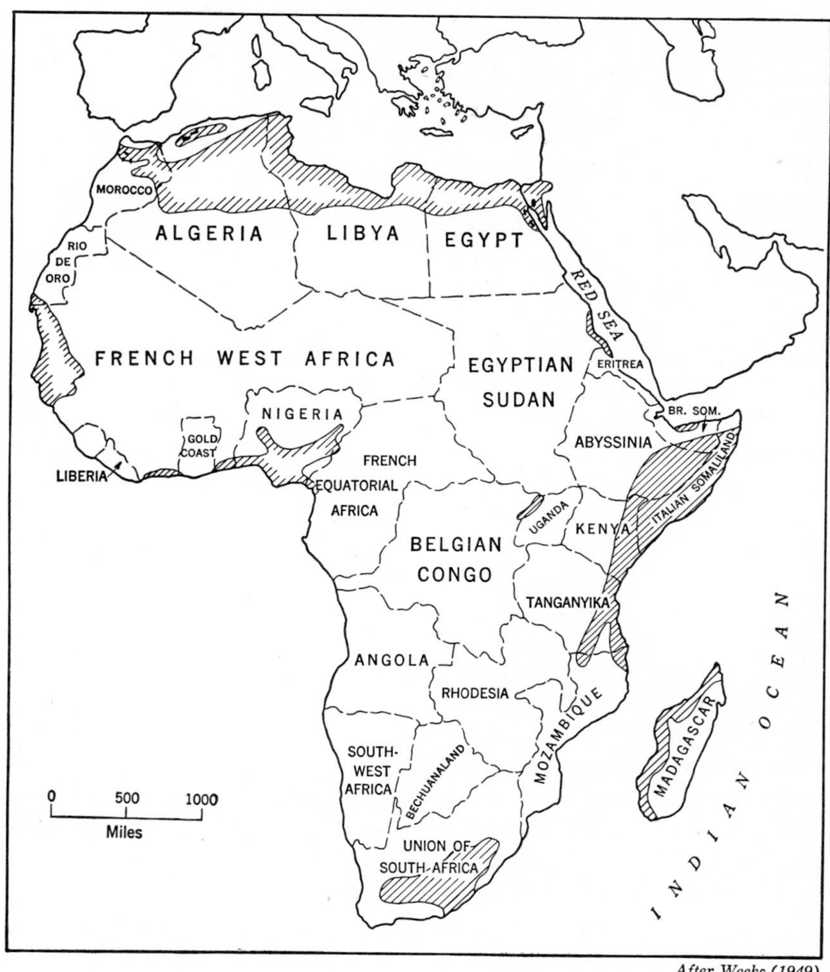

Fig. 215. Africa. Sedimentary basins and oil fields. *Courtesy American Association of Petroleum Geologists.*

General References. L. G. Weeks, "Highlights on 1948 Developments in Foreign Petroleum Fields," *Bull. Am. Assoc. Petrol. Geol.*, Vol. 33 (June, 1949), pp. 1095–1103; *Oil and Gas Jour., Review and Forecast Number,* Vol. 48 (Jan. 26, 1950); *Oil and Gas Jour., Inter-*

national Number, Vol. 48 (Dec. 22, 1949); *World Oil, International Operations Issue,* Vol. 131 (July 15, 1950).

Egypt [67]

New discoveries since 1945 have greatly increased Egypt's oil production. During 1949 this country produced 0.43 per cent of the total world yield. This is a little more than Peru and a little less than that of the state of Michigan for the same period.

Northernmost Egypt lies at the eastern end of the sedimentary basin that crosses the northern tip of Africa. This corner of Egypt has two distinct geographic divisions, one the mainland area west of the Gulf of Suez and the Suez Canal and the other the Sinai Peninsula, which lies at the head of the Red Sea between the Gulf of Suez and the Gulf of Aqaba. All the oil fields so far discovered in Egypt (Fig. 207) are on one side or the other of the Gulf of Suez, which is a rift valley. The older fields are on the west side, and the newer discoveries, beginning with Sudr in 1946, have been on the eastern, or Sinai Peninsula, side of the Gulf.

The first commercial discovery in Egypt was the Ras Gemsa field, since abandoned, in 1908. Two fields, the Asl and the Rasmataima, were discovered in 1947, and a successful wildcat well was drilled at Wadi Feiran in 1949. At the close of 1949, the latter two fields were still shut in, but the Asl was producing at the rate of 5400 barrels per day. One Asl well flowed initially at the rate of 3400 barrels per day. The largest field in both cumulative and current production is the Ras Gharib, which was discovered in 1938. The second field in cumulative production is the Hurghada (1913), and the second field in current output is the Sudr, which was producing nearly 13,000 barrels a day from six wells at the end of 1948. The Garib, Gemsa, and Hurghada fields lie on the west side of the Gulf of Suez, near its mouth, and the Sudr, Rasmataima, Asl, and Wadi Feiran fields are across the Gulf to the north (and even northwest) on the Sinai Peninsula.

The reservoirs in the Egyptian oil fields range in age from Miocene to Carboniferous. The newer discoveries in the Sinai Peninsula have been mainly in Eocene limestone, but the Asl field also produces from Miocene sandstone, and the shut-in Rasmataima field has a similar reservoir. The older fields have different reservoirs. The Hurghada

[67] P. Van der Ploeg, "Egypt," *Science of Petroleum* (Oxford Univ. Press, 1938), Vol. 1, pp. 150–151.

produces mainly from Cretaceous sands, but it also has some Miocene production, and the reservoirs in the Ras Gharib field include both Carboniferous and Cretaceous sands and Miocene limestone.

Trapping in Egypt has been in anticlines except in the Ras Gharib field, the largest in cumulative production, which is a faulted monocline. At Hurghada the upfold overlies a buried granite ridge.

Miscellaneous African Production

FRENCH MOROCCO (Fig. 216). The oil production of French Morocco during 1949 amounted to only 0.004 per cent of the world

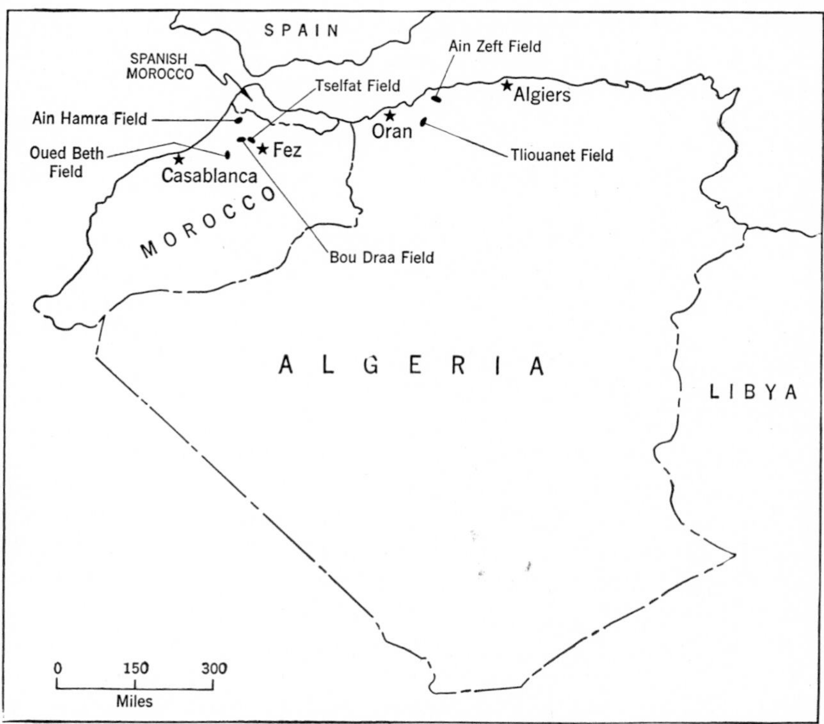

Fig. 216. French Morocco and Algeria. Index map of oil fields.

output. This was approximately the same as the amount of oil produced in Cuba during the same period. The accumulation of oil in Morocco is at the extreme opposite end of the sedimentary basin which crosses northern Africa from the oil fields of northeastern Egypt.

The same basin also extends across part of Spanish Morocco, but except for the discovery of some wet gas, exploration in this neighboring country has so far not been successful.

The oil fields in French Morocco lie in the northwestern part of the country. The first discovery was the Ain Hamra field in 1918. The Tselfat field was discovered in 1934 and the nearby one-well Bou Draa field in 1936. The only field currently producing much oil (about 280 barrels a day) is the Oued Beth, which was discovered in 1947. The discovery well in this field struck oil in a basal Miocene sand overlapping a Paleozoic hill. Accumulation appears to be the result of fault trapping.

ALGERIA (Fig. 216). The sedimentary basin at the northern end of Africa is broadest where it crosses Algeria, and it includes most of that country. However, here it does not extend all the way to the coast of the Mediterranean but cuts south of the Atlas Range. A very much smaller basin, the Chelif, overlaps a part of the coastal plain, and in this much smaller area all the oil so far discovered in Algeria has been found. The Chelif basin contains three fields, but one, the Ain Zeft, was shut down after yielding less than 25,000 barrels of oil. The greater part of the cumulative production of Algeria, about ¼ million barrels, has come from the Tliouanet field, which by 1949 was down to five wells and an average daily production of 2 barrels. The Qued Gueterini field was discovered in 1949, and by the end of the year two wells had been drilled, producing a total of 14 barrels per day from a Miocene reservoir at a depth of about 850 feet.

OCEANIA

Oil is obtained commercially in the islands of Oceania (Figs. 217–219) from Sumatra to the western tip of New Guinea. Politically, this entire area is a part of the Indonesian Republic (formerly Netherlands East Indies and Netherlands New Guinea), except the northwest coast of Borneo, which belongs to Great Britain. The oil fields occur on five islands. The largest number, with the greatest cumulative production, is on Sumatra. Considerable production has been obtained from Borneo, both the Indonesian side and the British side, and from Java. Ceram, which lies toward the eastern end of the archipelago, has one oil field, and eastern New Guinea has one producing field and two recently discovered fields that are not yet in active operation.

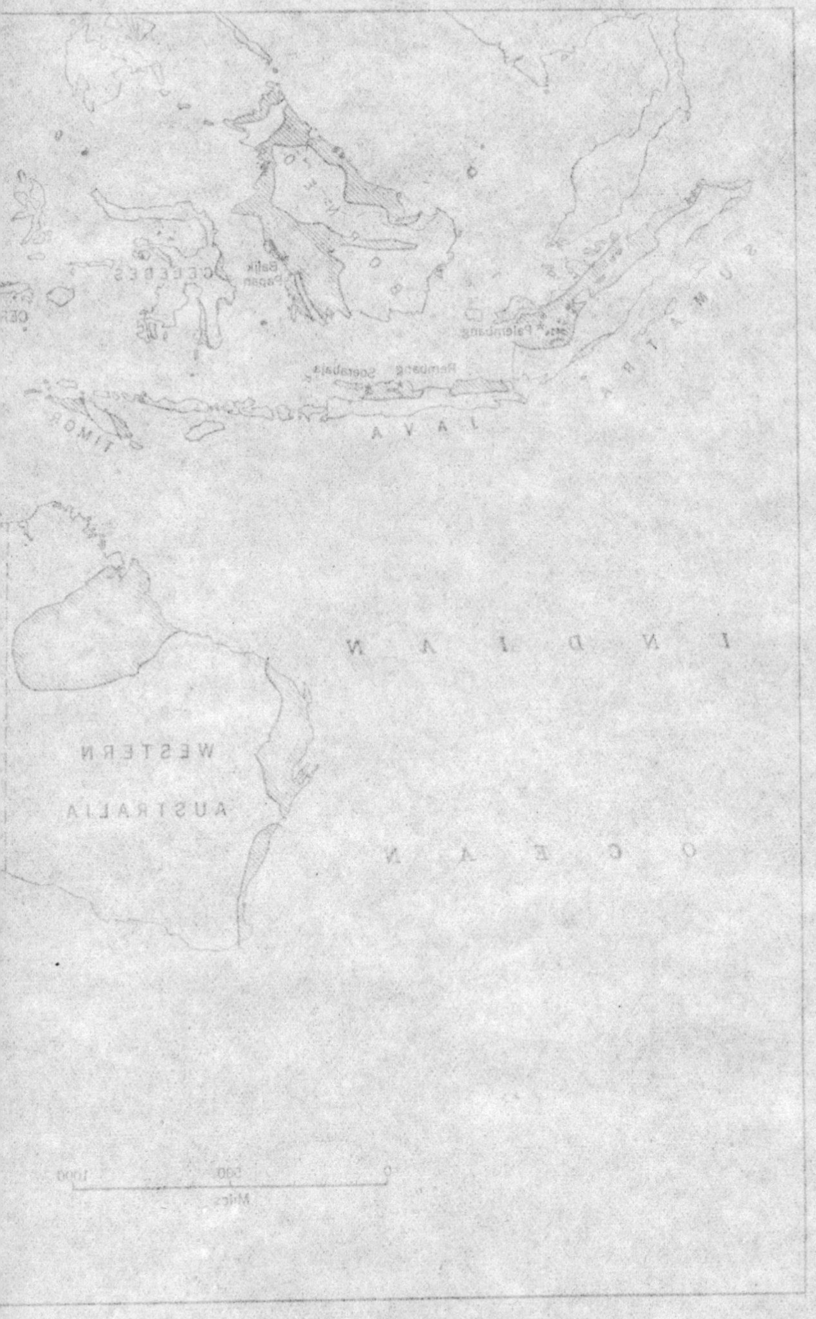

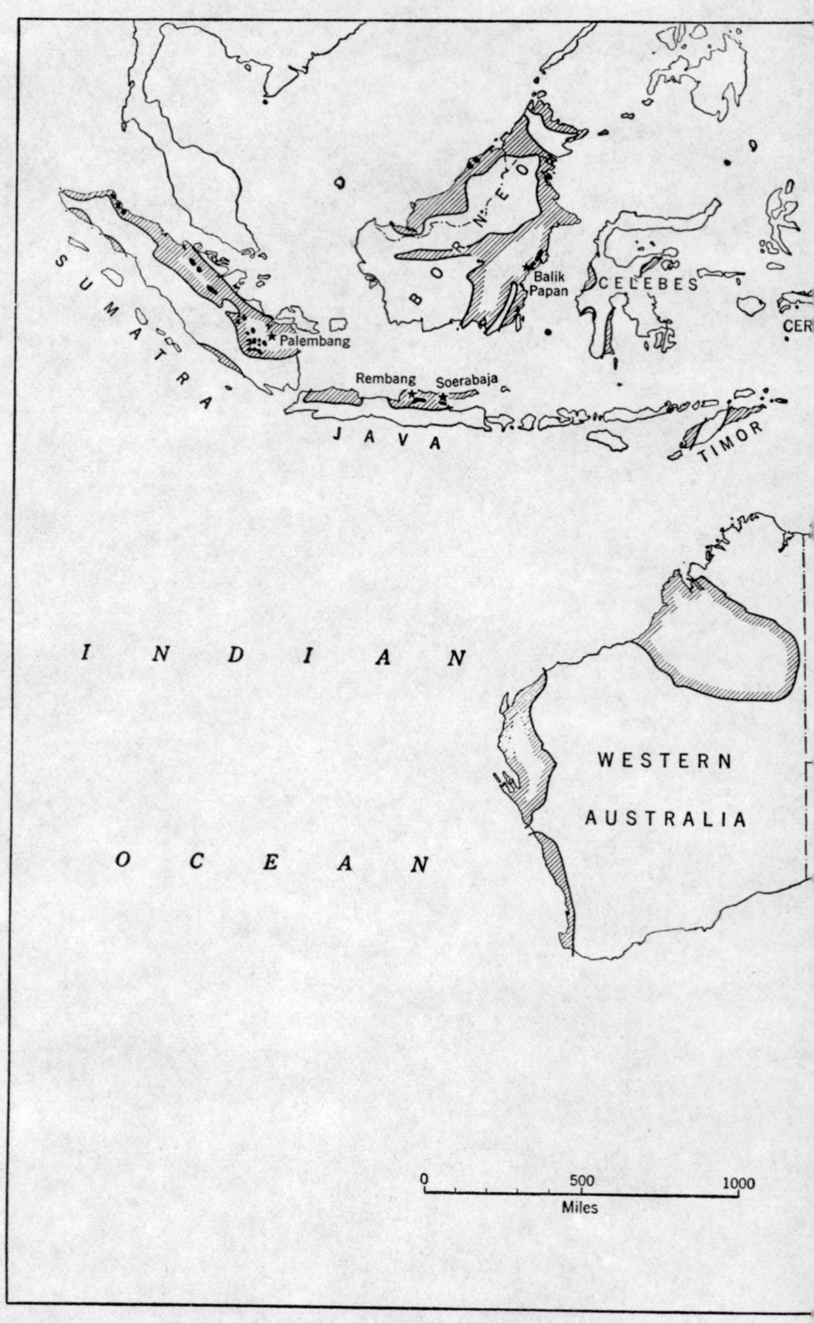

Fig. 217. Oceania. Sedimentary basins and oil fields. *Courtes*

. Weeks and American Association of Petroleum Geologists.

The oldest of the Oceania oil fields is one in north Sumatra that was discovered in 1893. During 1896 and 1897, three fields were discovered on Java, one field in western Borneo in what was then Dutch territory, and the one and only field on Ceram. The first commercial production was obtained in southern Sumatra in 1901, but it was not until 1922 that the Palembang district, which in recent years has produced about four-fifths of the Indonesian oil, was dis-

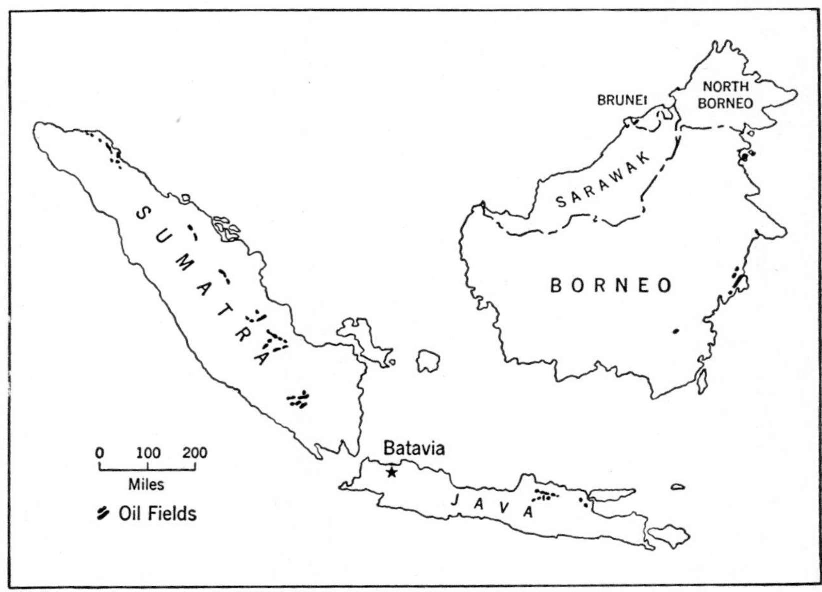

FIG. 218. Borneo and Indonesia. Oil and gas fields.

covered. The first discovery in British Borneo was the Miri in Sarawak in 1911. The oldest field of New Guinea, the Klamona, was discovered in 1936, but because the war delayed exploitation, it was not until 1949 that a pipe-line outlet was completed.

Oceania produced about 2 per cent of the world's oil output in 1949. Of this amount, a little over one-third came from British Borneo and the rest from the various Indonesian islands. Two per cent of the world's oil production is less than that of Kuwait (2.6 per cent), or approximately the equivalent of that of Illinois for 1949. However, Indonesia has not yet recovered from the war and from the political upheavals that followed. In Sarawak and Brunei in British Borneo, on the other hand, the production for 1949 was over three times the pre-war rate.

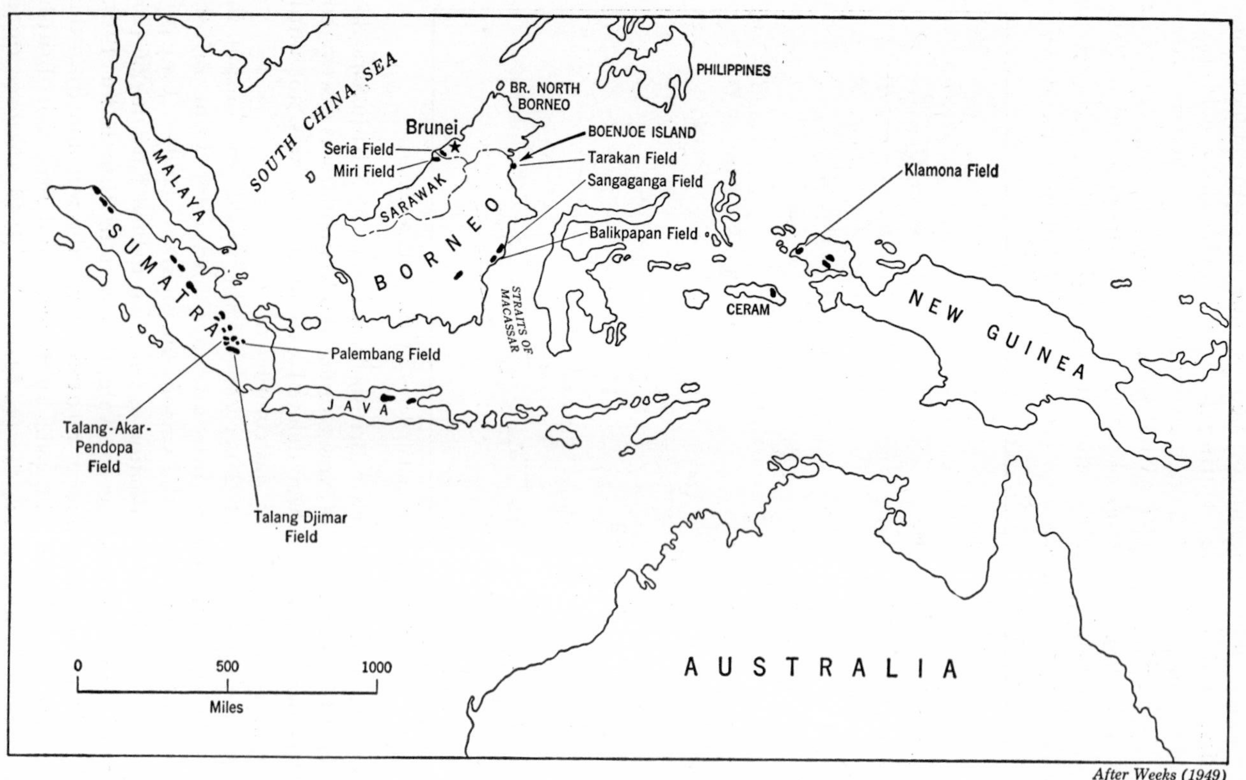

FIG. 219. Oceania index map.

The islands of Oceania extend over an east-west distance of nearly 4000 miles and a maximum north-south distance of 1000 miles. Sedimentary basins occupy the greater part of the northeast side of Sumatra and the north side of Java. Similar basins cover a considerable area along both the southeast and northwest coasts of Borneo. Except for the mountain core, New Guinea is covered with a thick veneer of sediments. Most of Papua (southeastern New Guinea, which now belongs to Australia), is covered with basin deposits and is at present the scene of an intensive search for oil accumulations. The other islands of the archipelago between New Guinea and Sumatra contain minor basin overlaps. The Ceram oil field lies in a basin that occupies the eastern tip of the island. Western and east central Australia are occupied in part by sedimentary basins, but the only oil so far discovered has been a very minor deposit (the Lakes Entrance field) in a sedimentary basin that just barely overlaps the southeastern Victoria coast.

High volcanic mountains, the Barisans, follow the southwestern coast line of Sumatra for nearly 1000 miles. The northeast side of the island consists of lowlands and jungle, and it is in this area that the oil deposits have been found. The fields occur in three districts. The northern district, with about ten fields, is at the northwestern end of the island west of the Malay Peninsula. The central district occupies the middle part of the island across the straits from Singapore and contains two fields. The southern district, with about twenty-two fields, covers a considerable area north of the Barisans near the southeastern end of the island. This district is responsible for the greater part of the Indonesian oil production, both current and cumulative.

The nine oil fields of Java are concentrated in an isolated sedimentary basin that occupies the eastern half of the island north of the chain of active and recent volcanic mountains. The oil fields of British Borneo are close to the South China Sea. The Miri field is in Sarawak, and the Seria is a short distance across the boundary in Brunei. Indonesian Borneo has two oil field districts, the Tarakan, which covers the islands of Tarakan and Boenjoe off the coast of northeastern Borneo, south of the British province of North Borneo, and the Balikpapan, to the south not far inland from the Strait of Makassar. There are about eight fields in the Balikpapan district.

The total cumulative production in Oceania is more than 1.3 billion barrels. Of this amount, all but 165 million barrels, the British Borneo production, has come from the former Dutch colonies. Sumatra has the greatest production of any of the islands, with over

600 millions, more than half of the Indonesian total. Borneo, counting both the Indonesian and British parts of the island, has produced about 584 million barrels. Most of the remainder has come from Java. The largest fields in cumulative production are first the Tarakan in northern Borneo, second the Sangasanga field in the Balikpapan district, third the Talang-Akar-Pendopa field in southern Sumatra, and fourth the Seria field in Brunei in British Borneo. First in current production is the Seria field, followed by the Talang-Akar-Pendopa and another southern Sumatra field, the Talang-Djimar.

The reservoir rocks throughout Oceania are of Tertiary age except on Ceram, where, in addition to Pliocene sandstone production, oil is obtained also from underlying Triassic rock. Most of the Tertiary production is from Miocene and Pliocene formations. In the central part of the basin, the maximum thickness of the Tertiary section approaches 30,000 feet. Most production is relatively shallow, coming from depths of less than 3000 feet.

In all the fields so far discovered in this vast petroliferous province, accumulation has been due to the presence of anticlines. Trapping has taken place mainly in belts of weak and moderate folds. Asymmetric anticlines are common, and some are overturned and thrust-faulted, but as a general rule, the exploration of strongly compressed and complicated anticlines has not resulted in the discovery of commercial oil deposits.

General References. H. M. Schuppli, "Geology of Oil Basins of East Indian Archipelago," *Bull. Am. Assoc. Petrol. Geol.*, Vol. 30 (January, 1946), pp. 1–22; E. W. Beltz, "Principal Sedimentary Basins in the East Indies," *Bull. Am. Assoc. Petrol. Geol.*, Vol. 28 (October, 1944), pp. 1440–1454; H. M. Schuppli, "The East Indian Archipelago," *Science of Petroleum* (Oxford Univ. Press, 1938), Vol. 1, pp. 131–132.

Chapter 11

FUTURE OIL SUPPLIES

The oil business is unusual in that it operates on a relatively small inventory. An enormous demand has been built up for a product with known supplies rarely exceeding twelve to fifteen times the annual consumption. The petroleum industry and the consuming public have both gambled on our continued ability to discover new supplies. The proven reserves are, as Levorsen puts it, merely working stock: "Much of the oil we are using today was unknown 20 years ago, and likewise the oil we will use 20 years hence is in a large part still undiscovered." [1]

But unfortunately for the peace of mind of all associated with the oil industry—producers, distributors, or consumers—the discovery curve is not a smooth one. As far as the quantity of oil discovered is concerned, the curve is most irregular. Several years may go by in which the new finds are inadequate to maintain a satisfactory inventory, and then a series of discoveries will take place, such as the almost simultaneous development of the reef accumulations of Alberta and Scurry County, Texas, that will make a notable improvement in the size of the working stock.

At the same time that discovery is proceeding in this erratic manner, the demand for petroleum products and natural gas increases markedly each year. This is largely due to a steadily increasing energy demand throughout the world. Since 1918, 95 per cent of the greater energy demand has been met by oil and gas. The remaining 5 per cent has been met by expanded water-power resources. Coal has not contributed to the increased consumption of energy-producing materials. As a matter of fact, in recent years the instability of the coal supply, and other factors, have created additional markets for liquid and gaseous hydrocarbons.

As a result of the constantly increasing demand and the unpredictable behavior of the discovery curve, the oil industry is alternately faced with an oil famine, with its threats of rationing and conversion

[1] A. I. Levorsen, "Our Petroleum Resources," *Bull. Geol. Soc. Am.*, Vol. 59 (April, 1948), p. 286.

to other energy sources, or with a flood of oil, depressing the market price.

However, except for these occasional periods of abundance, the oil industry is under incessant pressure to keep up with its ever-growing market. In the past, this demand has been met to some extent by the development of new processing techniques but mostly by discoveries of new oil and gas deposits. A part of the ballooning demand for gasoline brought about by the automobile was met by the invention of the cracking process of refining, which increased the gasoline yield two and one-half times. The fact that discovery of new deposits has been notably successful in the past is attested by the current crude-oil-reserve figure, which is greater than ever before in spite of the enormous withdrawals during the war and post-war years.

How the ever-increasing demand for petroleum products can be met in the future is the theme of this chapter. First the known oil and gas reserves will be considered. The next category of future oil supplies is the undiscovered hydrocarbon deposits. Some of these lie at greater depth than those heretofore explored, and others are in fields waiting to be found. These prospective new fields are both within current oil-producing districts and in sedimentary basins not yet productive. Last are what can be termed "technologic reserves." Included here are the hydrocarbon supplies that can be obtained by increasing the ultimate recovery within our known deposits, by developing dormant hydrocarbon supplies, and by the manufacture of synthetic hydrocarbons.

General References. A. I. Levorsen, *op. cit.*, pp. 283–299; Kirtley F. Mather, "Petroleum,—Today and Tomorrow," *Science,* Vol. 106 (Dec. 19, 1947), pp. 603–609; Leonard M. Fanning (editor), Wallace E. Pratt, Lyon F. Terry, K. C. Heald, Robert E. Wilson, *et al., Our Oil Resources* (McGraw-Hill, New York, 2nd Edition, 1950); William B. Heroy, "Oil for the Future," *Econ. Geol.,* Vol. 39 (December, 1944), pp. 593–599; Wallace E. Pratt, "Our Petroleum Resources," *Am. Scientist,* Vol. 3 (April, 1944), pp. 120–128; F. H. Lahee, "Our Oil and Gas Reserves: Their Meaning and Limitations," *Bull. Am. Assoc. Petrol. Geol.,* Vol. 34 (June, 1950), pp. 1283–1287.

KNOWN OIL AND GAS RESERVES

PROVEN OIL RESERVES.[2] Because the petroleum industry operates on such a narrow margin of known reserves, inventories are

[2] Charles J. Deegan, "Reserves Are Up," *Oil and Gas Jour.,* Vol. 48 (March 16, 1950), pp. 56–57; Dahl M. Duff, "Oil Reserves of World," *Oil and Gas Jour.,* Vol. 48

constantly being made, and a voluminous literature has developed on this subject.[3] In times of depleting stock, as during World War II, the general apprehension over the supply situation is reflected by a large increase in papers on this subject. A standing committee of the American Petroleum Institute prepares at the end of each calendar year an estimate of the reserves for each of the oil-producing states. Various individuals contribute to an annual inventory of estimated reserves in foreign countries published in the International Oil issue of the *Oil and Gas Journal.*[4] These reserve figures change from year to year, owing to withdrawals that diminish the reserve and to discoveries that increase it. During 1949, the proven reserves increased because discoveries more than compensated for withdrawals.

Table I gives the estimated proven reserves for the United States, by states, and for the other oil-producing countries of the world, as of Jan. 1, 1950. The second column gives the production (in round numbers for the foreign countries) during 1949. All figures are for thousands of barrels. The statistics for the United States include all liquid hydrocarbons, not only petroleum but also distillate and natural gasoline.

Several generalizations can be made from this table. One is that usually areas with the highest current production also have the highest reserve. This is, of course, based on the fact that the proven reserve is the oil still underground within the known oil fields, most of which are in active production. Exceptions occur where marketing facilities have not yet caught up with discovery. For example, Canada is far behind Mexico in production for 1949, but it is ahead in proven reserves because of the recent prolific discoveries in Alberta, most of which are still without adequate marketing outlet. The newer producing countries of Kuwait and Saudi Arabia are behind Iran in current production but are ahead in proven reserves.

It is obvious, from comparing the current production with the reserve estimates, that the rate of withdrawal from inventory is much greater in some places than in others. For most areas, the figure ranges from 4 per cent to 6 per cent, with the United States and Europe in the second bracket. However, in the immediately preceding years, the withdrawal rate in the United States has been 8 per cent and even higher; the drop in 1949 is largely due to the wave of new

(Dec. 22, 1949), pp. 180–182; G. C. Gester, "World Petroleum Reserves and Petroleum Statistics," *Bull. Am. Assoc. Petrol. Geol.,* Vol. 28 (October, 1944). pp. 1485–1505.

[3] See various petroleum bibliographies listed in Appendix.

[4] The issue for 1950 was published on Dec. 21.

TABLE I

ESTIMATED PROVEN OIL RESERVES AND PRODUCTION STATISTICS FOR 1949

(Thousands of Barrels)

	Proven Reserves	*Production during* 1949
United States		
Alabama	3,547	448
Arkansas	353,105	31,213
California	4,143,026	360,131
Colorado	369,002	30,242
Illinois	494,804	67,767
Indiana	50,335	9,503
Kansas	844,795	102,764
Kentucky	69,413	11,084
Louisiana	2,506,191	209,584
Michigan	67,699	16,666
Mississippi	459,267	38,432
Montana	116,103	9,880
Nebraska	1,624	291
New Mexico	677,941	51,895
New York	62,900	4,216
Ohio	29,373	3,611
Oklahoma	1,563,948	168,151
Pennsylvania	105,999	11,689
Texas	15,653,443	832,546
Utah	16,039	636
West Virginia	50,823	6,689
Wyoming	735,465	49,334
Miscellaneous	3,659	575
Total United States	28,378,501	2,017,347
Canada	1,200,000	21,300
Mexico	850,000	60,500
Cuba	2,800	200
Total North America	30,431,301	2,099,347
South America		
Argentina	250,000	22,800
Bolivia	20,000	650
Brazil	20,000	100
Chile	10,000	
Colombia	300,000	30,000
Ecuador	28,000	2,600
Peru	160,000	15,000
Trinidad	260,000	20,000
Venezuela	9,500,000	480,000
Total	10,548,000	571,150

	Proven Reserves	*Production during* 1949
Europe		
Albania	9,000	350
Austria	75,000	6,700
Czechoslovakia	2,000	330
France	4,250	400
Germany	150,000	6,000
Great Britain	3,700	330
Hungary	40,000	3,800
Italy	2,000	680
Netherlands	50,000	4,250
Poland	20,000	1,000
Rumania	350,000	32,300
U.S.S.R.	4,300,000	248,000
Yugoslavia	4,000	365
Total	5,009,950	305,505
Africa		
Algeria and French Morocco	2,500	145
Egypt	200,000	15,500
Total	202,500	15,645
Middle East		
Bahrein	160,000	11,000
Iran	7,000,000	201,000
Iraq	5,250,000	31,000
Kuwait	11,000,000	88,300
Saudi Arabia	9,000,000	168,000
Turkey	3,000	
Total	32,413,000	499,300
Other Asia and Oceania		
Burma	50,000	180
China	20,000	650
India	25,000	1,900
Japan	22,000	1,280
Pakistan	10,000	650
Indonesia	1,100,000	41,000
British Borneo	300,000	24,800
New Guinea	50,000	145
Total	1,577,000	70,605
Total foreign	51,803,250	1,544,205
Total United States	28,378,501	2,017,347
Total world	80,181,751	3,561,552

discoveries in west Texas, which added over a billion barrels of reserve oil. The withdrawal rate in the Middle East is only 1.5 per cent, which again is due to the lag between discovery and the completion of marketing facilities.

An outstanding disparity in the table is the ratio between production and reserves in the United States compared with the rest of the world. The current production of this country is about 57 per cent of the total world oil output, and the cumulative production is over 60 per cent. On the other hand, our share in the proven reserves of the world is about 35 per cent. Actually, the United States contains only about 15 per cent of the total prospective oil territory (Fig. 220), and Pratt believes that our share of the eventual oil production of the world will be closer to 15 per cent than 35 per cent.[5] In other words, since we have explored a much higher percentage of our prospective territory than the other countries, our proportion of the future oil must be less. As a matter of fact, many of the foreign countries have done little beyond prospecting the seep areas where the occurrence of hydrocarbons is obvious.

Evidence that the United States is experiencing the law of diminishing returns in oil exploration is shown by the fact that wildcat wells today discover only half as much oil as they once did. Furthermore, 70,000 wildcat wells are needed in the United States to discover as much oil as 100 wildcat wells in the Middle East.[6]

There are several reasons why the United States has developed a much higher percentage of its potential oil wealth than other countries.[7] The principal one is that the intensive mechanization within the United States has created a greater demand for petroleum products than that in any other part of the world, and necessity is the mother of discovery as well as of invention. Other important reasons are the relative political and economic freedom under which domestic exploration is permitted to operate, the technical skill of the American oil explorer, and the availability of capital for speculative purposes.

In the absence of any accurate statistical information from Russia, the estimate of 4.3 billion barrels of oil reserve for the U.S.S.R. has less basis in fact than most of the other estimates. As recently as 1947, one expert estimated the Russian proven reserve at about 8 billion

[5] Wallace E. Pratt, "Our Petroleum Resources," *Am. Scientist,* Vol. 3 (April, 1944), p. 123.

[6] Robert E. Wilson, address at Summer Session, University of Michigan, 1949.

[7] Wallace E. Pratt, *Oil in the Earth* (*Univ. Kans. Press,* 1942), and various articles by the same author.

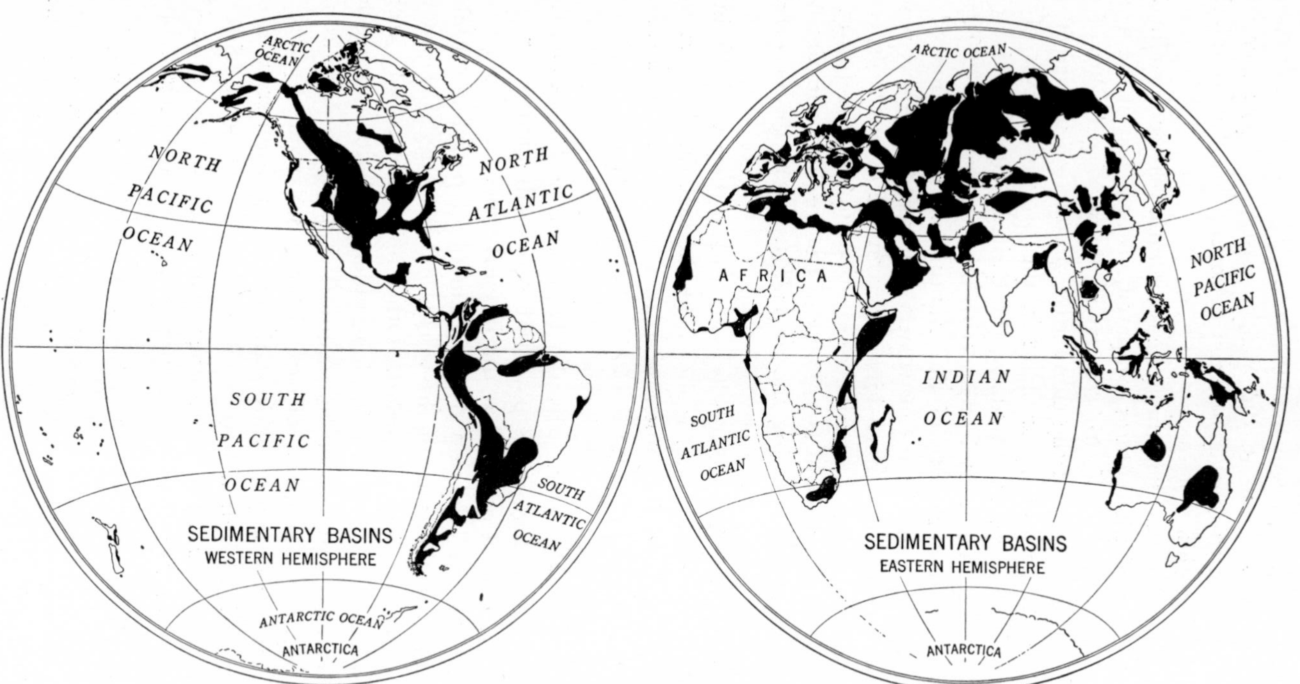

FIG. 220. Sedimentary basins of the world. Basins in black. *Courtesy L. G. Weeks and American Association of Petroleum Geologists.*

barrels.[8] This figure is high in comparison with the probable current production, and it led to downward revision of the figure given in Table I.

PROVEN GAS RESERVES.[9] A committee of the American Gas Association annually prepares estimates of the proven recoverable reserves of natural gas within the United States. Table II shows these estimates as of Jan. 1, 1950, for the various gas-producing states. The right-hand column shows the production during 1949. All figures are for millions of cubic feet, at atmospheric pressure and 60° F.

TABLE II

ESTIMATED PROVEN AND RECOVERABLE RESERVES OF NATURAL GAS

(Millions of Cubic Feet)

	Reserves *Jan.* 1, 1950	*Production* 1949
Arkansas	874,190	59,185
California	9,991,635	543,488
Colorado	1,227,095	24,828
Illinois	233,192	40,130
Indiana	25,200	6,250
Kansas	14,089,560	323,283
Kentucky	1,349,397	90,000
Louisiana	26,687,811	805,726
Michigan	214,911	17,438
Mississippi	2,528,969	68,950
Montana	803,471	37,925
New Mexico	6,241,003	256,706
New York	66,685	3,700
Ohio	652,571	47,000
Oklahoma	11,625,979	567,335
Pennsylvania	621,680	70,000
Texas	99,170,403	3,023,714
Utah	65,577	6,313
West Virginia	1,715,233	180,000
Wyoming	2,173,677	72,339
Miscellaneous	23,105	731
Total U. S.	180,381,344	6,245,041

[8] Quoted in L. G. Weeks, "Highlights on 1947 Developments in Foreign Petroleum Fields," *Bull. Am. Assoc. Petrol. Geol.*, Vol. 32 (June, 1948), p. 1139.

[9] Charles J. Deegan, "Reserves Are Up," *Oil and Gas Jour.*, Vol. 48 (March 16, 1950), p. 57; George G. Oberfell, "Reserves of Natural Gas," *Oil and Gas Jour.*, Vol. 47 (March 17, 1949), pp. 118 *et seq.;* Hugh D. Miser, "Geological Survey's Studies and Potential Reserves of Natural Gas," *U. S. Geol. Survey, Circular* 14, 1946; N. C. McGowen, "Natural Gas and Natural Gas Liquid Reserves in the United States," *World Oil,* Vol. 130 (June, 1950), p. 140.

Gas likewise shows a fairly direct relationship between annual production and size of reserve. There is also a relationship between the oil-producing states and the gas-producing states, but they are by no means parallel. For example, California, the second oil state, is fifth in gas production. Texas is outstanding in both oil and gas production and in reserves. It should also be noted that the domestic inventory of natural gas is considerably larger in respect to the annual withdrawals than that of petroleum. During 1949 gas production was only a little more than 3 per cent of the known recoverable reserve.

UNDISCOVERED HYDROCARBON DEPOSITS

RESERVES THAT MAY BE TAPPED BY DEEPER DRILLING. Cram refers to the unexplored section below the producing zones in the oil and gas districts as the "vertical frontier."[10] Experience in Kansas and California has shown that commercial accumulations of hydrocarbons can occur in the basement crystalline rocks, and so the exploration of the third dimension is not complete until the entire sedimentary section, regardless of its thickness, has been investigated. Relatively few tests have been drilled into the basement rock where the sedimentary column is over 5000 feet thick. Even where it lies at lesser depths, there is, in most areas, an inadequately explored zone between the deepest developed reservoir and the basement.

Deeper exploration has been handicapped by the increased drilling costs involved. However, this is more a psychological than an actual handicap, for a well testing deeper formations in a producing anticline is drilling through a succession of superimposed traps, whereas a lateral wildcat, because of inadequate structural or stratigraphic information, may not be testing a trap at all, and so the chances of discovery are less. Therefore, a single deep test may find as much oil at less expense than a series of relatively shallow wells. Unfortunately, many producing anticlines have been condemned as prospects for deeper oil or gas because the lower formations were explored by wells so far off structure that they missed the accumulations at lesser depths and so were carried deeper. A well that missed the trap in a producing zone is a poor test of deeper traps.

Almost every oil-producing district in the world has a history of a downward progression of discoveries. The sequence in many areas has been to proceed downward from a surface accumulation (oil seep

[10] Ira H. Cram, "Resources and Resourcefulness," *Bull. Am. Assoc. Petrol. Geol.*, Vol. 29 (July, 1945), pp. 857–864.

or asphalt deposit) to the first underground accumulation at a depth of a few hundred feet. Subsequently, one or more deeper reservoirs has been found, so a field may actually have many birthdays. Many examples are given in Chapters 8 and 9 of such a chronological sequence. The first discoveries in the salt dome province were in shallow cap rock, followed by the findings of oil deep on the flanks. Many California fields, including Santa Fe Springs, Ventura Avenue, and Sunset-Midway, had successively deeper discoveries. In 1947 an exploratory well on the middle dome at Kettleman Hills struck a flow of nearly 500 barrels of oil and more than 4 million cubic feet of gas per day from deep Eocene sands. The Rangely field of western Colorado produced relatively insignificant quantities of oil for many years from fissures in the Pierre shale before the much deeper and prolific Weber sandstone reservoir was tapped. Newly discovered Cretaceous reservoirs northwest of Lake Maracaibo are yet another example of the rewards that may follow exploration of the vertical frontier beneath already producing oil deposits, especially those structurally trapped.

Figure 221 shows the deeper basins and embayment areas [11] where a great thickness of sedimentary rock remains largely unexplored. Some of these deep areas have no production as yet and will be considered subsequently, but other areas, such as the San Joaquin basin of California and the Gulf Coast embayment of Louisiana and Texas, do contain producing fields, and considerable success has attended exploration beneath the hitherto productive zones. No one knows the exact depths to the basement rocks in these two areas, but the maximum thickness of the sedimentary section is probably somewhere between 40,000 and 60,000 feet. Except for an occasional isolated well the entire section below 14,000 feet is still unexplored. It will be a long time before the third dimension is adequately probed in both California [12] and the Gulf Coast. The prolific Santa Fe Springs field in the Los Angeles basin has been explored to more than 13,000 feet without getting below the Upper Miocene. The deepest well (in 1949) in the world, which was drilled to a depth of 20,521 feet in the Green River basin of southwestern Wyoming, did not test even all the possible reservoirs in the Upper Cretaceous.[13]

[11] Dorsey Hager, "Drilling the Deep Areas," *Oil and Gas Jour.*, Vol. 46 (Jan. 8, 1948), pp. 64–65.

[12] Albert Gregersen and Frank S. Parker, "Prospects for Deeper Zone Production in California," *Calif. Oil World*, Vol. 37 (September, Second Issue, 1944), pp. 12–21.

[13] Charles J. Deegan, "Deepest Well Confirms Theories of Regional Conditions," *Oil and Gas Jour.*, Vol. 48 (Aug. 11, 1949), pp. 56–57.

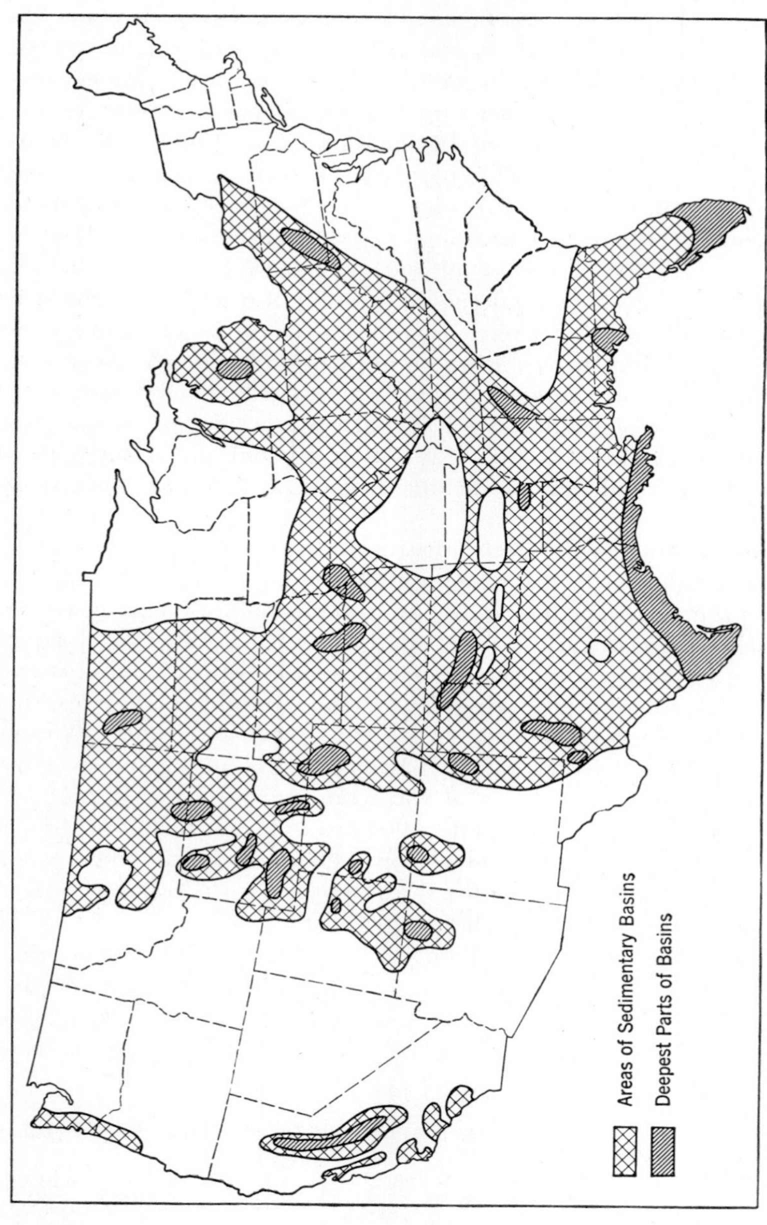

Fig. 221. United States. Sedimentary basins.

Denison [14] has described in considerable detail the possibilities of deeper exploration in the Mid-Continent basins, most of which are shallow in comparison with those of California and the Gulf embayment but yet have been inadequately explored. The Arbuckle possibilities in Kansas have been discussed by Paddleford.[15] Considerable deep testing remains to be done in the Permian basin of western Texas and southeastern New Mexico.[16] Only a beginning has been made in exploring the oil possibilities of the lower part of the stratigraphic section in the Michigan and Illinois [17] basins.

It can be concluded that an appreciable percentage of the oil supplies of the future will be obtained from beneath the oil fields that are being exploited today.

UNDISCOVERED HORIZONTAL RESERVES. By horizontal reserves is meant the oil and gas deposits that underlie areas not yet explored. These new areas may lie between producing fields, they may lie outside the periphery of the current producing districts, they may be offshore on the continental shelves, or they may be in sedimentary basins that have not hitherto been productive. The last is without doubt an important classification of future hydrocarbon supplies. However, it is probably more important in other countries than in the United States, for 85 per cent of the land in which oil accumulation is possible (Fig. 220) is foreign territory, and inasmuch as this vast area has produced less than 40 per cent of the world's oil, it is only reasonable to conclude that considerably more oil remains to be discovered there. This does not mean, however, that any immmediate decrease in discovery by lateral exploration is expected in the United States; we can continue to expect the discovery of an average of three or four new fields every day unless overproduction retards exploration.

Exploring the horizontal frontier has one advantage over deeper exploration in that it leads to the discovery of both structural and varying-permeability traps, whereas vertical exploration is likely to succeed only beneath structural traps. It is possible, of course, to

[14] A. R. Denison, "Deeper Drilling Prospects in the Mid-Continent," *Am. Inst. Min. Met. Engineers, Tech. Paper* 1650 (November, 1943).

[15] J. T. Paddleford, "Kansas Operators Neglect Deep Arbuckle," *Oil Weekly*, Vol. 115 (Nov. 6, 1944), pp. 174 *et seq*.

[16] Paul F. Osborne, "Permian Basin Pays Are Many and Deep," *World Petrol.*, Vol. 15 (March, 1944), pp. 44–49.

[17] Alfred H. Bell and M. M. Leighton, "Prospects for Oil Discoveries in Illinois beyond Proved Areas and from Deeper Horizons," *Ill. Geol. Survey, Circular* 150, 1949.

discover a stratigraphic trap by random drilling beneath any type of oil accumulation, but success in such drilling is more often the result of luck than of logic.

It has been stated earlier in this volume that structural traps are easier to find than stratigraphic traps, and therefore it is reasonable to assume that a higher proportion of stratigraphic traps remain to be discovered by further exploration. Levorsen[18] believes strongly that much of the future oil will come from newly discovered varying-permeability traps. Heroy[19] shows that the wedge-out type of trap is largely confined to the sedimentary basin rims, whereas the structural type can be found far down the flanks and, in fact, very close to the bottom of the basin. However, it is true that the pinchout trap, because of the large drainage area down-dip, may impound great quantities of oil, as shown by East Texas, Cutbank (Montana), and the fields on the east side of Lake Maracaibo.

Reserves within Producing Basins. Not only is all the 80-billion-barrel proven oil reserve of the world confined to the currently producing basins but so also is most of the new oil that will be found in the *near* future. This statement is based upon the fact that most of the successful wildcat wells completed in the United States are located between fields already producing. A lesser number of the new fields extend the periphery of the producing area within a sedimentary basin. Relatively few new fields are discovered annually by the exploration of hitherto unproductive basins. This is discussed in a subsequent section.

The opportunities for discovery of new oil fields by interpolation and extrapolation within producing basins are, of course, world wide. Of the four great depressed segments described by Pratt,[20] three are productive, and the fourth, the Arctic basin, is being explored by the United States and by Russia. The three mega-basins that are productive are Oceania, north and northwest of Australia; the eastern Mediterranean-Middle East-southern Russia basin, occupied in part by the Red, Black, and Caspian seas; and the depressed segment between North and South America, occupied in part by the Gulf of Mexico and the Caribbean. In addition to these intercontinental

[18] A. I. Levorsen, "Estimates of Undiscovered Petroleum Reserves," *Mines Mag.*, Vol. 39 (December, 1949), pp. 47 *et seq.*, and many other papers.

[19] William B. Heroy, "Oil for the Future," *Econ. Geol.*, Vol. 39 (December, 1944), pp. 593–599.

[20] Wallace E. Pratt, "Petroleum Resources," *Am. Scientist*, Vol. 32 (April, 1944). pp. 120–128.

basins, there are the smaller, but none the less prolific, basins entirely superimposed upon the continents.

Within the United States [21] there is a close parallel between current output for each of the productive sedimentary basins and the discovery rate. An even closer parallel exists between proven reserves and present and probable future discovery rate. For example, the greatest number of new discoveries are being made today in west Texas, where both the current production and the proven reserves are large. Conversely, the discovery rate is low in the older districts, where production and proven reserves have declined to far below their peak. But it is not possible to eliminate any area from potential discoveries. Even in the relatively old oil-producing districts of Lima-Indiana and Venango County, Pennsylvania, new field discoveries are still being made.

The oil fields of the future are by no means confined to the districts of greatest discovery at the present time. Such inadequately explored basins as the Anadarko [22] in western Oklahoma and the San Juan [23] in the Southwest contain many of the oil fields of the future. Considerable areas of the Gulf Coast embayment are as yet largely unexplored.

Heck [24] favors exploration in New York State east of the present area of oil production. Here are to be found the same succession of strata as are productive to the west, but probably not too metamorphosed. Practically no tests have been drilled. This is perhaps an example of misapplication of the carbon-ratio concept stifling exploration.

Many new oil fields remain to be found in producing basins in other countries and on other continents, including Alberta,[25] South America,[26] U.S.S.R.,[27] and other parts of Europe, Asia, Africa, and

[21] Frank B. Taylor, "Frontiers for the Wildcatter," *Independent Petrol. Assoc. Am. Monthly* (April, May, June, 1945) (Reprint); Seismograph Service Corporation, "Exploration Service" (compiled by the *Oil and Gas Jour.,* 1941).

[22] Robert R. Wheeler, "Anadarko Basin Geology and Oil Possibilities," *World Oil,* Vol. 127 (Sept. 22, 1947), pp. 38 *et seq.;* and Vol. 127 (Sept. 29, 1947), pp. 33 *et seq.*

[23] Frank C. Barnes, "San Juan Basin Eyed by Several Operators and Independents," *Oil and Gas Jour.,* Vol. 47 (May 27, 1948), pp. 73–77.

[24] E. T. Heck, "Possibilities of Oil and Gas in New York," *Petrol. Engineer,* Vol. 18 (August, 1947), pp. 163–172.

[25] Theodore A. Link, "Alberta's Oil Development and Problems," *World Oil,* Vol. 129 (July 1, 1949), pp. 205–208.

[26] John L. Rich, "Oil Possibilities of South America in the Light of Regional Geology," *Bull. Am. Assoc. Petrol. Geol.,* Vol. 29 (May, 1945), pp. 495–563.

[27] F. Julius Fohs, "Oil Reserve Provinces of Middle East and Southern Soviet Russia," *Bull. Am. Assoc. Petrol. Geol.,* Vol. 31 (August, 1947), pp. 1372–1383.

Oceania. Syria, for example, lies in the same sedimentary basin that is so productive elsewhere in the Middle East, but as yet it contains not a single field.[28]

Reserves beneath Continental Shelves.[29] All production today from beneath continental shelves is merely an extrapolation of onshore producing areas; no new oil provinces have been discovered as yet by offshore drilling. California has been producing oil from the continental shelf for many years. Development of these accumulations has been both by drilling from piers extending out into the ocean and by directionally drilled wells along the shoreline.

The most recent activity has been on the Gulf Coast of Texas and Louisiana, especially in offshore Louisiana. Even before the first discovery in the open waters of the Gulf, oil was being produced in areas only recently landlocked by the deposition of sediment at the mouth of the Mississippi. Many of these wells were drilled in bayous that required underwater drilling in the same way as the offshore operations but without the storm-wave hazard. Open-water drilling has been carried on for many years in Lake Maracaibo, Venezuela. The greatest seafloor depth in which exploration has taken place off the Louisiana coast is 50 feet, but wells have been put down in Lake Maracaibo, where the depth of the bottom has been as great as 100 feet. New equipment is being planned in California for working in as much as 350 feet of water.[30] The water depth at the edge of the shelves bordering the continents is approximately 100 fathoms,[31] or 600 feet, but no equipment is available as yet that will permit exploration of the entire continental shelf zone.

By Jan. 1, 1950, nine oil fields and eleven gas and gas-condensate fields had been discovered in the post-war exploration of the Gulf

[28] Anon., "Syria Becomes Hot Spot of Middle East Oil," *World Oil,* Vol. 129 (May, 1949), pp. 232–234.

[29] Emory N. Kemler, *Bibliography on Offshore Petroleum Development* (approximately 400 titles) (Southwest Research Institute, Houston-San Antonio, Texas, 1949); *Offshore Drilling Operations in the Gulf of Mexico* (assembled reprints from various journals) (Langham, Langston and Burnett, Houston, Texas, 1949, supplements, 1950); J. R. Latimer, Jr., "The Search for Oil on the Continental Shelf," *World Oil,* Vol. 129 (December, 1949), pp. 50 *et seq.;* Wallace E. Pratt, "Petroleum on the Continental Shelves," *Bull. Am. Assoc. Petrol. Geol.,* Vol. 31 (April, 1947), pp. 657–672.

[30] Robert Harwick, "Deep Water Drilling," *Oil and Gas Jour.,* Vol. 48 (Jan. 26, 1950), p. 161.

[31] W. E. Wrather, "Statement Made during Hearings before a Special Committee Investigating Petroleum Resources," *Investigation of Petroleum Resources* (Government Printing Office, Washington, 1945), pp. 360–372.

of Mexico. All these discoveries were made in offshore Louisiana. Considerable doubt has been cast upon the economic feasibility of exploiting such deposits.[32] The oil fields currently are producing about 5500 barrels per day, which is only 1 per cent of the Louisiana total. All the gas and gas-condensate fields are shut-in, owing to the difficulty of marketing offshore gas, but plans are under way (June, 1950) to tap at least one field with a submarine gas pipe line. The development costs are about three times what they are on land, mainly because of the expense of constructing the drilling platform. This cost is offset in part by the considerably smaller percentage of wildcat wells necessary so far to discover oil, in comparison with those that are necessary onshore, where all the more or less obvious structural traps were tested long ago. But even after oil has been discovered, the production costs also run about three times what they are on land. For these reasons, the oil industry is currently getting back only about 10 per cent of the money it has invested in offshore exploration and exploitation.

The continental shelf beneath the waters of the Gulf of Mexico contains about 200,000 square miles.[33] About one-fourth of this total lies off the Louisiana and Texas shorelines. Most of the trapping in the shelf area is in either piercement or deep-seated salt domes, just as it is in the adjacent fields onshore. However, the Creole field, illustrated in Chapter 8 (Fig. 66), is an offshore field in which faulting is responsible for oil accumulation.

The exploration method of continental shelf prospecting tends to be the same as that on the nearby land areas. Thus, in California divers have been instructed in the use of the Brunton compass, and the structure of the seafloor bed rock has been mapped in this manner. In the Gulf Coast, on the other hand, geophysical prospecting is used offshore as well as onshore, and at a cost little, if any, greater. If it can be assumed that the offshore leases mark salt domes discovered by geophysical surveys, then there are at least 87 known salt domes off the Louisiana coast and 33 off the Texas coast, a total of 120.[34] In addition, there are 164 topographic features determined by contour-

[32] Leigh S. McCaslin, Jr., "Offshore Loss," *Oil and Gas Jour.*, Vol. 48 (Jan. 5, 1950), p. 32.

[33] Dean A. McGee, "Continental Shelf Exploration Off Louisiana and Texas," *Am. Assoc. Petrol. Geol., Program Annual Meeting* (1949), pp. 10–11.

[34] J. Ben Carsey, "Geology of Gulf Coastal Area and Continental Shelf," *Bull. Am. Assoc. Petrol. Geol.*, Vol. 34 (March, 1950), p. 385.

ing the floor of the Gulf of Mexico that are probably salt domes also, making a grand total of 284 possible underwater oil traps already known in this area. Of this total, only a few have been tested, and the proportion of discoveries has been high.

The conclusion appears justified that the density of prospective oil fields is just as great on the continental shelves as it is in the adjacent land areas. Therefore, wherever oil-producing districts reach the shore, on any continent (for continental shelves are universal although of widely varying width), an oil reserve can be assumed for the contiguous offshore area. Whether exploitation is economically possible depends entirely upon the price of oil; a potential reserve becomes an actual one when an excess of demand over supply creates a shortage that increases the price to the level necessary for development.

Reserves in Sedimentary Basins Which Are Not Yet Productive. Since the earliest days of the profession, petroleum geologists have enjoyed looking into the crystal ball in an attempt to determine the oil provinces of the future. The possible future oil provinces of the United States and Canada have been the subject of two symposiums of the American Association of Petroleum Geologists.[35] In addition to the participants in these symposiums, many other geologists have written articles on the possibilities of finding oil fields in sedimentary basins not yet productive. Some of these will be referred to in the following paragraphs.

The Arctic basin (Fig. 220) is the only one of the four intercontinental basins described by Pratt[36] that is not yet a major source of oil. This structural depression is occupied by the Arctic Sea and the northern extremities of the North American, European, and Asiatic continents and the circumpolar archipelagos. The continental rim of the depressed area contains oil and gas seeps in various places, including the vicinity of Point Barrow, Alaska. Exploration in this area (Chapter 9) has resulted so far in one gas well. Similar oil seeps have been found in the Canadian Arctic and along the north coast of Siberia. It is believed that the Russians are actively exploring their Arctic possessions for petroleum at the present time.

[35] "Possible Future Oil Provinces of the United States and Canada," *Bull. Am. Assoc. Petrol. Geol.,* Vol. 25 (August, 1941); "Symposium on Possible Future Oil Provinces of North America," *Am. Assoc. Petrol. Geol., Program Annual Meeting* (1950).

[36] Wallace E. Pratt, "Our Petroleum Resources," *Am. Scientist,* Vol. 32 (April, 1944), p. 126; Wallace E. Pratt, "Distribution of Petroleum in the Earth's Crust," *Bull. Am. Assoc. Petrol. Geol.,* Vol. 28 (October, 1944), pp. 1506–1509.

The Atlantic coastal plain [37] contains three superimposed basins in Maryland, eastern North Carolina, and southwestern Georgia that have not yet been thoroughly explored. Northern Florida [38] is possible future oil-producing territory in spite of many unsuccessful tests. Alabama [39] is occupied in part by the largely untested Black Warrior basin in the Paleozoic rocks in the northwestern part of the state; in addition, there are, of course, possibilities of further coastal-plain discoveries east of the Gilbertown field.

One large basin, the Williston, which covers parts of Nebraska, the two Dakotas, Wyoming, Montana, Saskatchewan, and Alberta, has excited considerable interest but is still largely untested.[40] Most of the Rocky Mountain basins [41] contain oil fields except the Colorado River salt basin, in southeastern Utah, and the Black Mesa basin, mainly in northeastern Arizona.[42] Some attention is being paid to the oil possibilities of basins marked by lava flows. Exploration is fairly active in Arizona. The basin and range province of western Nevada is also getting a play. Some of the valleys in this area have been described as geologically similar to parts of California that produce oil.[43]

Several opportunities exist in California for the discovery of oil in new provinces, especially in the wedge-shaped basin re-entrants into

[37] Horace G. Richards, "The Atlantic Coastal Plain, Its Geology and Oil Possibilities," *World Oil,* Vol. 127 (Sept. 15, 1947), pp. 44 *et seq.;* F. M. Swain, "Two Recent Wells in Coastal Plain of North Carolina," *Bull. Am. Assoc. Petrol. Geol.,* Vol. 31 (November, 1947), pp. 2054–2060.

[38] John D. Todd, "North Florida Province Is Geologically Attractive," *World Petrol.,* Vol. 17 (March, 1946), pp. 44 *et seq.;* Miss. Geol. Soc., "Possible Future Oil Provinces of Southeastern U. S.," *Bull. Am. Assoc. Petrol. Geol.,* Vol. 25 (August, 1941), pp. 1575–1586.

[39] Walter B. Jones, "Alabama: Its Geology and Oil Prospects," *Oil Weekly,* Vol. 120 (Jan. 14, 1946), pp. 51 *et seq.*

[40] Tulsa Geol. Soc., "Possible Future Oil Provinces of Northern Mid-Continent States," *Bull. Am. Assoc. Petrol. Geol.,* Vol. 25 (August, 1941), pp. 1508–1512; William Norval Ballard, "Regional Geology of Dakota Basin," *Bull. Am. Assoc. Petrol. Geol.,* Vol. 26 (October, 1942), pp. 1557–1584; Ray V. Hennen, "Tertiary Geology and Oil and Gas Prospects in Dakota Basin, North Dakota," *Bull. Am. Assoc. Petrol. Geol.,* Vol. 27 (December, 1943), pp. 1567–1594; Wallace E. Pratt, *Oil in the Earth* (Univ. Kans. Press, 1942), p. 43.

[41] Rocky Mountain Assoc. Petrol. Geol., "Possible Future Oil Provinces in Rocky Mountain Region," *Bull. Am. Assoc. Petrol. Geol.,* Vol. 25 (August, 1941), pp. 1469–1507.

[42] Gail F. Moulton, "Oil Prospects in Basin Areas," *World Oil,* Vol. 128 (March, 1949), p. 62.

[43] Frank B. Taylor, "Frontiers for the Wildcatter," *Independent Petrol. Assoc. Am. Monthly* (April, May, June, 1945) (assembled reprint), p. 5.

the Coast Range. One such synclinal valley, the Salinas,[44] has recently entered the oil-producing column (Chapter 9). The great Sacramento Valley, north of San Francisco Bay, has some commercial gas production, and therefore it is a decided prospect as a future oil province. Sedimentary basins in western Washington and Oregon [45] contain oil and gas seeps that have been known for many years, but sporadic testing has so far been negative. Alaska [46] has two large and several smaller basins that are largely untested, in addition to the Katalla field and the Arctic rim described in Chapter 9. Canada, besides the producing basins of the northwest plains and southwestern Ontario, has oil and gas possibilities in the Maritime provinces. This sedimentary basin has one small oil field, the Stony Creek; repeated testing has failed so far to find a second field.[47]

Lower California, in the opposite corner of the continent, contains three basins of deposition on the west slope of the peninsula.[48] A thick section of carbonate rock underlies the Bahama Islands, but one deep well drilled there recently failed to find any encouraging signs of oil. Sedimentary basins also occur in Cuba (Chapter 9) and on other islands of the West Indian archipelago, but except for Cuba no oil production has been found as yet. British Honduras and northern Guatemala are occupied by the south rim of the great Gulf of Mexico sedimentary basin. The only oil production on the south side of the basin is in the Isthmus of Tehuantepec district in Mexico. Parts of Nicaragua and Costa Rica are also underlain by basin sediments. These prospective oil provinces are largely unexplored.

The Sub-Andean basin of South America, although containing a few fields in the Salta-Camiri area of Argentina, Brazil, and Bolivia, and the Agua Caliente field of Peru, has been barely scratched.[49] The

[44] J. E. Kilkenny, "Geology and Exploration for Oil in Salinas Valley, California," *Bull. Am. Assoc. Petrol. Geol.,* Vol. 32 (December, 1948), pp. 2254–2268.

[45] Hampton Smith, "Oil and Gas Prospects of Washington and Oregon," *Bull. Am. Assoc. Petrol. Geol.,* Vol. 31 (December, 1947), p. 2240; Charles E. Weaver, "Geology of Oregon and Washington and Its Relation to Occurrence of Oil and Gas," *Bull. Am. Assoc. Petrol. Geol.,* Vol. 29 (October, 1945), pp. 1377–1415; Pacific Section, Am. Assoc. Petrol. Geol., "Possible Future Oil Provinces of Pacific Coast States," *Bull. Am. Assoc. Petrol. Geol.,* Vol. 25 (August, 1941), pp. 1457–1461.

[46] Philip S. Smith, "Possible Future Oil Provinces in Alaska," *Bull. Am. Assoc. Petrol. Geol.,* Vol. 25 (August, 1941), pp. 1440–1446.

[47] Geol. Survey of Canada, Quebec Bur. Mines, and Newfoundland Geol. Survey, "Possible Future Oil Provinces of Eastern Canada," *Bull. Am. Assoc. Petrol. Geol.,* Vol. 25 (August, 1941), pp. 1539–1562.

[48] C. H. Beal, "Reconnaissance of the Geology and Oil Possibilities of Baja California, Mexico," *Geol. Soc. Am., Memoir* 31 (December, 1948).

[49] John L. Rich, "Oil Possibilities of South America in the Light of Regional Geology," *Bull. Am. Assoc. Petrol. Geol.,* Vol. 29 (May, 1945), pp. 495–563.

same is true for the southwestern part of the Orinoco (Apure) basin, which covers a large area in southwestern Venezuela and eastern Colombia. Two large basins in Brazil are virtually unexplored.[50] One of these is the Amazon trough, and the other is the Piaui basin, which lies between the Amazon trough and the producing Bahia basin.

Many sedimentary basins in Europe contain not a single oil field and yet they are prospective future oil provinces. One such basin covers the southern end of England; another is the large Paris basin of northern France. Spain [51] has three basins, and Portugal [52] one. Even the northern half of relatively tiny Switzerland, crossed from east to west by a sedimentary basin, is assumed to have possibilities for commercial oil production.[53]

By far the greatest area of unexplored sedimentary basins is in Asia (Fig. 220), especially in Siberia and China. If the assumption is correct that the ultimate yield of oil is proportional to the area of basin sediments, then a considerable share of the world's total eventual oil output remains to be discovered in this vast territory. Only in the Ferghana and Khaudag districts of southwestern Siberia and in the Yumen district of western China has there been any development of the hydrocarbon resources. To the north and northeast of the Ferghana district, beyond the Karaganda uplift, are the great Siberian basins, which extend from the Urals to the Pacific and from Mongolia to the Arctic.[54] Eastern China contains nearly a dozen sedimentary basins [55] of varying size, all virtually non-productive at present, and in the province of Sinkiang in western China is the largest basin,

[50] Avelino Ignacio de Oliveira, "Brazil Has Extensive Sedimentary Areas Favorable to Accumulation of Petroleum," *Oil and Gas Jour.,* Vol. 46 (Jan. 15, 1948), pp. 48–50; Victor Oppenheim, "Brazil's Oil," *Oil Weekly,* Vol. 117 (April 9, 1945), pp. 60–62.

[51] P. H. Sampelayo, "Spain's Possibilities," *World Oil,* Vol. 130 (Feb. 1, 1950), pp. 197–199.

[52] Fernando A. C. Conçalves Maciera, "Search for Petroleum in Portugal," reviewed by Glen M. Ruby, *Bull. Am. Assoc. Petrol. Geol.,* Vol. 33 (November, 1949), pp. 1910–1911.

[53] J. Kopp, "The Search for Oil in Switzerland," *World Oil,* Vol. 129 (May, 1949), pp. 226 *et seq.*

[54] Dimitry A. Shanazarov, "Petroleum Problem of Siberia," *Bull. Am. Assoc. Petrol. Geol.,* Vol. 32 (February, 1948), pp. 153–197; Wallace Pratt, "Undiscovered Reserves Equal to Those Already Found Held Probable," *Oil and Gas Jour.,* Vol. 42 (Dec. 30, 1943), p. 80.

[55] J. Marvin Weller, "Petroleum Possibilities of Red Basin of Szechuan Province, China," *Bull. Am. Assoc. Petrol. Geol.,* Vol. 28 (October, 1944), pp. 1430–1439; Frederick G. Clapp, "China," *Science of Petroleum* (Oxford Univ. Press, 1938), Vol. 1, p. 139.

already productive at the eastern end, which may well be one of the great petroleum provinces of the future.

Scattered islands in the Philippine archipelago are covered in part by sedimentary basins, and the discovery of oil in this area is by no means an impossibility. Oil and gas seeps have been found on at least six of the islands.[56]

Unlike Asia, only a relatively small part of the African continent is covered by a veneer of sedimentary rock, but the basin at the northern end contains a few oil fields, and the smaller basins elsewhere, especially around the periphery of the continent, are also thought to have petroleum possibilities.[57] The oil possibilities of Ethiopia are currently being explored not only by geological investigation but also by the actual drilling of wildcat tests.[58]

The continent of Australia contains two large basins, and at least three smaller basins overlap upon coastal areas. Much time and effort have been spent since World War I in an attempt to develop commercial production on this continent but with virtually no success as yet.[59]

TECHNOLOGIC RESERVES

INCREASING THE PERCENTAGE OF ULTIMATE RECOVERY.[60] A major reserve is the liquid hydrocarbon still left in the

[56] Juan S. Teves, "Oil Possibilities in the Philippines," *World Oil,* Vol. 130 (March, 1950), pp. 207–209; Wallace E. Pratt, "Possible Petroleum Reserves of Philippine Islands," *Trans. Am. Inst. Min. Met. Engineers,* 1175-P (July, 1922).

[57] Anon., "Oil Possibilities in Lesser Known African Territories," *World Oil,* Vol. 128 (August, 1948), pp. 244–246; G. D. Hobson, "Africa and Madagascar," *Science of Petroleum* (Oxford Univ. Press, 1938), Vol. 1, pp. 152–154.

[58] Hall Taylor, "Geology of Ethiopia Being Developed by Sinclair in Exploring Concession," *Oil and Gas Jour.,* Vol. 47 (Aug. 12, 1948), pp. 48–51.

[59] Eric C. Craig, "Structure of the Northwest Basin in Western Australia," *World Oil,* Vol. 130 (March, 1950), pp. 210–214; Curt Teichert, "Stratigraphy of Western Australia," *Bull. Am. Assoc. Petrol. Geol.,* Vol. 31 (January, 1947), pp. 1–70; W. G. Woolnough, "Australia," *Science of Petroleum* (Oxford Univ. Press, 1938), Vol. 1, pp. 124–129.

[60] Morris Muskat, "Secondary Recovery," *Physical Principles of Oil Production* (McGraw-Hill, New York, 1949), Chapter 12, pp. 645–737; Paul D. Torrey, "Secondary Methods for Increasing Oil Recovery," *Elements of the Petroleum Industry* (Am. Inst. Min. Met. Engineers, New York, 1940), Chapter 13, pp. 289–309; *Secondary Recovery of Oil in the United States* (Am. Petrol. Inst., 2nd edition, 1950); H. C. Miller and Ben E. Lindsly, "Report on Petroleum Development and Production," *Petroleum Investigations* (U. S. Superintendent of Documents, 1934), pp. 1193–1214; Oscar F. Spencer, *Secondary Recovery of Oil* (Pennsylvania State College, State College, Penn., 1949); A. E. Sweeney, Jr., "Secondary Recovery," *Mines Mag.,* Vol. 38 (December, 1948), pp. 80–81; S. F. Shaw, "Increasing the Ultimate Recovery of Oil," *Am. Inst. Min. Met. Engineers, Tech. Pub.* 358 (1930).

reservoir rock when a field is abandoned owing to exhaustion of the oil that can profitably be extracted by wells. In some of the older fields, exploited before the development of modern production methods, as much as 80 per cent of the original petroleum may still be in the reservoir. Various procedures have been devised for the purpose of extracting this oil; they are known collectively as "secondary recovery" methods. In older fields, such as the Bradford, of Pennsylvania and New York, secondary recovery can be expected to produce ultimately as much oil as was originally obtained by natural flow and pumping. There are no doubt many areas where the reserves of abandoned oil in the reservoir are at least as great as the oil already produced.

Modern production methods, especially the maintenance of pressure in the reservoir, result in a much higher percentage of ultimate recovery and, conversely, a lower percentage of residual oil left underground. Muskat has pointed out that, "from a physical point of view," secondary recovery operations "may be considered simply as an extreme form of delayed pressure-maintenance operation. In fact, in contrast to the more common type of so-called 'pressure maintenance operations,' which generally result only in pressure-decline retardation, with an incomplete replacement of the space voidage created by the fluid redrawals, there is usually some build-up of reservoir pressure in secondary-recovery gas or water injection." [61]

Nine or ten different methods of secondary recovery have been investigated. Two methods are being used widely today in the United States: gas repressuring and water flooding, which are described in later paragraphs. Although originally invoked to stimulate or revive production as a field approached abandonment, there is a growing tendency to dovetail one or the other of these methods with the normal production procedure, beginning early in the life of a field. For example, recycling the gas to maintain reservoir pressure may obviate the necessity of installing gas-repressuring equipment later, and the return of oil-field brines to the reservoir as a conservation measure at the same time assists the natural water drive. A third type of secondary recovery, oil mining, is strictly a salvage method and can be carried out only after exploitation by drilled wells is no longer profitable. Oil mining is practiced commercially in Europe but not as yet in the United States.

[61] Morris Muskat, "Secondary Recovery," *Physical Principles of Oil Production* (McGraw-Hill, New York, 1949), p. 645.

Among other secondary recovery methods that have been tried commercially or experimentally are vacuum pumping,[62] hot water injection, and repressuring with carbon dioxide or nitrogen. A longer life has been given some wells, about to be abandoned because of large water yield, by installing centrifugal pumps which can raise a great quantity of fluid at a cost low enough so that operations can continue.[63] A suggested method of secondary recovery is the use of bacteria.[64] Some bacteria are able to liberate oil from oil-containing sands. Experimentation has been carried out at Bradford, Pennsylvania, on possible commercial applications of bacterial release.

The choice of a secondary recovery method is dictated largely by the geologic environment of the oil deposit. Water flooding is best adapted to sands of fine texture and hence relatively low permeability, whereas gas repressuring is at its best in coarse-grained, highly permeable sandstone and in porous limestone.[65] Underground mining can take place as a profitable venture only where the oil is not amenable to extraction by surface methods of secondary recovery and where the reservoirs lie at shallow depth.

Gas Repressuring.[66] The repressuring of oil formations by the injection of gas was first tried in Ohio in the early years of the century, but it was not attempted on a large scale until the middle 1920's, when many plants were established in Kansas, Oklahoma, and Texas for the purpose of repressuring depleted oil fields. The usual procedure is to take over as input wells the bore holes that enter the reservoir rock at the structurally highest point. Gas is compressed at the surface and injected into these wells, where it both rebuilds the depleted gas cap and goes into solution in the oil, thereby greatly increasing the oil's mobility. The combination of the pressure exerted by the gas cap and the increased liquidity of the fluid accelerates the movement of the laggard oil into the output wells which tap the reservoir below the gas cap. In some places, the output wells flow under the

[62] H. B. Hill, Kenneth H. Johnston, T. L. Coleman, and J. M. Seward, "West Red River Field, Oklahoma," *Oil and Gas Jour.*, Vol. 47 (April 7, 1949), pp. 70 *et seq.*

[63] Victor Kotschoubey, "New Type Secondary Recovery in Dupo, Illinois Field," *Oil and Gas Jour.*, Vol. 40 (March 5, 1942), pp. 39–40.

[64] Claude E. ZoBell, "Bacterial Release of Oil from Oil-Bearing Materials," *World Oil*, Vol. 126 (Aug. 25, 1947), pp. 36 *et seq.;* Vol. 127 (Sept. 1, 1947), pp. 35 *et seq.;* Charles J. Deegan, "Effect of Bacteria on Oil Production," *Oil and Gas Jour.*, Vol. 46 (June 21, 1947), pp. 78 *et seq.*

[65] Paul D. Torrey, "Secondary Methods for Increasing Oil Recovery," *Elements of the Petroleum Industry* (Am. Inst. Min. Met. Engineers, New York, 1940), p. 290.

[66] S. F. Shaw, "Oilfield Repressuring," *Science of Petroleum* (Oxford Univ. Press, 1938), Vol. 1, pp. 577–582.

stimulus of gas injection, but usually they continue to pump, although with increased yield.

The return of gas to the reservoir for secondary recovery, pressure maintenance, and lifting operations has become so prevalent in Texas that more than one-fourth of the natural gas produced during 1949 was reinjected into the reservoir.[67]

Water Flooding.[68] The beneficial effects of water flooding were discovered, accidentally, at Bradford, Pennsylvania, during the closing years of the last century, when water from shallow aquifers got into the oil reservoir rock by way of abandoned wells and increased markedly the production of nearby oil wells. However, water drive by design remained illegal in that state until 1921. Since then, great strides have been made in the Bradford pool, and in other parts of the world, in pumping water from the surface into the reservoir rock and driving the oil ahead of the water flood into output wells. At least two techniques are employed. One, which has been used extensively at Bradford, is the so-called "five spot" method, in which a water input well is established in the center of a square formed by four producing wells. The other method, which is preferable in anticlinal accumulations, is to inject the water into wells down-dip below the oil-water interface, thereby assisting the natural water drive in forcing the oil up the structure toward its highest point. The input wells may be "dry" holes drilled beyond the confines of the accumulation during the development of the field; they may be wells toward the outer edge which were originally oil wells but became water wells as the oil was driven into higher parts of the structure; or they may be wells drilled especially as brine-disposal wells. The water for flooding operations may be water produced with the oil and thus returned to its source, or it may be water from higher aquifers obtained from wells that were drilled for that purpose. The water usually has to be treated at the surface in order to remove compounds in solution that tend to precipitate in the reservoir and clog the pores, thereby preventing further input.

67 Leigh S. McCaslin, Jr., "Texas' Gas Utilization," *Oil and Gas Jour.*, Vol. 48 (March 16, 1950), p. 51.

68 Morris Muskat and R. D. Wyckoff, "A Theoretical Analysis of Water Flooding Networks," *Am. Inst. Min. Met. Engineers, Tech. Paper* 507 (1933); Donald L. Katz, "Possibilities of Secondary Recovery for the Oklahoma City Wilcox Sand," *Am. Inst. Min. Met. Engineers, Tech. Paper* 1400 (1941); H. K. Holland, Jr., "West Burkburnett Field Waterflood Project," *Oil and Gas Jour.*, Vol. 47 (April 28, 1949), pp. 88 *et seq.;* Kenneth B. Barnes, "Biggest Waterflood," *Oil and Gas Jour.*, Vol. 48 (Dec. 1, 1949), p. 37; John Mark Jewett, "Subsurface Aspects in Kansas Water-Flooding," *World Oil,* Vol. 128 (December, 1948), pp. 142–152.

Oil Mining.[69] Although the exploitation of oil by means of open pits, dug wells, and tunnels extends back into prehistory, apparently the first systematic commercial mining of oil was carried out by the Germans in the old Pechelbronn fields of Alsace during World War I. This project proved to be feasible, and eventually three successful mines were operating in that district. The success at Pechelbronn also led to mining oil at Wietze, near Hannover in north Germany, beginning in 1919. A German attempt during World War II to mine oil from the chalk reservoir of the Heide Meldorf field was not successful, owing to the plasticity of the chalk. Within the United States, the nearest approach to successful oil-mining operation was also the oldest attempt. Drainage tunnels driven into an oil-bearing sandstone in California in 1866 yielded oil for many years. More recent attempts in Kentucky and Texas have not been commercially successful.

Methods of oil mining can be classified into two types: direct and indirect. The direct method is practiced at Wietze, Germany, where the uppermost of four reservoir rocks is mined and brought to the surface and the oil is extracted by hot alkaline solutions. The spent sand is returned underground for back filling. The indirect method can be subdivided into three types. In one procedure, the reservoir rock itself is penetrated by either drifts or horizontal bore holes radiating out from a shaft. The drift method is used at Pechelbronn and in the three lower reservoirs at Wietze. The oil oozes from the surrounding rock into the drifts and drains into sumps, whence it is pumped to the surface. Radial horizontal bore holes have recently been drilled from the base of a 1200-foot shaft in the Lakes Entrance field in southeastern Australia (Victoria) in an attempt to obtain oil commercially from the sandstone reservoir rock.[70] The other indirect methods are to tunnel into the beds either directly above or directly below the reservoir rock. If the operation is from above, slits or narrow channels may be cut into the reservoir rock through which the oil will drain.[71] If drifts are driven below the reservoir rock, the oil could be tapped by holes drilled upward. Obviously, of

[69] A. E. Gunther, "Oil Mining in Europe," *Petrol. Engineer,* Vol. 19 (May, 1948), pp. 74 *et seq.;* John L. Rich, "Mining for Oil," *Mines Mag.,* Vol. 27 (May, 1937), pp. 23 *et seq.;* George S. Rice, "Mining Petroleum by Underground Methods," *U. S. Bur. Mines, Bull.* 351, 1932.

[70] L. G. Weeks, "Highlights on 1948 Developments in Foreign Petroleum Fields," *Bull. Am. Assoc. Petrol. Geol.,* Vol. 33 (June, 1949), p. 1122.

[71] John L. Rich, *op. cit.*

course, underground mining of oil is not without considerable fire and explosion hazard.

There are many shallow oil fields in the United States which have been abandoned but in which a large amount of oil remains. Western Pennsylvania and eastern Kansas contain a number of such fields. When, and if, the price of oil makes mining feasible, this considerable reserve will no doubt be drawn upon.

INCREASING THE PERCENTAGE OF DESIRED PRODUCT. During the relatively brief history of the petroleum industry, not only has the demand for petroleum products increased by astronomic progression but also the relative demand for the various petroleum products has changed through the years. In the early days, the greatest demand was for kerosene, but later the automobile age moved gasoline into first place. At the present time, the demand for Diesel fuel and furnace oils is rising rapidly. Under straight-run refining there was little or no flexibility in the proportions of petroleum products obtained. The refinery run was based upon the demand for the leading product; the surpluses that accumulated in the other fractions were sometimes burned to get rid of them.

At least three times since the start of the century, chemists have developed processes that permitted considerably greater flexibility in the type of the refinery output. The first invention was the cracking process, which increased the possible gasoline yield by 150 per cent. The second development was hydrogenation, by means of which any lighter hydrocarbon, such as gasoline, can be created by adding hydrogen under the influence of a catalyst to heavier carbon compounds. These carbon compounds may be in heavy crude oils or in synthetic hydrocarbons obtained from coal, oil shale, or other carbon-containing material. A third process, polymerization, permits the transformation of lighter hydrocarbon molecules into heavier hydrocarbons.

There is no reason to believe that the chemists are through discovering and developing new processing techniques. It is entirely possible (if not probable) that the current reserves will be extended in the future, as they have been in the past, by chemical discoveries yet to be made.

DEVELOPING DORMANT HYDROCARBON SUPPLIES. An enormous reserve of petroleum products is locked up within known hydrocarbon deposits that are not being utilized to their fullest capacity. The asphalt deposits of North America alone are considered to be capable of yielding more barrels of liquid hydrocarbons than the sum of the past domestic production and the proven oil reserve.

The natural-gas deposits can also be considered to constitute a liquid hydrocarbon reserve.[72] By means of a modified Fischer-Tropsch synthesis, gas can be converted into gasoline or Diesel fuel. About 13,500 feet of natural gas are used in producing one barrel of synthetic oil. One commercial plant with a capacity of about 7000 barrels of gasoline per day has been built at Brownsville, Texas. Plans for a similar plant in the Hugoton gas field of Kansas have been tabled, at least for the time being. If all the known natural gas in the United States were to be converted into liquid hydrocarbon, it would add about 12 billion barrels to our eventual oil output. However, it is questionable logic to consider this to be additional reserve; such use of natural gas would be merely converting one hydrocarbon energy supply into another, or robbing Peter to pay Paul.

The greatest single oil reserve so far discovered in the world is locked up in the heavy oil ("tar") sands of the Athabaska Valley in northern Alberta.[73] Estimates of the reserve of petroleum products in this single deposit range from 100 billion barrels to 250 billion barrels. This compares with a total known petroleum reserve of 80 billion barrels for the entire world.

The Athabaska oil sands, of Lower Cretaceous age, crop out along the Athabaska River and its tributaries near Fort McMurray about 230 miles northeast of Edmonton. The location of the deposit is shown in Fig. 168. Enough oil-impregnated sand to produce about a billion barrels of oil is readily available; the rest can be obtained only by shaft mining. Since the oil is not fluid enough either to flow or to be driven into wells, the only feasible method of exploitation is to mine the sand and extract the oil from it by steam, hot water, or solvents. Experiments to do this on a commercial scale were carried on for some years, first by private interests and then by the Canadian government, but they have been abandoned.

[72] Robert E. Wilson and J. K. Roberts, "Petroleum and Natural Gas: Uses and Possible Replacements," *Seventy-Five Years of Progress in the Mineral Industry* (Am. Inst. Min. Met. Engineers, New York, 1947), pp. 735–737; E. V. Murphree, "The Synthetic Fuels Picture," *World Oil,* Vol. 128 (Feb. 1, 1949), pp. 46–50.

[73] Max W. Ball, *This Fascinating Oil Business* (Bobbs-Merrill, Indianapolis, 1940), p. 373; G. S. Hume, "Petroleum Geology of Canada," *Can. Geol. Survey, Econ. Geol. Series* 14 (1944), pp. 30–34; K. A. Clark, "Bituminous Sands of Alberta," *Oil Weekly,* Vol. 118 (Aug. 13, 1945), pp. 46–51; Dept. of Mines and Resources (Canada), "Drilling and Sampling of Bituminous Sands of Northern Alberta," *Results of Investigations, 1942–1947, Pub.* 826 (1949).

Although they are less well known than the Athabaskan deposits, bituminous sand and sandstone deposits in the United States are estimated to contain a potential gasoline reserve of nearly 3 billion barrels. These deposits are principally in Utah and California, with smaller occurrences in Alabama, Kentucky, and Oklahoma.[74] Asphalt and bituminous sands are abundant in the Coast Ranges, especially at Point Arena, about 110 miles north of San Francisco, and to the south in the counties of San Luis Obispo, Santa Barbara, and Ventura. Oil-bearing sands which crop out near McKittrick and elsewhere in western Kern County are additional possible sources of recoverable oil. Near Vernal, Utah, the asphaltic sands range in thickness from 90 to 130 feet, and for the last two years these sands have been worked at the outcrop and treated in a pilot plant, which may be the forerunner of a small-scale extraction plant.[75] Many of the black "oil" sands in the oil fields of eastern Kansas actually contain asphalt rather than oil, but because these deposits occur at depths of several hundred feet, they could be exploited only by shaft mining.

THE MANUFACTURE OF SYNTHETIC HYDROCARBONS.[76] The dearth of local supplies of petroleum in western Europe caused the establishment of synthetic hydrocarbon industries in that area some years ago. In preparation for World War II, and during the war, both Germany and Japan developed a full-scale oil synthetics industry, largely from coal (Germany) and from Manchurian oil shale (Japan).

Activity in synthetic petroleum within the United States has followed a definite cycle. First there has been an oil shortage, or at least a threatened shortage. This has brought about the construction of

[74] G. B. Shea, "Bituminous Sands and Shales, and Partly Depleted Subsurface Sands as Sources of Additional Oil in California," *Calif. Oil World,* Vol. 36 (December, 1943), pp. 9–13; E. M. Spieker, "Bituminous Sandstone Near Vernal, Utah," *U. S. Geol. Survey, Bull.* 822-C (1930); Clifford N. Holmes, Benjamin Page, and Paul Averitt, "Geology of the Bituminous Sandstone Deposits Near Sunnyside, Carbon County, Utah," *U. S. Geol. Survey, Oil and Gas Investigation, Preliminary Map* 86 (1948), and other maps and charts in this series.

[75] Anon., "Profitable Sand," *Oil and Gas Jour.,* Vol. 48 (Jan. 12, 1950), pp. 34–35.

[76] Walter M. Fuchs, *When the Oil Wells Run Dry* (Industrial Research Service, Dover, N. H., 1946); George Roberts, Jr., and Paul R. Schultz, "Liquid Fuels from Coal and Oil Shale," *Petrol. Technology,* Vol. 1 (September, 1949), pp. 24–30; A. C. Fieldner, "Reserves of Solid Fuels," *Oil and Gas Jour.,* Vol. 47 (March 17, 1949), pp. 138 *et seq.;* E. V. Murphree, "Synthetic Fuels Picture," *World Oil,* Vol. 128 (Feb. 1, 1949), pp. 46–50; E. V. Murphree, "Natural Gas, Coal, Oil Shale as Source of Liquid Fuels," *Mines Mag.,* Vol. 38 (December, 1948), pp. 89 *et seq.;* K. C. Heald and Eugene Ayres, "Our Reserves of Coal and Shale," *Our Oil Resources* (Leonard M. Fanning, editor, McGraw-Hill, New York, 1945), Chapter 6, pp. 157–209; Robert E. Wilson, "Oil from Coal and Shale," *ibid.,* Chapter 7, pp. 210–229.

pilot plants for the conversion of organic shale or coal into synthetic hydrocarbons. The next event in the cycle has been the belated discovery of vast new supplies of crude oil. This has led to the temporary abandonment of activity, and even interest, in the manufacture of synthetics. Before too long another oil shortage appears, and the entire cycle is repeated. The domestic synthetic industry is like the spinster with many proposals (not to mention propositions!) but no wedding bells. A statement made by Snider and Brooks [77] in 1936, to the effect that large-scale investments in synthetic plants "would be questionable investments so long as there are chances of a new oil field like East Texas reducing the price of petroleum products below the scale at which the plants could operate" is as true today as it was then. In the latest cycle, the famine turned to a feast with the great oil-bearing reef discoveries in Alberta and West Texas.

The most successful synthetic operations abroad have used either oil shale or coal as a raw material. However, synthetic petroleum can be obtained from any carbonaceous matter, including peat,[78] various agricultural products such as soy and castor beans, farm waste, and fish.

Oil Shale.[79] Although both France and Scotland have had successful oil-shale industries for many years, the greatest exploitation of this raw material was achieved by the Japanese in Manchuria during World War II. Sweden began making oil from shale in 1942. Other countries known to have processed shale to produce oil are Estonia, Spain, South Africa, and Australia. The petroleum shortage within the United States in the years immediately following World War I

[77] L. C. Snider and B. T. Brooks, "Probable Petroleum Shortage in the United States, and Methods for Its Alleviation," *Bull. Am. Assoc. Petrol. Geol.,* Vol. 20 (January, 1936), p. 49.

[78] Bertram F. Linz, "Liquid Fuel from Peat," *Oil and Gas Jour.,* Vol. 48 (April 6, 1950), pp. 47–49.

[79] Carl Belser, "Oil Shale Resources of Colorado, Utah, and Wyoming," *Petroleum Development and Technology* (Am. Inst. Min. Met. Engineers, 1949), Vol. 179, pp. 72–82; Ernest E. Burgh and J. D. Lankford, "Liquid Fuels from Colorado Oil Shale," *Mines Mag.,* Vol. 39 (December, 1949), pp. 65 *et seq.;* A. J. Kraemer, "Liquid Fuels from Oil Shale," *World Oil,* Vol. 128 (December, 1948), pp. 48–54; James Boyd, "Progress in Oil Shale Development and Research," *Mines Mag.,* Vol. 38 (December, 1948), pp. 47 *et seq.;* Emery M. Sipprelle, "Oil Shale Mining Investigations, Rifle, Colorado," *ibid.,* pp. 61 *et seq.;* E. D. Gardner, "Progress of Mining Studies at Bureau of Mines, Oil Shale Mine, Anvil Point, Rifle, Colorado," *Am. Inst. Min. Met. Engineers, Tech. Publication* 2286 (1947); Martin J. Gavin, "Oil Shale, an Historical, Technical, and Economic Study," *U. S. Bur. Mines, Bull.* 210 (1924); S. Fróes Abreu, "Brazilian Oil Fields and Oil Shale Reserves," *Bull. Am. Assoc. Petrol. Geol.,* Vol. 33 (September, 1949), pp. 1590–1599; H. E. Linden, "Sweden's Shale Oil Industry," *World Oil,* Vol. 129 (September, 1949), pp. 213 *et seq.;* J. B. Mull, "American Oil Shale Developments," *Jour. Petrol. Tech.,* Vol. 2 (May, 1950), pp. 14–16.

led to investigations into the enormous resources of the Green River shale of Colorado, Utah, and Wyoming. Although the greatest area covered by these shales is in Wyoming (Fig. 222), the richest deposits and the largest estimated reserve are in Colorado and the second

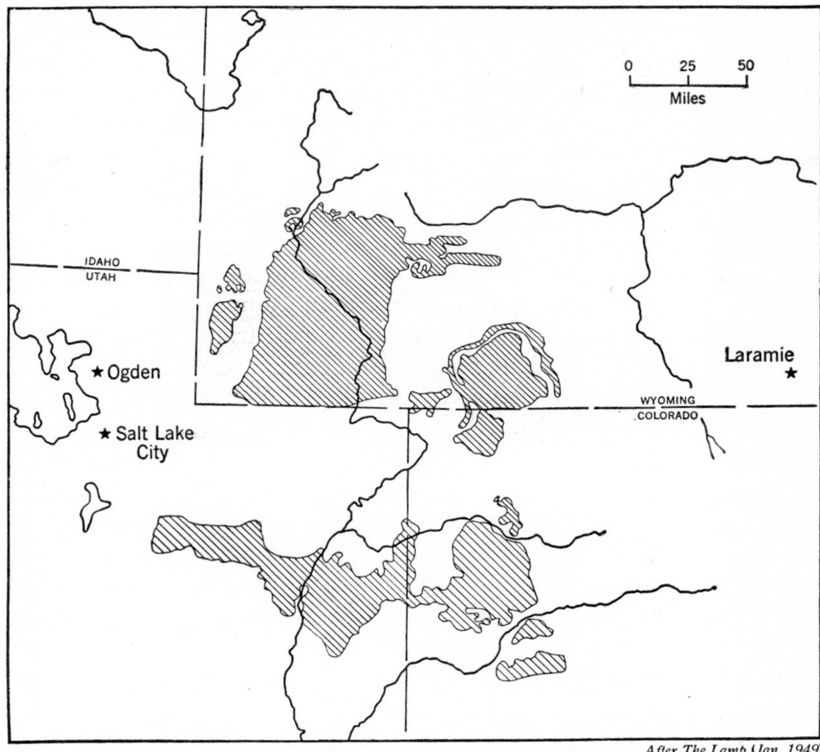

FIG. 222. Oil shale deposits of Colorado, Utah, and Wyoming. *Courtesy The Lamp and the Standard Oil Company (New Jersey).*

largest in Utah. It has been estimated that the total reserve of liquid fuel available from the Colorado oil shales alone is 300 billion barrels. This is greater than even the most optimistic estimates of the reserve tied up in the Athabaska sands. The Utah reserve is estimated at 42.8 billion barrels, and the Wyoming reserve at 3 billion barrels. However, it was calculated by Gardner [80] that "close to 500 underground oil shale mines, each with a capacity of 20,000 tons per day,

[80] E. D. Gardner, "Progress of Mining Studies at Bureau of Mines, Oil Shale Mine, Anvil Point, Rifle, Colorado," *Am. Inst. Min. Met. Engineers, Tech. Publication* 2286 (1947), p. 11.

would be required to produce the same amount of oil as our domestic production in 1947." A very strong deterrent to widespread oil shale processing is the necessity for water in quantity during the operation. Many tons of water are needed to treat one ton of shale; therefore only riverside plants are feasible.

Governmental research into the possibility of a synthetic-oil industry in the United States was started after World War I but was closed down in the early 1920's after the discovery of several large oil fields. This research was resumed during World War II, and considerable progress has been made in pilot-mine and pilot-plant operation. The Navy owns a large oil-shale reserve near Rifle in Garfield County, Colorado. On this property the Bureau of Mines has established and operates a demonstration oil-shale mine. The Bureau also has built a pilot plant at Rifle and an experiment station at Laramie, Wyoming; in addition, commercial refineries in Baton Rouge and Los Angeles have experimented in the treatment of shale oil from Colorado.

Large, but leaner, oil-shale reserves also occur in Indiana, Kentucky, and Ohio, and smaller deposits have been noted in some fourteen other states and in Alaska.

Coal. Enormous as are the possible reserves of synthetic petroleum from oil shale, they are dwarfed by the statistics of the volume of liquid hydrocarbons that could be obtained from the domestic and world deposits of coal. The Germans extensively exploited their brown-coal deposits during World War II, combining the carbon in the coal with hydrogen, by the hydrogenation process, to form gasoline and other desired liquid hydrocarbons. The Congress of the United States has appropriated funds to the Bureau of Mines to carry out studies of the possibilities of obtaining oil from coal within the United States. Pilot plants were erected at Louisiana, Missouri, and substantial experimentation has been carried on there. In addition, both the government [81] and private industry have carried on experiments in the conversion of coal (either in surface plants or in place underground) into gas, which could in turn be converted into synthetic liquid fuel. Recently such activities on the part of industry have been suspended because of the greatly increased gasoline supply and the high cost of mined coal.[82] Although underground gasification of coal is technically possible, it is also of questionable economic feasibility.

[81] James J. Dowd, James L. Elder, J. P. Capp, and Paul Cohen, "Experiment in Underground Gasification of Coal, Gorgas, Alabama," *U. S. Bur. Mines, Rept. of Investigation* 4164 (August, 1947).

[82] George Weber, "Synthetics Reverse," *Oil and Gas Jour.*, Vol. 48 (Jan. 5, 1950), p. 23.

The problems of making synthetic oil from coal are similar to those of obtaining oil from oil shale in that first the raw material must be mined (or otherwise prepared) and then processed. The coal industry has one less problem, however, in that it does not have to dispose of enormous quantities of spent shale. The best coals for synthetic-oil manufacture are those that are high in volatiles, such as the lignites of the northern Great Plains. The Paleocene Fort Union coal alone could supply all the domestic oil demand for many years, but the cost of mining and converting this coal, and of delivering it to market (it could not be much farther away in terms of transportation costs from the largest markets and still be in the United States), is no doubt several times the current cost of delivering crude-oil products to the same markets.

CONCLUSIONS

The following conclusions can be drawn from this brief survey:

1. The actually proven oil reserves are the equivalent of only a few years' supply.

2. The amount of undiscovered oil reserve is unknown, but no doubt it is many times the present proven reserve.

3. A considerable body of oil lies at greater depths than those so far explored in most oil fields. No sedimentary section can be considered to be completely explored until many wells have entered the basement rock.

4. There are still many new oil fields to be found within the periphery of the present oil-producing districts.

5. Other fields will be discovered by exploration beyond the peripheries of the oil districts. The continental shelf bordering oil-producing areas is a case in point, but also the land-locked sedimentary basins have not been explored in all directions to the very edge of the possibly productive area.

6. Entirely new petroliferous provinces will be discovered in the future as in the past. None of the sedimentary basins not productive have been thoroughly explored; some have not been explored at all.

7. The reserves of undiscovered oil are no doubt much greater outside the United States than within the borders of this country.

8. The reserves of liquid hydrocarbons from natural gas are large, but they cannot be considered new reserves.

9. Enormous reserves are available on the North American continent alone, from asphalt deposits, oil shales, and coals. Liquid hydro-

carbon obtained from such sources, however, will inevitably cost more than crude oil products.

10. The crude-oil products themselves will become more expensive as petroleum becomes more difficult to find.

11. As long as there is the suspicion of an undiscovered drop of petroleum within the earth's crust, there will be employment for geologists.

Appendix

THE LITERATURE OF PETROLEUM GEOLOGY[1]

Only the more recent and generally available publications of interest and value to the petroleum geologist will be mentioned here. The cited chapter written by DeGolyer contains a much more detailed account of oil and gas literature.

The most recent bibliography is:

E. DeGolyer and Harold Vance, "Bibliography on the Petroleum Industry," *Texas Engineering Experiment Station, Bull.* 83 (1944).

Other bibliographies of exceptional value are:

U. S. Geol. Survey, *Bibliography of North American Geology.* Published biennially, with periodic cumulative compilations.

Geol. Soc. America, *Bibliography and Index of Geology Exclusive of North America.* Published annually.

Soc. Econ. Geol., *Annotated Bibliography of Economic Geology.* Published semiannually.

Am. Assoc. Petrol. Geol., *Comprehensive Index, 1917–1945.* Covers both the *Bulletin* and special volumes of the Association.

Colo. School of Mines. *Annual Review of Petroleum Geology,* 1942–1947 inclusive.

J. V. Howell and A. I. Levorsen, "Directory of Geological Material in North America," *Bull. Am. Assoc. Petrol. Geol.,* Vol. 30 (August, 1946, Part 2), pp. 1321–1432.

Russell C. Fleming, *Source Book; a Directory of Public Agencies in the United States Engaged in the Publication of Literature on Mining and Geology* (Am. Inst. Min. Met. Engineers, New York, 1933).

The most comprehensive but now out of date monograph is:

Science of Petroleum (Oxford Univ. Press, 1938). Consists of four volumes, but the geological aspects are confined to the first volume.

Comparable in size and weight, but highly variable in degree of coverage, is the

Compte Rendu IIme Congrès Mondial du Pétrole, Paris, 1937. Five volumes; Vol. 1 is devoted to geology, geophysics, and drilling.

1 E. DeGolyer, "Introduction to the Literature of Oil and Gas," *Elements of the Petroleum Industry* (Am. Inst. Min. Met. Engineers, 1940), pp. 502–512.

Much more convenient to carry around with one is:

Elements of the Petroleum Industry (Am. Inst. Min. Met. Engineers, New York, 1940).

A very readable and relatively brief account of the ramifications of the oil industry is:

Max Ball, *This Fascinating Oil Business* (Bobbs-Merrill, Indianapolis, 1940).

Production and other statistics can be found in:

U. S. Bur. Mines, *Minerals Yearbook*. Published annually. Am. Inst. Min. Met. Engineers, *Statistics of Oil and Gas Development and Production*. Annual.
National Oil Scouts and Landmen's Association, *Oil and Gas Development in the United States*. Annual yearbook.
DeGolyer and McNaughton, *Twentieth Century Petroleum Statistics* (published annually) (Dallas, Texas).
Oil and Gas Jour. Annual statistics in third issue each January; semi-annual figures, in third issue in July.

Congressional hearings on the petroleum reserve situation have yielded two reports, in which the geological parts have been written mainly by members of the staff of the Geological Survey:

Petroleum Investigation Hearings before a Subcommittee of the Committee on Interstate and Foreign Commerce, House of Representatives, 73rd Congress (Recess) on H.R. 441, Part 2 (1934).
Investigation of Petroleum Resources, Hearings before a Special Committee Investigating Petroleum Resources, U. S. Senate, 79th Congress, First Session, S.R. 36 (1945).

The most comprehensive survey of American oil fields, as of 1930, is:

Ralph Arnold and William J. Kemnitzer, *Petroleum in the United States and Possessions* (New York, 1931).

A more recent compilation is:

W. A. Ver Wiebe, *North American and Middle East Oil Fields* (Wichita, 1950).

Petroleum geology in general and the geology of European oil fields in particular are given monographic treatment in:

O. Stutzer, *Erdöl* (Gebrüder Borntraeger, Berlin, 1931).

World oil distribution is the theme of the newly published:

Wallace E. Pratt and Dorothy Good, editors, and 20 authors, "World Geography of Petroleum," *Am. Geol. Soc., Spec. Pub.* 31 (1950).

The American Association of Petroleum Geologists has published a series of special volumes on geology. Among them are:

Structure of Typical American Oil Fields, Vols. 1 and 2 (1929), Vol. 3 (1948).
Problems of Petroleum Geology (1934).
Stratigraphic Type Oil Fields (1941).
Geology of Salt Dome Oil Fields (1926).
Gulf Coast Oil Fields (1936).
Geology of Natural Gas (1935).

Subsurface geology is given monographic treatment in:

L. W. LeRoy, *Subsurface Geologic Methods* (Colo. School of Mines, 1950. 2nd Edition).

Another subsurface text, with some emphasis on the engineering aspects, is:

Harold Vance, *Elements of Petroleum Subsurface Engineering* (St. Louis, 1950).

Petroleum origin, especially the possible source materials, is discussed in:

Parker D. Trask, *Origin and Environment of Source Sediments of Petroleum* (Houston, 1932).
Parker D. Trask and H. W. Patnode, *Source Beds of Petroleum,* Am. Assoc. Petrol. Geol. (Tulsa, 1942).

Field and office methods in petroleum geology are included in several field geologies, especially:

F. H. Lahee, *Field Geology,* 4th edition (New York, 1941).
Dorsey Hager, Practical Oil Geology, 5th edition (New York, 1938).

A contemporary textbook is:

Cecil G. Lalicker, *Principles of Petroleum Geology* (New York, 1949).

Among the several journal publications, the most valuable to the petroleum geologist is the monthly:

Bull. Am. Assoc. Petrol. Geol.

The American Institute of Mining and Metallurgical Engineers publishes or has published:

Jour. Petrol. Technology (monthly).
Petroleum Development and Technology (Transactions Petroleum Division) (annually).

The Institute of Petroleum (London) publishes at irregular intervals:

Reviews of Petrol. Technology.

Of the many journals devoted to various aspects of the petroleum industry, those which most frequently contain articles on geology are:

Oil and Gas Jour. (weekly).
World Oil (monthly). Formerly the *Oil Weekly.*
World Petrol. (monthly).

Index